PEARSON

ALWAYS LEARNING

Margaret L. Lial • John Hornsby • Terry Mcginnis

Intermediate Algebra

Custom Edition for University of Nebraska-Lincoln

Taken from:
Intermediate Algebra, Twelfth Edition
by Margaret L. Lial, John Hornsby, and Terry Mcginnis

Pearson Learning Solutions, 330 Hudson Street, New York, New York 10013
A Pearson Education Company
www.pearsoned.com

Printed in the United States of America

1 2 3 4 5 6 7 8 9 10 V0UD 19 18 17 16 15

000200010271973110

AD

ISBN 10: 1-323-14719-5
ISBN 13: 978-1-323-14719-1

CONTENTS

Additional topics available in MyMathLab®: Solving Systems of Linear Equations by Matrix Methods; Determinants and Cramer's Rule; Piecewise Linear Functions; Conic Sections; Nonlinear Systems of Equations; Second-Degree Inequalities and Systems of Inequalities; Linear Programming; Sequences and Series; The Binomial Theorem

R Review of the Real Number System

R.1 Basic Concepts

R.2 Operations on Real Numbers

R.3 Exponents, Roots, and Order of Operations

R.4 Properties of Real Numbers

Study Skills Reading Your Math Textbook

R.1 Basic Concepts

OBJECTIVES

1. Write sets using set notation.
2. Use number lines.
3. Know the common sets of numbers.
4. Find additive inverses.
5. Use absolute value.
6. Use inequality symbols.

VOCABULARY

☐ set
☐ elements (members)
☐ finite set
☐ natural (counting) numbers
☐ infinite set
☐ whole numbers
☐ empty (null) set
☐ variable
☐ number line
☐ integers
☐ coordinate
☐ graph
☐ rational numbers
☐ irrational numbers
☐ real numbers
☐ additive inverse (opposite, negative)
☐ signed numbers
☐ absolute value
☐ equation
☐ inequality

OBJECTIVE 1 Write sets using set notation.

A **set** is a collection of objects called the **elements,** or **members,** of the set. In algebra, the elements of a set are usually numbers. Set braces, $\{\ \}$, are used to enclose the elements.

For example, 2 is an element of the set $\{1, 2, 3\}$. Because we can count the number of elements in the set $\{1, 2, 3\}$ and the counting comes to an end, it is a **finite set.**

In our study of algebra, we refer to certain sets of numbers by name. The set

$$N = \{1, 2, 3, 4, 5, 6, \ldots\} \quad \text{Natural (counting) numbers}$$

is the **natural numbers,** or the **counting numbers.** The three dots (*ellipsis* points) show that the list continues in the same pattern indefinitely. We cannot list all of the elements of the set of natural numbers, so it is an **infinite set.**

Including 0 with the set of natural numbers gives the set of **whole numbers.**

$$W = \{0, 1, 2, 3, 4, 5, 6, \ldots\} \quad \text{Whole numbers}$$

The set containing no elements, such as the set of whole numbers less than 0, is the **empty set,** or **null set,** usually written $\varnothing$ or $\{\ \}$.

! CAUTION Do not write $\{\varnothing\}$ for the empty set. $\{\varnothing\}$ is a set with one element: $\varnothing$. Use the notation $\varnothing$ or $\{\ \}$ for the empty set.

To indicate that 2 is an element of the set $\{1, 2, 3\}$, we use the symbol $\in$ (read "is an element of").

$$2 \in \{1, 2, 3\}$$

The number 2 is also an element of the set of natural numbers N.

$$2 \in N$$

To show that 0 is *not* an element of set N, we draw a slash through the symbol $\in$.

$$0 \notin N$$

Two sets are equal if they contain exactly the same elements. For example, $\{1, 2\} = \{2, 1\}$. (Order doesn't matter.) However, $\{1, 2\} \neq \{0, 1, 2\}$ ($\neq$ means "is not equal to"), because one set contains the element 0 while the other does not.

A **variable** is a symbol, usually a letter, used to represent a number or to define a set of numbers. For example,

$$\{x \mid x \text{ is a natural number between 3 and 15}\}$$

(read "the set of all elements x such that x is a natural number between 3 and 15") defines the following set.

$$\{4, 5, 6, 7, \ldots, 14\}$$

The notation $\{x \mid x \text{ is a natural number between 3 and 15}\}$ is an example of **set-builder notation.**

$$\{x \mid x \text{ has property } P\}$$

the set of   all elements x such that x has a given property P

NOW TRY
EXERCISE 1

List the elements in the set.

$$\{p \mid p \text{ is a natural number less than 6}\}$$

EXAMPLE 1   Listing the Elements in Sets

List the elements in each set.

(a) $\{x \mid x \text{ is a natural number less than 4}\}$

The natural numbers less than 4 are 1, 2, and 3. This set is $\{1, 2, 3\}$.

(b) $\{x \mid x \text{ is one of the first five even natural numbers}\}$ is $\{2, 4, 6, 8, 10\}$.

(c) $\{x \mid x \text{ is a natural number greater than or equal to 7}\}$

The set of natural numbers greater than or equal to 7 is an infinite set, written with ellipsis points as

$$\{7, 8, 9, 10, \ldots\}.$$

NOW TRY

NOW TRY
EXERCISE 2

Use set-builder notation to describe the set.

$$\{9, 10, 11, 12\}$$

EXAMPLE 2   Using Set-Builder Notation to Describe Sets

Use set-builder notation to describe each set.

(a) $\{1, 3, 5, 7, 9\}$

There are often several ways to describe a set in set-builder notation. One way to describe the given set is

$$\{x \mid x \text{ is one of the first five odd natural numbers}\}.$$

(b) $\{5, 10, 15, \ldots\}$

This set can be described as $\{x \mid x \text{ is a positive multiple of 5}\}$.   NOW TRY

OBJECTIVE 2   Use number lines.

A good way to picture a set of numbers is to use a **number line.** See **FIGURE 1.**

The number 0 is neither positive nor negative.

Negative numbers   Positive numbers

$$-5 \quad -4 \quad -3 \quad -2 \quad -1 \quad 0 \quad 1 \quad 2 \quad 3 \quad 4 \quad 5$$

FIGURE 1

To draw a number line, choose any point on the line and label it 0. Then choose any point to the right of 0 and label it 1. Use the distance between 0 and 1 as the scale to locate, and then label, other points.

NOW TRY ANSWERS
1. $\{1, 2, 3, 4, 5\}$
2. One answer is $\{x \mid x \text{ is a natural number between 8 and 13}\}$.

The set of numbers identified on the number line in **FIGURE 1**, including positive and negative numbers and 0, is part of the set of **integers.**

$$I = \{\ldots, -3, -2, -1, 0, 1, 2, 3, \ldots\}$$ Integers

Each number on a number line is the **coordinate** of the point that it labels, while the point is the **graph** of the number. **FIGURE 2** shows a number line with several points graphed on it.

FIGURE 2

The fractions $-\frac{1}{2}$ and $\frac{3}{4}$, graphed on the number line in **FIGURE 2**, are *rational numbers.* A **rational number** can be expressed as the quotient of two integers, with denominator not 0. The set of all rational numbers is written as follows.

$$\left\{\frac{p}{q} \,\middle|\, p \text{ and } q \text{ are integers, where } q \neq 0\right\}$$ Rational numbers

The set of rational numbers includes the natural numbers, whole numbers, and integers because these numbers can be written as fractions. For example,

$$14 = \frac{14}{1}, \quad -3 = \frac{-3}{1}, \quad \text{and} \quad 0 = \frac{0}{1}.$$

A rational number written as a fraction, such as $\frac{1}{8}$ or $\frac{2}{3}$, can also be expressed as a decimal by dividing the numerator by the denominator.

$$\begin{array}{r} 0.125 \\ 8\overline{)1.000} \\ \underline{8} \\ 20 \\ \underline{16} \\ 40 \\ \underline{40} \\ 0 \end{array}$$ ← Terminating decimal (rational number)

← Remainder is 0.

$$\frac{1}{8} = 0.125$$

$$\begin{array}{r} 0.666\ldots \\ 3\overline{)2.000\ldots} \\ \underline{18} \\ 20 \\ \underline{18} \\ 20 \\ \underline{18} \\ 2 \end{array}$$ ← Repeating decimal (rational number)

← Remainder is never 0.

$$\frac{2}{3} = 0.\overline{6}$$ ← A bar is written over the repeating digit(s).

Thus, terminating decimals, such as $0.125 = \frac{1}{8}$, $0.8 = \frac{4}{5}$, and $2.75 = \frac{11}{4}$, and repeating decimals, such as $0.\overline{6} = \frac{2}{3}$ and $0.\overline{27} = \frac{3}{11}$, are rational numbers.

Decimal numbers that neither terminate nor repeat, which include many square roots, are **irrational numbers.**

$$\sqrt{2} = 1.414213562\ldots \quad \text{and} \quad -\sqrt{7} = -2.6457513\ldots$$ Irrational numbers

NOTE Some square roots, such as $\sqrt{16} = 4$ and $\sqrt{\frac{9}{25}} = \frac{3}{5}$, are rational.

A decimal number such as 0.010010001 . . . has a pattern, but it is irrational because there is no fixed block of digits that repeat. Another irrational number is π. See **FIGURE 3**.

π, the ratio of the circumference of a circle to its diameter, is approximately equal to 3.141592653....

$$\pi = \frac{C}{d}$$

FIGURE 3

Some rational and irrational numbers are graphed on the number line in **FIGURE 4**. The rational numbers together with the irrational numbers make up the set of **real numbers**.

Every point on a number line corresponds to a real number, and every real number corresponds to a point on the number line.

FIGURE 4

OBJECTIVE 3 Know the common sets of numbers.

Sets of Numbers	
Natural numbers, or counting numbers	$\{1, 2, 3, 4, 5, 6, \dots\}$
Whole numbers	$\{0, 1, 2, 3, 4, 5, 6, \dots\}$
Integers	$\{\dots, -3, -2, -1, 0, 1, 2, 3, \dots\}$
Rational numbers	$\left\{\frac{p}{q} \mid p \text{ and } q \text{ are integers, where } q \neq 0\right\}$ *Examples:* $\frac{4}{1}$, 1.3, $-\frac{9}{2}$ or $-4\frac{1}{2}$, $\frac{16}{8}$ or 2, $\sqrt{9}$ or 3, $0.\overline{6}$
Irrational numbers	$\{x \mid x \text{ is a real number that cannot be represented by a terminating or repeating decimal}\}$ *Examples:* $\sqrt{3}$, $-\sqrt{2}$, π, 0.010010001 . . .
Real numbers	$\{x \mid x \text{ is a rational number or an irrational number}\}^*$

---

*An example of a number that is not real is $\sqrt{-1}$. This number, part of the *complex number system*, is discussed in **Chapter 7**.

FIGURE 5 shows the set of real numbers. *Every real number is either rational or irrational.* Notice that the integers are elements of the set of rational numbers and that the whole numbers and natural numbers are elements of the set of integers.

Real numbers

Rational numbers	Irrational numbers
$-\dfrac{1}{4}$ $\dfrac{4}{9}$ $\dfrac{11}{7}$ $-3\dfrac{2}{5}$	$-\sqrt{7}$
-0.125 1.5 $0.\overline{18}$ $\sqrt{4}$	$\sqrt{15}$
Integers $\ldots, -3, -2, -1,$	$\sqrt{23}$
Whole numbers 0	π
Natural numbers $1, 2, 3, \ldots$	$\dfrac{\pi}{4}$

FIGURE 5

NOW TRY EXERCISE 3

List the numbers in the following set that are elements of each set.

$$\left\{-2.4, -\sqrt{1}, -\tfrac{1}{2}, 0, 0.\overline{3}, \sqrt{5}, \pi, 5\right\}$$

(a) Whole numbers

(b) Rational numbers

EXAMPLE 3   Identifying Examples of Number Sets

List the numbers in the following set that are elements of each set.

$$\left\{-8, -\sqrt{5}, -\frac{9}{64}, 0, 0.5, \frac{1}{3}, 1.\overline{12}, \sqrt{3}, 2, \pi\right\}$$

(a) Integers
  $-8, 0,$ and 2

(b) Rational numbers
  $-8, -\dfrac{9}{64}, 0, 0.5, \dfrac{1}{3}, 1.\overline{12},$ and 2

(c) Irrational numbers
  $-\sqrt{5}, \sqrt{3},$ and π

(d) Real numbers
  All are real numbers.   NOW TRY

NOW TRY EXERCISE 4

Decide whether each statement is *true* or *false*. If it is false, tell why.

(a) All integers are irrational numbers.

(b) Every whole number is an integer.

EXAMPLE 4   Determining Relationships between Sets of Numbers

Decide whether each statement is *true* or *false*. If it is false, tell why.

(a) All irrational numbers are real numbers.

  This is true. As shown in **FIGURE 5**, the set of real numbers includes all irrational numbers.

(b) Every rational number is an integer.

  This is false. Although some rational numbers are integers, other rational numbers, such as $\dfrac{2}{3}$ and $-\dfrac{1}{4}$, are not.   NOW TRY

NOW TRY ANSWERS

3. (a) $\{0, 5\}$

  (b) $\left\{-2.4, -\sqrt{1}, -\tfrac{1}{2}, 0, 0.\overline{3}, 5\right\}$

4. (a) false; All integers are rational numbers.

  (b) true

OBJECTIVE 4   Find additive inverses.

In **FIGURE 6**, for each positive number, there is a negative number on the opposite side of 0 that lies the same distance from 0. These pairs of numbers are *additive inverses, opposites,* or *negatives* of each other. For example, 3 and -3 are additive inverses.

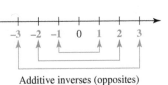

Additive inverses (opposites)

FIGURE 6

Additive Inverse

For any real number a, the number $-a$ is the **additive inverse** of a.

We change the sign of a number to find its additive inverse. As we shall see later, the sum of a number and its additive inverse is always 0.

Uses of the Symbol −

The symbol "−" can be used to indicate any of the following.

1. A negative number, as in −9, read "negative 9"

2. The additive inverse of a number, as in "−4 is the additive inverse of 4"

3. Subtraction, as in 12 − 3, read "12 minus 3"

In the expression $-(-5)$, the symbol "−" is being used in two ways. The first symbol − indicates the additive inverse (or opposite) of −5, and the second indicates a negative number, −5. Because the additive inverse of −5 is 5,

$$-(-5) = 5.$$

▼ **Additive Inverses of Signed Numbers**

Number	Additive Inverse
6	−6
−4	4
$\frac{2}{3}$	$-\frac{2}{3}$
−8.7	8.7
0	0

The number 0 is its own additive inverse.

$-(-a)$

For any real number a, $-(-a) = a.$

Numbers written with positive or negative signs, such as +4, +8, −9, and −5, are **signed numbers.** A positive number can be called a signed number even though the positive sign is usually left off.

OBJECTIVE 5 Use absolute value.

Geometrically, the **absolute value** of a number a, written $|a|$, is the distance on the number line from 0 to a. For example, the absolute value of 5 is the same as the absolute value of −5 because each number lies five units from 0. See **FIGURE 7**.

FIGURE 7

⚠ **CAUTION** *Because absolute value represents undirected distance, the absolute value of a number is always positive or 0.*

The formal definition of absolute value follows.

Absolute Value

For any real number a, $|a| = \begin{cases} a & \text{if } a \text{ is positive or 0,} \\ -a & \text{if } a \text{ is negative.} \end{cases}$

Consider the second part of this definition, $|a| = -a$ if a is negative. If a is a *negative* number, then $-a$, the additive inverse or opposite of a, is a positive number. Thus, $|a|$ is positive. For example, let $a = -3$.

$$|a| = |-3| = -(-3) = 3 \qquad \text{\footnotesize |a| = -a if a is negative.}$$

**NOW TRY
EXERCISE 5**

Evaluate each expression involving absolute value.

(a) $|-7|$ **(b)** $-|-15|$
(c) $|4| - |-4|$

EXAMPLE 5 Finding Absolute Value

Evaluate each expression involving absolute value.

(a) $|13| = 13$

(b) $|-2| = -(-2) = 2$

(c) $|0| = 0$

(d) $|-0.75| = 0.75$

(e) $-|8| = -(8) = -8$ — Evaluate the absolute value. Then find the additive inverse.

(f) $-|-8| = -(8) = -8$ — Work as in part (e); $|-8| = 8$.

(g) $|-2| + |5| = 2 + 5 = 7$ — Evaluate each absolute value, and then add.

(h) $-|5 - 2| = -|3| = -3$ — Subtract inside the absolute value bars first.

NOW TRY

**NOW TRY
EXERCISE 6**

Refer to the table in **Example 6**. Of the interpreters and translators, postal service clerks, and locomotive firers, which occupation is expected to see the least change (without regard to sign)?

EXAMPLE 6 Comparing Rates of Change in Industries

The projected total rates of change in employment (in percent) in some of the fastest-growing and in some of the most rapidly declining occupations from 2012 through 2022 are shown in the table.

Occupation (2012–2022)	Total Rate of Change (in percent)
Interpreters and translators	46.1
Personal care aides	48.8
Physicians assistants	38.4
Word processors and typists	−25.1
Postal service clerks	−31.8
Locomotive firers	−42.0

Source: Bureau of Labor Statistics.

What occupation in the table is expected to see the greatest change? The least change?

We want the greatest change, without regard to whether the change is an increase or a decrease. Look for the number in the table with the greatest absolute value. That number is for personal care aides.

$$|48.8| = 48.8$$

Similarly, the least change is for word processors and typists.

$$|-25.1| = 25.1$$

NOW TRY

NOW TRY ANSWERS
5. (a) 7 **(b)** −15 **(c)** 0
6. postal service clerks

OBJECTIVE 6 Use inequality symbols.

The statement

$$4 + 2 = 6$$

is an **equation**—a statement that two quantities are equal. The statement

$$4 \neq 6 \quad \text{(read "4 is not equal to 6")}$$

is an **inequality**—a statement that two quantities are *not* equal. When two numbers are not equal, one must be less than the other. When reading from left to right, the symbol $<$ means "is less than."

$$8 < 9, \quad -6 < 15, \quad -6 < -1, \quad \text{and} \quad 0 < \frac{4}{3} \quad \text{All are true.}$$

Reading from left to right, the symbol $>$ means "is greater than."

$$12 > 5, \quad 9 > -2, \quad -4 > -6, \quad \text{and} \quad \frac{6}{5} > 0 \quad \text{All are true.}$$

In each case, the symbol "points" toward the lesser number.

The number line in **FIGURE 8** shows the graphs of the numbers 4 and 9. On the graph, 4 is to the *left* of 9, so $4 < 9$. *The lesser of two numbers is always to the left of the other on a number line.*

FIGURE 8

Inequalities on a Number Line

On a number line, the following hold.

$a < b$ if a is to the left of b. $a > b$ if a is to the right of b.

NOW TRY
EXERCISE 7
Use a number line to determine whether each statement is *true* or *false*.
(a) $-5 > -1$
(b) $-7 < -6$

EXAMPLE 7 Determining Order on a Number Line

Use a number line to compare -6 and 1 and to compare -5 and -2.

As shown on the number line in **FIGURE 9**, -6 is located to the left of 1. For this reason, $-6 < 1$. Also, $1 > -6$. From **FIGURE 9**, $-5 < -2$, or $-2 > -5$. In each case, the symbol points to the lesser number.

FIGURE 9   NOW TRY

The following table summarizes this discussion.

▼ Results about Positive and Negative Numbers

Words	Symbols
Every negative number is less than 0.	If a is negative, then $a < 0$.
Every positive number is greater than 0.	If a is positive, then $a > 0$.
0 is neither positive nor negative.	

NOW TRY ANSWERS
7. (a) false **(b)** true

In addition to the symbols $\neq$, $<$, and $>$, the symbols $\leq$ and $\geq$ are often used.

▼ Inequality Symbols

Symbol	Meaning	Example
$\neq$	is not equal to	$3 \neq 7$
$<$	is less than	$-4 < -1$
$>$	is greater than	$3 > -2$
$\leq$	is less than or equal to	$6 \leq 6$
$\geq$	is greater than or equal to	$-8 \geq -10$

NOW TRY EXERCISE 8

Determine whether each statement is *true* or *false*.

(a) $-5 \leq -6$

(b) $-2 \geq -10$

(c) $0.5 \leq 0.5$

(d) $10(6) > 8(7)$

EXAMPLE 8 Using Inequality Symbols

The table shows several uses of inequalities and why each is true.

Inequality	Why It Is True
$6 \leq 8$	$6 < 8$
$-2 \leq -2$	$-2 = -2$
$-9 \geq -12$	$-9 > -12$
$-3 \geq -3$	$-3 = -3$
$6 \cdot 4 \leq 5(5)$	$24 < 25$

Notice the reason why $-2 \leq -2$ is true. *With the symbol $\leq$, if either the $<$ part or the $=$ part is true, then the inequality is true. This is also the case with the $\geq$ symbol.*

In the last row of the table, recall that the dot in $6 \cdot 4$ indicates the product 6×4, or 24, and $5(5)$ means 5×5, or 25. Thus, the inequality $6 \cdot 4 \leq 5(5)$ becomes $24 \leq 25$, which is true.   **NOW TRY**

NOW TRY ANSWERS

8. (a) false **(b)** true
   (c) true **(d)** $60 > 56$; true

R.1 Exercises

▶ MyMathLab®

▶ *Complete solution available in MyMathLab*

1. *Concept Check* A student claimed that $\{x \mid x \text{ is a natural number greater than } 3\}$ and $\{y \mid y \text{ is a natural number greater than } 3\}$ actually name the same set, even though different variables are used. Was this student correct?

2. *Concept Check* Give a real number that satisfies each condition.

(a) An integer between 6.75 and 7.75

(b) A rational number between $\frac{1}{4}$ and $\frac{3}{4}$

(c) A whole number that is not a natural number

(d) An integer that is not a whole number

(e) An irrational number between $\sqrt{4}$ and $\sqrt{9}$

(f) An irrational number that is negative

List the elements in each set. See Example 1.

▶ **3.** $\{x \mid x \text{ is a natural number less than } 6\}$

4. $\{m \mid m \text{ is a natural number less than } 9\}$

5. $\{z \mid z \text{ is an integer greater than } 4\}$

6. $\{y \mid y \text{ is an integer greater than } 8\}$

7. $\{z \mid z \text{ is an integer less than or equal to } 4\}$

8. $\{p \mid p \text{ is an integer less than } 3\}$

9. $\{a \mid a \text{ is an even integer greater than } 8\}$

10. $\{k \mid k \text{ is an odd integer less than } 1\}$

11. $\{p \mid p$ is a number whose absolute value is 4$\}$

12. $\{w \mid w$ is a number whose absolute value is 7$\}$

13. $\{x \mid x$ is an irrational number that is also rational$\}$

14. $\{r \mid r$ is a number that is both positive and negative$\}$

Use set-builder notation to describe each set. See Example 2. (More than one description is possible.)

15. $\{2, 4, 6, 8\}$ **16.** $\{11, 12, 13, 14\}$

17. $\{4, 8, 12, 16, \dots\}$ **18.** $\{\dots, -6, -3, 0, 3, 6, \dots\}$

Graph the elements of each set on a number line. See Objective 2.

19. $\{-4, -2, 0, 3, 5\}$ **20.** $\{-3, -1, 0, 4, 6\}$

21. $\left\{-\dfrac{6}{5}, -\dfrac{1}{4}, 0, \dfrac{5}{6}, \dfrac{13}{4}, 5.2, \dfrac{11}{2}\right\}$ **22.** $\left\{-\dfrac{2}{3}, 0, \dfrac{4}{5}, \dfrac{12}{5}, \dfrac{9}{2}, 4.8\right\}$

*Which elements of each set are **(a)** natural numbers, **(b)** whole numbers, **(c)** integers, **(d)** rational numbers, **(e)** irrational numbers, **(f)** real numbers? See Example 3.*

23. $\left\{-9, -\sqrt{6}, -0.7, 0, \dfrac{6}{7}, \sqrt{7}, 4.\overline{6}, 8, \dfrac{21}{2}, 13, \dfrac{75}{5}\right\}$

24. $\left\{-8, -\sqrt{5}, -0.6, 0, \dfrac{3}{4}, \sqrt{3}, \pi, 5, \dfrac{13}{2}, 17, \dfrac{40}{2}\right\}$

Decide whether each statement is true or false. If it is false, tell why. See Example 4.

25. Every integer is a whole number.   **26.** Every natural number is an integer.

27. Every irrational number is an integer.   **28.** Every integer is a rational number.

29. Every natural number is a whole number.   **30.** Some rational numbers are irrational.

31. Some rational numbers are whole numbers.   **32.** Some real numbers are integers.

33. The absolute value of any number is the same as the absolute value of its additive inverse.

34. The absolute value of any nonzero number is positive.

35. *Concept Check*   Match each expression in parts (a)–(d) with its value in choices A–D. Choices may be used once, more than once, or not at all.

I		II	
(a) $-(-4)$	**(b)** $\lvert -4 \rvert$	**A.** 4	**B.** -4
(c) $-\lvert -4 \rvert$	**(d)** $-\lvert -(-4) \rvert$	**C.** Both A and B	**D.** Neither A nor B

36. *Concept Check*   For what value(s) of x is $\lvert x \rvert = 4$ true?

*Give **(a)** the additive inverse and **(b)** the absolute value of each number. See Objective 4 and Example 5.*

37. 6   **38.** 9   **39.** -12 **40.** -14 **41.** $\dfrac{6}{5}$ **42.** 0.16

Evaluate each expression involving absolute value. See Example 5.

43. $\lvert -8 \rvert$ **44.** $\lvert -19 \rvert$ **45.** $\left\lvert \dfrac{3}{2} \right\rvert$ **46.** $\left\lvert \dfrac{3}{4} \right\rvert$

47. $-\lvert 5 \rvert$ **48.** $-\lvert 12 \rvert$ **49.** $-\lvert -2 \rvert$ **50.** $-\lvert -6 \rvert$

51. $-|4.5|$ **52.** $-|12.4|$ ▶ **53.** $|-2| + |3|$

54. $|-16| + |14|$ **55.** $|-9| - |-3|$ **56.** $|-10| - |-7|$

57. $|-1| + |-2| - |-3|$ **58.** $|-7| + |-3| - |-10|$

Solve each problem. ***See Example 6.***

59. The table shows the percent change in population from 2000 through 2012 for selected metropolitan areas.

Metropolitan Area	Percent Change
Las Vegas	45.4
San Francisco	8.0
Chicago	4.7
New Orleans	−8.3
Phoenix	33.1
Detroit	−3.6

Source: U.S. Census Bureau.

(a) Which metropolitan area had the greatest change in population? What was this change? Was it an increase or a decrease?

(b) Which metropolitan area had the least change in population? What was this change? Was it an increase or a decrease?

60. The table gives the net trade balance, in millions of U.S. dollars, for selected U.S. trade partners for October 2013.

Country	Trade Balance (in millions of dollars)
India	−1967
China	−28,862
Netherlands	2325
France	−1630
Turkey	396

Source: U.S. Census Bureau.

A negative balance means that imports to the United States exceeded exports from the United States, while a positive balance means that exports exceeded imports.

(a) Which country had the greatest discrepancy between exports and imports? Explain.

(b) Which country had the least discrepancy between exports and imports? Explain.

Sea level refers to the surface of the ocean. The depth of a body of water can be expressed as a negative number, representing average depth in feet below sea level. The altitude of a mountain can be expressed as a positive number, indicating its height in feet above sea level.

Body of Water	Average Depth in Feet (as a negative number)	Mountain	Altitude in Feet (as a positive number)
Pacific Ocean	−14,040	McKinley	20,237
South China Sea	−4802	Point Success	14,164
Gulf of California	−2375	Matlalcueyetl	14,636
Caribbean Sea	−8448	Rainier	14,416
Indian Ocean	−12,800	Steele	16,624

Source: World Almanac and Book of Facts.

61. List the bodies of water in order, starting with the deepest and ending with the shallowest.

62. List the mountains in order, starting with the shortest and ending with the tallest.

63. *True* or *false:*   The absolute value of the depth of the Pacific Ocean is greater than the absolute value of the depth of the Indian Ocean.

64. *True* or *false:*   The absolute value of the depth of the Gulf of California is greater than the absolute value of the depth of the Caribbean Sea.

Use a number line to determine whether each statement in true *or* false. ***See Example 7.***

65. $-6 < -1$ **66.** $-4 < -2$ **67.** $-4 > -3$ **68.** $-3 > -1$

69. $3 > -2$ **70.** $6 > -3$ **71.** $-3 \geq -3$ **72.** $-5 \leq -5$

Rewrite each statement with $>$ *so that it uses* $<$ *instead. Rewrite each statement with* $<$ *so that it uses* $>$. ***See Example 7.***

73. $6 > 2$ **74.** $5 > 1$ **75.** $-9 < 4$ **76.** $-6 < 1$

77. $-5 > -10$ **78.** $-7 > -12$ **79.** $0 < x$ **80.** $-3 < x$

Use an inequality symbol to write each statement. ***See Example 8.***

81. 7 is greater than y.

82. -4 is less than 10.

83. 5 is greater than or equal to 5.

84. -6 is less than or equal to -6.

85. $3t - 4$ is less than or equal to 10.

86. $5x + 4$ is greater than or equal to 21.

87. $5x + 3$ is not equal to 0.

88. $6x + 7$ is not equal to -9.

89. t is less than or equal to -3.

90. r is greater than or equal to -5.

91. $3x$ is less than 4.

92. $6x$ is less than -2.

Determine whether each statement is true *or* false. ***See Example 8.***

93. $-6 < 7 + 3$ **94.** $-7 < 4 + 1$ **95.** $2 \cdot 5 \geq 4 + 6$

96. $8 + 7 \leq 3 \cdot 5$ **97.** $-|-3| \geq -3$ **98.** $-|-4| \leq -4$

99. $-8 > -|-6|$ **100.** $-10 > -|-4|$ **101.** $|-5| \geq -|-5|$

102. *Concept Check*   *True or false:* $-|\pi| < -3$ (*Hint:* See **FIGURE 3**.)

The graph shows egg production in millions of eggs in selected states for 2011 and 2012. Use this graph to work Exercises 103–106.

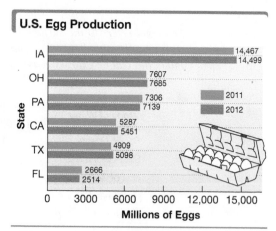

U.S. Egg Production

Source: U.S. Department of Agriculture.

103. In 2012, which states had production greater than 6000 million eggs?

104. In which of the states was 2012 egg production less than 2011 egg production?

105. If x represents 2012 egg production for Texas (TX) and y represents 2012 egg production for Ohio (OH), which is true, $x < y$ or $x > y$?

106. If x represents 2011 egg production for Iowa (IA) and y represents 2011 egg production for Pennsylvania (PA), write two inequalities, one with $>$ and one with $<$, that compare the production in these two states.

R.2 Operations on Real Numbers

OBJECTIVES

1. Add real numbers.
2. Subtract real numbers.
3. Find the distance between two points on a number line.
4. Multiply real numbers.
5. Find reciprocals and divide real numbers.

VOCABULARY

☐ sum
☐ difference
☐ product
☐ quotient
☐ reciprocal
  (multiplicative inverse)

NOW TRY EXERCISE 1

Find each sum.

(a) $-4 + (-9)$

(b) $-7.25 + (-3.57)$

(c) $-\dfrac{2}{5} + \left(-\dfrac{3}{10}\right)$

OBJECTIVE 1 Add real numbers.

Recall that the answer to an addition problem is a **sum.**

Adding Real Numbers

Same sign To add two numbers with the *same* sign, add their absolute values. The sum has the same sign as the given numbers.

Examples: $2 + 7 = 9$, $-2 + (-7) = -9$

Different signs To add two numbers with *different* signs, find the absolute values of the numbers, and subtract the lesser absolute value from the greater. The sum has the same sign as the number with the greater absolute value.

Examples: $-8 + 3 = -5$, $15 + (-9) = 6$

EXAMPLE 1 Adding Two Negative Real Numbers

Find each sum.

(a) $-12 + (-8)$

First find the absolute values: $|-12| = 12$ and $|-8| = 8$.

Because -12 and -8 have the *same* sign, add their absolute values.

$$-12 + (-8)$$

Both numbers are negative, so the sum will be negative.

$$= -(12 + 8) \quad \text{Add the absolute values.}$$

$$= -(20)$$

$$= -20$$

(b) $-6 + (-3)$

$$= -(|-6| + |-3|)$$

$$= -(6 + 3)$$

$$= -9$$

(c) $-1.2 + (-0.4)$

$$= -(1.2 + 0.4)$$

$$= -1.6$$

(d) $-\dfrac{5}{6} + \left(-\dfrac{1}{3}\right)$

$$= -\left(\dfrac{5}{6} + \dfrac{1}{3}\right) \quad \text{Add the absolute values. Both numbers are negative, so the sum will be negative.}$$

$$= -\left(\dfrac{5}{6} + \dfrac{2}{6}\right) \quad \text{The least common denominator is 6.} \quad \dfrac{1 \cdot 2}{3 \cdot 2} = \dfrac{2}{6}$$

$$= -\dfrac{7}{6} \quad \begin{array}{l}\text{Add numerators.} \\ \text{Keep the same denominator.}\end{array}$$

NOW TRY

NOW TRY ANSWERS

1. (a) -13 **(b)** -10.82

(c) $-\dfrac{7}{10}$

NOW TRY
EXERCISE 2

Find each sum.

(a) $-15 + 7$

(b) $4.6 + (-2.8)$

(c) $-\dfrac{5}{9} + \dfrac{2}{7}$

EXAMPLE 2 Adding Real Numbers with Different Signs

Find each sum.

(a) $-17 + 11$

First find the absolute values: $|-17| = 17$; and $|11| = 11$. Because -17 and 11 have *different* signs, subtract their absolute values.

$$17 - 11 = 6$$

The number -17 has a greater absolute value than 11, so the answer is negative.

$$-17 + 11 = -6 \quad \text{The sum is negative because } |-17| > |11|.$$

(b) $4 + (-1)$

Subtract the absolute values, 4 and 1. Because 4 has the greater absolute value, the sum must be positive.

$$4 + (-1) = 4 - 1 = 3 \quad \text{The sum is positive because } |4| > |-1|.$$

(c) $-9 + 17$

$$= 17 - 9$$
$$= 8$$

(d) $-2.3 + 5.6$

$$= 5.6 - 2.3$$
$$= 3.3$$

(e) $-16 + 12$

The absolute values are 16 and 12. Subtract the absolute values.

$$-16 + 12 = -(16 - 12) = -4 \quad \text{The sum is negative because } |-16| > |12|.$$

(f) $-\dfrac{4}{5} + \dfrac{2}{3}$

$$= -\frac{12}{15} + \frac{10}{15} \qquad \text{The least common denominator is 15.} \quad -\frac{4 \cdot 3}{5 \cdot 3} = -\frac{12}{15}; \frac{2 \cdot 5}{3 \cdot 5} = \frac{10}{15}$$

$$= -\left(\frac{12}{15} - \frac{10}{15}\right) \qquad \text{Subtract the absolute values. } -\frac{12}{15} \text{ has the greater absolute value, so the answer will be negative.}$$

$$= -\frac{2}{15} \qquad \text{Subtract numerators.} \\ \text{Keep the same denominator.}$$

NOW TRY

OBJECTIVE 2 Subtract real numbers.

Recall that the answer to a subtraction problem is a **difference.** Compare the following two statements.

$$6 - 4 = 2$$
$$6 + (-4) = 2$$

Thus,

$$6 - 4 = 6 + (-4).$$

To subtract 4 from 6, we add the additive inverse of 4 to 6. This example suggests the following definition of subtraction.

NOW TRY ANSWERS
2. (a) -8 **(b)** 1.8 **(c)** $-\frac{17}{63}$

Subtraction

For all real numbers a and b, the following holds.

$$a - b = a + (-b)$$

To subtract b from a, add the additive inverse (or opposite) of b to a.

Examples: $5 - 12 = 5 + (-12) = -7,$ $6 - (-3) = 6 + 3 = 9$

**NOW TRY
EXERCISE 3**

Find each difference.

(a) $-4 - 11$

(b) $-5.67 - (-2.34)$

(c) $\dfrac{4}{9} - \dfrac{3}{5}$

EXAMPLE 3 Subtracting Real Numbers

Find each difference.

Change to addition.

The additive inverse of 8 is -8.

(a) $6 - 8 = 6 + (-8) = -2$

Change to addition.

The additive inverse of 4 is -4.

(b) $-12 - 4 = -12 + (-4) = -16$

(c) $-10 - (-7)$

$\qquad = -10 + 7$ The additive inverse of -7 is 7.

$\qquad = -3$

(d) $-2.4 - (-8.1)$

$\qquad = -2.4 + 8.1$

$\qquad = 5.7$

(e) $\dfrac{5}{6} - \left(-\dfrac{3}{8}\right)$

$\qquad = \dfrac{5}{6} + \dfrac{3}{8}$ To subtract $a - b$, add the additive inverse (opposite) of b to a.

$\qquad = \dfrac{20}{24} + \dfrac{9}{24}$ Write each fraction with the least common denominator, 24.

$\qquad = \dfrac{29}{24}$ Add numerators. Keep the same denominator.

NOW TRY

When working a problem that involves both addition and subtraction, add and subtract in order from left to right. Work inside brackets or parentheses first.

EXAMPLE 4 Adding and Subtracting Real Numbers

Perform the indicated operations.

(a) $15 - (-3) - 5 - 12$

$\qquad = (15 + 3) - 5 - 12$ Work in order from left to right.

$\qquad = 18 - 5 - 12$ Add inside the parentheses.

$\qquad = 13 - 12$ Subtract from left to right.

$\qquad = 1$ Subtract.

NOW TRY ANSWERS

3. (a) -15 **(b)** -3.33 **(c)** $-\dfrac{7}{45}$

NOW TRY
EXERCISE 4
Perform the indicated operations.

$$-4 - (-2 - 7) - 12$$

(b) $-9 - [-8 - (-4)] + 6$

$= -9 - [-8 + 4] + 6$	Work inside the brackets.
$= -9 - [-4] + 6$	Add.
$= -9 + 4 + 6$	Add the additive inverse.
$= -5 + 6$	Add from left to right.
$= 1$	Add.

NOW TRY

OBJECTIVE 3 Find the distance between two points on a number line.

The number line in **FIGURE 10** shows several points.

FIGURE 10

To find the distance between the points 4 and 7, we subtract $7 - 4 = 3$. Because distance is positive (or 0), we must be careful to subtract in such a way that the answer is positive (or 0). To avoid this problem altogether, we can find the absolute value of the difference. Then the distance between 4 and 7 is found as follows.

$$|7 - 4| = |3| = 3 \quad \text{or} \quad |4 - 7| = |-3| = 3 \qquad \text{Distance between 4 and 7}$$

Distance

The **distance** between two points on a number line is the absolute value of the difference of their coordinates.

**NOW TRY
EXERCISE 5**
Find the distance between the points -7 and 12.

EXAMPLE 5 Finding Distance between Points on the Number Line

Find the distance between each pair of points. Refer to **FIGURE 10**.

(a) 8 and -4

Find the absolute value of the difference of the numbers, taken in either order.

$$|8 - (-4)| = 12, \quad \text{or} \quad |-4 - 8| = 12$$

(b) -4 and -6

$$|-4 - (-6)| = 2, \quad \text{or} \quad |-6 - (-4)| = 2 \qquad \text{NOW TRY} \ \ \image$$

OBJECTIVE 4 Multiply real numbers.

Recall that the answer to a multiplication problem is a **product.**

Multiplying Real Numbers

Same sign   The product of two numbers with the *same* sign is positive.

Examples: $4(8) = 32, \quad -4(-8) = 32$

Different signs   The product of two numbers with *different* signs is negative.

Examples: $-8(9) = -72, \quad 6(-7) = -42$

The **multiplication property of 0** states that the product of any real number and 0 is 0.

Multiplication Property of 0

For any real number a, the following hold.

$$a \cdot 0 = 0 \quad \text{and} \quad 0 \cdot a = 0$$

Examples: $12 \cdot 0 = 0, \quad 0 \cdot 12 = 0$

NOW TRY
EXERCISE 6
Find each product.

(a) $-3(-10)$

(b) $0.7(-1.2)$

(c) $-\dfrac{8}{11}(33)$

(d) $14(0)$

EXAMPLE 6 Multiplying Real Numbers

Find each product.

(a) $-3(-9) = 27$ The numbers have the same sign, so the product is positive.

(b) $-0.5(-0.4) = 0.2$

(c) $-\dfrac{3}{4}\left(-\dfrac{5}{6}\right)$

  $= \dfrac{15}{24}$ Multiply numerators. Multiply denominators.

  $= \dfrac{5 \cdot 3}{8 \cdot 3}$ Factor to write in lowest terms.

  $= \dfrac{5}{8}$ Divide out the common factor, 3.

(d) $6(-9) = -54$ The numbers have different signs, so the product is negative. $-6 = -\dfrac{6}{1}$

(e) $-0.05(0.3) = -0.015$ (f) $-\dfrac{5}{8}\left(\dfrac{12}{13}\right) = -\dfrac{15}{26}$ (g) $\dfrac{2}{3}(-6) = -4$

NOW TRY

OBJECTIVE 5 Find reciprocals and divide real numbers.

The definition of division uses the concept of a **multiplicative inverse,** or *reciprocal.*
Two numbers are *reciprocals* if they have a product of 1.

Reciprocal

The **reciprocal** of a nonzero number a is $\dfrac{1}{a}$.

▼ Reciprocals

Number	Reciprocal
$-\dfrac{2}{5}$	$-\dfrac{5}{2}$
-6, or $-\dfrac{6}{1}$	$-\dfrac{1}{6}$
$\dfrac{7}{11}$	$\dfrac{11}{7}$
0.05	20
0	None

$\left.\begin{array}{l} -\dfrac{2}{5}\left(-\dfrac{5}{2}\right) = 1 \\[4pt] -6\left(-\dfrac{1}{6}\right) = 1 \\[4pt] \dfrac{7}{11}\left(\dfrac{11}{7}\right) = 1 \\[4pt] 0.05(20) = 1 \end{array}\right\}$ Reciprocals have a product of 1.

There is no reciprocal for 0 because there is no number that can be multiplied by 0 to
give a product of 1.

> ⓘ **CAUTION**   Remember the following.
>
> *A number and its additive inverse have* opposite *signs, such as 3 and* -3.
> *A number and its reciprocal always have the* same *sign, such as 3 and* $\frac{1}{3}$.

The result of dividing one number by another is a **quotient.** For example, we can write the quotient of 45 and 3 as $\frac{45}{3}$, which equals 15. We obtain the same answer if we multiply 45 and $\frac{1}{3}$.

$$45 \div 3 = \frac{45}{3} = 15 \quad \text{and} \quad 45 \cdot \frac{1}{3} = 15$$

This suggests the following definition of division of real numbers.

Division

For all real numbers a and b (where $b \neq 0$), the following holds.

$$a \div b = \frac{a}{b} = a \cdot \frac{1}{b}$$

To divide a by b, multiply a (the **dividend**) by the reciprocal of b (the **divisor**).

There is no reciprocal for the number 0, so *division by 0 is undefined.* For example, $\frac{15}{0}$ is undefined and $-\frac{1}{0}$ is undefined.

ⓘ **CAUTION**   Although division by 0 is undefined, dividing 0 by a nonzero number gives the quotient 0. For example,

$$\frac{6}{0} \text{ is undefined,} \quad \text{but} \quad \frac{0}{6} = 0 \quad (\text{because } 0 \cdot 6 = 0).$$

Be careful when 0 is involved in a division problem.

Because division is defined as multiplication by the reciprocal, the rules for signs of quotients are the same as those for signs of products.

Dividing Real Numbers

Same sign   The quotient of two nonzero real numbers with the *same* sign is positive.

Examples: $\dfrac{24}{6} = 4, \quad \dfrac{-24}{-6} = 4$

Different signs   The quotient of two nonzero real numbers with *different* signs is negative.

Examples: $\dfrac{-36}{3} = -12, \quad \dfrac{36}{-3} = -12$

**NOW TRY
EXERCISE 7**

Find each quotient.

(a) $\dfrac{-10}{-5}$ **(b)** $\dfrac{-\dfrac{10}{3}}{\dfrac{3}{8}}$

(c) $-\dfrac{6}{5} \div \left(-\dfrac{3}{7}\right)$

EXAMPLE 7   **Dividing Real Numbers**

Find each quotient.

(a) $\dfrac{-12}{4} = -3$ The numbers have opposite signs, so the quotient is negative.   **(b)** $\dfrac{6}{-3} = -2$

(c) $\dfrac{-\dfrac{2}{3}}{-\dfrac{5}{9}}$ This is a *complex fraction* (**Section 6.3**). A complex fraction has a fraction in the numerator, the denominator, or both.

$= -\dfrac{2}{3}\left(-\dfrac{9}{5}\right)$ The reciprocal of $-\frac{5}{9}$ is $-\frac{9}{5}$.

$= \dfrac{18}{15}$ Multiply.

$= \dfrac{6}{5}$ Write in lowest terms; $\frac{18}{15} = \frac{3 \cdot 6}{3 \cdot 5} = \frac{6}{5}$

(d) $-\dfrac{9}{14} \div \dfrac{3}{7}$

$= -\dfrac{9}{14} \cdot \dfrac{7}{3}$ Multiply $-\frac{9}{14}$ by the reciprocal of $\frac{3}{7}$.

$= -\dfrac{63}{42}$ Multiply numerators and multiply denominators.

$= -\dfrac{3}{2}$ Write in lowest terms.   **NOW TRY**

Every fraction has three signs: the sign of the numerator, the sign of the denominator, and the sign of the fraction itself.

Equivalent Forms of a Fraction

The fractions $\dfrac{-x}{y}$, $\dfrac{x}{-y}$, and $-\dfrac{x}{y}$ are equivalent (where $y \neq 0$).

Example: $\dfrac{-4}{7} = \dfrac{4}{-7} = -\dfrac{4}{7}$

The fractions $\dfrac{x}{y}$ and $\dfrac{-x}{-y}$ are equivalent (where $y \neq 0$).

Example: $\dfrac{4}{7} = \dfrac{-4}{-7}$

NOW TRY ANSWERS

7. (a) 2 **(b)** $-\frac{80}{9}$ **(c)** $\frac{14}{5}$

R.2 Exercises

 FOR EXTRA HELP   MyMathLab®

▶ *Complete solution available in MyMathLab*

Concept Check   *Complete each statement and give an example.*

1. The sum of two positive numbers is a _____ number.

2. The sum of two negative numbers is a _____ number.

3. The sum of a positive number and a negative number is negative if the negative number has the _____ absolute value.

4. The sum of a positive number and a negative number is positive if the positive number has the _____ absolute value.

5. The difference between two positive numbers is negative if _____.

6. The difference between two negative numbers is negative if _____.

7. The sum of a positive number and a negative number is 0 if the numbers are _____.

8. The product of two numbers with the same sign is _____.

9. The product of two numbers with different signs is _____.

10. The quotient formed by any nonzero number divided by 0 is _____, and the quotient formed by 0 divided by any nonzero number is _____.

Add or subtract as indicated. **See Examples 1–3.**

▶ **11.** $-6 + (-13)$ **12.** $-8 + (-16)$ ▶ **13.** $13 + (-4)$

14. $19 + (-18)$ **15.** $-\dfrac{7}{3} + \dfrac{3}{4}$ **16.** $-\dfrac{5}{6} + \dfrac{4}{9}$

17. $-2.3 + 0.45$ **18.** $-0.238 + 4.58$ ▶ **19.** $-6 - 5$

20. $-8 - 17$ **21.** $8 - (-13)$ **22.** $12 - (-22)$

23. $-16 - (-3)$ **24.** $-21 - (-6)$ **25.** $-12.31 - (-2.13)$

26. $-15.88 - (-9.42)$ **27.** $\dfrac{9}{10} - \left(-\dfrac{4}{3}\right)$ **28.** $\dfrac{3}{14} - \left(-\dfrac{3}{4}\right)$

29. $|-8 - 6|$ **30.** $|-7 - 15|$ **31.** $-|-4 + 9|$

32. $-|-5 + 6|$ **33.** $-2 - |-4|$ **34.** $16 - |-13|$

Perform the indicated operations. **See Example 4.**

35. $-7 + 5 - 9$ **36.** $-12 + 14 - 18$

37. $6 - (-2) + 8$ **38.** $7 - (-4) + 11$

▶ **39.** $-9 - 4 - (-3) + 6$ **40.** $-10 - 6 - (-12) + 9$

41. $-8 - (-12) - (2 - 6)$ **42.** $-3 + (-14) + (-6 + 4)$

43. $-0.382 + 4 - 0.6$ **44.** $3 - 2.95 - (-0.63)$

45. $\left(-\dfrac{5}{4} - \dfrac{2}{3}\right) + \dfrac{1}{6}$ **46.** $\left(-\dfrac{5}{8} + \dfrac{1}{4}\right) - \left(-\dfrac{1}{4}\right)$

47. $-\dfrac{3}{4} - \left(\dfrac{1}{2} - \dfrac{3}{8}\right)$ **48.** $\dfrac{7}{5} - \left(\dfrac{9}{10} - \dfrac{3}{2}\right)$

49. $|-11| - |-5| - |7| + |-2|$ **50.** $|-6| + |-3| - |4| - |-8|$

The number line has several points labeled. Find the distance between each pair of points. **See Example 5.**

▶ **51.** A and B **52.** A and C **53.** D and F **54.** E and C

55. *Concept Check*   A statement that is often heard is "Two negatives give a positive." When is this true? When is it not true? Give a more precise statement that conveys this message.

56. *Concept Check*   Why must the reciprocal of a nonzero number have the same sign as the number?

Multiply. See Example 6.

57. $5(-7)$ **58.** $6(-9)$ ◗ **59.** $-8(-5)$ **60.** $-20(-4)$

61. $-10\left(-\dfrac{1}{5}\right)$ **62.** $-\dfrac{1}{2}(-18)$ ◗ **63.** $\dfrac{3}{4}(-16)$ **64.** $\dfrac{3}{5}(-35)$

65. $-\dfrac{5}{2}\left(-\dfrac{12}{25}\right)$ **66.** $-\dfrac{9}{7}\left(-\dfrac{21}{36}\right)$ **67.** $-\dfrac{3}{8}\left(-\dfrac{24}{9}\right)$ **68.** $-\dfrac{2}{11}\left(-\dfrac{77}{4}\right)$

69. $4(0)$ **70.** $\dfrac{1}{2}(0)$ **71.** $0(-8)$ **72.** $0(-4.5)$

Divide where possible. See Example 7.

◗ **73.** $\dfrac{-14}{2}$ **74.** $\dfrac{-39}{13}$ ◗ **75.** $\dfrac{-24}{-4}$ **76.** $\dfrac{-45}{-9}$ **77.** $\dfrac{100}{-25}$

78. $\dfrac{150}{-30}$ **79.** $\dfrac{0}{-8}$ **80.** $\dfrac{0}{-14}$ **81.** $\dfrac{5}{0}$ **82.** $\dfrac{13}{0}$

83. $-\dfrac{10}{17}\div\left(-\dfrac{12}{5}\right)$ **84.** $-\dfrac{22}{23}\div\left(-\dfrac{33}{5}\right)$ **85.** $\dfrac{\frac{12}{13}}{-\frac{4}{3}}$ **86.** $\dfrac{\frac{7}{6}}{-\frac{1}{30}}$

87. $\dfrac{-27.72}{13.2}$ **88.** $\dfrac{-162.9}{36.2}$ **89.** $\dfrac{-100}{-0.01}$ **90.** $\dfrac{-60}{-0.06}$

Exercises 91–120 provide more practice on operations with fractions and decimals. Perform the indicated operations.

91. $\dfrac{1}{6}-\left(-\dfrac{7}{9}\right)$ **92.** $\dfrac{7}{10}-\left(-\dfrac{1}{6}\right)$ **93.** $-\dfrac{1}{9}+\dfrac{7}{12}$ **94.** $-\dfrac{1}{12}+\dfrac{13}{16}$

95. $-\dfrac{3}{8}-\dfrac{5}{12}$ **96.** $-\dfrac{11}{15}-\dfrac{4}{9}$ **97.** $-\dfrac{7}{30}+\dfrac{2}{45}-\dfrac{3}{10}$

98. $-\dfrac{8}{15}-\dfrac{3}{20}+\dfrac{7}{6}$ **99.** $\dfrac{8}{25}\left(-\dfrac{5}{12}\right)$ **100.** $\dfrac{9}{20}\left(-\dfrac{7}{15}\right)$

101. $\dfrac{5}{6}\left(-\dfrac{9}{10}\right)\left(-\dfrac{4}{5}\right)$ **102.** $\dfrac{4}{3}\left(-\dfrac{9}{20}\right)\left(-\dfrac{5}{12}\right)$ **103.** $\dfrac{7}{6}\div\left(-\dfrac{9}{10}\right)$

104. $\dfrac{12}{5}\div\left(-\dfrac{18}{25}\right)$ **105.** $\dfrac{\frac{2}{3}}{-2}$ **106.** $\dfrac{\frac{3}{4}}{-6}$

107. $\dfrac{-\frac{8}{9}}{\frac{2}{3}}$ **108.** $\dfrac{-\frac{15}{16}}{\frac{3}{8}}$ **109.** $-8.6-3.751$

110. $-37.8-13.582$ **111.** $-4.2(1.4)(2.7)$ **112.** $2.9(-10.3)(0.04)$

113. $-24.84\div 6$ **114.** $-32.84\div 8$ **115.** $-2496\div(-0.52)$

116. $-161.7\div(-0.25)$ **117.** $\dfrac{-0.5}{-1.5}$ **118.** $\dfrac{-1.5}{-0.5}$

119. $-14.23 + 9.81 + 74.63$ **120.** $-89.416 + 21.32 - 478.91$

121. *Concept Check* How can the answer to **Exercise 118** be determined without showing work if the correct answer to **Exercise 117** is known?

122. *Concept Check* Without showing work, determine the difference between the high and low Fahrenheit temperatures on three consecutive days in Cedar Rapids, Iowa, during the winter of 2014. Express each as a positive number.

  (a) *Sunday:* high: 0;   low: -6 **(b)** *Monday:* high: -15;   low: -24

  (c) *Tuesday:* high: -4;   low: -20

Solve each problem.

123. The highest temperature ever recorded in Juneau, Alaska, was 90°F. The lowest temperature ever recorded there was -22°F. What is the difference between these two temperatures? (*Source: World Almanac and Book of Facts.*)

124. The highest temperature ever recorded in Illinois was 117°F. The lowest temperature ever recorded there was -36°F. What is the difference between these two temperatures? (*Source: World Almanac and Book of Facts.*)

125. Andrew has $48.35 in his checking account. He uses his debit card to make purchases of $35.99 and $20.00, which overdraws his account. His bank charges his account an overdraft fee of $28.50. He then deposits his paycheck for $66.27 from his part-time job at Arby's. What is the balance in his account?

126. Kayla has $37.60 in her checking account. She uses her debit card to make purchases of $25.99 and $19.34, which overdraws her account. Her bank charges her account an overdraft fee of $25.00. She then deposits her paycheck for $58.66 from her part-time job at Subway. What is the balance in her account?

127. Ahmad owes $382.45 on his Visa account. He returns two items costing $25.10 and $34.50 for credit. Then he makes purchases of $45.00 and $98.17.

  (a) How much should his payment be if he wants to pay off the balance on the account?

  (b) Instead of paying off the balance, he makes a payment of $300 and then incurs a finance charge of $24.66. What is the balance on his account?

128. Charlene owes $237.59 on her MasterCard account. She returns one item costing $47.25 for credit and then makes two purchases of $12.39 and $20.00.

  (a) How much should her payment be if she wants to pay off the balance on the account?

  (b) Instead of paying off the balance, she makes a payment of $75.00 and incurs a finance charge of $32.06. What is the balance on her account?

129. The graph shows annual returns in percent for class A shares of the Invesco Charter Fund for the years 2007–2013.

  (a) Find the sum of the percents for the years shown in the graph.

  (b) Find the difference between the returns in 2008 and 2007.

  (c) Find the difference between the returns in 2009 and 2008.

Invesco Charter Fund Annual Returns

Year	Percent
2007	8.41
2008	-28.46
2009	30.18
2010	8.10
2011	-0.11
2012	13.07
2013	28.34

Source: Morningstar, Invesco.

130. The graph shows profits and losses in thousands of dollars for a private company for the years 2012 through 2015.

(a) What was the total profit or loss for the years 2012 through 2015?

(b) The company showed an increase from 2012 to 2013, despite still having an overall loss. Illustrate using a subtraction problem how this increase can be determined. What was the increase?

(c) By how much did the company increase between 2012 and 2015? Illustrate using a subtraction problem.

Company Profits and Losses

The table shows receipts (income) and outlays (spending) in billions of dollars for the U.S. government in selected years.

Fiscal Year	Receipts	Outlays
1995	1352	1516
2000	2025	1789
2005	2154	2472
2012	2450	3537

Source: Office of Management and Budget.

131. Find the difference between U.S. government receipts and outlays for each year shown in the table.

132. During which years did the budget show a surplus? A deficit? Use the results from **Exercise 131** to explain the answers.

R.3 Exponents, Roots, and Order of Operations

OBJECTIVES

1 Use exponents.
2 Find square roots.
3 Use the rules for order of operations.
4 Evaluate algebraic expressions for given values of variables.

Two (or more) numbers whose product is a third number are **factors** of that third number. For example, 2 and 6 are factors of 12 because $2 \cdot 6 = 12$.

OBJECTIVE 1 Use exponents.

In algebra, we use *exponents* as a way of writing products of repeated factors.

$$\underbrace{2 \cdot 2 \cdot 2 \cdot 2 \cdot 2}_{5 \text{ factors of } 2} = 2^5$$

The number 5 shows that 2 is used as a factor 5 times. The number 5 is the *exponent,* and 2 is the *base.*

$$2^5 \leftarrow \text{Exponent}$$
$$\uparrow$$
$$\text{Base}$$

Read 2^5 as "2 to the fifth power," or "2 to the fifth." Multiplying five 2s gives 32.

2^5 means $2 \cdot 2 \cdot 2 \cdot 2 \cdot 2$, which equals 32.

VOCABULARY

☐ factors
☐ exponent (power)
☐ base
☐ exponential expression
☐ square root
☐ positive (principal) square root
☐ negative square root
☐ constant
☐ algebraic expression

> **Exponential Expression**
>
> If a is a real number and n is a natural number, then
>
> $$a^n = \underbrace{a \cdot a \cdot a \cdot \ldots \cdot a,}_{n \text{ factors of } a}$$
>
> where n is the **exponent,** a is the **base,** and a^n is an **exponential expression.**
> Exponents are also called **powers.**

NOW TRY
EXERCISE 1
Write using exponents.
(a) $(-3)(-3)(-3)$
(b) $(0.5)(0.5)$
(c) $t \cdot t \cdot t \cdot t \cdot t$

EXAMPLE 1 Using Exponential Notation

Write using exponents.

(a) $\underbrace{4 \cdot 4 \cdot 4}_{3 \text{ factors of } 4} = 4^3$

   Read 4^3 as "4 **cubed.**"

(b) $\dfrac{3}{5} \cdot \dfrac{3}{5} = \left(\dfrac{3}{5}\right)^2$ 2 factors of $\frac{3}{5}$

   Read $\left(\dfrac{3}{5}\right)^2$ as "$\dfrac{3}{5}$ **squared.**"

(c) $(-6)(-6)(-6)(-6) = (-6)^4$ 4 factors of -6

   Read $(-6)^4$ as "-6 to the fourth power," or "-6 to the fourth."

(d) $(0.3)(0.3)(0.3)(0.3)(0.3) = (0.3)^5$ **(e)** $x \cdot x \cdot x \cdot x \cdot x \cdot x = x^6$

NOW TRY

NOTE In **Example 1,** we used the terms *squared* and *cubed* to refer to powers of 2 and 3, respectively. The term *squared* comes from the figure of a square, which has the same measure for both length and width, as shown in **FIGURE 11(a).** Similarly, the term *cubed* comes from the figure of a cube, where the length, width, and height have the same measure, as shown in **FIGURE 11(b).**

(a) $3 \cdot 3$ means 3 squared, or 3^2.   **(b)** $6 \cdot 6 \cdot 6$ means 6 cubed, or 6^3.

FIGURE 11

EXAMPLE 2 Evaluating Exponential Expressions

Evaluate.

(a) 5^2 means $5 \cdot 5$, which equals 25.   5 is used as a factor 2 times.

   5^2 means $5 \cdot 5$, **not** $5 \cdot 2$.

(b) $\left(\dfrac{2}{3}\right)^3$ means $\dfrac{2}{3} \cdot \dfrac{2}{3} \cdot \dfrac{2}{3}$, which equals $\dfrac{8}{27}$. $\frac{2}{3}$ is used as a factor 3 times.

(c) 2^6 means $2 \cdot 2 \cdot 2 \cdot 2 \cdot 2 \cdot 2$, which equals 64.

NOW TRY ANSWERS
1. (a) $(-3)^3$ **(b)** $(0.5)^2$ **(c)** t^5

(d) $(-3)^5$ means $(-3)(-3)(-3)(-3)(-3)$, which equals -243.   The base is -3.

NOW TRY
EXERCISE 2

Evaluate.

(a) 7^2 **(b)** $(-7)^2$ **(c)** -7^2

(e) $(-2)^6$ means $(-2)(-2)(-2)(-2)(-2)(-2)$, which equals 64.   The base is −2.

(f) -2^6

There are no parentheses. The exponent 6 applies *only* to the number 2, not to -2.

-2^6 means $-(2 \cdot 2 \cdot 2 \cdot 2 \cdot 2 \cdot 2)$, which equals -64.   The base is 2.

NOW TRY

Examples 2(d) and (e) suggest the following generalizations.

Sign of an Exponential Expression

The product of an *even* number of negative factors is positive.

Example: $(-2)(-2)(-2)(-2) = 16$

The product of an *odd* number of negative factors is negative.

Example: $(-2)(-2)(-2) = -8$

⚠ CAUTION   As shown in **Examples 2(e)** and **(f)**, it is important to distinguish between $-a^n$ and $(-a)^n$.

$$-a^n \quad \text{means} \quad -1\underbrace{(a \cdot a \cdot a \cdot \ldots \cdot a)}_{n \text{ factors of } a} \quad \text{The base is } a.$$

$$(-a)^n \quad \text{means} \quad \underbrace{(-a)(-a) \cdot \ldots \cdot (-a)}_{n \text{ factors of } -a} \quad \text{The base is } -a.$$

Be careful when evaluating an exponential expression with a negative sign.

OBJECTIVE 2   Find square roots.

As we saw in **Example 2(a),** 5 squared (or 5^2) equals 25. The inverse procedure of squaring a number is taking its **square root.** For example, a square root of 25 is 5. Another square root of 25 is -5 because $(-5)^2 = 25$. Thus, 25 has two square roots, 5 and -5.

We write the **positive** or **principal square root** of a number using a **radical symbol** $\sqrt{}$. The positive or principal square root of 25 is written

$$\sqrt{25} = 5.$$

The **negative square root** of 25 is written

$$-\sqrt{25} = -5.$$

Because the square of any nonzero real number is positive, the square root of a negative number, such as $\sqrt{-25}$, is not a real number.

EXAMPLE 3   Finding Square Roots

Find each square root that is a real number.

(a) $\sqrt{36} = 6$ because 6 is positive and $6^2 = 36$.

(b) $\sqrt{0} = 0$ because $0^2 = 0$.

(c) $\sqrt{\dfrac{9}{16}} = \dfrac{3}{4}$ because $\left(\dfrac{3}{4}\right)^2 = \dfrac{9}{16}$.

NOW TRY
EXERCISE 3
Find each square root that is a
real number.

(a) $-\sqrt{144}$ **(b)** $\sqrt{\dfrac{100}{9}}$

(c) $\sqrt{-144}$

(d) $\sqrt{0.16} = 0.4$ because $(0.4)^2 = 0.16$.   **(e)** $\sqrt{100} = 10$ because $10^2 = 100$.

(f) $-\sqrt{100} = -10$ because the negative sign is outside the radical symbol.

(g) $\sqrt{-100}$ is not a real number because the negative sign is inside the radical symbol. No *real number* squared equals -100.

Notice that part (e) is the positive or principal square root of 100, part (f) is the negative square root of 100, and part (g) is the square root of -100, which is not a real number.

NOW TRY

⚠ **CAUTION**   The symbol $\sqrt{a}$ is used only for the *positive* square root of a. When $a = 0$, $\sqrt{0} = 0$. The symbol $-\sqrt{a}$ is used for the negative square root of a.

OBJECTIVE 3   Use the rules for order of operations.

To simplify the following expression, what should we do first—add 5 and 2 or multiply 2 and 3?

$$5 + 2 \cdot 3$$

When an expression involves more than one operation symbol, we use the following rules for **order of operations.**

Order of Operations

If grouping symbols are present, work within them, innermost first (and above and below fraction bars separately), in the following order.

Step 1   Apply all **exponents.**

Step 2   Do any **multiplications** or **divisions** in order from left to right.

Step 3   Do any **additions** or **subtractions** in order from left to right.

If no grouping symbols are present, start with Step 1.

NOW TRY
EXERCISE 4
Simplify.

$$15 - 3 \cdot 4 + 2$$

EXAMPLE 4   **Using the Rules for Order of Operations**

Simplify.

(a) $5 + 2 \cdot 3$

$\qquad = 5 + 6$ Multiply.

$\qquad = 11$ Add.

(b) $24 \div 3 \cdot 2 + 6$ Multiplications and divisions are done in order from left to right. So we divide first here.

$\qquad = 8 \cdot 2 + 6$

$\qquad = 16 + 6$ Multiply.

$\qquad = 22$ Add.

NOW TRY

NOW TRY ANSWERS
3. (a) -12 **(b)** $\frac{10}{3}$
  (c) not a real number
4. 5

NOW TRY
EXERCISE 5

Simplify.

(a) $-5^2 + 10 \div 5 - |3 - 7|$

(b) $6 + \dfrac{2}{3}(-9) - \dfrac{5}{8} \cdot 16$

EXAMPLE 5   Using the Rules for Order of Operations

Simplify.

(a) $10 \div 5 + 2\,|3 - 4|$ Work inside the absolute value bars first.

$= 10 \div 5 + 2\,|-1|$ Subtract inside the absolute value bars.

$= 10 \div 5 + 2 \cdot 1$ Take the absolute value.

$= 2 + 2$ Divide first, and then multiply.

$= 4$ Add.

(b) $4 \cdot 3^2 + 7 - (2 + 8)$ Work inside the parentheses first.

$= 4 \cdot 3^2 + 7 - 10$ Add inside the parentheses.

$= 4 \cdot 9 + 7 - 10$ Evaluate the power.

> 3^2 means $3 \cdot 3$, **not** $3 \cdot 2$.

$= 36 + 7 - 10$ Multiply.

$= 43 - 10$ Add.

$= 33$ Subtract.

(c) $\dfrac{1}{2} \cdot 4 + (6 \div 3 - 7)$ Work inside the parentheses first.

$= \dfrac{1}{2} \cdot 4 + (2 - 7)$ Divide inside the parentheses.

$= \dfrac{1}{2} \cdot 4 + (-5)$ Subtract inside the parentheses.

$= 2 + (-5)$ Multiply.

$= -3$ Add.   **NOW TRY**

NOW TRY
EXERCISE 6

Simplify.

$$\dfrac{\sqrt{36} - 4 \cdot 3^2}{-2^2 - 8 \cdot 3 + 28}$$

EXAMPLE 6   Using the Rules for Order of Operations

Simplify.

$$\dfrac{5 - (-2^3)(2)}{6 \cdot \sqrt{9} - 9 \cdot 2}$$ Work separately above and below the fraction bar.

$$= \dfrac{5 - (-8)(2)}{6 \cdot 3 - 9 \cdot 2}$$ Evaluate the power and the root.

$$= \dfrac{5 + 16}{18 - 18}$$ Multiply and use the definition of subtraction.

$$= \dfrac{21}{0}$$ Add and subtract.

Because division by 0 is undefined, the given expression is undefined.   **NOW TRY**

OBJECTIVE 4 Evaluate algebraic expressions for given values of variables.

A **constant** is a fixed, unchanging number.

$$1, \quad 6, \quad -10, \quad \frac{2}{5}, \quad -3.75 \qquad \text{Constants}$$

A collection of constants, variables, operation symbols, and/or grouping symbols is an **algebraic expression.**

$$6ab, \quad 5m - 9n, \quad -2(x^2 + 4y) \qquad \text{Algebraic expressions}$$

Algebraic expressions have different numerical values for different values of the variables. We evaluate such expressions by *substituting* given values for the variables.

> **NOW TRY**
> **EXERCISE 7**
>
> Evaluate each expression for $x = -4$, $y = 7$, and $z = 36$.
>
> (a) $3y - 2x$ (b) $\dfrac{x^2 - \sqrt{z}}{-3xy}$

EXAMPLE 7 Evaluating Algebraic Expressions

Evaluate each expression for $m = -4$, $n = 5$, $p = -6$, and $q = 25$.

(a) $\qquad 5m - 9n$

> Use parentheses around substituted values to avoid errors.

$$= 5(-4) - 9(5) \qquad \text{Substitute } m = -4 \text{ and } n = 5.$$

$$= -20 - 45 \qquad \text{Multiply.}$$

$$= -65 \qquad \text{Subtract.}$$

(b) $\dfrac{m + 2n}{4p}$ Work separately above and below the fraction bar.

$$= \frac{-4 + 2(5)}{4(-6)} \qquad \text{Substitute } m = -4, n = 5, \text{ and } p = -6.$$

$$= \frac{-4 + 10}{-24} \qquad \begin{array}{l}\text{Multiply in the numerator.}\\ \text{Multiply in the denominator.}\end{array}$$

$$= \frac{6}{-24} \qquad \text{Add in the numerator.}$$

$$= -\frac{1}{4} \qquad \text{Write in lowest terms, and rewrite using } \frac{a}{-b} = -\frac{a}{b}.$$

(c) $-3m^3 - n^2\left(\sqrt{q}\right)$

$$= -3(-4)^3 - (5)^2\left(\sqrt{25}\right) \qquad \text{Substitute } m = -4, n = 5, \text{ and } q = 25.$$

$$= -3(-64) - 25(5) \qquad \text{Evaluate the powers and the root.}$$

$$= 192 - 125 \qquad \text{Multiply.}$$

$$= 67 \qquad \text{Subtract.} \qquad \text{NOW TRY}$$

NOW TRY ANSWERS

7. (a) 29 **(b)** $\frac{5}{42}$

R.3 Exercises

FOR EXTRA HELP   ▶ MyMathLab®

▶ *Complete solution available in MyMathLab*

Concept Check   Decide whether each statement is true *or* false. *If it is false, correct the statement so that it is true.*

1. $-7^6 = (-7)^6$

2. $-5^7 = (-5)^7$

3. $\sqrt{25}$ is a positive number.

4. $3 + 5 \cdot 8 = 3 + (5 \cdot 8)$

5. $(-6)^7$ is a negative number.

6. $(-6)^8$ is a positive number.

7. The product of 10 positive factors and 10 negative factors is positive.

8. The product of 5 positive factors and 5 negative factors is positive.

9. In the exponential expression -8^5, the base is -8.

10. $\sqrt{a}$ is positive for all positive numbers a.

Concept Check   Evaluate each exponential expression.

11. (a) 8^2 **(b)** -8^2 **(c)** $(-8)^2$ **(d)** $-(-8)^2$

12. (a) 4^3 **(b)** -4^3 **(c)** $(-4)^3$ **(d)** $-(-4)^3$

Write each expression using exponents. See Example 1.

▶ **13.** $10 \cdot 10 \cdot 10 \cdot 10$ **14.** $8 \cdot 8 \cdot 8$ ▶ **15.** $\dfrac{3}{4} \cdot \dfrac{3}{4} \cdot \dfrac{3}{4} \cdot \dfrac{3}{4} \cdot \dfrac{3}{4}$

16. $\dfrac{3}{2} \cdot \dfrac{3}{2}$ ▶ **17.** $(-9)(-9)(-9)$ **18.** $(-9)(-9)(-9)(-9)$

▶ **19.** $z \cdot z \cdot z \cdot z \cdot z \cdot z \cdot z$ **20.** $a \cdot a \cdot a \cdot a \cdot a$ **21.** $0 \cdot 0 \cdot 0 \cdot 0 \cdot 0 \cdot 0$

22. *Concept Check   True* or *false:* If n is odd and a is a positive integer, then $(-a)^n = -a^n$ in all cases.

Evaluate each expression. See Example 2.

▶ **23.** 4^2 **24.** 2^4 **25.** 0.28^3 **26.** 0.91^3

27. $\left(\dfrac{1}{5}\right)^3$ **28.** $\left(\dfrac{1}{6}\right)^4$ ▶ **29.** $\left(\dfrac{4}{5}\right)^4$ **30.** $\left(\dfrac{7}{10}\right)^3$

▶ **31.** $(-5)^3$ **32.** $(-2)^5$ ▶ **33.** $(-2)^8$ **34.** $(-3)^6$

35. -3^6 **36.** -4^6 **37.** -8^4 **38.** -10^3

Find each square root. If it is not a real number, say so. See Example 3.

▶ **39.** $\sqrt{81}$ **40.** $\sqrt{64}$ **41.** $\sqrt{169}$ **42.** $\sqrt{225}$

▶ **43.** $-\sqrt{400}$ **44.** $-\sqrt{900}$ ▶ **45.** $\sqrt{\dfrac{100}{121}}$ **46.** $\sqrt{\dfrac{225}{169}}$

47. $-\sqrt{0.49}$ **48.** $-\sqrt{0.64}$ ▶ **49.** $\sqrt{-36}$ **50.** $\sqrt{-121}$

51. *Concept Check   In these questions, x represents a positive number.*

     (a) Is $-\sqrt{-x}$ positive, negative, or not a real number?

     (b) Is $-\sqrt{x}$ positive, negative, or not a real number?

52. *Concept Check   Frank's grandson was asked to evaluate the following expression.*

$$9 + 15 \div 3$$

Frank gave the answer as 8, but his grandson gave the answer as 14. The grandson explained that the answer is 14 because of the "Order of Process rule," which says that when evaluating an expression like this, we proceed from right to left rather than left to right. (*Note:* This is a true story.)

     (a) Whose answer was correct for this expression, Frank's or his grandson's?

     (b) Was the *reasoning* for the correct answer valid? Explain.

Simplify each expression. See Examples 4–6.

▶ **53.** $12 + 3 \cdot 4$ **54.** $15 + 5 \cdot 2$ **55.** $6 \cdot 3 - 12 \div 4$

56. $9 \cdot 4 - 8 \div 2$ **57.** $10 + 30 \div 2 \cdot 3$ **58.** $12 + 24 \div 3 \cdot 2$

59. $-3(5)^2 - (-2)(-8)$

60. $-9(2)^2 - (-3)(-2)$

61. $5 - 7 \cdot 3 - (-2)^3$

62. $-4 - 3 \cdot 5 + 6^2$

63. $-7(\sqrt{36}) - (-2)(-3)$

64. $-8(\sqrt{64}) - (-3)(-7)$

▶ **65.** $6|4 - 5| - 24 \div 3$

66. $-4|2 - 4| + 8 \cdot 2$

67. $|-6 - 5|(-8) + 3^2$

68. $(-6 - 3)|-2 - 3| \div 9$

69. $6 + \frac{2}{3}(-9) - \frac{5}{8} \cdot 16$

70. $7 - \frac{3}{4}(-8) + 12 \cdot \frac{5}{6}$

71. $-14\left(-\frac{2}{7}\right) \div (2 \cdot 6 - 10)$

72. $-12\left(-\frac{3}{4}\right) - (6 \cdot 5 \div 3)$

73. $\dfrac{(-5 + \sqrt{4})(-2^2)}{-5 - 1}$

74. $\dfrac{(-9 + \sqrt{16})(-3^2)}{-4 - 1}$

▶ **75.** $\dfrac{2(-5) + (-3)(-2)}{-8 + 3^2 - 1}$

76. $\dfrac{3(-4) + (-5)(-8)}{2^3 - 2 - 6}$

77. $\dfrac{5 - 3\left(\dfrac{-5 - 9}{-7}\right) - 6}{-9 - 11 + 3 \cdot 7}$

78. $\dfrac{-4\left(\dfrac{12 - (-8)}{3 \cdot 2 + 4}\right) - 5(-1 - 7)}{-9 - (-7) - [-5 - (-8)]}$

Evaluate each expression for $a = -3$, $b = 64$, and $c = 6$. **See Example 7.**

▶ **79.** $3a + \sqrt{b}$

80. $-2a - \sqrt{b}$

81. $\sqrt{b} + c - a$

82. $\sqrt{b} - c + a$

83. $4a^3 + 2c$

84. $-3a^4 - 3c$

▶ **85.** $\dfrac{2c + a^3}{4b + 6a}$

86. $\dfrac{3c + a^2}{2b - 6c}$

Evaluate each expression for $w = 4$, $x = -\frac{3}{4}$, $y = \frac{1}{2}$, and $z = 1.25$. **See Example 7.**

87. $wy - 8x$

88. $wz - 12y$

89. $xy + y^4$

90. $xy - x^2$

91. $-w + 2x + 3y + z$

92. $w - 6x + 5y - 3z$

93. $\dfrac{7x + 9y}{w}$

94. $\dfrac{7y - 5x}{2w}$

Residents of Linn County, Iowa, in the Cedar Rapids Community School District can use the expression

$$(v \times 0.5485 - 4850) \div 1000 \times 31.44$$

to determine their property taxes, where v is assessed home value. (Source: The Gazette.) Use the expression to calculate the amount of property taxes to the nearest dollar that the owner of a home with each of the following values would pay. Follow the rules for order of operations.

95. $100,000

96. $150,000

97. $200,000

The Blood Alcohol Concentration (BAC) of a person who has been drinking is given by the expression

number of oz × % alcohol × 0.075 ÷ body weight in lb − hr of drinking × 0.015.

(*Source:* Lawlor, J., *Auto Math Handbook: Calculations, Formulas, Equations and Theory for Automotive Enthusiasts,* Penguin, © 1991.)
  Use this formula in Exercises 98–100.

98. Suppose a policeman stops a 190-lb man who, in 2 hr, has ingested four 12-oz beers (48 oz), each having a 3.2% alcohol content.

    (a) Substitute the values into the formula, and write the expression for the man's BAC.

    (b) Calculate the man's BAC to the nearest thousandth. Follow the rules for order of operations.

99. Find the BAC to the nearest thousandth for a 135-lb woman who, in 3 hr, has drunk three 12-oz beers (36 oz), each having a 4.0% alcohol content.

100. (a) Calculate the BACs in **Exercises 98 and 99** if each person weighs 25 lb more and the rest of the variables stay the same. How does increased weight affect a person's BAC?

    (b) Predict how decreased weight would affect the BAC of each person in **Exercises 98 and 99.** Calculate the BACs if each person weighs 25 lb less and the rest of the variables stay the same.

Solve each problem.

101. The amount in billions of dollars that Americans have spent on their pets from 2001 to 2013 can be approximated by substituting a given year for x in the expression

$$2.311x - 4596.$$

(*Source:* American Pet Products Manufacturers Association.) Find the amount spent in each year. Round answers to the nearest tenth.

    (a) 2001   **(b)** 2007   **(c)** 2013

    (d) How has the amount Americans have spent on their pets changed from 2001 to 2013?

Dotty

102. The average price in dollars of a movie ticket in the United States from 1997 to 2012 can be approximated using the expression

$$0.2363x - 467.2,$$

where x represents the year. (*Source:* National Association of Theater Owners.)

Year	Average Price (in dollars)
1997	
2002	5.87
2007	
2012	

    (a) Use the expression to complete the table. Round answers to the nearest cent.

    (b) How has the average price of a theater ticket in the United States changed from 1997 to 2012?

R.4 Properties of Real Numbers

VOCABULARY

☐ identity element for addition (additive identity)
☐ identity element for multiplication (multiplicative identity)
☐ term
☐ coefficient (numerical coefficient)
☐ like terms
☐ unlike terms

In **Section R.2** we used the *multiplication property of 0*. There are other basic properties of real numbers that reflect results that occur consistently in mathematics.

OBJECTIVE 1 Use the distributive property.

Notice the following.

$$2(3 + 5) = 2 \cdot 8 = 16$$

and

$$2 \cdot 3 + 2 \cdot 5 = 6 + 10 = 16,$$

so

$$2(3 + 5) = 2 \cdot 3 + 2 \cdot 5.$$

This idea is illustrated by the divided rectangle in **FIGURE 12**.

Similarly, observe these facts.

$$-4[5 + (-3)] = -4(2) = -8$$

and

$$-4(5) + (-4)(-3) = -20 + 12 = -8,$$

so

$$-4[5 + (-3)] = -4(5) + (-4)(-3).$$

These two examples are generalized to the set of *all* real numbers as the **distributive property of multiplication with respect to addition,** or simply the **distributive property.**

Area of left part is $2 \cdot 3 = 6$.
Area of right part is $2 \cdot 5 = 10$.
Area of total rectangle is $2(3 + 5) = 16$.

FIGURE 12

Distributive Property

For any real numbers a, b, and c, the following hold.

$$a(b + c) = ab + ac \quad \text{and} \quad (b + c)a = ba + ca$$

Examples: $12(4 + 2) = 12 \cdot 4 + 12 \cdot 2 \quad$ and

$$(4 + 2)12 = 4 \cdot 12 + 2 \cdot 12$$

The distributive property can also be applied "in reverse."

$$ab + ac = a(b + c) \quad \text{and} \quad ba + ca = (b + c)a$$

Examples: $6 \cdot 8 + 6 \cdot 9 = 6(8 + 9) \quad$ and $\quad 8 \cdot 6 + 9 \cdot 6 = (8 + 9)6$

This property can be extended to more than two numbers as well.

$$a(b + c + d) = ab + ac + ad$$

The distributive property provides a way to rewrite a product $a(b + c)$ as a sum $ab + ac$, or a sum as a product.

NOTE When we rewrite $a(b + c)$ as $ab + ac$, we sometimes refer to the process as "removing" or "clearing" parentheses.

**NOW TRY
EXERCISE 1**

Use the distributive property
to rewrite each expression.

(a) $-2(3x - y)$

(b) $4k - 12k$

EXAMPLE 1 Using the Distributive Property

Use the distributive property to rewrite each expression.

(a) $3(x + y)$

$= 3x + 3y$ Use the first form of the property to rewrite the given product as a sum.

(b) $-2(5 + k)$

$= -2(5) + (-2)(k)$ Distributive property

$= -10 - 2k$ Multiply.

(c) $4x + 8x$

$= (4 + 8)x$ Use the distributive property in reverse to rewrite the given sum as a product.

$= 12x$ Add inside the parentheses.

(d) $3r - 7r$

$= 3r + (-7r)$ Definition of subtraction

$= [3 + (-7)]r$ Distributive property in reverse

$= -4r$ Add.

(e) $5p + 7q$ This expression *cannot* be rewritten as 12*pq*.

Because there is no common number or variable here, we cannot use the distributive property to rewrite the expression.

(f) $6(x + 2y - 3z)$

$= 6x + 6(2y) + 6(-3z)$ Distributive property

$= 6x + 12y - 18z$ Multiply.   **NOW TRY**

The distributive property can also be used for subtraction as in **Example 1(d).**

$$a(b - c) = ab - ac$$

OBJECTIVE 2 Use the identity properties.

The number 0 is the only number that can be added to any number to get that number, leaving the identity of the number unchanged. Thus, 0 is the **identity element for addition,** or the **additive identity.**

In a similar way, multiplying any number by 1 leaves the identity of the number unchanged. Thus, 1 is the **identity element for multiplication,** or the **multiplicative identity.** The **identity properties** summarize this discussion.

Identity Properties

For any real number a, the following hold.

$$a + 0 = a \quad \text{and} \quad 0 + a = a$$

Examples: $9 + 0 = 9$ and $0 + 9 = 9$

$$a \cdot 1 = a \quad \text{and} \quad 1 \cdot a = a$$

Examples: $9 \cdot 1 = 9$ and $1 \cdot 9 = 9$

NOW TRY ANSWERS

1. (a) $-6x + 2y$ **(b)** $-8k$

The identity properties leave the identity of a real number unchanged. Think of a child wearing a costume on Halloween. The child's appearance is changed, but his or her identity is unchanged.

NOW TRY EXERCISE 2

Simplify each expression.

(a) $7x + x$　(b) $-(5p - 3q)$

EXAMPLE 2　Using the Identity Property $1 \cdot a = a$

Simplify each expression.

(a) $12m + m$

$\quad = 12m + 1m$　　Identity property

$\quad = (12 + 1)m$　　Distributive property

$\quad = 13m$　　　　Add inside the parentheses.

(b) $y + y$

$\quad = 1y + 1y$　　Identity property

$\quad = (1 + 1)y$　　Distributive property

$\quad = 2y$　　　　Add inside the parentheses.

(c) $\qquad -(m - 5n)$

$\quad = -1(m - 5n)$　　　　Identity property

$\quad = -1(m) + (-1)(-5n)$　　Distributive property

> Multiply *each* term by -1. Be careful with signs.

$\quad = -m + 5n$　　　　Multiply.　　**NOW TRY**

OBJECTIVE 3　Use the inverse properties.

The *additive inverse* (or *opposite*) of a number a is $-a$. Additive inverses have a sum of 0 (the additive identity).

$$5 \text{ and } -5, \quad -\frac{1}{2} \text{ and } \frac{1}{2}, \quad -34 \text{ and } 34$$ Additive inverses (sum of 0)

The *multiplicative inverse* (or *reciprocal*) of a number a is $\frac{1}{a}$ (where $a \neq 0$). Multiplicative inverses have a product of 1.

$$5 \text{ and } \frac{1}{5}, \quad -\frac{1}{2} \text{ and } -2, \quad \frac{3}{4} \text{ and } \frac{4}{3}$$ Multiplicative inverses (product of 1)

This discussion leads to the **inverse properties.**

Inverse Properties

For any real number a, the following hold.

$$a + (-a) = 0 \quad \text{and} \quad -a + a = 0$$

Examples:　$7 + (-7) = 0$　and　$-7 + 7 = 0$

$$a \cdot \frac{1}{a} = 1 \quad \text{and} \quad \frac{1}{a} \cdot a = 1 \quad (\text{where } a \neq 0)$$

Examples:　$7 \cdot \frac{1}{7} = 1$　and　$\frac{1}{7} \cdot 7 = 1$

NOW TRY ANSWERS
2. (a) $8x$　(b) $-5p + 3q$

▼ Terms and Their Coefficients

Term	Numerical Coefficient
$-7y$	-7
$34r^3$	34
$-26x^5yz^4$	-26
$-k = -1k$	-1
$r = 1r$	1
$\dfrac{3x}{8} = \dfrac{3}{8}x$	$\dfrac{3}{8}$
$\dfrac{x}{3} = \dfrac{1x}{3} = \dfrac{1}{3}x$	$\dfrac{1}{3}$

The inverse properties "undo" addition or multiplication. Think of putting on your shoes when you get up in the morning and then taking them off before you go to bed at night. These are inverse operations that undo each other.

Expressions such as $12m$ and $5n$ from **Example 2** are examples of *terms*. A **term** is a number or the product of a number and one or more variables raised to powers. The numerical factor in a term is the **numerical coefficient,** or just the **coefficient.**

Terms with exactly the same variables raised to exactly the same powers are **like terms.** Otherwise, they are **unlike terms.**

$5p$ and $-21p$ $-6x^2$ and $9x^2$ Like terms

$3m$ and $16x$ $7y^3$ and $-3y^2$ Unlike terms

Different variables   Different exponents on the same variable

OBJECTIVE 4 Use the commutative and associative properties.

Simplifying expressions as in **Examples 2(a) and (b)** is called **combining like terms.** *Only like terms may be combined.* To combine like terms in an expression such as

$$-2m + 5m + 3 - 6m + 8,$$

we need two more properties. From arithmetic, we know that

$$3 + 9 = 12 \quad \text{and} \quad 9 + 3 = 12$$
$$3 \cdot 9 = 27 \quad \text{and} \quad 9 \cdot 3 = 27.$$

The order of the numbers being added or multiplied does not matter. The same answers result. The following computations illustrate this fact.

$$(5 + 7) + 2 = 12 + 2 = 14$$
$$5 + (7 + 2) = 5 + 9 = 14$$

$$(5 \cdot 7) \cdot 2 = 35 \cdot 2 = 70$$
$$5 \cdot (7 \cdot 2) = 5 \cdot 14 = 70$$

The grouping of the numbers being added or multiplied does not matter. The same answers result.

These arithmetic examples can be extended to algebra.

Commutative and Associative Properties

For any real numbers a, b, and c, the following hold.

$$a + b = b + a$$
$$ab = ba$$
Commutative properties

(The *order* of the two terms or factors changes.)

Examples: $9 + (-3) = -3 + 9$ and $9(-3) = (-3)9$

$$a + (b + c) = (a + b) + c$$
$$a(bc) = (ab)c$$
Associative properties

(The *grouping* among the three terms or factors changes, but the order stays the same.)

Examples: $7 + (8 + 9) = (7 + 8) + 9$ and $7 \cdot (8 \cdot 9) = (7 \cdot 8) \cdot 9$

The commutative properties are used to change the order of the terms or factors in an expression. Think of *commuting* from home to work and then from work to home. The associative properties are used to regroup the terms or factors of an expression. The grouped terms or factors are *associated*.

NOW TRY
EXERCISE 3

Simplify.

$-7x + 10 - 3x - 4 + x$

EXAMPLE 3 Using the Commutative and Associative Properties

Simplify.

$$-2m + 5m + 3 - 6m + 8$$

$$= (-2m + 5m) + 3 - 6m + 8 \qquad \text{Associative property}$$

$$= (-2 + 5)m + 3 - 6m + 8 \qquad \text{Distributive property}$$

$$= 3m + 3 - 6m + 8 \qquad \text{Add inside parentheses.}$$

The next step would be to add $3m$ and 3, but they are unlike terms. To get $3m$ and $-6m$ together, we use the associative and commutative properties, inserting parentheses and brackets according to the order of operations.

$$= [(3m + 3) - 6m] + 8$$

$$= [3m + (3 - 6m)] + 8 \qquad \text{Associative property}$$

$$= [3m + (-6m + 3)] + 8 \qquad \text{Commutative property}$$

$$= [(3m + [-6m]) + 3] + 8 \qquad \text{Associative property}$$

$$= (-3m + 3) + 8 \qquad \text{Combine like terms.}$$

$$= -3m + (3 + 8) \qquad \text{Associative property}$$

$$= -3m + 11 \qquad \text{Add.}$$

In practice, many of these steps are not written down, but it is important to realize that the commutative and associative properties are used whenever the terms in an expression are rearranged to combine like terms. NOW TRY

EXAMPLE 4 Using the Properties of Real Numbers

Simplify each expression.

(a) $5y - 8y - 6y + 11y$

$$= (5 - 8 - 6 + 11)y \qquad \text{Distributive property}$$

$$= 2y \qquad \text{Subtract and add.}$$

(b) $3x + 4 - 5(x + 1) - 8$

Be careful with signs.

$$= 3x + 4 - 5x - 5 - 8 \qquad \text{Distributive property}$$

$$= 3x - 5x + 4 - 5 - 8 \qquad \text{Commutative property}$$

$$= -2x - 9 \qquad \text{Combine like terms. Subtract.}$$

(c) $8 - (3m + 2)$

$$= 8 - 1(3m + 2) \qquad \text{Identity property}$$

$$= 8 - 3m - 2 \qquad \text{Distributive property}$$

$$= 6 - 3m \qquad \text{Subtract.}$$

NOW TRY ANSWER
3. $-9x + 6$

NOW TRY
EXERCISE 4

Simplify each expression.

(a) $-3(t - 4) - t + 15$

(b) $7x - (4x - 2)$

(c) $5x(6y)$

(d) $3x(5)(y)$

$= [3x(5)]y$ Associative property

$= [3(x \cdot 5)]y$ Associative property

$= [3(5x)]y$ Commutative property

$= [(3 \cdot 5)x]y$ Associative property

$= (15x)y$ Multiply.

$= 15(xy)$ Associative property

$= 15xy$

As previously mentioned, many of these steps are not usually written out.

NOW TRY

⚠ **CAUTION** Be careful. The distributive property does not apply in **Example 4(d)** because there is no addition or subtraction involved.

$$(3x)(5)(y) \neq (3x)(5) \cdot (3x)(y)$$

NOW TRY ANSWERS

4. **(a)** $-4t + 27$ **(b)** $3x + 2$
    (c) $30xy$

R.4 Exercises

FOR EXTRA HELP   ▶   MyMathLab®

▶ *Complete solution available in MyMathLab*

Concept Check   *Choose the correct response.*

1. The identity element for addition is

    A. $-a$ **B.** 0   **C.** 1   **D.** $\dfrac{1}{a}$.

2. The identity element for multiplication is

    A. $-a$ **B.** 0   **C.** 1   **D.** $\dfrac{1}{a}$.

3. The additive inverse of a is

    A. $-a$ **B.** 0   **C.** 1   **D.** $\dfrac{1}{a}$.

4. The multiplicative inverse of a, where $a \neq 0$, is

    A. $-a$ **B.** 0   **C.** 1   **D.** $\dfrac{1}{a}$.

Concept Check   *Complete each statement.*

5. The commutative property is used to change the _____ of two terms or factors.

6. The associative property is used to change the _____ of three terms or factors.

7. Like terms are terms with the _____ variables raised to the _____ powers.

8. When simplifying an expression, only _____ terms can be combined.

9. The numerical coefficient in the term $-7yz^2$ is _____ .

10. The multiplication property of 0 (**Section R.2**) says that the _____ of 0 and any real number is _____ .

Simplify each expression. ***See Examples 1 and 2.***

▶ **11.** $2(m + p)$ **12.** $3(a + b)$ **13.** $-12(x - y)$ **14.** $-10(p - q)$

15. $5k + 3k$ **16.** $6a + 5a$ **17.** $7r - 9r$ **18.** $4n - 6n$

19. $-8z + 4w$ **20.** $-12k + 3r$ ▶ **21.** $a + 7a$ **22.** $s + 9s$

23. $-(2d - f)$ **24.** $-(3m - n)$ **25.** $-(-x - y)$ **26.** $-(-3x - 4y)$

*Simplify each expression. **See Examples 1–4.***

27. $-12y + 4y + 3 + 2y$

28. $-5r - 9r + 8r - 5$

▶ **29.** $-6p + 5 - 4p + 6 + 11p$

30. $-8x - 12 + 3x - 5x + 9$

▶ **31.** $3(k + 2) - 5k + 6 + 3$

32. $5(r - 3) + 6r - 2r + 4$

33. $-2(m + 1) - (m - 4)$

34. $6(a - 5) - (a + 6)$

35. $0.25(8 + 4p) - 0.5(6 + 2p)$

36. $0.4(10 - 5x) - 0.8(5 + 10x)$

37. $-(2p + 5) + 3(2p + 4) - 2p$

38. $-(7m - 12) - 2(4m + 7) - 8m$

39. $2 + 3(2z - 5) - 3(4z + 6) - 8$

40. $-4 + 4(4k - 3) - 6(2k + 8) + 7$

Concept Check   *Complete each statement so that the indicated property is illustrated. Simplify each answer if possible.*

41. $5x + 8x =$ _____
(distributive property)

42. $9y - 6y =$ _____
(distributive property)

43. $5(9r) =$ _____
(associative property)

44. $-4 + (12 + 8) =$ _____
(associative property)

45. $5x + 9y =$ _____
(commutative property)

46. $-5 \cdot 7 =$ _____
(commutative property)

47. $1 \cdot 7 =$ _____
(identity property)

48. $-12x + 0 =$ _____
(identity property)

49. $-\dfrac{1}{4}ty + \dfrac{1}{4}ty =$ _____
(inverse property)

50. $-\dfrac{9}{8}\left(-\dfrac{8}{9}\right) =$ _____
(inverse property)

51. $8(-4 + x) =$ _____
(distributive property)

52. $3(x - y + z) =$ _____
(distributive property)

53. $0(0.875x + 9y - 88z) =$ _____
(multiplication property of 0)

54. $0(35t^2 - 8t + 12) =$ _____
(multiplication property of 0)

55. *Concept Check*   Give an "everyday" example of a commutative operation and of an operation that is not commutative.

56. *Concept Check*   Give an "everyday" example of inverse operations.

The distributive property can be used to mentally perform calculations. For example, calculate $38 \cdot 17 + 38 \cdot 3$ *as follows.*

$$38 \cdot 17 + 38 \cdot 3$$
$$= 38(17 + 3) \qquad \text{Distributive property}$$
$$= 38(20) \qquad \text{Add inside the parentheses.}$$
$$= 760 \qquad \text{Multiply.}$$

Use the distributive property to calculate each value mentally.

57. $96 \cdot 19 + 4 \cdot 19$

58. $27 \cdot 60 + 27 \cdot 40$

59. $58 \cdot \dfrac{3}{2} - 8 \cdot \dfrac{3}{2}$

60. $8.75(15) - 8.75(5)$

61. $4.31(69) + 4.31(31)$

62. $\dfrac{8}{5}(17) + \dfrac{8}{5}(13)$

Write a short answer to each problem.

63. By the distributive property, $a(b + c) = ab + ac$. This property is more completely named the distributive property of multiplication with respect to addition. Is there a distributive property of addition with respect to multiplication? In other words, is

$$a + (b \cdot c) = (a + b)(a + c)$$

true for all real numbers, a, b, and c? To find out, try some sample values of a, b, and c.

64. Explain how the distributive property is used to combine like terms. Give an example.

RELATING CONCEPTS   For Individual or Group Work   **(Exercises 65–70)**

When simplifying the expression $3x + 4 + 2x + 7$ to $5x + 11$, some steps are usually done mentally. **Work Exercises 65–70 in order,** *providing the property that justifies each statement in the given simplification. (These steps could be done in other orders.)*

$$3x + 4 + 2x + 7$$

65.	$= (3x + 4) + (2x + 7)$	_____
66.	$= 3x + (4 + 2x) + 7$	_____
67.	$= 3x + (2x + 4) + 7$	_____
68.	$= (3x + 2x) + (4 + 7)$	_____
69.	$= (3 + 2)x + (4 + 7)$	_____
70.	$= 5x + 11$	_____

Chapter R | Summary

Key Terms

R.1

set
elements (members)
finite set
natural (counting) numbers
infinite set
whole numbers
empty (null) set
variable
number line
integers
coordinate
graph

rational numbers
irrational numbers
real numbers
additive inverse
  (opposite, negative)
signed numbers
absolute value
equation
inequality

R.2

sum
difference

product
quotient
reciprocal
  (multiplicative inverse)

R.3

factors
exponent (power)
base
exponential expression
square root
positive (principal)
  square root
negative square root

constant
algebraic expression

R.4

identity element for addition
  (additive identity)
identity element for
  multiplication
  (multiplicative identity)
term
coefficient
  (numerical coefficient)
like terms
unlike terms

New Symbols

$\{a, b\}$	set containing the elements a and b
$\varnothing$ or $\{\ \}$	empty set
$\in$	is an element of (a set)
$\notin$	is not an element of
$\neq$	is not equal to

$\{x \mid x \text{ has property } P\}$	set-builder notation
$\mid x \mid$	absolute value of x
$<$	is less than
$\leq$	is less than or equal to
$>$	is greater than

$\geq$	is greater than or equal to
a^m	m factors of a
$\sqrt{\ }$	radical symbol
$\sqrt{a}$	positive (principal) square root of a

Test Your Word Power

See how well you have learned the vocabulary in this chapter.

1. The **empty set** is a set
   A. with 0 as its only element
   B. with an infinite number of elements
   C. with no elements
   D. of ideas.

2. A **variable** is
   A. a symbol used to represent an unknown number
   B. a value that makes an equation true
   C. a solution of an equation
   D. the answer in a division problem.

3. The **absolute value** of a number is
   A. the graph of the number
   B. the reciprocal of the number
   C. the opposite of the number
   D. the distance between 0 and the number on a number line.

4. The **reciprocal** of a nonzero number a is
   A. a B. $\frac{1}{a}$ C. $-a$ D. 1.

5. A **factor** is
   A. the answer in an addition problem
   B. the answer in a multiplication problem
   C. one of two or more numbers that are added to get another number
   D. any number that divides evenly into a given number.

6. An **exponential expression** is
   A. a number that is a repeated factor in a product
   B. a number or a variable written with an exponent
   C. a number that shows how many times a factor is repeated in a product

D. an expression that involves addition.

7. A **term** is
   A. a numerical factor
   B. a number or a product of a number and one or more variables raised to powers
   C. one of several variables with the same exponents
   D. a sum of numbers and variables raised to powers.

8. A **numerical coefficient** is
   A. the numerical factor in a term
   B. the number of terms in an expression
   C. a variable raised to a power
   D. the variable factor in a term.

ANSWERS

1. C; *Example:* The set of whole numbers less than 0 is the empty set, written $\emptyset$.   2. A; *Examples: a, b, c*   3. D; *Examples:* $|2| = 2$ and $|-2| = 2$
4. B; *Examples:* 3 is the reciprocal of $\frac{1}{3}$; $-\frac{5}{2}$ is the reciprocal of $-\frac{2}{5}$.   5. D; *Example:* 2 and 5 are factors of 10 because both divide evenly (without remainder) into 10.   6. B; *Examples:* 3^4 and x^{10} 7. B; *Examples:* $6, \frac{x}{2}, -4ab^2$ 8. A; *Examples:* The term $8z$ has numerical coefficient 8, and the term $-10x^3y$ has numerical coefficient -10.

| Chapter R | Test | FOR EXTRA HELP | *Step-by-step test solutions are found on the Chapter Test Prep Videos available in* MyMathLab® *or on* YouTube. |

▶ *View the complete solutions to all Chapter Test exercises in MyMathLab.*

[R.1]

1.

2. $0, 3, \sqrt{25}$ (or 5), $\frac{24}{2}$ (or 12)

3. $-1, 0, 3, \sqrt{25}$ (or 5), $\frac{24}{2}$ (or 12)

4. $-1, -0.5, 0, 3, \sqrt{25}$ (or 5)

   $7.5, \frac{24}{2}$ (or 12)

5. All are real numbers except $\sqrt{-4}$.

6. false

7. true

[R.2]

8. 0

1. Graph $\left\{-3, 0.75, \frac{5}{3}, 5, 6.3\right\}$ on a number line.

Let $A = \left\{-\sqrt{6}, -1, -0.5, 0, 3, \sqrt{25}, 7.5, \frac{24}{2}, \sqrt{-4}\right\}$. *Simplify the elements of A as necessary, and then list those elements of A which belong to the specified set.*

2. Whole numbers

3. Integers

4. Rational numbers

5. Real numbers

Decide whether each statement is true *or* false.

6. Every real number is an integer.

7. Every whole number is an integer.

Perform the indicated operations.

8. $-6 + 14 + (-11) - (-3)$

9. $10 - 4 \cdot 3 + 6(-4)$

10. $7 - 4^2 + 2(6) + (-4)^2$

11. $\dfrac{10 - 24 + (-6)}{\sqrt{16}(-5)}$

12. $\dfrac{-2[3 - (-1 - 2) + 2]}{\sqrt{9}(-3) - (-2)}$

13. $\dfrac{8 \cdot 4 - 3^2 \cdot 5 - 2(-1)}{-3 \cdot 2^3 + 24}$

[R.3]
9. -26 10. 19
11. 1 12. $\dfrac{16}{7}$
13. undefined

[R.2]
14. 50,395 ft
15. 37,487 ft
16. 1345 ft

[R.3]
17. 14 18. -15
19. not a real number
20. (a) a must be positive.
    (b) a must be negative.
    (c) a must be 0.

21. $-\dfrac{6}{23}$

[R.4]
22. $10k - 10$
23. It changes the sign of each term. The simplified form is $7r + 2$.

[R.2, R.4]
24. B
25. D   26. A
27. F   28. C
29. C   30. E

The table shows the heights in feet of some selected mountains and the depths in feet (as negative numbers) of some selected ocean trenches.

Mountain	Height	Trench	Depth
Foraker	17,400	Philippine	−32,995
Wilson	14,252	Cayman	−24,721
Pikes Peak	14,111	Java	−23,376

Source: *World Almanac and Book of Facts.*

14. What is the difference between the height of Mt. Foraker and the depth of the Philippine Trench?

15. What is the difference between the height of Pikes Peak and the depth of the Java Trench?

16. How much deeper is the Cayman Trench than the Java Trench?

Find each square root. If the number is not real, say so.

17. $\sqrt{196}$ 18. $-\sqrt{225}$ 19. $\sqrt{-16}$

20. For the expression $\sqrt{a}$, under what conditions will its value be each of the following?

   (a) positive   (b) not real   (c) 0

21. Evaluate $\dfrac{8k + 2m^2}{r - 2}$ for $k = -3$, $m = -3$, and $r = 25$.

22. Simplify $-3(2k - 4) + 4(3k - 5) - 2 + 4k$.

23. How does the subtraction sign affect the terms $-4r$ and 6 when

$$(3r + 8) - (-4r + 6)$$

   is simplified? What is the simplified form?

Match each statement in Column I with the appropriate property in Column II. Answers may be used more than once.

I	**II**
24. $6 + (-6) = 0$	**A.** Distributive property
25. $-2 + (3 + 6) = (-2 + 3) + 6$	**B.** Inverse property
26. $5x + 15x = (5 + 15)x$	**C.** Identity property
27. $13 \cdot 0 = 0$	**D.** Associative property
28. $-9 + 0 = -9$	**E.** Commutative property
29. $4 \cdot 1 = 4$	**F.** Multiplication property of 0
30. $(a + b) + c = (b + a) + c$	

Reading Your Math Textbook

Take time to read each section and its examples before doing your homework. You will learn more and be better prepared to work the exercises your instructor assigns.

Approaches to Reading Your Math Textbook

Student A learns best by listening to her teacher explain things. She "gets it" when she sees the instructor work problems. She previews the section before the lecture, so she knows generally what to expect. **Student A carefully reads the section in her text *AFTER* she hears the classroom lecture on the topic.**

Student B learns best by reading on his own. He reads the section and works through the examples before coming to class. That way, he knows what the teacher is going to talk about and what questions he wants to ask. **Student B carefully reads the section in his text *BEFORE* he hears the classroom lecture on the topic.**

Which of these reading approaches works best for you—that of Student A or Student B?

Tips for Reading Your Math Textbook

- **Turn off your cell phone.** You will be able to concentrate more fully on what you are reading.

- **Survey the material.** Glance over the assigned material to get an idea of the "big picture." Look at the list of objectives to see what you will be learning.

- **Read slowly.** Read only one section—or even part of a section—at a sitting, with paper and pencil in hand.

- **Pay special attention to important information given in colored boxes or set in boldface type.**

- **Study the examples carefully.** Pay particular attention to the blue side comments and any pointer balloons.

- **Do the Now Try exercises in the margin on separate paper as you go.** These mirror the examples and prepare you for the exercise set. The answers are given at the bottom of the page.

- **Make study cards as you read.** Make cards for new vocabulary, rules, procedures, formulas, and sample problems.

- **Mark anything you don't understand. *ASK QUESTIONS*** in class—everyone will benefit. Follow up with your instructor, as needed.

Think through and answer each question.

1. Which two or three reading tips will you try this week?

2. Did the tips you selected improve your ability to read and understand the material? Explain.

1

Linear Equations, Inequalities, and Applications

The concept of balance can be applied to solving *linear equations in one variable,* a topic of this chapter.

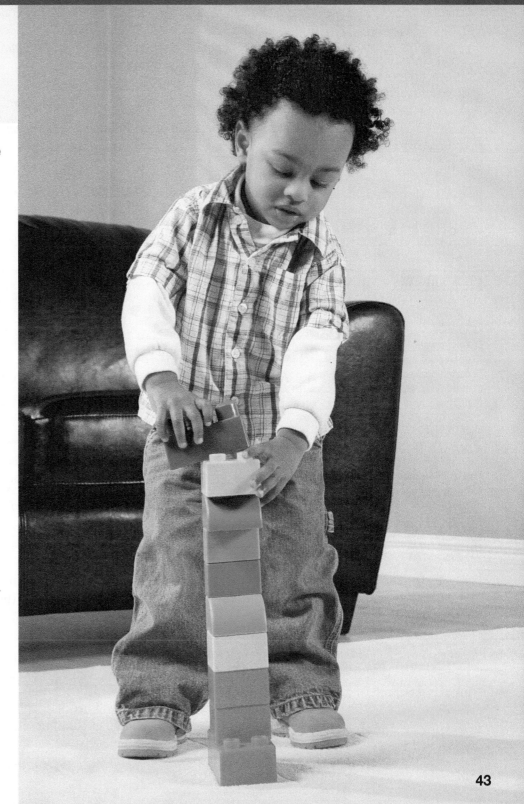

43

1.1 Linear Equations in One Variable

VOCABULARY

☐ linear (first-degree) equation in one variable
☐ solution
☐ solution set
☐ equivalent equations
☐ conditional equation
☐ identity
☐ contradiction

 NOW TRY EXERCISE 1

Decide whether each of the following is an *expression* or an *equation*.

(a) $2x + 17 - 3x$

(b) $2x + 17 = 3x$

NOW TRY ANSWERS
1. **(a)** expression **(b)** equation

OBJECTIVE 1 Distinguish between expressions and equations.

In our work in **Chapter R,** we reviewed *algebraic expressions.*

$$8x + 9, \quad y - 4, \quad \text{and} \quad \frac{x^3 y^8}{z} \qquad \text{Algebraic expressions}$$

Equations and inequalities compare algebraic expressions, just as a balance scale compares the weights of two quantities. Recall that an *equation* is a statement that two algebraic expressions are equal. ***An equation always contains an equality symbol, while an expression does not.***

EXAMPLE 1 **Distinguishing between Expressions and Equations**

Decide whether each of the following is an *expression* or an *equation.*

(a) $3x - 7 = 2$ **(b)** $3x - 7$

In part (a) we have an equation because there is an equality symbol. In part (b), there is no equality symbol, so it is an expression.

Equation
Left side   Right side
$$\overbrace{3x - 7} = \overbrace{2}$$
An equation can be *solved.*

Expression
$$3x - 7$$
An expression **cannot** be solved.
It can often be *evaluated* or *simplified.*

NOW TRY

OBJECTIVE 2 Identify linear equations.

A *linear equation in one variable* involves only real numbers and one variable raised to the first power.

Linear Equation in One Variable

A **linear equation in one variable** (here x) can be written in the form

$$Ax + B = C,$$

where A, B, and C are real numbers and $A \neq 0$.

Examples: $x + 1 = -2$, $x - 3 = 5$, and $2x + 5 = 10$ Linear equations

A linear equation is a **first-degree equation** because the greatest power on the variable is 1. Some equations that are not linear (that is, *nonlinear*) follow.

$$x^2 + 3x = 5, \quad \frac{8}{x} = -22, \quad \text{and} \quad \sqrt{x} = 6 \qquad \text{Nonlinear equations}$$

If the variable in an equation can be replaced by a real number that makes the statement true, then that number is a **solution** of the equation. For example, 8 is a solution of the equation $x - 3 = 5$ because replacing x with 8 gives a true statement. An equation is *solved* by finding its **solution set,** the set of all solutions. The solution set of the equation $x - 3 = 5$ is $\{8\}$.

Equivalent equations are related equations that have the same solution set. To solve an equation, we usually start with the given equation and replace it with a series of simpler equivalent equations. The following are all equivalent because each has solution set $\{3\}$.

$$5x + 2 = 17, \quad 5x = 15, \quad \text{and} \quad x = 3 \qquad \text{Equivalent equations}$$

OBJECTIVE 3 Solve linear equations using the addition and multiplication properties of equality.

We use two important properties of equality to produce equivalent equations.

Addition and Multiplication Properties of Equality

Addition Property of Equality

If A, B, and C represent real numbers, then the equations

$$A = B \quad \text{and} \quad A + C = B + C \quad \text{are equivalent.}$$

That is, the same number may be added to each side of an equation without changing the solution set.

Multiplication Property of Equality

If A, B, and C represent real numbers, where $C \neq 0$, then the equations

$$A = B \quad \text{and} \quad AC = BC \quad \text{are equivalent.}$$

That is, each side of an equation may be multiplied by the same nonzero number without changing the solution set.

Because subtraction and division are defined in terms of addition and multiplication, respectively, the preceding properties can be extended.

The same number may be subtracted from each side of an equation, and each side of an equation may be divided by the same nonzero number, without changing the solution set.

EXAMPLE 2 Solving a Linear Equation

Solve $4x - 2x - 5 = 4 + 6x + 3$.

The goal is to isolate x on one side of the equation.

$$4x - 2x - 5 = 4 + 6x + 3$$

$2x - 5 = 7 + 6x$	Combine like terms.
$2x - 5 + 5 = 7 + 6x + 5$	Add 5 to each side.
$2x = 12 + 6x$	Combine like terms.
$2x - 6x = 12 + 6x - 6x$	Subtract 6x from each side.
$-4x = 12$	Combine like terms.
$\dfrac{-4x}{-4} = \dfrac{12}{-4}$	Divide each side by −4.
$x = -3$	

NOW TRY EXERCISE 2

Solve.

$$5x + 11 = 2x - 13 - 3x$$

CHECK   Substitute -3 for x in the original equation.

$$4x - 2x - 5 = 4 + 6x + 3 \qquad \text{Original equation}$$

$$4(-3) - 2(-3) - 5 \stackrel{?}{=} 4 + 6(-3) + 3 \qquad \text{Let } x = -3.$$

> Use parentheses around substituted values to avoid errors.

$$-12 + 6 - 5 \stackrel{?}{=} 4 - 18 + 3 \qquad \text{Multiply.}$$

$$-11 = -11 \; \checkmark \qquad \text{True}$$

> This is *not* the solution.

The true statement indicates that $\{-3\}$ is the solution set.   NOW TRY

⚠ **CAUTION**   In **Example 2**, the equality symbols are aligned in a column. **Use only one equality symbol in a horizontal line of work when solving an equation.**

> **Solving a Linear Equation in One Variable**
>
> **Step 1**   **Simplify each side separately.** Use the distributive property as needed.
> - Clear any parentheses.
> - Clear any fractions or decimals.
> - Combine like terms.
>
> **Step 2**   **Isolate the variable terms on one side.** Use the addition property of equality so that all terms with variables are on one side of the equation and all constants (numbers) are on the other side.
>
> **Step 3**   **Isolate the variable.** Use the multiplication property of equality to obtain an equation that has just the variable with coefficient 1 on one side.
>
> **Step 4**   **Check.** Substitute the proposed solution into the *original* equation. If a true statement results, write the solution set. If not, rework the problem.

OBJECTIVE 4   Solve linear equations using the distributive property.

EXAMPLE 3   Solving a Linear Equation

Solve $2(x - 5) + 3x = x + 6$.

Step 1   Clear parentheses using the distributive property. Then combine like terms.

> Be sure to distribute over *all* terms within the parentheses.

$$2(x - 5) + 3x = x + 6$$

$$2x + 2(-5) + 3x = x + 6 \qquad \text{Distributive property}$$

$$2x - 10 + 3x = x + 6 \qquad \text{Multiply.}$$

$$5x - 10 = x + 6 \qquad \text{Combine like terms.}$$

Step 2   Isolate the variable terms on one side and constants on the other.

$$5x - 10 - x = x + 6 - x \qquad \text{Subtract } x.$$

$$4x - 10 = 6 \qquad \text{Combine like terms.}$$

$$4x - 10 + 10 = 6 + 10 \qquad \text{Add 10.}$$

$$4x = 16 \qquad \text{Combine like terms.}$$

NOW TRY ANSWER
2. $\{-4\}$

**NOW TRY
EXERCISE 3**

Solve.

$5(x - 4) - 12 = 3 - 2x$

Step 3 Use the multiplication property of equality to isolate x on the left.

$$\frac{4x}{4} = \frac{16}{4} \qquad \text{Divide by 4.}$$

$$x = 4$$

Step 4 Check by substituting 4 for x in the original equation.

CHECK

$$2(x - 5) + 3x = x + 6 \qquad \text{Original equation}$$

$$2(4 - 5) + 3(4) \stackrel{?}{=} 4 + 6 \qquad \text{Let } x = 4.$$

Always check
your work.

$$2(-1) + 12 \stackrel{?}{=} 10 \qquad \text{Simplify.}$$

$$10 = 10 \ \checkmark \qquad \text{True}$$

The proposed solution 4 checks, so the solution set is $\{4\}$.

NOW TRY

**NOW TRY
EXERCISE 4**

Solve.

$2 - 3(2 + 6x) = 4(x + 1) + 36$

EXAMPLE 4 Solving a Linear Equation

Solve $4(3x - 2) = 38 - 2(2x - 1)$.

$$4(3x - 2) = 38 - 2(2x - 1) \qquad \text{Clear parentheses using the distributive property.}$$

Step 1 $4(3x) + 4(-2) = 38 - 2(2x) - 2(-1)$

Be careful with signs
when distributing.

$$12x - 8 = 38 - 4x + 2 \qquad \text{Multiply.}$$

$$12x - 8 = 40 - 4x \qquad \text{Combine like terms.}$$

Step 2 $12x - 8 + 4x = 40 - 4x + 4x \qquad \text{Add } 4x.$

$$16x - 8 = 40 \qquad \text{Combine like terms.}$$

$$16x - 8 + 8 = 40 + 8 \qquad \text{Add 8.}$$

$$16x = 48 \qquad \text{Combine like terms.}$$

Step 3 $\dfrac{16x}{16} = \dfrac{48}{16} \qquad \text{Divide by 16.}$

$$x = 3$$

Step 4 CHECK $4(3x - 2) = 38 - 2(2x - 1) \qquad \text{Original equation}$

$$4[3(3) - 2] \stackrel{?}{=} 38 - 2[2(3) - 1] \qquad \text{Let } x = 3.$$

$$4[7] \stackrel{?}{=} 38 - 2[5] \qquad \text{Work inside the brackets.}$$

$$28 = 28 \ \checkmark \qquad \text{True}$$

The proposed solution 3 checks, so the solution set is $\{3\}$.

NOW TRY

OBJECTIVE 5 Solve linear equations with fractions or decimals.

When fractions appear as coefficients in an equation, we multiply each side by the least common denominator (LCD) of all the fractions. This is an application of the multiplication property of equality.

NOW TRY ANSWERS
3. $\{5\}$ **4.** $\{-2\}$

**NOW TRY
EXERCISE 5**

Solve.

$$\frac{x-4}{4} + \frac{2x+4}{8} = 5$$

EXAMPLE 5   Solving a Linear Equation with Fractions

Solve $\dfrac{x+7}{6} + \dfrac{2x-8}{2} = -4$.

Step 1 $6\left(\dfrac{x+7}{6} + \dfrac{2x-8}{2}\right) = 6(-4)$ Eliminate the fractions.
Multiply each side by the LCD, 6.

$6\left(\dfrac{x+7}{6}\right) + 6\left(\dfrac{2x-8}{2}\right) = 6(-4)$ Distributive property

$x + 7 + 3(2x-8) = -24$ Multiply.

$x + 7 + 3(2x) + 3(-8) = -24$ Distributive property

$x + 7 + 6x - 24 = -24$ Multiply.

$7x - 17 = -24$ Combine like terms.

Step 2 $7x - 17 + 17 = -24 + 17$ Add 17.

$7x = -7$ Combine like terms.

Step 3 $\dfrac{7x}{7} = \dfrac{-7}{7}$ Divide by 7.

$x = -1$

Step 4   CHECK $\dfrac{x+7}{6} + \dfrac{2x-8}{2} = -4$ Original equation

$\dfrac{-1+7}{6} + \dfrac{2(-1)-8}{2} \overset{?}{=} -4$ Let $x = -1$.

$\dfrac{6}{6} + \dfrac{-10}{2} \overset{?}{=} -4$ Add and subtract in the numerators.

$1 - 5 \overset{?}{=} -4$ Simplify each fraction.

$-4 = -4$ ✓   True

The proposed solution -1 checks, so the solution set is $\{-1\}$.   NOW TRY

When an equation involves decimal coefficients, we can clear the decimals by multiplying by a power of 10, such as

$$10^1 = 10, \quad 10^2 = 100, \quad \text{and so on,}$$

to obtain an equivalent equation with integer coefficients.

EXAMPLE 6   Solving a Linear Equation with Decimals

Solve $0.06x + 0.09(15 - x) = 0.07(15)$.

$0.06x + 0.09(15 - x) = 0.07(15)$ Clear parentheses first.

Step 1 $0.06x + 0.09(15) + 0.09(-x) = 0.07(15)$ Distributive property

$0.06x + 1.35 - 0.09x = 1.05$ Multiply.

Now clear the decimals. Because each decimal number is given in hundredths, multiply each term of the equation by 100. A number can be multiplied by 100 by moving the decimal point two places to the right.

NOW TRY ANSWER
5. $\{11\}$

NOW TRY
EXERCISE 6

Solve.

$$0.08x - 0.12(x - 4)$$
$$= 0.03(x - 5)$$

$$0.06x + 1.35 - 0.09x = 1.05 \qquad \text{Multiply } each \text{ term by 100.}$$

$$6x + 135 - 9x = 105 \qquad \boxed{\text{This is an equivalent equation without decimals.}}$$

$$\boxed{\text{Move decimal points 2 places to the right.}}$$

$$-3x + 135 = 105 \qquad \text{Combine like terms.}$$

Step 2 $\qquad -3x + 135 - 135 = 105 - 135 \qquad$ Subtract 135.

$$-3x = -30 \qquad \text{Combine like terms.}$$

Step 3 $\qquad \dfrac{-3x}{-3} = \dfrac{-30}{-3} \qquad$ Divide by -3.

$$x = 10$$

Step 4 **CHECK** $\qquad 0.06x + 0.09(15 - x) = 0.07(15)$

$$0.06(10) + 0.09(15 - 10) \overset{?}{=} 0.07(15) \qquad \text{Let } x = 10.$$

$$0.6 + 0.09(5) \overset{?}{=} 1.05 \qquad \text{Multiply and subtract.}$$

$$0.6 + 0.45 \overset{?}{=} 1.05 \qquad \text{Multiply.}$$

$$1.05 = 1.05 \ \checkmark \qquad \text{True}$$

The solution set is $\{10\}$.

NOW TRY

OBJECTIVE 6 Identify conditional equations, contradictions, and identities.

Some equations have one solution, some have no solutions, and others have an infinite number of solutions. The table gives the names of these types of equations.

▼ **Solution Sets of Equations**

Type of Linear Equation	Number of Solutions	Indication When Solving
Conditional	One solution; solution set: {a number}	Final line is $x = $ a number. (See **Example 7(a)**.)
Identity	Infinitely many solutions; solution set: {all real numbers}	Final line is true, such as $0 = 0$. (See **Example 7(b)**.)
Contradiction	No solution; solution set: ∅	Final line is false, such as $-15 = -20$. (See **Example 7(c)**.)

EXAMPLE 7 Recognizing Conditional Equations, Identities, and Contradictions

Solve each equation. Decide whether it is a *conditional equation,* an *identity,* or a *contradiction.*

(a) $\qquad 5(2x + 6) - 2 = 7(x + 4)$

$$10x + 30 - 2 = 7x + 28 \qquad \text{Distributive property}$$

$$10x + 28 = 7x + 28 \qquad \text{Combine like terms.}$$

$$10x + 28 - 7x - 28 = 7x + 28 - 7x - 28 \qquad \text{Subtract } 7x. \text{ Subtract 28.}$$

$$3x = 0 \qquad \text{Combine like terms.}$$

$$\boxed{\text{The last line has a variable. The number following "=" is a solution.}} \quad \dfrac{3x}{3} = \dfrac{0}{3} \qquad \text{Divide by 3.}$$

$$x = 0 \qquad \tfrac{0}{3} = 0 \text{ (See **Section R.2**.)}$$

Solve each equation. Decide whether it is a *conditional equation,* an *identity,* or a *contradiction.*

(a) $9x - 3(x + 4) = 6(x - 2)$

(b) $-3(2x - 1) - 2x = 3 + x$

(c) $10x - 21 = 2(x - 5) + 8x$

CHECK

$$5(2x + 6) - 2 = 7(x + 4) \qquad \text{Original equation}$$

$$5[2(0) + 6] - 2 \overset{?}{=} 7(0 + 4) \qquad \text{Let } x = 0.$$

$$5(6) - 2 \overset{?}{=} 7(4) \qquad \text{Multiply and then add.}$$

$$28 = 28 \checkmark \qquad \text{True}$$

The value 0 checks, so the solution set is $\{0\}$. Because the solution set has only one element, $5(2x + 6) - 2 = 7(x + 4)$ is a conditional equation.

(b)
$$5x - 15 = 5(x - 3)$$

$$5x - 15 = 5x - 15 \qquad \text{Distributive property}$$

$$5x - 15 - 5x + 15 = 5x - 15 - 5x + 15 \qquad \text{Subtract } 5x. \text{ Add } 15.$$

The variable has disappeared. $\quad 0 = 0 \qquad \text{True}$

The *true* statement $0 = 0$ indicates that the solution set is $\{\text{all real numbers}\}$. The equation $5x - 15 = 5(x - 3)$ is an identity. Notice that the first step yielded

$$5x - 15 = 5x - 15, \quad \text{which is true for } all \text{ values of } x.$$

We could have identified the equation as an identity at that point.

(c)
$$5x - 15 = 5(x - 4)$$

$$5x - 15 = 5x - 20 \qquad \text{Distributive property}$$

$$5x - 15 - 5x = 5x - 20 - 5x \qquad \text{Subtract } 5x.$$

The variable has disappeared. $\quad -15 = -20 \qquad \text{False}$

Because the result, $-15 = -20$, is *false,* the equation has no solution. The solution set is $\varnothing$, so the equation $5x - 15 = 5(x - 4)$ is a contradiction. **NOW TRY**

NOW TRY ANSWERS

7. **(a)** $\{\text{all real numbers}\}$; identity

(b) $\{0\}$; conditional equation

(c) $\varnothing$; contradiction

> **! CAUTION** A common error in solving an equation like that in **Example 7(a)** is to think that the equation has no solution and write the solution set as $\varnothing$. This equation has one solution, the number 0, so it is a conditional equation with solution set $\{0\}$.

1.1 Exercises

FOR EXTRA HELP MyMathLab°

 Complete solution available in MyMathLab

Concept Check   Complete each statement. The following key terms may be used once, more than once, or not at all.

| linear equation | solution | algebraic expression | contradiction | all real numbers |
| solution set | identity | conditional equation | first-degree equation | empty set $\varnothing$ |

1. A collection of numbers, variables, operation symbols, and grouping symbols, such as $2(8x - 15)$, is a(n) _____ . While an equation (*does/does not*) include an equality symbol, there (*is/is not*) an equality symbol in an algebraic expression.

2. A(n) _____ in one variable (here x) can be written in the form $Ax + B (=/>/<) C$, with $A \neq 0$. Another name for a linear equation is a(n) _____ , because the greatest power on the variable is (*one/two/three*).

3. If we let $x = 2$ in the linear equation $2x + 5 = 9$, a (*true/false*) statement results. The number 2 is a(n) _____ of the equation, and $\{2\}$ is the _____ .

4. A linear equation with one solution in its _____, such as the equation in **Exercise 3,** is a(n) _____.

5. A linear equation with an infinite number of solutions is a(n)_____. Its solution set is {_____}.

6. A linear equation with no solution is a(n) _____. Its solution set is the _____.

7. *Concept Check*   Which equations are linear equations in *x*?

   A. $3x + x - 2 = 0$ **B.** $12 = x^2$ **C.** $9x - 4 = 9$ **D.** $\dfrac{1}{8}x - \dfrac{1}{x} = 0$

8. *Concept Check*   Which of the equations in **Exercise 7** are nonlinear equations in *x*? Explain why.

9. *Concept Check*   Decide whether 6 is a solution of $3(x + 4) = 5x$ by substituting 6 for *x*. If it is not a solution, explain why.

10. *Concept Check*   Use substitution to decide whether -2 is a solution of the equation $5(x + 4) - 3(x + 6) = 9(x + 1)$. If it is not a solution, explain why.

Decide whether each of the following is an expression *or an* equation. ***See Example 1.***

11. $-3x + 2 - 4 = x$

12. $-3x + 2 - 4 - x = 4$

13. $4(x + 3) - 2(x + 1) - 10$

14. $4(x + 3) - 2(x + 1) + 10$

15. $-10x + 12 - 4x = -3$

16. $-10x + 12 - 4x + 3 = 0$

17. *Concept Check*   This work contains a common error.

$$8x - 2(2x - 3) = 3x + 7$$
$$8x - 4x - 6 = 3x + 7 \qquad \text{Distributive property}$$
$$4x - 6 = 3x + 7 \qquad \text{Combine like terms}$$
$$x = 13 \qquad \text{Subtract 3x. Add 6.}$$

WHAT WENT WRONG?   Give the correct solution.

18. *Concept Check*   When clearing parentheses in the expression

$$-5x - (2x - 4) + 5 \qquad \text{See Exercise 47, the right side of the equation.}$$

the $-$ sign before the parenthesis acts like a factor representing what number? Clear parentheses and simplify this expression.

Solve each equation, and check the solution. If applicable, tell whether the equation is an identity *or a* contradiction. ***See Examples 2–4 and 7.***

19. $7x + 8 = 1$

20. $5x - 4 = 21$

21. $5x + 2 = 3x - 6$

22. $9x + 1 = 7x - 9$

▶ **23.** $7x - 5x + 15 = x + 8$

24. $2x + 4 - x = 4x - 5$

▶ **25.** $12w + 15w - 9 + 5 = -3w + 5 - 9$

26. $-4x + 5x - 8 + 4 = 6x - 4$

▶ **27.** $3(2t - 4) = 20 - 2t$

28. $2(3 - 2x) = x - 4$

29. $-5(x + 1) + 3x + 2 = 6x + 4$

30. $5(x + 3) + 4x - 5 = 4 - 2x$

▶ **31.** $-2x + 5x - 9 = 3(x - 4) - 5$

32. $-6x + 2x - 11 = -2(2x - 3) + 4$

33. $2(x + 3) = -4(x + 1)$

34. $4(x - 9) = 8(x + 3)$

35. $3(2x + 1) - 2(x - 2) = 5$

36. $4(x - 2) + 2(x + 3) = 6$

37. $2x + 3(x - 4) = 2(x - 3)$

38. $6x - 3(5x + 2) = 4(1 - x)$

39. $6x - 4(3 - 2x) = 5(x - 4) - 10$

40. $-2x - 3(4 - 2x) = 2(x - 3) + 2$

▶ **41.** $-2(x + 3) - x - 4 = -3(x + 4) + 2$ **42.** $4(2x + 7) = 2x + 25 + 3(2x + 1)$

43. $2[x - (2x + 4) + 3] = 2(x + 1)$ **44.** $4[2x - (3 - x) + 5] = -(2 + 7x)$

45. $-[2x - (5x + 2)] = 2 + (2x + 7)$ **46.** $-[6x - (4x + 8)] = 9 + (6x + 3)$

47. $-3x + 6 - 5(x - 1) = -5x - (2x - 4) + 5$

48. $4(x + 2) - 8x - 5 = -3x + 9 - 2(x + 6)$

49. $7[2 - (3 + 4x)] - 2x = -9 + 2(1 - 15x)$

50. $4[6 - (1 + 2x)] + 10x = 2(10 - 3x) + 8x$

51. $-[3x - (2x + 5)] = -4 - [3(2x - 4) - 3x]$

52. $2[-(x - 1) + 4] = 5 + [-(6x - 7) + 9x]$

Concept Check   *Answer each question.*

53. To solve the linear equation

$$\frac{3}{4}x - \frac{1}{3}x = \frac{5}{6}x - 5,$$

we multiply each side by the least common denominator of all the fractions in the equation. What is this LCD?

54. Suppose that in solving the equation

$$\frac{1}{3}x + \frac{1}{2}x = \frac{1}{6}x,$$

we begin by multiplying each side by 12, rather than the *least* common denominator, 6. Would we get the correct solution? Explain.

55. To solve a linear equation with decimals, we usually begin by multiplying by a power of 10 so that all coefficients are integers. What is the least power of 10 that will accomplish this goal in each equation?

    (a) $0.04x + 0.06 + 0.03x = 0.03x + 1.46$ **(Exercise 71)**

    (b) $0.006x - 0.02x + 0.03 = 0.008x + 0.25$ **(Exercise 73)**

56. The expression $0.06(10 - x)(100)$ is equivalent to which one of the following?

    A. $0.06 - 0.06x$ **B.** $60 - 6x$ **C.** $6 - 6x$ **D.** $6 - 0.06x$

Solve each equation, and check the solution. ***See Examples 5 and 6.***

57. $-\frac{5}{9}x = 2$ **58.** $\frac{3}{11}x = -5$ **59.** $\frac{6}{5}x = -1$

60. $-\frac{7}{8}x = 6$ **61.** $\frac{x}{2} + \frac{x}{3} = 5$ **62.** $\frac{x}{5} - \frac{x}{4} = 1$

63. $\frac{3x}{4} + \frac{5x}{2} = 13$ **64.** $\frac{8x}{3} - \frac{x}{2} = -13$ **65.** $\frac{x - 10}{5} + \frac{2}{5} = -\frac{x}{3}$

66. $\frac{5 - x}{6} + \frac{5}{6} = \frac{x}{54}$ ▶ **67.** $\frac{3x - 1}{4} + \frac{x + 3}{6} = 3$ **68.** $\frac{3x + 2}{7} - \frac{x + 4}{5} = 2$

69. $\frac{4x + 1}{3} = \frac{x + 5}{6} + \frac{x - 3}{6}$ **70.** $\frac{2x + 5}{5} = \frac{3x + 1}{2} + \frac{-x + 8}{16}$

71. $0.04x + 0.06 + 0.03x = 0.03x + 1.46$ **72.** $0.05x + 0.08 + 0.06x = 0.07x + 0.68$

73. $0.006x - 0.02x + 0.03 = 0.008x + 0.25$ **74.** $0.05x - 0.1x + 0.6 = 0.04x + 2.22$

▶ **75.** $0.05x + 0.12(x + 5000) = 940$ **76.** $0.09x + 0.13(x + 300) = 61$

77. $0.02(50) + 0.08x = 0.04(50 + x)$ **78.** $0.04(90) + 0.12x = 0.06(460 + x)$

79. $0.05x + 0.10(200 - x) = 0.45x$ **80.** $0.08x + 0.12(260 - x) = 0.48x$

81. $0.006(x + 2) = 0.007x + 0.009$ **82.** $0.006(50 - x) = 0.272 - 0.004x$

STUDY SKILLS

Completing Your Homework

You are ready to do your homework **AFTER** you have read the corresponding textbook section and worked through the examples and Now Try exercises.

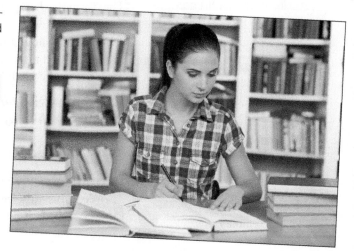

Homework Tips

- **Survey the exercise set.** Glance over the problems that your instructor has assigned to get a general idea of the types of exercises you will be working. Skim directions, and note any references to section examples.

- **Work problems neatly.** Use pencil and write legibly, so others can read your work. Skip lines between steps. Clearly separate problems from each other.

- **Show all your work.** It is tempting to take shortcuts. Include ALL steps.

- **Check your work frequently to make sure you are on the right track.** It is hard to unlearn a mistake. For all odd-numbered problems, answers are given in the back of the book.

- **If you have trouble with a problem, refer to the corresponding worked example in the section.** The exercise directions will often reference specific examples to review. Pay attention to every line of the worked example to see how to get from step to step.

- **If you are having trouble with an even-numbered problem, work the corresponding odd-numbered problem.** Check your answer in the back of the book, and apply the same steps to work the even-numbered problem.

- **Mark any problems you don't understand.** Ask your instructor about them.

- **Do some homework problems every day.** This is a good habit, even if your math class does not meet each day.

Think through and answer each question.

1. What is your instructor's policy regarding homework?

2. Think about your current approach to doing homework. What are you doing well? What improvements could you make?

3. Which one or two homework tips will you try this week? Why?

1.2 Formulas and Percent

VOCABULARY

☐ mathematical model
☐ formula
☐ percent
☐ percent increase
☐ percent decrease

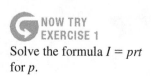

NOW TRY EXERCISE 1

Solve the formula $I = prt$ for p.

A **mathematical model** is an equation or inequality that describes a real situation. Models for many applied problems, called *formulas,* already exist. A **formula** is an equation in which variables are used to describe a relationship. For example, the formula for finding the area $\mathscr{A}^*$ of a triangle is

$$\mathscr{A} = \frac{1}{2}bh.$$

Here, b is the length of the base and h is the height. See **FIGURE 1**. A list of formulas used in algebra is given inside the back cover of this book.

FIGURE 1

OBJECTIVE 1 Solve a formula for a specified variable.

The formula $I = prt$ says that interest on a loan or investment equals principal (amount borrowed or invested) times rate (percent) times time at interest (in years). To determine how long it will take for an investment at a stated interest rate to earn a predetermined amount of interest, it would help to first solve the formula for t. This process is called **solving for a specified variable** or **solving a literal equation.**

> *When solving for a specified variable, the key is to treat that variable as if it were the only one. Treat all other variables like numbers (constants).*

EXAMPLE 1 Solving for a Specified Variable

Solve the formula $I = prt$ for t.

We solve this formula for t by treating I, p, and r as constants (having fixed values) and treating t as the only variable.

$$prt = I \qquad \text{Our goal is to isolate } t.$$

$$(pr)t = I \qquad \text{Associative property}$$

$$\frac{(pr)t}{pr} = \frac{I}{pr} \qquad \text{Divide by } pr.$$

$$t = \frac{I}{pr}$$

The result is a formula for t, time in years.

NOW TRY

Solving for a Specified Variable

Step 1 **Clear any parentheses and fractions.** If the equation contains parentheses, clear them using the distributive property. Clear any fractions by multiplying both sides by the LCD.

Step 2 **Isolate all terms with the specified variable.** Transform so that all terms containing the specified variable are on one side of the equation and all terms without that variable are on the other side.

Step 3 **Isolate the specified variable.** Divide each side by the factor that is the coefficient of the specified variable.

NOW TRY ANSWER

1. $p = \frac{I}{rt}$

---

*In this book, we use $\mathscr{A}$ to denote area.

NOW TRY
EXERCISE 2

Solve the formula for b.

$$P = a + 2b + c$$

EXAMPLE 2   Solving for a Specified Variable

Solve the formula $P = 2L + 2W$ for W.

This formula gives the relationship between perimeter of a rectangle, P, length of the rectangle, L, and width of the rectangle, W. See **FIGURE 2**.

Perimeter, P, the sum of the lengths of the sides of this rectangle, is given by

$$P = 2L + 2W.$$

FIGURE 2

$$P = 2L + 2W \quad \boxed{\text{Our goal is to isolate } W.}$$

Step 1   is not needed here because there are no parentheses or fractions to clear in this formula.

Step 2

$$P - 2L = 2L + 2W - 2L \qquad \text{Subtract } 2L.$$

$$P - 2L = 2W \qquad \text{Combine like terms.}$$

Step 3

$$\frac{P - 2L}{2} = \frac{2W}{2} \qquad \text{Divide by 2.}$$

$$\frac{P - 2L}{2} = W \qquad \frac{2W}{2} = \frac{2}{2} \cdot W = 1 \cdot W = W$$

$$\boxed{\text{Although } W \text{ is isolated, we simplify the right side further.}} \quad W = \frac{P - 2L}{2} \qquad \text{Interchange sides.}$$

$$\boxed{\begin{array}{c}\text{Be careful here.} \\ \frac{P - 2L}{2} \neq P - L\end{array}} \quad W = \frac{P}{2} - \frac{2L}{2} \qquad \frac{a - b}{c} = \frac{a}{c} - \frac{b}{c}$$

$$W = \frac{P}{2} - L \qquad \frac{2L}{2} = \frac{2}{2} \cdot L = 1 \cdot L = L \quad \textbf{NOW TRY} \; \text{↻}$$

⚠ **CAUTION**   In Step 3 of **Example 2**, we cannot simplify the fraction by dividing 2 into the term $2L$. The fraction bar serves as a grouping symbol. Thus, the subtraction in the numerator must be done before the division.

$$\frac{P - 2L}{2} \neq P - L$$

EXAMPLE 3   Solving a Formula Involving Parentheses

The formula

$$s = \frac{1}{2}(a + b + c)$$

is used with another formula, called *Heron's formula,* for finding the area of a triangle. Here, the variable s represents the *semiperimeter* (which is one-half the perimeter), and a, b, and c represent the lengths of the sides of the triangle.

Solve the formula for a.

NOW TRY ANSWER

2. $b = \frac{P - a - c}{2}$

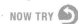

**NOW TRY
EXERCISE 3**
Solve $P = 2(L + W)$ for L.

$$s = \frac{1}{2}(a + b + c)$$

Step 1 $s = \frac{1}{2}a + \frac{1}{2}b + \frac{1}{2}c$ Distributive property

$$2s = 2\left(\frac{1}{2}a + \frac{1}{2}b + \frac{1}{2}c\right)$$ Multiply by 2 to clear the fractions.

$$2s = a + b + c$$ Distributive property

Step 2 $2s - b - c = a + b + c - b - c$ Subtract b and c.

Step 3 $2s - b - c = a$, or $a = 2s - b - c$ Combine like terms. Interchange sides.

NOW TRY

In **Examples 1–3,** we solved formulas for specified variables. In **Example 4,** we solve an equation with two variables for one of these variables. This process will be useful when we work with *linear equations in two variables* in **Chapter 2.**

**NOW TRY
EXERCISE 4**
Solve $5x - 6y = 12$ for y.

EXAMPLE 4   **Solving an Equation for One of the Variables**

Solve $3x - 4y = 12$ for y.

$$3x - 4y = 12$$ *Our goal is to isolate y.*

$$3x - 4y - 3x = 12 - 3x$$ Subtract $3x$.

$$-4y = -3x + 12$$ Combine like terms; commutative property

$$\frac{-4y}{-4} = \frac{-3x + 12}{-4}$$ Divide by -4.

$$y = \frac{-3x}{-4} + \frac{12}{-4}$$ $\frac{a + b}{c} = \frac{a}{c} + \frac{b}{c}$

$\frac{-3x}{-4} = \frac{-3}{-4} \cdot \frac{x}{1} = \frac{3}{4}x$ → $y = \frac{3}{4}x - 3$ Simplify the expression on the right.

NOW TRY

OBJECTIVE 2   Solve applied problems using formulas.

EXAMPLE 5   **Finding Average Rate**

Phyllis found that on average it took her $\frac{3}{4}$ hr each day to drive a distance of 15 mi to work. What was her average rate (or speed)?

The distance formula $d = rt$ relates d, the distance traveled, r, the rate or speed, and t, the travel time. Solve the formula for r.

$$d = rt$$

$$\frac{d}{t} = \frac{rt}{t}$$ Divide by t.

$$\frac{d}{t} = r, \text{ or } r = \frac{d}{t}$$

NOW TRY ANSWERS
3. $L = \frac{P - 2W}{2}$ or $L = \frac{P}{2} - W$,
4. $y = \frac{5}{6}x - 2$

NOW TRY EXERCISE 5

It takes $\frac{1}{2}$ hr for Dorothy to drive 21 mi to work each day. What is her average rate?

We find the desired rate by substituting the given values of d and t into this formula.

$$r = \frac{15}{\frac{3}{4}} \qquad \text{Let } d = 15, t = \frac{3}{4}.$$

$$r = 15 \cdot \frac{4}{3} \qquad \text{To divide by } \tfrac{3}{4}, \text{ multiply by its reciprocal, } \tfrac{4}{3}.$$

$$r = 20$$

Her average rate was 20 mph. (That is, at times she may have traveled a little faster or slower than 20 mph, but overall her rate was 20 mph.) **NOW TRY**

OBJECTIVE 3 Solve percent problems.

An important everyday use of mathematics involves the concept of percent, written with the symbol **%**. The word **percent** means **"per one hundred."** One percent means "one per one hundred" or "one one-hundredth."

$$1\% = 0.01 \quad \text{or} \quad 1\% = \frac{1}{100}$$

Solving a Percent Problem

Let a represent a partial amount of b, the whole amount (or base). Then the following equation can be used to solve a percent problem.

$$\frac{\text{partial amount } a}{\text{whole amount } b} = \text{decimal value (which is converted to a percent)}$$

For example, if a class consists of 50 students and 32 are males, then the percent of males in the class is found as follows.

$$\frac{\text{partial amount } a}{\text{whole amount } b} = \frac{32}{50} \qquad \text{Let } a = 32, b = 50.$$

$$= \frac{64}{100} \qquad \tfrac{32}{50} \cdot \tfrac{2}{2} = \tfrac{64}{100}$$

$$= 0.64 \qquad \text{Write as a decimal.}$$

$$= 64\% \qquad \text{Convert to a percent.}$$

NOTE When interpreting the "partial amount" in the formula for solving a percent problem, understand that it may represent a quantity that is actually *larger* than the whole amount. In these cases, the percent will be greater than 100%. For example,

25 is 250% of 10.

Here 25 is the partial amount and 10 is the whole amount.

NOW TRY ANSWER
5. 42 mph

NOW TRY EXERCISE 6

Solve each problem.

(a) A 5-L mixture of water and antifreeze contains 2 L of antifreeze. What is the percent of antifreeze in the mixture?

(b) If a savings account earns 2.5% interest on a balance of $7500 for one year, how much interest is earned?

EXAMPLE 6 Solving Percent Problems

(a) A 50-L mixture of acid and water contains 10 L of acid. What is the percent of acid in the mixture?

The given amount of the mixture is 50 L, and the part that is acid is 10 L. Let x represent the percent of acid in the mixture.

$$x = \frac{10}{50} \quad \leftarrow \text{ partial amount} \atop \leftarrow \text{ whole amount}$$

$$x = 0.20 \qquad \text{Divide to write as a decimal.}$$

$$x = 20\% \qquad 0.20 = \frac{20}{100} = 20\%$$

The mixture is 20% acid.

(b) If $4780 earns 5% interest in one year, how much interest is earned?

Let x represent the amount of interest earned (that is, the part of the whole amount invested). Because $5\% = 0.05$, the equation is written as follows.

$$\frac{x}{4780} = 0.05 \qquad \frac{\text{partial amount } a}{\text{whole amount } b} = \text{decimal value}$$

$$4780 \cdot \frac{x}{4780} = 4780(0.05) \qquad \text{Multiply by 4780.}$$

$$x = 239$$

The interest earned is $239.

NOW TRY

NOW TRY EXERCISE 7

Refer to **FIGURE 3**. How much was spent on vet care? Round the answer to the nearest tenth of a billion dollars.

EXAMPLE 7 Interpreting Percents from a Graph

In 2012, Americans spent about $53.3 billion on their pets. Use the graph in **FIGURE 3** to determine how much of this amount was spent on pet food.

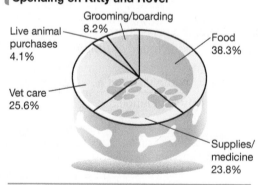

Spending on Kitty and Rover

Grooming/boarding 8.2%
Live animal purchases 4.1%
Food 38.3%
Vet care 25.6%
Supplies/medicine 23.8%

Pythagoras

Source: American Pet Products Manufacturers Association Inc.

FIGURE 3

The graph shows that 38.3% was spent on food. Let x = this amount in billions of dollars.

$$\text{partial amount} \longrightarrow \frac{x}{53.3} = 0.383 \qquad 38.3\% = 0.383 \atop \text{whole amount} \longrightarrow$$

$$53.3 \cdot \frac{x}{53.3} = 53.3(0.383) \qquad \text{Multiply by 53.3.}$$

$$x \approx 20.4 \qquad \text{Nearest tenth}$$

Therefore, about $20.4 billion was spent on pet food.

NOW TRY

NOW TRY ANSWERS
6. **(a)** 40%   **(b)** $187.50
7. $13.6 billion

OBJECTIVE 4 Solve problems involving percent increase or decrease.

Percent is often used to express a change in some quantity. Buying an item that has been marked up and getting a raise at a job are applications of **percent increase.** Buying an item on sale and finding population decline are applications of **percent decrease.**

To solve problems of this type, we use the following equation.

$$\text{percent change (as a decimal)} = \frac{\text{amount of change}}{\text{original amount}}$$

Subtract to find this.

EXAMPLE 8 Solving Problems about Percent Increase or Decrease

Use the percent change equation in each application.

(a) An electronics store marked up a laptop computer from their cost of $1200 to a selling price of $1464. What was the percent markup?

"Markup" is a name for an increase. Let x = the percent increase (as a decimal).

$$\text{percent increase} = \frac{\text{amount of increase}}{\text{original amount}}$$

Subtract to find the *amount* of increase.

$$x = \frac{1464 - 1200}{1200} \qquad \text{Substitute the given values.}$$

Use the original cost.

$$x = \frac{264}{1200}$$

$$x = 0.22 \qquad \text{Use a calculator.}$$

$$x = 22\% \qquad \text{Convert to a percent.}$$

The computer was marked up 22%.

(b) The enrollment at a community college declined from 12,750 during one school year to 11,350 the following year. Find the percent decrease.

Let x = the percent decrease (as a decimal).

$$\text{percent decrease} = \frac{\text{amount of decrease}}{\text{original amount}}$$

Subtract to find the *amount* of decrease.

$$x = \frac{12{,}750 - 11{,}350}{12{,}750} \qquad \text{Substitute the given values.}$$

Use the original number.

$$x = \frac{1400}{12{,}750}$$

$$x \approx 0.11 \qquad \text{Use a calculator.}$$

$$x = 11\% \qquad \text{Convert to a percent.}$$

The college enrollment decreased by about 11%.   NOW TRY

CAUTION When calculating a percent increase or decrease, be sure to use the original number (*before* the increase or decrease) as the denominator of the fraction. A common error is to use the final number (*after* the increase or decrease).

**NOW TRY
EXERCISE 8**

Use the percent change equation in each application.

(a) Jane bought a jacket on sale for $56. The regular price of the jacket was $80. What was the percent markdown?

(b) When it was time for Horatio to renew the lease on his apartment, the landlord raised his monthly rent from $650 to $689. What was the percent increase?

NOW TRY ANSWERS
8. (a) 30% **(b)** 6%

OBJECTIVE 5 Solve problems from the health care industry.

NOW TRY
EXERCISE 9

Use the formula in **Example 9** to find the body surface area, to the nearest hundredth, of a child who weighs 32 lb. Use $k = 14.515$.

EXAMPLE 9 Determining a Child's Body Surface Area

If a child weighs k kilograms, then the child's body surface area S in square meters (m^2) is determined by the formula

$$S = \frac{4k + 7}{k + 90}.$$

What is the body surface area of a child who weighs 40 lb? (*Source:* Hegstad, L., and W. Hayek, *Essential Drug Dosage Calculations,* Fourth Edition, Prentice Hall.)

Tables and web sites for conversion between the metric and English measurement systems are readily available. Using www.metric-conversions.org, we find that 40 lb is approximately 18.144 kg. Use this value for k in the above formula.

$$S = \frac{4(18.144) + 7}{18.144 + 90} \qquad \text{Let } k = 18.144 \text{ in the formula.}$$

$$S = 0.74 \qquad\qquad\quad \text{Use a calculator. Round to the nearest hundredth.}$$

The child's body surface area is 0.74 m². **NOW TRY**

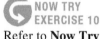
NOW TRY
EXERCISE 10

Refer to **Now Try Exercise 9.** Determine the appropriate dose, to the nearest unit, for this child if the usual adult dose is 100 mg.

EXAMPLE 10 Determining a Child's Dose of a Medication

If D represents the usual adult dose of a medication in milligrams, the corresponding child's dose C in milligrams is calculated using the formula

$$C = \frac{\text{body surface area in square meters}}{1.7} \times D.$$

Determine the appropriate dose for a child weighing 40 lb if the usual adult dose is 50 mg. (*Source:* Hegstad, L., and W. Hayek, *Essential Drug Dosage Calculations,* Fourth Edition, Prentice Hall.)

From **Example 9,** the body surface area of a child weighing 40 lb is 0.74 m². Use this value in the above formula to find the child's dose.

$$C = \frac{0.74}{1.7} \times 50 \qquad \text{Body surface area = 0.74,} \atop \text{D = 50}$$

$$C = 22 \qquad\qquad \text{Use a calculator.} \atop \text{Round to the nearest unit.}$$

NOW TRY ANSWERS
9. 0.62 m²
10. 36 mg

The child's dose is 22 mg. **NOW TRY**

1.2 Exercises

FOR EXTRA HELP   ▶ MyMathLab°

⬤ *Complete solution available in MyMathLab*

Concept Check   *Fill in each blank with the correct response.*

1. A(n) _____ is an equation in which variables are used to describe a relationship.

2. To solve a formula for a specified variable, treat that _____ as if it were the only one and treat all other variables like _____ (numbers).

Concept Check   *Work Exercises 3 and 4 to review converting between decimals and percents.*

3. Write each decimal as a percent.

   (a) 0.35   **(b)** 0.18   **(c)** 0.02   **(d)** 0.075   **(e)** 1.5

4. Write each percent as a decimal.

    (a) 60%　　**(b)** 37%　　**(c)** 8%　　**(d)** 3.5%　　**(e)** 210%

Solve each formula for the specified variable. **See Examples 1–3.**

5. $I = prt$ for r (simple interest)

6. $d = rt$ for t (distance)

7. $\mathcal{A} = bh$ (area of a parallelogram)

    (a) for b　　　**(b)** for h

8. $\mathcal{A} = LW$ (area of a rectangle)

    (a) for W　　　**(b)** for L

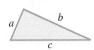

▶ **9.** $P = 2L + 2W$ for L
(perimeter of a rectangle)

10. $P = a + b + c$ (perimeter of a triangle)

    (a) for b　　　**(b)** for c

11. $V = LWH$
(volume of a rectangular solid)

    (a) for W　　　**(b)** for H

12. $\mathcal{A} = \dfrac{1}{2}bh$ (area of a triangle)

    (a) for h　　　**(b)** for b

13. $C = 2\pi r$ for r
(circumference of a circle)

14. $V = \pi r^2 h$ for h
(volume of a right circular cylinder)

▶ **15.** $\mathcal{A} = \dfrac{1}{2}h(b + B)$ (area of a trapezoid)

    (a) for b　　　**(b)** for B

16. $V = \dfrac{1}{3}\pi r^2 h$ for h (volume of a cone)

17. $F = \dfrac{9}{5}C + 32$ for C

(Celsius to Fahrenheit)

18. $C = \dfrac{5}{9}(F - 32)$ for F

(Fahrenheit to Celsius)

19. $Ax + B = C$
(linear equation in x)

    (a) for x　　　**(b)** for A

20. $y = mx + b$
(slope-intercept form of a linear equation)

    (a) for x　　　**(b)** for m

21. $A = P(1 + rt)$ for t
(future value for simple interest)

22. $M = C(1 + r)$ for r
(markup)

23. *Concept Check* When a formula is solved for a particular variable, several different equivalent forms may be possible. If we solve $\mathcal{A} = \frac{1}{2}bh$ for h, one possible correct answer is

$$h = \frac{2\mathcal{A}}{b}.$$

Which one of the following is *not* equivalent to this?

A. $h = 2\left(\dfrac{\mathcal{A}}{b}\right)$ **B.** $h = 2\mathcal{A}\left(\dfrac{1}{b}\right)$ **C.** $h = \dfrac{\mathcal{A}}{\frac{1}{2}b}$ **D.** $h = \dfrac{\frac{1}{2}\mathcal{A}}{b}$

24. *Concept Check* The answer to **Exercise 17** is given as $C = \frac{5}{9}(F - 32)$. Which one of the following is *not* equivalent to this?

A. $C = \dfrac{5}{9}F - \dfrac{160}{9}$ **B.** $C = \dfrac{5F}{9} - \dfrac{160}{9}$ **C.** $C = \dfrac{5F - 160}{9}$ **D.** $C = \dfrac{5}{9}F - 32$

Solve each equation for y. See Example 4.

25. $4x + y = 1$ **26.** $3x + y = 9$ **27.** $x - 2y = -6$

28. $x - 5y = -20$ **29.** $4x + 9y = 11$ **30.** $7x + 8y = 11$

31. $-3x + 2y = 5$ **32.** $-5x + 3y = 12$ **33.** $6x - 5y = 7$

34. $8x - 3y = 4$ **35.** $\dfrac{1}{2}x - \dfrac{1}{3}y = 1$ **36.** $\dfrac{2}{3}x - \dfrac{2}{5}y = 2$

Solve each problem. See Example 5.

37. Jimmie Johnson won the Daytona 500 (mile) race with a rate of 159.250 mph in 2013. Find his time to the nearest thousandth. (*Source: World Almanac and Book of Facts.*)

38. In 2007, rain shortened the Indianapolis 500 race to 415 mi. It was won by Dario Franchitti, who averaged 151.774 mph. What was his time to the nearest thousandth? (*Source:* www.indy500.com)

39. Nora traveled from Kansas City to Louisville, a distance of 520 mi, in 10 hr. Find her rate in miles per hour.

40. The distance from Melbourne to London is 10,500 mi. If a jet averages 500 mph between the two cities, what is its travel time in hours?

41. As of 2013, the highest temperature ever recorded in Tennessee was 45°C. Find the corresponding Fahrenheit temperature. (*Source:* National Climatic Data Center.)

42. As of 2013, the lowest temperature ever recorded in South Dakota was −58°F. Find the corresponding Celsius temperature. (*Source:* National Climatic Data Center.)

43. The base of the Great Pyramid of Cheops is a square whose perimeter is 920 m. What is the length of each side of this square? (*Source: Atlas of Ancient Archaeology.*)

Perimeter = 920 m

44. Marina City in Chicago is a complex of two residential towers that resemble corncobs. Each tower has a concrete cylindrical core with a 35-ft diameter and is 588 ft tall. Find the volume of the core of one of the towers to the nearest whole number. (*Hint:* Use the π key on your calculator.) (*Source:* www.architechgallery.com; www.aviewoncities.com)

45. The circumference of a circle is 480π in.

(a) What is its radius?

(b) What is its diameter?

46. The radius of a circle is 2.5 in.

(a) What is its diameter?

(b) What is its circumference?

$r = 2.5$ in.

47. A sheet of standard-size copy paper measures 8.5 in. by 11 in. If a ream (500 sheets) of this paper has a volume of 187 in.^{3}, how thick is the ream?

48. Copy paper (**Exercise 47**) also comes in legal size, which has the same width, but is longer than standard size. If a ream of legal-size paper has the same thickness as standard-size paper and a volume of 238 in.^{3}, what is the length of a sheet of legal paper?

Solve each problem. ***See Example 6.***

▶ **49.** A mixture of alcohol and water contains a total of 36 oz of liquid. There are 9 oz of pure alcohol in the mixture. What percent of the mixture is water? What percent is alcohol?

50. A mixture of acid and water is 35% acid. If the mixture contains a total of 40 L, how many liters of pure acid are in the mixture? How many liters of pure water are in the mixture?

51. A real-estate agent earned $6300 commission on a property sale of $210,000. What is her rate of commission?

52. A certificate of deposit for 1 yr pays $25.50 simple interest on a principal of $3400. What is the interest rate being paid on this deposit?

In baseball, winning percentage (Pct.) is commonly expressed as a decimal rounded to the nearest thousandth. To find the winning percentage of a team, divide the number of wins (W) *by the total number of games played* (W + L).

53. The final 2013 standings of the American League West division in Major League Baseball are shown in the table. Find the winning percentage of each team.

(a) Texas   (b) L.A. Angels

(c) Seattle   (d) Houston

	W	L	Pct.
Oakland	96	66	.593
Texas*	91	72	
L.A. Angels	78	84	
Seattle	71	91	
Houston	51	111	

*Texas played one more game than the others. It was an extra playoff game, which counted in the regular season statistics.

Source: World Almanac and Book of Facts.

54. The final 2013 standings of the National League Central division in Major League Baseball are shown in the table. Find the winning percentage of each team.

(a) Pittsburgh   (b) Cincinnati

(c) Milwaukee   (d) Chicago Cubs

	W	L	Pct.
St. Louis	97	65	.599
Pittsburgh	94	68	
Cincinnati	90	72	
Milwaukee	74	88	
Chicago Cubs	66	96	

Source: World Almanac and Book of Facts.

In 2013, 114.2 million U.S. households owned at least one TV set. (Source: Nielsen Media Research.) Use this to work Exercises 55–58. Round answers to the nearest percent in Exercises 55 and 56, and to the nearest tenth million in Exercises 57 and 58. **See Example 6.**

55. About 38.4 million U.S. households owned 4 or more TV sets in 2013. What percent of those owning at least one TV set was this?

56. About 94.2 million households that owned at least one TV set in 2013 had a DVD player. What percent of those owning at least one TV set had a DVD player?

57. Of the households owning at least one TV set in 2013, 90.5% received basic cable. How many households received basic cable?

58. Of the households owning at least one TV set in 2013, 47.6% received premium cable. How many households received premium cable?

An average middle-income family will spend $241,080 to raise a child born in 2013 from birth through age 17. The graph shows the percents spent for various categories. Use the graph to answer Exercises 59–62. **See Example 7.**

59. To the nearest dollar, how much will be spent to provide housing for the child?

60. To the nearest dollar, how much will be spent for child care and education?

61. Use the answer from **Exercise 60** to find how much will be spent on clothing.

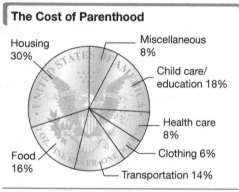

The Cost of Parenthood

Housing 30%

Miscellaneous 8%

Child care/ education 18%

Health care 8%

Clothing 6%

Transportation 14%

Food 16%

Source: U.S. Department of Agriculture.

62. About $38,500 will be spent for food. To the nearest percent, what percent of the cost of raising a child from birth through age 17 is this? Does the answer agree with the graph?

Solve each problem. **See Example 8.**

63. After 1 yr on the job, Grady got a raise from $10.50 per hour to $11.76 per hour. What was the percent increase in his hourly wage?

64. Clayton bought a ticket to a rock concert at a discount. The regular price of the ticket was $70.00, but he only paid $56.00. What was the percent discount?

65. Between 2000 and 2012, the population of New Orleans, Louisiana, declined from 484,674 to 369,250. What was the percent decrease to the nearest tenth? (*Source:* U.S. Census.)

66. Between 2000 and 2012, the estimated population of Naperville, Illinois, grew from 128,358 to 143,684. What was the percent increase to the nearest tenth? (*Source:* U.S. Census.)

67. The movie *Lincoln* in Blu-Ray was on sale for $19.52. The list price (full price) of this two-disc combo pack was $39.00. To the nearest tenth, what was the percent discount? (*Source:* www.amazon.com)

68. *The Dark Night Trilogy* in Blu-Ray was on sale for $31.99. The list price (full price) of this five-disc set was $52.99. To the nearest tenth, what was the percent discount? (*Source:* www.amazon.com)

In Exercises 69–72, apply the formulas for determining a child's body surface area and a child's dose of a medication. **See Examples 9 and 10.**

$$S = \frac{4k + 7}{k + 90}$$

Child's body surface area S, in square meters; k = weight in kilograms

$$C = \frac{\text{body surface area in square meters}}{1.7} \times D$$

Child's dose of medication C, in milligrams; D = usual adult dose, in milligrams

69. Find the body surface area, to the nearest hundredth, of a child with each weight.

(a) 20 kg   (b) 26 kg

70. Find the body surface area, to the nearest hundredth, of a child with each weight.

(a) 30 lb (Use $k = 13.608$.)   (b) 26 lb (Use $k = 11.793$.)

71. If the usual adult dose of a medication is 250 mg, what is the child's dose, to the nearest unit, for a child with each weight? (*Hint:* Use the results of **Exercise 69.**)

(a) 20 kg   (b) 26 kg

72. If the usual adult dose of a medication is 500 mg, what is the child's dose, to the nearest unit, for a child with each weight? (*Hint:* Use the results of **Exercise 70.**)

(a) 30 lb   (b) 26 lb

STUDY SKILLS

Taking Lecture Notes

Study the set of sample math notes given here.

- **Use a new page** for each day's lecture.
- **Include the date and title** of the day's lecture topic.
- **Skip lines and write neatly** to make reading easier.
- **Include cautions and warnings** to emphasize common errors to avoid.
- **Mark important concepts** with stars, underlining, circling, boxes, etc.
- **Use two columns,** which allows an example and its explanation to be close together.
- **Use brackets and arrows** to clearly show steps, related material, etc.

With a partner or in a small group, compare lecture notes. Answer each question.

1. What are you doing to show main points in your notes (such as boxing, using stars or capital letters, etc.)?

2. In what ways do you set off explanations from worked problems and sub-points (such as indenting, using arrows, circling, etc.)?

3. What new ideas did you learn by examining your classmates' notes?

4. What new techniques will you try in your note taking?

1.3 Applications of Linear Equations

OBJECTIVE 1 Translate from words to mathematical expressions.

Producing a mathematical model of a real situation often involves translating verbal statements into mathematical statements.

PROBLEM-SOLVING HINT Usually there are key words and phrases in a verbal problem that translate into mathematical expressions involving addition, subtraction, multiplication, and division. Translations of some commonly used expressions follow.

Use this table for reference when solving applications in this chapter.

▼ **Translating from Words to Mathematical Expressions**

Verbal Expression	Mathematical Expression (where x and y are numbers)
Addition	
The **sum** of a number and 7	$x + 7$
6 **more than** a number	$x + 6$
3 **plus** a number	$3 + x$
24 **added to** a number	$x + 24$
A number **increased by** 5	$x + 5$
The **sum** of two numbers	$x + y$
Subtraction	
2 **less than** a number	$x - 2$
2 **less** a number	$2 - x$
12 **minus** a number	$12 - x$
A number **decreased by** 12	$x - 12$
A number **subtracted from** 10	$10 - x$
10 **subtracted from** a number	$x - 10$
The **difference of** two numbers	$x - y$
Multiplication	
16 **times** a number	$16x$
A number **multiplied by** 6	$6x$
$\frac{2}{3}$ **of** a number (used with fractions and percent)	$\frac{2}{3}x$
$\frac{3}{4}$ **as much as** a number	$\frac{3}{4}x$
Twice (2 times) a number	$2x$
Triple (3 times) a number	$3x$
The **product** of two numbers	xy
Division	
The **quotient** of 8 and a number	$\frac{8}{x}$ $(x \neq 0)$
A number **divided by** 13	$\frac{x}{13}$
The **ratio** of two numbers	$\frac{x}{y}$ $(y \neq 0)$
The **quotient** of two numbers	$\frac{x}{y}$ $(y \neq 0)$

⚠ **CAUTION** *Because subtraction and division are not commutative operations, it is important to correctly translate expressions involving them.* For example,

"2 less than a number" is translated as $x - 2$, **not** $2 - x$.

"A number subtracted from 10" is expressed as $10 - x$, **not** $x - 10$.

For division, the number *by which* we are dividing is the denominator, and the number *into which* we are dividing is the numerator.

"A number divided by 13" and "13 divided into x" both translate as $\frac{x}{13}$.

"The quotient of x and y" is translated as $\frac{x}{y}$.

OBJECTIVE 2 Write equations from given information.

Any words that indicate equality or "sameness," such as *is*, translate as $=$.

**NOW TRY
EXERCISE 1**

Translate each verbal sentence into an equation, using x as the variable.

(a) The quotient of a number and 10 is twice the number.

(b) The product of a number and 5, decreased by 7, is 0.

EXAMPLE 1 Translating Words into Equations

Translate each verbal sentence into an equation, using x as the variable.

Verbal Sentence	Equation
Twice a number, decreased by 3, is 42.	$2x - 3 = 42$
The product of a number and 12, decreased by 7, is 105.	$12x - 7 = 105$
The quotient of a number and the number plus 4 is 28.	$\frac{x}{x + 4} = 28$
The quotient of a number and 4, plus the number, is 10.	$\frac{x}{4} + x = 10$

NOW TRY 🔄

OBJECTIVE 3 Distinguish between simplifying expressions and solving equations.

An expression translates as a phrase. An equation includes the equality symbol ($=$), with expressions on both sides, and translates as a sentence.

**NOW TRY
EXERCISE 2**

Decide whether each is an *expression* or an *equation*. Simplify any expressions, and solve any equations.

(a) $3(x - 5) + 2x - 1$

(b) $3(x - 5) + 2x = 1$

EXAMPLE 2 Simplifying Expressions vs. Solving Equations

Decide whether each is an *expression* or an *equation*. Simplify any expressions, and solve any equations.

(a) $2(3 + x) - 4x + 7$

Clear parentheses and combine like terms to **simplify**. $\quad 2(3 + x) - 4x + 7$	There is no equality symbol. This is an **expression**.
$= 6 + 2x - 4x + 7$	Distributive property
$= -2x + 13$	Simplified expression

(b) $2(3 + x) - 4x + 7 = -1$

Find the value of x to **solve**. $\quad 2(3 + x) - 4x + 7 = -1$	There is an equality symbol. This is an **equation**.
$6 + 2x - 4x + 7 = -1$	Distributive property
$-2x + 13 = -1$	Combine like terms.
$-2x = -14$	Subtract 13.
$x = 7$	Divide by -2.

The solution set is $\{7\}$.

NOW TRY 🔄

NOW TRY ANSWERS
1. (a) $\frac{x}{10} = 2x$ **(b)** $5x - 7 = 0$
2. (a) expression; $5x - 16$
   (b) equation; $\left\{\frac{16}{5}\right\}$

OBJECTIVE 4 Use the six steps in solving an applied problem.

The following six steps are helpful when solving applied problems.

> **Solving an Applied Problem**
>
> *Step 1*   **Read** the problem carefully. *What information is given? What is to be found?*
>
> *Step 2*   **Assign a variable** to represent the unknown value. Make a sketch, diagram, or table, as needed. If necessary, express any other unknown values in terms of the variable.
>
> *Step 3*   **Write an equation** using the variable expression(s).
>
> *Step 4*   **Solve** the equation.
>
> *Step 5*   **State the answer.** Label it appropriately. *Does it seem reasonable?*
>
> *Step 6*   **Check** the answer in the words of the *original* problem.

NOW TRY
EXERCISE 3

The length of a rectangle is 2 ft more than twice the width. The perimeter is 34 ft. Find the length and the width of the rectangle.

EXAMPLE 3   Solving a Perimeter Problem

The length of a rectangle is 1 cm more than twice the width. The perimeter of the rectangle is 110 cm. Find the length and the width of the rectangle.

Step 1   **Read** the problem. *What must be found?* We must find the length and width of the rectangle. *What is given?* The length is 1 cm more than twice the width and the perimeter is 110 cm.

Step 2   **Assign a variable.**

W

$2W + 1$

FIGURE 4

$$\text{Let} \qquad W = \text{the width.}$$
$$\text{Then } 2W + 1 = \text{the length.}$$

Make a sketch, as in **FIGURE 4**.

Step 3   **Write an equation.** Use the formula for the perimeter of a rectangle.

$P = 2L + 2W$	Perimeter of a rectangle
$110 = 2(2W + 1) + 2W$	$P = 110$ and $L = 2W + 1$

Step 4   **Solve.**

$110 = 4W + 2 + 2W$	Distributive property
$110 = 6W + 2$	Combine like terms.
$110 - 2 = 6W + 2 - 2$	Subtract 2.
$108 = 6W$	Combine like terms.
$\dfrac{108}{6} = \dfrac{6W}{6}$	Divide by 6.
$18 = W$	

We also need to find the length.

Step 5   **State the answer.** The width of the rectangle is 18 cm and the length is

$$2(18) + 1 = 37 \text{ cm.}$$

Step 6   **Check.** The length, 37 cm, is 1 cm more than $2(18)$ cm (twice the width). The perimeter is

$$2(37) + 2(18) = 110 \text{ cm,} \quad \text{as required.} \qquad \text{NOW TRY}$$

NOW TRY
EXERCISE 4
During the 2013 regular NFL
season, Peyton Manning of
the Denver Broncos threw
16 more touchdown passes
than Drew Brees of the New
Orleans Saints. Together, these
two quarterbacks completed a
total of 94 touchdown passes.
How many passes did each
player complete? (*Source:*
www.nfl.com)

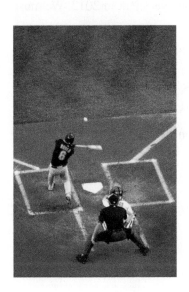

EXAMPLE 4   **Finding Unknown Numerical Quantities**

During the 2013 regular Major League Baseball season, Yu Darvish of the Texas
Rangers and Max Scherzer of the Detroit Tigers were the top major league pitchers
for strikeouts. The two pitchers had a total of 517 strikeouts. Darvish had 37 more
strikeouts than Scherzer. How many strikeouts did each pitcher have? (*Source:*
www.mlb.com)

Step 1   **Read** the problem. We are asked to find the number of strikeouts each
pitcher had.

Step 2   **Assign a variable** to represent the number of strikeouts for one of the men.

Let s = the number of strikeouts for Max Scherzer.

We must also find the number of strikeouts for Yu Darvish. Because he had
37 more strikeouts than Scherzer,

$s + 37$ = the number of strikeouts for Darvish.

Step 3   **Write an equation.** The sum of the numbers of strikeouts is 517.

Scherzer's strikeouts   +   Darvish's strikeouts   =   total strikeouts.

$$s + (s + 37) = 517$$

Step 4   **Solve** the equation.

$$s + (s + 37) = 517$$

$$2s + 37 = 517 \qquad \text{Combine like terms.}$$

$$2s + 37 - 37 = 517 - 37 \qquad \text{Subtract 37.}$$

$$2s = 480 \qquad \text{Combine like terms.}$$

$$\frac{2s}{2} = \frac{480}{2} \qquad \text{Divide by 2.}$$

Don't stop
here.

$$s = 240$$

Step 5   **State the answer.** The variable s represents the number of strikeouts for
Scherzer, so he had 240. Then Darvish had $s + 37$, which is

$$240 + 37 = 277 \text{ strikeouts.}$$

Step 6   **Check.** 277 is 37 more than 240, and $240 + 277 = 517$. The conditions of
the problem are satisfied, and our answer checks.   NOW TRY

> **⚠ CAUTION**   *Be sure to answer all the questions asked in the problem.* In **Example 4,**
> we were asked for the number of strikeouts for *each* player, so there was extra work in
> Step 5 in order to find Darvish's number.

PROBLEM-SOLVING HINT   In **Example 4,** we chose to let the variable represent the number
of strikeouts for Scherzer. Students often ask, "Can I let the variable represent the *other* unknown?" The answer is yes. The equation will be different, but in the end the answers will be
the same. Let s represent the number of strikeouts for Darvish, and confirm this.

$$s + (s - 37) = 517 \qquad \text{Alternative equation for Example 4}$$

NOW TRY ANSWER
4. Manning: 55; Brees: 39

OBJECTIVE 5 Solve percent problems.

Recall from **Section 1.2** that percent means "per one hundred," so 5% means 0.05, 14% means 0.14, and so on.

EXAMPLE 5   **Solving a Percent Problem**

Total annual health expenditures in the United States were about $2800 billion (or $2.8 trillion) in 2012. This is an increase of 287% over the total for 1990. What were the approximate total health expenditures in billions of dollars in the United States in 1990? (*Source:* U.S. Centers for Medicare & Medicaid Services.)

Step 1   **Read** the problem. We are given that the total health expenditures increased by 287% from 1990 to 2012, and $2800 billion was spent in 2012. We must find the expenditures in 1990.

Step 2   **Assign a variable.** Let x = the total health expenditures for 1990.

$$287\% = 287(0.01) = 2.87,$$

so $2.87x$ represents the expenditures compared to those of 1990.

Step 3   **Write an equation** from the given information.

The expenditures in 1990 + the increase = 2800.

$$x \quad + \quad 2.87x \quad = \quad 2800$$

Note the x in $2.87x$.

Step 4   **Solve** the equation. (We do so without clearing the decimal.)

$$1x + 2.87x = 2800 \qquad \text{Identity property}$$
$$3.87x = 2800 \qquad \text{Combine like terms.}$$
$$x \approx 724 \qquad \text{Divide by 3.87.}$$

Step 5   **State the answer.** Total health expenditures in the United States for 1990 were about $724 billion.

Step 6   **Check** that the increase, which is $2800 - $724 = $2076 billion, is about 287% of $724 billion.   NOW TRY

🛑 **CAUTION**   Avoid two common errors that occur in solving problems like the one in **Example 5.**

1. Do not try to find 287% of 2800 and subtract that amount from 2800. The 287% should be applied to *the amount in 1990, not the amount in 2012.*

2. Do not write the equation as

$$x + 2.87 = 2800. \qquad \text{Incorrect}$$

The percent must be multiplied by some number. In this case, the number is the amount spent in 1990, that is, $2.87x$.

NOW TRY EXERCISE 5

In the fall of 2015, there were 96 Introductory Statistics students at a certain community college, an increase of 700% over the number of Introductory Statistics students in the fall of 1992. How many Introductory Statistics students were there in the fall of 1992?

NOW TRY ANSWER
5. 12

OBJECTIVE 6 Solve investment problems.

The investment problems in this chapter deal with *simple interest*. In most real-world applications, *compound interest* (covered in a later chapter) is used.

**NOW TRY
EXERCISE 6**

Gary received a $20,000 inheritance from his grandfather. He invested some of the money in an account earning 3% annual interest and the remaining amount in an account earning 2.5% annual interest. If the total annual interest earned is $575, how much is invested at each rate?

EXAMPLE 6 Solving an Investment Problem

Thomas invested $40,000. He put part of the money in an account paying 2% interest and the remainder into stocks paying 3% interest. The total annual income from these investments was $1020. How much did he invest at each rate?

Step 1 **Read** the problem again. We must find the two amounts.

Step 2 **Assign a variable.**

$$\text{Let} \qquad x = \text{the amount invested at 2\%;}$$
$$40{,}000 - x = \text{the amount invested at 3\%.}$$

The formula for interest is $I = prt$. Here the time t is 1 yr. Use a table to organize the given information.

Principal (in dollars)	Rate (as a decimal)	Interest (in dollars)	
x	0.02	0.02x	Multiply principal, rate, and time (here, 1 yr) to find interest.
$40{,}000 - x$	0.03	$0.03(40{,}000 - x)$	
40,000		1020	← Total

Step 3 **Write an equation.** The last column of the table gives the equation.

Interest at 2%   +   interest at 3%   =   total interest.

$$0.02x \quad + \quad 0.03(40{,}000 - x) \quad = \quad 1020$$

Step 4 **Solve** the equation. Clear the parentheses and then the decimals.

$$0.02x + 1200 - 0.03x = 1020 \qquad \text{Distributive property}$$
$$100(0.02x + 1200 - 0.03x) = 100(1020) \qquad \text{Multiply by 100.}$$
$$2x + 120{,}000 - 3x = 102{,}000 \qquad \substack{\text{Distributive property;} \\ \text{Multiply.}}$$
$$-x + 120{,}000 = 102{,}000 \qquad \text{Combine like terms.}$$
$$-x = -18{,}000 \qquad \text{Subtract 120,000.}$$
$$x = 18{,}000 \qquad \text{Multiply by } -1.$$

Move decimal points 2 places to the right.

Step 5 **State the answer.** Thomas invested $18,000 of the money at 2%. At 3%, he invested $40,000 − $18,000 = $22,000.

Step 6 **Check.** Find the annual interest at each rate. The sum of these two amounts should total $1020.

$$0.02(\$18{,}000) = \$360 \quad \text{and} \quad 0.03(\$22{,}000) = \$660$$
$$\$360 + \$660 = \$1020, \quad \text{as required.} \qquad \text{NOW TRY}$$

NOW TRY ANSWER
6. $15,000 at 3%; $5000 at 2.5%

NOW TRY
EXERCISE 7

How many liters of a 20% acid solution must be mixed with 5 L of a 30% acid solution to make a 24% acid solution?

OBJECTIVE 7 Solve mixture problems.

Mixture problems involving rates of concentration can be solved with linear equations.

EXAMPLE 7   Solving a Mixture Problem

A chemist must mix 8 L of a 40% acid solution with some 70% solution to make a 50% solution. How much of the 70% solution should be used?

Step 1   **Read** the problem. The problem asks for the amount of 70% solution to be used.

Step 2   **Assign a variable.**

Let $x =$ the number of liters of 70% solution.

The information in the problem is illustrated in **FIGURE 5**. We use it to complete a table.

After mixing

8 L   Unknown $(8 + x)$ L
number of liters, x

FIGURE 5

Liters of Solution	Percent (as a decimal)	Liters of Pure Acid	
8	0.40	$0.40(8) = 3.2$	← Sum must
x	0.70	$0.70x$	equal
$8 + x$	0.50	$0.50(8 + x)$	

The values in the last column were found by multiplying the strengths by the numbers of liters.

Step 3   **Write an equation** using the values in the last column of the table.

Liters of pure acid in 40% solution		liters of pure acid in 70% solution		liters of pure acid in 50% solution.
3.2	$+$	$0.70x$	$=$	$0.50(8 + x)$

Step 4   **Solve.** $3.2 + 0.70x = 4 + 0.50x$ Distributive property

$32 + 7x = 40 + 5x$ Multiply by 10 to clear the decimals.

> Move decimal points 1 place to the right.

$2x = 8$ Subtract 32 and 5x.

$x = 4$ Divide by 2.

Step 5   **State the answer.** The chemist should use 4 L of the 70% solution.

Step 6   **Check.** 8 L of 40% solution plus 4 L of 70% solution is

$$8(0.40) + 4(0.70) = 6 \text{ L of acid.}$$

Similarly, 8 + 4 or 12 L of 50% solution has

$$12(0.50) = 6 \text{ L of acid.}$$

The total amount of pure acid is 6 L both before and after mixing, so the answer checks.

NOW TRY

NOW TRY ANSWER

7. $7\frac{1}{2}$ L

> **PROBLEM-SOLVING HINT** When pure water is added to a solution, water is 0% of the chemical (acid, alcohol, etc.). Similarly, pure chemical is 100% chemical.

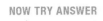

NOW TRY EXERCISE 8

How much pure antifreeze must be mixed with 3 gal of 30% antifreeze solution to obtain 40% antifreeze solution?

EXAMPLE 8 Solving a Mixture Problem When One Ingredient Is Pure

The octane rating of gasoline is a measure of its antiknock qualities. For a standard fuel, the octane rating is the percent of isooctane. How many liters of pure isooctane should be mixed with 200 L of 94% isooctane, referred to as 94 octane, to obtain a mixture that is 98% isooctane?

Step 1 **Read** the problem. We must find the amount of pure isooctane.

Step 2 **Assign a variable.** Let x = the number of liters of pure (100%) isooctane. Complete a table. Recall that $100\% = 100(0.01) = 1$.

Liters of Solution	Percent (as a decimal)	Liters of Pure Isooctane
x	1	x
200	0.94	0.94(200)
$x + 200$	0.98	0.98($x + 200$)

Step 3 **Write an equation** using the values in the last column of the table.

$$x + 0.94(200) = 0.98(x + 200)$$ Refer to the table.

Step 4 **Solve.** $x + 188 = 0.98x + 196$ Multiply; distributive property

$$100(x + 188) = 100(0.98x + 196)$$ Multiply by 100 to clear the decimal.

$$100x + 18{,}800 = 98x + 19{,}600$$ Distributive property

$$2x = 800$$ Subtract 98x and 18,800.

$$x = 400$$ Divide by 2.

Step 5 **State the answer.** 400 L of isooctane is needed.

Step 6 **Check** by substituting 400 for x in the equation from Step 3.

$$400 + 0.94(200) \overset{?}{=} 0.98(400 + 200)$$ Let x = 400.

$$400 + 188 \overset{?}{=} 0.98(600)$$ Multiply. Add.

$$588 = 588 \checkmark$$ True

NOW TRY ANSWER

8. $\frac{1}{2}$ gal

A true statement results, so the answer checks.   NOW TRY

1.3 Exercises

FOR EXTRA HELP   MyMathLab®

● *Complete solution available in MyMathLab*

Concept Check *In each of the following, translate part (a) as an expression and translate part (b) as an equation or inequality. Use x to represent the number.*

1. **(a)** 15 more than a number
   (b) 15 is more than a number.

2. **(a)** 5 greater than a number
   (b) 5 is greater than a number.

3. **(a)** 8 less than a number
   (b) 8 is less than a number.

4. **(a)** 6 less than a number
   (b) 6 is less than a number.

5. *Concept Check*   Which one of the following is *not* a valid translation of "40% of a number," where x represents the number?

    A. $0.40x$ **B.** $0.4x$ **C.** $\dfrac{2x}{5}$ **D.** $40x$

6. *Concept Check*   Why is $13 - x$ *not* a correct translation of "13 less than a number?"

Translate each verbal phrase into a mathematical expression using x as the variable. **See Objective 1.**

▶ 7. Twice a number, decreased by 13

8. Triple a number, decreased by 14

9. 12 increased by four times a number

10. 15 more than one-half of a number

11. The product of 8 and 16 less than a number

12. The product of 8 more than a number and 5 less than the number

13. The quotient of three times a number and 10

14. The quotient of 9 and five times a non-zero number

Translate each verbal sentence into an equation, using x as the variable. Then solve the equation. **See Example 1.**

15. The sum of a number and 6 is -31. Find the number.

16. The sum of a number and -4 is 18. Find the number.

17. If the product of a number and -4 is subtracted from the number, the result is 9 more than the number. Find the number.

18. If the quotient of a number and 6 is added to twice the number, the result is 8 less than the number. Find the number.

19. When $\frac{2}{3}$ of a number is subtracted from 14, the result is 10. Find the number.

20. When 75% of a number is added to 6, the result is 3 more than the number. Find the number.

Decide whether each is an expression *or an* equation. *Simplify any expressions, and solve any equations.* **See Example 2.**

▶ 21. $5(x + 3) - 8(2x - 6)$

22. $-7(x + 4) + 13(x - 6)$

23. $5(x + 3) - 8(2x - 6) = 12$

24. $-7(x + 4) + 13(x - 6) = 18$

25. $\dfrac{1}{2}x - \dfrac{1}{6}x + \dfrac{3}{2} - 8$

26. $\dfrac{1}{3}x + \dfrac{1}{5}x - \dfrac{1}{2} + 7$

Complete the six suggested problem-solving steps to solve each problem.

27. In 2012, the corporations securing the most U.S. patents were IBM and Samsung. Together, the two corporations secured a total of 11,500 patents, with Samsung receiving 1414 fewer patents than IBM. How many patents did each corporation secure? (*Source:* U.S. Patent and Trademark Office.)

  Step 1 **Read** the problem carefully. We are asked to find _____ .

  Step 2 **Assign a variable.**   Let $x =$ the number of patents that IBM secured. Then

$$x - 1414 = \text{the number of} \underline{\hspace{1.5cm}}.$$

  Step 3 **Write an equation.**   _____ + _____ = 11,500

  Step 4 **Solve** the equation. $x =$ _____

  Step 5 **State the answer.**   IBM secured _____ patents. Samsung secured _____ patents.

  Step 6 **Check.**   The number of Samsung patents was _____ fewer than the number of _____ . The total number of patents was $6457 +$ _____ $=$ _____ .

28. In 2011, 8.5 million more U.S. residents traveled to Mexico than to Canada. There was a total of 31.7 million U.S. residents traveling to these two countries. How many traveled to each country? (*Source:* U.S. Department of Commerce.)

Step 1   **Read** the problem carefully. We are asked to find _____ .

Step 2   **Assign a variable.**   Let x = the number of travelers to Mexico (in millions).

Then $x - 8.5$ = the number of _____ .

Step 3   **Write an equation.**   _____ + _____ = 31.7

Step 4   **Solve** the equation. $x =$ _____

Step 5   **State the answer.**   There were _____ travelers to Mexico and _____ travelers to Canada.

Step 6   **Check.**   The number of _____ was _____ more than the number of travelers to _____ . The total number of travelers was 20.1 + _____ = _____ .

Solve each problem. ***See Examples 3 and 4.***

▶ **29.** The John Hancock Center in Chicago has a rectangular base. The length of the base measures 65 ft less than twice the width. The perimeter of the base is 860 ft. What are the dimensions of the base?

30. The John Hancock Center (**Exercise 29**) tapers as it rises. The top floor is rectangular and has perimeter 520 ft. The width of the top floor measures 20 ft more than one-half its length. What are the dimensions of the top floor?

The perimeter of the top floor is 520 ft.

$2W - 65$ W
The perimeter of the base is 860 ft.

31. Grant Wood painted his most famous work, *American Gothic,* in 1930 on composition board with perimeter 108.44 in. If the rectangular painting is 5.54 in. taller than it is wide, find the dimensions of the painting. (*Source: The Gazette.*)

32. The perimeter of a certain rectangle is 16 times the width. The length is 12 cm more than the width. Find the length and width of the rectangle.

$W + 12$

W

33. The Bermuda Triangle supposedly causes trouble for aircraft pilots. It has a perimeter of 3075 mi. The shortest side measures 75 mi less than the middle side, and the longest side measures 375 mi more than the middle side. Find the lengths of the three sides.

34. The Vietnam Veterans Memorial in Washington, DC, is in the shape of two sides of an isosceles triangle. If the two walls of equal length were joined by a straight line of 438 ft, the perimeter of the resulting triangle would be 931.5 ft. Find the lengths of the two walls. (*Source:* Pamphlet obtained at Vietnam Veterans Memorial.)

x x
438 ft

35. The two companies with top revenues in the Fortune 500 list for 2012 were Exxon Mobil and Wal-Mart. Their revenues together totaled $919.1 billion. Exxon Mobil revenues were $19.3 billion less than those of Wal-Mart. What were the revenues of each corporation? (*Source: Fortune* magazine.)

36. Two of the longest-running Broadway shows were *Cats* and *Les Misérables*. Together, there were 14,165 performances of these two shows during their Broadway runs. There were 805 fewer performances of *Les Misérables* than of *Cats*. How many performances were there of each show? (*Source:* The Broadway League.)

37. Galileo Galilei conducted experiments involving Italy's famous Leaning Tower of Pisa to investigate the relationship between an object's speed of fall and its weight. The Leaning Tower is 804 ft shorter than the Eiffel Tower in Paris, France. The two towers have a total height of 1164 ft. How tall is each tower? (*Source: World Almanac and Book of Facts.*)

38. In 2013, the New York Yankees and the Los Angeles Dodgers had the highest payrolls in Major League Baseball. The Dodgers' payroll was $0.1 million less than the Yankees' payroll, and the two payrolls totaled $473.9 million. What was the payroll for each team? (*Source: Kansas City Star.*)

39. In the 2012 presidential election, Barack Obama and Mitt Romney together received 538 electoral votes. Obama received 126 more votes than Romney. How many votes did each candidate receive? (*Source: World Almanac and Book of Facts.*)

40. Ted Williams and Rogers Hornsby were two great hitters in Major League Baseball. Together, they had 5584 hits in their careers. Hornsby had 276 more hits than Williams. How many hits did each have? (*Source:* Neft, D. S., and R. M. Cohen, *The Sports Encyclopedia: Baseball,* St. Martins Griffin, New York.)

Rogers Hornsby

Solve each percent problem. ***See Example 5.***

41. In 2012, the number of graduating seniors taking the ACT exam was 1,666,017. In 2002, a total of 1,116,082 graduating seniors took the exam. By what percent did the number increase over this period of time, to the nearest tenth of a percent? (*Source:* ACT.)

42. Composite scores on the ACT exam rose from 20.8 in 2002 to 21.1 in 2012. What percent increase was this, to the nearest tenth of a percent? (*Source:* ACT.)

43. For 1993–1994, the average cost of tuition and fees at public four-year universities in the United States was $2431 for full-time in-state students. Twenty years later, it had increased 240%. To the nearest dollar, what was the approximate cost for 2013–2014? (*Source:* The College Board.)

44. For 1993–1994, the average cost of tuition and fees at private four-year universities in the United States was $9399 for full-time students. Twenty years later, it had increased 173.3%. To the nearest dollar, what was the approximate cost for 2013–2014? (*Source:* The College Board.)

45. In 2013, the average cost of a traditional Thanksgiving dinner for 10, featuring turkey, stuffing, cranberries, pumpkin pie, and trimmings, was $49.04, a decrease of 0.89% over the cost in 2012. What was the cost, to the nearest cent, in 2012? (*Source:* American Farm Bureau.)

46. Refer to **Exercise 45.** The cost of a traditional Thanksgiving dinner in 2013 was $49.04, an increase of 83.3% over the cost in 1987 when data was first collected. What was the cost, to the nearest cent, in 1987? (*Source:* American Farm Bureau.)

47. At the end of a day, Lawrence found that the total cash register receipts at the motel where he works were $2725. This included the 9% sales tax charged. Find the amount of tax.

48. David sold his house for $159,000. He got this amount knowing that he would have to pay a 6% commission to his agent. What amount did he have after the agent was paid?

Solve each investment problem. ***See Example 6.***

▶ **49.** Mario earned $12,000 last year giving tennis lessons. He invested part of the money at 3% simple interest and the rest at 4%. In one year, he earned a total of $440 in interest. How much did he invest at each rate?

Principal (in dollars)	Rate (as a decimal)	Interest (in dollars)
x	0.03	
	0.04	
	✕✕✕✕	

50. Sheryl won $60,000 on a slot machine in Las Vegas. She invested part of the money at 2% simple interest and the rest at 3%. In one year, she earned a total of $1600 in interest. How much was invested at each rate?

Principal (in dollars)	Rate (as a decimal)	Interest (in dollars)
x	0.02	
	✕✕✕✕	

51. Jennifer invested some money at 4.5% simple interest and $1000 less than twice this amount at 3%. Her total annual income from the interest was $1020. How much was invested at each rate?

52. Piotr invested some money at 3.5% simple interest, and $5000 more than three times this amount at 4%. He earned $1440 in annual interest. How much did he invest at each rate?

53. Dan has invested $12,000 in bonds paying 6%. How much additional money should he invest in a certificate of deposit paying 3% simple interest so that the total return on the two investments will be 4%?

54. Mona received a year-end bonus of $17,000 from her company and invested the money in an account paying 6.5%. How much additional money should she deposit in an account paying 5% so that the return on the two investments will be 6%?

Solve each problem. ***See Examples 7 and 8.***

▶ **55.** How many liters of a 10% acid solution must be mixed with 10 L of a 4% solution to obtain a 6% solution?

Liters of Solution	Percent (as a decimal)	Liters of Pure Acid
10	0.04	
x	0.10	
	0.06	

56. How many liters of a 14% alcohol solution must be mixed with 20 L of a 50% solution to obtain a 30% solution?

Liters of Solution	Percent (as a decimal)	Liters of Pure Alcohol
x	0.14	
	0.50	

57. In a chemistry class, 12 L of a 12% alcohol solution must be mixed with a 20% solution to obtain a 14% solution. How many liters of the 20% solution are needed?

58. How many liters of a 10% alcohol solution must be mixed with 40 L of a 50% solution to obtain a 40% solution?

▶ **59.** How much pure dye must be added to 4 gal of a 25% dye solution to increase the solution to 40%? (*Hint:* Pure dye is 100% dye.)

60. How much water must be added to 6 gal of a 4% insecticide solution to reduce the concentration to 3%? (*Hint:* Water is 0% insecticide.)

61. Randall wants to mix 50 lb of nuts worth $2 per lb with some nuts worth $6 per lb to make a mixture worth $5 per lb. How many pounds of $6 nuts must he use?

Pounds of Nuts	Cost per Pound (in dollars)	Total Cost (in dollars)

62. Lee Ann wants to mix tea worth 2¢ per oz with 100 oz of tea worth 5¢ per oz to make a mixture worth 3¢ per oz. How much 2¢ tea should be used?

Ounces of Tea	Cost per Ounce (in dollars)	Total Cost (in dollars)

63. *Concept Check*   Why is it impossible to mix candy worth $4 per lb and candy worth $5 per lb to obtain a final mixture worth $6 per lb?

64. *Concept Check*   Write an equation based on the following problem, solve the equation, and explain why the problem has no solution.

How much 30% acid should be mixed with 15 L of 50% acid to obtain a mixture that is 60% acid?

RELATING CONCEPTS   For Individual or Group Work   (Exercises 65–68)

Consider each problem.

Problem A   Jack has $800 invested in two accounts. One pays 5% annual interest and the other pays 10% annual interest. The amount of annual interest is the same as he would earn if the entire $800 was invested at 8.75%. How much does he have invested at each rate?

Problem B   Jill has 800 L of acid solution. She obtained it by mixing some 5% acid with some 10% acid. Her final mixture of 800 L is 8.75% acid. How much of each of the 5% and 10% solutions did she use to make her final mixture?

In Problem A, let x represent the amount invested at 5% interest, and in Problem B, let y represent the amount of 5% acid used. **Work Exercises 65–68 in order.**

65. (a) Write an expression in x that represents the amount of money Jack invested at 10% in Problem A.

 (b) Write an expression in y that represents the amount of 10% acid solution Jill used in Problem B.

66. (a) Write expressions that represent the amount of annual interest Jack earns at 5% and at 10%.

 (b) Write expressions that represent the amount of pure acid in Jill's 5% and 10% acid solutions.

67. (a) The sum of the two expressions in part (a) of **Exercise 66** must equal the total amount of annual interest earned. Write an equation representing this fact.

 (b) The sum of the two expressions in part (b) of **Exercise 66** must equal the amount of pure acid in the final mixture. Write an equation representing this fact.

68. (a) Solve Problem A.

 (b) Solve Problem B.

 (c) Explain the similarities between the processes used in solving Problems A and B.

1.4 Further Applications of Linear Equations

VOCABULARY

☐ consecutive integers
☐ consecutive even integers
☐ consecutive odd integers

NOW TRY EXERCISE 1

Steven has a collection of 52 coins worth $3.70. His collection contains only dimes and nickels. How many of each type of coin does he have?

OBJECTIVE 1 Solve problems about different denominations of money.

PROBLEM-SOLVING HINT   In problems involving money, use the following basic fact.

$$\begin{array}{c}\text{number of monetary} \\ \text{units of the same kind}\end{array} \times \text{denomination} = \begin{array}{c}\text{total monetary} \\ \text{value}\end{array}$$

Examples: 30 dimes have a monetary value of 30($0.10) = $3.00.

15 five-dollar bills have a value of 15($5) = $75.

EXAMPLE 1   **Solving a Money Denomination Problem**

For a bill totaling $5.65, a cashier received 25 coins consisting of nickels and quarters. How many of each denomination of coin did the cashier receive?

Step 1   **Read** the problem. We must find the number of nickels and the number of quarters the cashier received.

Step 2   **Assign a variable.**

Let x = the number of nickels.

Then $25 - x$ = the number of quarters.

	Number of Coins	Denomination (in dollars)	Value (in dollars)	
Nickels	x	0.05	0.05x	Organize the information in a table.
Quarters	$25 - x$	0.25	0.25(25 − x)	
			5.65	← Total

Step 3   **Write an equation.** Use the values from the last column of the table.

$$0.05x + 0.25(25 - x) = 5.65$$

Step 4   **Solve.**   Clear the parentheses and then the decimals.

$0.05x + 6.25 - 0.25x = 5.65$	Distributive property
$100(0.05x + 6.25 - 0.25x) = 100(5.65)$	Multiply by 100.
$5x + 625 - 25x = 565$	Distributive property; Multiply.
$-20x = -60$	Subtract 625. Combine like terms.
$x = 3$	Divide by −20.

Move decimal points 2 places to the right.

Step 5   **State the answer.** There are 3 nickels and $25 - 3 = 22$ quarters.

Step 6   **Check.** The cashier has $3 + 22 = 25$ coins. The value is

$$\$0.05(3) + \$0.25(22) = \$5.65, \quad \text{as required.} \qquad \text{NOW TRY} \, $$

⚠ CAUTION   *Be sure that your answer is reasonable* when working problems like **Example 1.** Because we are dealing with a number of coins, the correct answer can neither be negative nor a fraction.

NOW TRY ANSWER
1. 22 dimes; 30 nickels

OBJECTIVE 2 Solve problems about uniform motion.

PROBLEM-SOLVING HINT   Uniform motion problems use the distance formula $d = rt$. **When rate (or speed) is given in miles per hour, time must be given in hours. Draw a sketch** to illustrate what is happening. **Make a table** to summarize given information.

**NOW TRY
EXERCISE 2**

Two trains leave a city traveling in opposite directions. One travels at a rate of 80 km per hr and the other at a rate of 75 km per hr. How long will it take before they are 387.5 km apart?

EXAMPLE 2 Solving a Motion Problem (Opposite Directions)

Two cars leave the same place at the same time, one going east and the other west. The eastbound car averages 40 mph, while the westbound car averages 50 mph. In how many hours will they be 300 mi apart?

Step 1 **Read** the problem. We are looking for the time it takes for the two cars to be 300 mi apart.

Step 2 **Assign a variable.** A sketch shows what is happening in the problem. The cars are going in *opposite* directions. See **FIGURE 6**.

Total distance = 300 mi

FIGURE 6

Let $x =$ the time traveled by each car.

	Rate	Time	Distance
Eastbound Car	40	x	40x
Westbound Car	50	x	50x
			300

Fill in each distance by multiplying rate by time, using the formula $d = rt$, or $rt = d$. The sum of the two distances is 300.

Step 3 **Write an equation.** $40x + 50x = 300$

Step 4 **Solve.** $90x = 300$ Combine like terms.

$$x = \frac{300}{90}$$ Divide by 90.

$$x = \frac{10}{3}$$ Lowest terms

Step 5 **State the answer.** The cars travel $\frac{10}{3} = 3\frac{1}{3}$ hr, or 3 hr, 20 min.

Step 6 **Check.** The eastbound car traveled $40\left(\frac{10}{3}\right) = \frac{400}{3}$ mi. The westbound car traveled $50\left(\frac{10}{3}\right) = \frac{500}{3}$ mi, for a total distance of $\frac{400}{3} + \frac{500}{3} = \frac{900}{3}$, or 300 mi, as required.

NOW TRY

!CAUTION   It is a common error to write 300 as the distance traveled by each car in **Example 2**. Three hundred miles is the *total* distance traveled.

As in **Example 2,** in general, the equation for a problem involving motion in *opposite* directions is of the following form.

partial distance + partial distance = total distance

**NOW TRY
EXERCISE 3**

Michael can drive to work in $\frac{1}{2}$ hr. When he rides his bicycle, it takes $1\frac{1}{2}$ hours. If his average rate while driving to work is 30 mph faster than his rate while bicycling to work, determine the distance that he lives from work.

EXAMPLE 3   Solving a Motion Problem (Same Direction)

Geoff can bike to work in $\frac{3}{4}$ hr. When he takes the bus, the trip takes $\frac{1}{4}$ hr. If the bus travels 20 mph faster than Geoff rides his bike, how far is it to his workplace?

Step 1   **Read** the problem. We must find the distance between Geoff's home and his workplace.

Step 2   **Assign a variable.** Make a sketch to show what is happening. See **FIGURE 7.**

FIGURE 7

The problem asks for a distance, but it is easier here to let x be Geoff's rate when he rides his bike to work. Then the rate of the bus is $(x + 20)$ mph.

For the trip by bike, $d = rt = x \cdot \dfrac{3}{4} = \dfrac{3}{4}x.$

For the trip by bus, $d = rt = (x + 20) \cdot \dfrac{1}{4} = \dfrac{1}{4}(x + 20).$

	Rate	Time	Distance
Bike	x	$\dfrac{3}{4}$	$\dfrac{3}{4}x$
Bus	$x + 20$	$\dfrac{1}{4}$	$\dfrac{1}{4}(x + 20)$

← Same distance

Step 3   **Write an equation.**

$$\frac{3}{4}x = \frac{1}{4}(x + 20)$$ The distance is the same in each case.

Step 4   **Solve.**

$$\frac{3}{4}x = \frac{1}{4}x + 5$$ Distributive property

$$4\left(\frac{3}{4}x\right) = 4\left(\frac{1}{4}x + 5\right)$$ Multiply by 4 to clear the fractions.

$$3x = x + 20$$ Multiply; $4\left(\frac{1}{4}\right) = 1$ and $1x = x$

$$2x = 20$$ Subtract x.

$$x = 10$$ Divide by 2.

Step 5   **State the answer.** The required distance is

$$d = \frac{3}{4}x = \frac{3}{4}(10) = \frac{30}{4} = 7.5 \text{ mi.}$$

Step 6   **Check** by finding the distance using

The same distance results.

$$d = \frac{1}{4}(x + 20) = \frac{1}{4}(10 + 20) = \frac{30}{4} = 7.5 \text{ mi.}$$ NOW TRY

NOW TRY ANSWER
3. 22.5 mi

As in **Example 3,** the equation for a problem involving motion in the *same* direction is often of the following form.

$$\text{one distance} = \text{other distance}$$

PROBLEM-SOLVING HINT   In **Example 3,** it was easier to let the variable represent a quantity other than the one that we were asked to find. It takes practice to learn when this approach works best.

OBJECTIVE 3   Solve problems about angles.

An important result of Euclidean geometry (the geometry of the Greek mathematician Euclid) is as follows.

The sum of the angle measures of any triangle is 180°.

**NOW TRY
EXERCISE 4**

Find the value of *x*, and determine the measure of each angle.

EXAMPLE 4   Finding Angle Measures

Find the value of *x*, and determine the measure of each angle in **FIGURE 8**.

Step 1   **Read** the problem. We are asked to find the measure of each angle.

Step 2   **Assign a variable.**

Let $x =$ the measure of one angle.

Step 3   **Write an equation.** The sum of the three measures shown in the figure must be 180°.

$$x + (x + 20) + (210 - 3x) = 180 \qquad \begin{array}{l}\text{Measures are}\\ \text{in degrees.}\end{array}$$

Step 4   **Solve.** $-x + 230 = 180$ Combine like terms.

$$-x = -50 \qquad \text{Subtract 230.}$$

$$x = 50 \qquad \text{Multiply by } -1.$$

Step 5   **State the answer.** One angle measures 50°. The other two angles measure

$$x + 20 = 50 + 20 = 70°$$

and $$210 - 3x = 210 - 3(50) = 60°.$$

Step 6   **Check.** Because $50° + 70° + 60° = 180°$ is true, the answers are correct.

NOW TRY

OBJECTIVE 4   Solve problems about consecutive integers.

Recall that the set of integers is $\{\ldots, -3, -2, -1, 0, 1, 2, 3, \ldots\}$. **Consecutive integers** are integers that are next to each other on a number line. Two consecutive integers differ by 1. Some examples of consecutive integers are 4, 5 and $-6, -5$.

Consecutive even integers always differ by 2. Examples are 4, 6 and $-4, -2$. Similarly, **consecutive odd integers** also differ by 2, such as 1, 3 and $-5, -3$.

NOW TRY ANSWER
4. 41°, 52°, 87°

PROBLEM-SOLVING HINT If x = the lesser (least) integer in a consecutive integer problem, then the following apply.

- For two consecutive integers, use $x,\ x + 1.$
- For three consecutive integers, use $x,\ x + 1,\ x + 2.$
- For two consecutive even or odd integers, use $x,\ x + 2.$
- For three consecutive even or odd integers, use $x,\ x + 2,\ x + 4.$

In this book, we list consecutive integers in increasing order.

NOW TRY EXERCISE 5

Find three consecutive integers such that the sum of the first and second is 43 less than three times the third.

EXAMPLE 5 Solving a Consecutive Integer Problem

Find three consecutive integers such that the sum of the first and third, increased by 3, is 50 more than the second.

Step 1 **Read** the problem. We are told to find three consecutive integers satisfying the given conditions.

Step 2 **Assign a variable.**

Let x = the least of the three consecutive integers.

Then $x + 1$ = the second (middle) integer,

and $x + 2$ = the greatest of the three consecutive integers.

Step 3 **Write an equation.**

Sum of the first and third,	increased by 3,	is	50 more than the second.
$\downarrow$	$\downarrow$	$\downarrow$	$\downarrow$
$x + (x + 2)$	$+ 3$	$=$	$(x + 1) + 50$

Step 4 **Solve.** $2x + 5 = x + 51$ Combine like terms.

$x = 46$ Subtract x and 5.

Step 5 **State the answer.** The solution is 46, so the first integer is $x = 46$, the second is $46 + 1 = 47$, and the third is $46 + 2 = 48$. The three integers are 46, 47, and 48.

Step 6 **Check.** The sum of the first and third is $46 + 48 = 94$. If this is increased by 3, the result is $94 + 3 = 97$, which is indeed 50 more than the second (47). The answer is correct.

NOW TRY ANSWER
5. 38, 39, 40

NOW TRY

1.4 Exercises

FOR EXTRA HELP

▶ MyMathLab®

▶ *Complete solution available in MyMathLab*

Concept Check *Solve each problem.*

1. What amount of money is found in a coin hoard containing 12 dimes and 18 quarters?

2. The distance between Cape Town, South Africa, and Miami is 7700 mi. If a jet averages 550 mph between the two cities, what is its travel time in hours?

3. Tri traveled from Chicago to Des Moines, a distance of 300 mi, in 10 hr. What was his rate in miles per hour?

4. A square has perimeter 160 in. What would be the perimeter of an equilateral triangle whose sides each measure the same length as the side of the square?

Concept Check   *Answer each question.*

5. Read over **Example 3** in this section. The solution of the equation is 10. Why is *10 mph* not the answer to the problem?

6. Suppose that we know that two angles of a triangle have equal measures and the third angle measures 36°. How would we find the measures of the equal angles without actually writing an equation?

7. In a problem about the number of coins of different denominations, would an answer that is a fraction be reasonable? Would a negative answer be reasonable?

8. In a motion problem the rate is given as *x* mph and the time is given as 10 min. What variable expression represents the distance in miles?

*Solve each problem. **See Example 1.***

9. Otis has a box of coins that he uses when he plays poker with his friends. The box contains 44 coins, consisting of pennies, dimes, and quarters. The number of pennies is equal to the number of dimes. The total value is $4.37. How many of each denomination of coin does he have in the box?

Number of Coins	Denomination (in dollars)	Value (in dollars)
x	0.01	0.01x
x		
	0.25	
		4.37 ←Total

10. Nana found some coins while looking under her sofa pillows. There were equal numbers of nickels and quarters and twice as many half-dollars as quarters. If she found $2.60 in all, how many of each denomination of coin did she find?

Number of Coins	Denomination (in dollars)	Value (in dollars)
x	0.05	0.05x
x		
2x	0.50	
		2.60 ←Total

11. In Canada, $1 and $2 bills have been replaced by coins. The $1 coins are called "loonies" because they have a picture of a loon (a well-known Canadian bird) on the reverse, and the $2 coins are called "toonies." When Marissa returned home to San Francisco from a trip to Vancouver, she found that she had acquired 37 of these coins, with a total value of 51 Canadian dollars. How many coins of each denomination did she have?

12. Dan works at an ice cream shop. At the end of his shift, he counted the bills in his cash drawer and found 119 bills with a total value of $347. If all of the bills are $5 bills and $1 bills, how many of each denomination were in his cash drawer?

13. Dave collects U.S. gold coins. He has a collection of 41 coins. Some are $10 coins, and the rest are $20 coins. If the face value of the coins is $540, how many of each denomination does he have?

14. In the 19th century, the United States minted two-cent and three-cent pieces. Frances has three times as many three-cent pieces as two-cent pieces, and the face value of these coins is $2.42. How many of each denomination does she have?

15. In 2014, general admission to the Art Institute of Chicago cost $23 for adults and $17 for children and seniors. If $30,052 was collected from the sale of 1460 general admission tickets, how many adult tickets were sold? (*Source:* www.artic.edu)

16. For a high school production of *A Funny Thing Happened on the Way to the Forum*, student tickets cost $5 each while nonstudent tickets cost $8. If 480 tickets were sold and a total of $2895 was collected, how many tickets of each type were sold?

In Exercises 17–20, find the rate on the basis of the information provided. Use a calculator and round answers to the nearest hundredth. All events were at the 2012 Summer Olympics in London, England. (Source: World Almanac and Book of Facts.)

	Event	Winner	Distance	Time
17.	100-m hurdles, women	Sally Pearson, Australia	100 m	12.35 sec
18.	400-m hurdles, women	Natalya Antyukh, Russia	400 m	52.70 sec
19.	200-m run, men	Usain Bolt, Jamaica	200 m	19.32 sec
20.	400-m run, men	Kirani James, Grenada	400 m	43.94 sec

Solve each problem. **See Examples 2 and 3.**

21. Two steamers leave a port on a river at the same time, traveling in opposite directions. Each is traveling 22 mph. How long will it take for them to be 110 mi apart?

	Rate	Time	Distance
First Steamer		t	
Second Steamer	22		
			110

22. A train leaves Kansas City, Kansas, and travels north at 85 km per hr. Another train leaves at the same time and travels south at 95 km per hr. How long will it take before they are 315 km apart?

	Rate	Time	Distance
First Train	85	t	
Second Train			
			315

23. Mulder and Scully are driving to Georgia to investigate "Big Blue," a giant reptile reported in one of the local lakes. Mulder leaves the office at 8:30 A.M. averaging 65 mph. Scully leaves at 9:00 A.M., following the same path and averaging 68 mph. At what time will Scully catch up with Mulder?

	Rate	Time	Distance
Mulder			
Scully			

24. Lois and Clark, two elderly reporters, are covering separate stories and have to travel in opposite directions. Lois leaves the *Daily Planet* building at 8:00 A.M. and travels at 35 mph. Clark leaves at 8:15 A.M. and travels at 40 mph. At what time will they be 140 mi apart?

	Rate	Time	Distance
Lois			
Clark			

25. It took Charmaine 3.6 hr to drive to her mother's house on Saturday morning for a weekend visit. On her return trip on Sunday night, traffic was heavier, so the trip took her 4 hr. Her average rate on Sunday was 5 mph slower than on Saturday. What was her average rate on Sunday?

	Rate	Time	Distance
Saturday			
Sunday			

26. Sharon commutes to her office by train. When she walks to the train station, it takes her 40 min. When she rides her bike, it takes her 12 min. Her average walking rate is 7 mph less than her average biking rate. Find the distance from her house to the train station.

	Rate	Time	Distance
Walking			
Biking			

27. Johnny leaves Memphis to visit his cousin Anne, who lives in the town of Hornsby, Tennessee, 80 mi away. He travels at an average rate of 50 mph. One-half hour later, Anne leaves to visit Johnny, traveling at an average rate of 60 mph. How long after Anne leaves will it be before they meet?

28. On an automobile trip, Laura maintained a steady rate for the first two hours. Rush-hour traffic slowed her rate by 25 mph for the last part of the trip. The entire trip, a distance of 125 mi, took $2\frac{1}{2}$ hr. What was her rate during the first part of the trip?

Find the measure of each angle in the triangles shown. ***See Example 4.***

29.

30.

▶ **31.**

32.

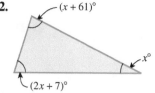

In Exercises 33 and 34, the angles marked with variable expressions are ***vertical angles.*** *It is shown in geometry that vertical angles have equal measures. Find the measure of each angle.*

33.

34.

Two angles whose sum is 90° are ***complementary angles.*** *In Exercises 35 and 36, find the measures of the complementary angles shown in the figure.*

35.

36.

Two angles whose sum is 180° are ***supplementary angles.*** *In Exercises 37 and 38, find the measures of the supplementary angles shown in the figure.*

37.

38.

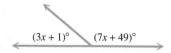

Solve each problem involving consecutive integers. ***See Example 5.***

39. Find three consecutive integers such that the sum of the first and twice the second is 17 more than twice the third.

40. Find three consecutive integers such that the sum of the first and twice the third is 39 more than twice the second.

41. Find four consecutive integers such that the sum of the first three is 54 more than the fourth.

42. Find four consecutive integers such that the sum of the last three is 86 more than the first.

43. If I add my current age to the age I will be next year on this date, the sum is 103 yr. How old will I be 10 yr from today?

44. If I add my current age to the age I will be next year on this date, the sum is 129 yr. How old will I be 5 yr from today?

45. Find three consecutive *even* integers such that the sum of the least integer and the middle integer is 26 more than the greatest integer.

46. Find three consecutive *even* integers such that the sum of the least integer and the greatest integer is 12 more than the middle integer.

47. Find three consecutive *odd* integers such that the sum of the least integer and the middle integer is 19 more than the greatest integer.

48. Find three consecutive *odd* integers such that the sum of the least integer and the greatest integer is 13 more than the middle integer.

RELATING CONCEPTS For Individual or Group Work (Exercises 49–52)

Consider the following two figures. ***Work Exercises 49–52 in order.***

FIGURE A   FIGURE B

49. Solve for the measures of the unknown angles in **FIGURE A**. (*Hint:* What is the sum of the angle measures of any triangle?)

50. Solve for the measure of the unknown angle marked $y°$ in **FIGURE B**. (*Hint:* See **Exercises 37 and 38.**)

51. Add the measures of the two angles found in **Exercise 49.** How does the sum compare to the measure of the angle found in **Exercise 50?**

52. Based on the answers to **Exercises 49–51,** make a conjecture (an educated guess) about the relationship among the angles marked ①, ②, and ③ in the figure below.

SUMMARY EXERCISES Applying Problem-Solving Techniques

Solve each problem.

1. length: 8 in.; width: 5 in.
2. length: 60 m; width: 30 m
3. $399.99
4. $425
5. $800 at 4%; $1600 at 5%
6. $12,000 at 3%; $14,000 at 4%
7. Durant: 2280; Bryant: 2133
8. *Titanic:* $600.8 million;
    The Dark Knight: $533.3 million
9. 5 hr

1. The length of a rectangle is 3 in. more than its width. If the length were decreased by 2 in. and the width were increased by 1 in., the perimeter of the resulting rectangle would be 24 in. Find the dimensions of the original rectangle.

$x + 3$

x

2. A farmer wishes to enclose a rectangular region with 210 m of fencing in such a way that the length is twice the width and the region is divided into two equal parts, as shown in the figure. What length and width should be used?

Width

Length

3. After a discount of 20.5%, the sale price for a Samsung Galaxy tablet computer was $317.99. What was the regular price of the computer to the nearest cent? (*Source:* www.amazon.com)

4. An electronics store offered a new HD television for $255, the sale price after the regular price was discounted 40%. What was the regular price?

5. An amount of money is invested at 4% annual simple interest, and twice that amount is invested at 5%. The total annual interest is $112. How much is invested at each rate?

6. An amount of money is invested at 3% annual simple interest, and $2000 more than that amount is invested at 4%. The total annual interest is $920. How much is invested at each rate?

7. Kevin Durant of the Oklahoma City Thunder and Kobe Bryant of the Los Angeles Lakers were the leading scorers in the NBA for the 2012–2013 regular season. Together they scored 4413 points, with Bryant scoring 147 fewer points than Durant. How many points did each of them score? (*Source:* www.espn.go.com)

8. Two top-grossing American movies were *Titanic* and *The Dark Knight*. *Titanic* grossed $67.5 million more than *The Dark Knight*. Together, the two films brought in $1134.1 million. How much did each movie gross? (*Source:* Rentrak Corporation.)

9. Atlanta and Cincinnati are 440 mi apart. John leaves Cincinnati, driving toward Atlanta at an average rate of 60 mph. Pat leaves Atlanta at the same time, driving toward Cincinnati in her antique auto, averaging 28 mph. How long will it take them to meet?

Pat
Atlanta
John
Cincinnati
440 mi

10. $1\frac{1}{2}$ cm

11. $13\frac{1}{3}$ L   **12.** $53\frac{1}{3}$ kg

13. 84 fives; 42 tens

14. 1650 tickets at \$9;
810 tickets at \$7

15. 20°, 30°, 130°

16. 107°, 73°

17. 31, 32, 33

18. 9, 11

19. 6 in., 12 in., 16 in.

20. 23 in.

10. Joshua has a sheet of tin 12 cm by 16 cm. He plans to make a box by cutting equal squares out of each of the four corners and folding up the remaining edges. How large a square should he cut so that the finished box will have a length that is 5 cm less than twice the width?

11. A pharmacist has 20 L of a 10% drug solution. How many liters of 5% solution must be added to obtain a mixture that is 8%?

12. A certain metal is 20% tin. How many kilograms of this metal must be mixed with 80 kg of a metal that is 70% tin to obtain a metal that is 50% tin?

13. A cashier has a total of 126 bills in fives and tens. The total value of the money is \$840. How many of each denomination of bill does he have?

Kilograms of Metal	Percent (as a decimal)	Kilograms of Tin
	0.20	
	0.50	

Number of Bills	Denomination (in dollars)	Value (in dollars)
✕✕✕✕✕✕✕		840

14. The top-grossing domestic movie in 2013 was *The Hunger Games: Catching Fire*. On opening weekend, one theater showing this movie took in \$20,520 by selling a total of 2460 tickets, some at \$9 and the rest at \$7. How many tickets were sold at each price? (*Source:* www.boxofficemojo.com)

15. Find the measure of each angle.

16. Find the measure of each marked angle.

17. The sum of the least and greatest of three consecutive integers is 32 more than the middle integer. What are the three integers?

18. If the lesser of two consecutive odd integers is doubled, the result is 7 more than the greater of the two integers. Find the two integers.

19. The perimeter of a triangle is 34 in. The middle side is twice as long as the shortest side. The longest side is 2 in. less than three times the shortest side. Find the lengths of the three sides.

20. The perimeter of a rectangle is 43 in. more than the length. The width is 10 in. Find the length of the rectangle.

1.5 Linear Inequalities in One Variable

VOCABULARY

☐ inequality
☐ interval
☐ linear inequality in one variable
☐ equivalent inequalities
☐ three-part inequality

An **inequality** consists of algebraic expressions related by one of the following symbols.

$<$ "is less than" $\leq$ "is less than or equal to"

$>$ "is greater than" $\geq$ "is greater than or equal to"

These symbols are read as shown when the inequality is read from left to right.

We *solve an inequality* by finding all real number solutions for it. For example, the solution set of $x \leq 2$ includes *all* real numbers that are less than or equal to 2, not just the integers less than or equal to 2.

OBJECTIVE 1 Graph intervals on a number line.

We graph all the real numbers satisfying $x \leq 2$ by placing a square bracket at 2 and drawing an arrow to the left to represent the fact that all numbers less than 2 are also part of the graph. See **FIGURE 9**.

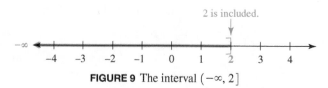

FIGURE 9 The interval $(-\infty, 2]$

The set of numbers less than or equal to 2 is an example of an **interval** on a number line. To write intervals, we use **interval notation,** which includes the **infinity symbols, ∞** or $-\infty$. We write the interval of *all* numbers less than or equal to 2 as

$$(-\infty, 2].$$ Interval notation

The negative infinity symbol $-\infty$ does not indicate a number, but shows that the interval includes all real numbers less than 2. On both the number line and in interval notation, the square bracket indicates that 2 is included in the solution set.

Remember the following important concepts regarding interval notation.

- A parenthesis indicates that an endpoint is *not* included.

- A square bracket indicates that an endpoint is included.

- A parenthesis is always used next to an infinity symbol, $-\infty$ or ∞.

- The set of real numbers is written in interval notation as $(-\infty, \infty)$.

EXAMPLE 1 Using Interval Notation

Write each inequality in interval notation and graph the interval.

(a) $x > -5$

This statement says that x can represent any number greater than -5, but x cannot equal -5. This interval is written $(-5, \infty)$. We graph it by placing a parenthesis at -5 and drawing an arrow to the right, as in **FIGURE 10**. The parenthesis at -5 shows that -5 is *not* part of the graph.

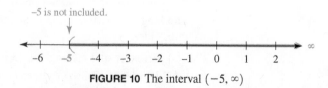

FIGURE 10 The interval $(-5, \infty)$

**NOW TRY
EXERCISE 1**

Write each inequality in interval notation and graph the interval.

(a) $x < -1$

(b) $-4 \le x < 2$

(b) $-1 \le x < 3$

This statement is read "-1 is less than or equal to x and x is less than 3." We want the set of numbers that are *between* -1 and 3, with -1 included and 3 excluded. In interval notation, we write $[-1, 3)$, using a bracket at -1 because it is part of the graph and a parenthesis at 3 because it is not part of the graph. See **FIGURE 11**.

FIGURE 11 The interval $[-1, 3)$

NOW TRY

▼ **Summary of Types of Intervals**

Type of Interval	Set-Builder Notation	Interval Notation	Graph
Open interval	$\{x \mid a < x < b\}$	(a, b)	
Closed interval	$\{x \mid a \le x \le b\}$	$[a, b]$	
Half-open (or half-closed) interval	$\{x \mid a \le x < b\}$	$[a, b)$	
	$\{x \mid a < x \le b\}$	$(a, b]$	
Disjoint interval*	$\{x \mid x < a \text{ or } x > b\}$	$(-\infty, a) \cup (b, \infty)$	
Infinite interval	$\{x \mid x > a\}$	(a, ∞)	
	$\{x \mid x \ge a\}$	$[a, \infty)$	
	$\{x \mid x < a\}$	$(-\infty, a)$	
	$\{x \mid x \le a\}$	$(-\infty, a]$	
	$\{x \mid x \text{ is a real number}\}$	$(-\infty, \infty)$	

! CAUTION A parenthesis is *always* used next to an infinity symbol, $-\infty$ or ∞.

Solving inequalities is similar to solving equations.

Linear Inequality in One Variable

A **linear inequality in one variable** (here x) can be written in the form

$$Ax + B < C, \quad Ax + B \le C, \quad Ax + B > C, \quad \text{or} \quad Ax + B \ge C,$$

where A, B, and C are real numbers and $A \ne 0$.

Examples: $x + 5 < 2$, $x - 3 \ge 5$, and $2x + 5 \le 10$ Linear inequalities

NOW TRY ANSWERS
1. (a) $(-\infty, -1)$

(b) $[-4, 2)$

*We will work with disjoint intervals in **Section 1.6** when we study *set operations* and *compound inequalities*.

OBJECTIVE 2 Solve linear inequalities using the addition property.

We solve an inequality by finding all numbers that make the inequality true. Usually, an inequality has an infinite number of solutions. These solutions, like solutions of equations, are found by producing a series of simpler equivalent inequalities. **Equivalent inequalities** are inequalities with the same solution set.

We use two important properties to produce equivalent inequalities.

Addition Property of Inequality

If A, B, and C represent real numbers, then the inequalities

$$A < B \quad \text{and} \quad A + C < B + C \quad \text{are equivalent.*}$$

That is, the same number may be added to each side of an inequality without changing the solution set.

*This also applies to $A \leq B$, $A > B$, and $A \geq B$.

NOW TRY EXERCISE 2

Solve $x - 10 > -7$, and graph the solution set.

EXAMPLE 2 Using the Addition Property of Inequality

Solve $x - 7 < -12$, and graph the solution set.

$$x - 7 < -12$$
$$x - 7 + 7 < -12 + 7 \qquad \text{Add 7.}$$
$$x < -5 \qquad \qquad \text{Combine like terms.}$$

CHECK   Substitute -5 for x in the *equation* $x - 7 = -12$.

$$x - 7 = -12$$
$$-5 - 7 \overset{?}{=} -12 \qquad \text{Let } x = -5.$$
$$-12 = -12 \quad \checkmark \quad \text{True}$$

The result, a true statement, shows that -5 is the boundary point. Now test a number on each side of -5 to verify that numbers *less than* -5 make the inequality true. We choose -4 and -6.

$$x - 7 < -12$$

$-4 - 7 \overset{?}{<} -12$ Let $x = -4.$		$-6 - 7 \overset{?}{<} -12$ Let $x = -6.$
$-11 < -12$ False		$-13 < -12$ ✓ True
-4 is *not* in the solution set.		-6 *is* in the solution set.

The check confirms that the interval $(-\infty, -5)$ is the solution set. See **FIGURE 12**.

FIGURE 12

 NOW TRY

As with equations, the addition property can be used to *subtract* the same number from each side of an inequality.

**NOW TRY
EXERCISE 3**
Solve $4x + 1 \geq 5x$, and graph
the solution set.

EXAMPLE 3   Using the Addition Property of Inequality

Solve $14 + 2x \leq 3x$, and graph the solution set.

$$14 + 2x \leq 3x$$

$$14 + 2x - 2x \leq 3x - 2x \qquad \text{Subtract } 2x.$$

$$14 \leq x \qquad \text{Combine like terms.}$$

Be careful. $\qquad x \geq 14 \qquad \text{Rewrite.}$

The inequality $14 \leq x$ (14 is less than or equal to x) can also be written $x \geq 14$ (x is greater than or equal to 14). *Notice that in each case the inequality symbol points to the lesser number,* **14.**

CHECK $\qquad\qquad\qquad 14 + 2x = 3x$

$$14 + 2(14) \stackrel{?}{=} 3(14) \qquad \text{Let } x = 14.$$

$$42 = 42 \;\checkmark \qquad \text{True}$$

So 14 satisfies the equality part of $\leq$. Choose 10 and 15 as test values.

$$14 + 2x < 3x$$

$14 + 2(10) \stackrel{?}{<} 3(10) \quad$ Let $x = 10$.	$14 + 2(15) \stackrel{?}{<} 3(15) \quad$ Let $x = 15$.
$34 < 30 \qquad$ False	$44 < 45 \;\checkmark \quad$ True
10 is not in the solution set.	15 is in the solution set.

The check confirms that the interval $[14, \infty)$ is the solution set. See **FIGURE 13**.

FIGURE 13

NOW TRY

OBJECTIVE 3   Solve linear inequalities using the multiplication property.

Consider the following true statement.

$$-2 < 5$$

Multiply each side by some positive number—for example, 8.

$$-2(8) < 5(8) \qquad \text{Multiply by 8.}$$

$$-16 < 40 \qquad \text{True}$$

The result is true. Start again with $-2 < 5$, and multiply each side by some negative number—for example, -8.

$$-2(-8) < 5(-8) \qquad \text{Multiply by } -8.$$

$$16 < -40 \qquad \text{False}$$

The result, $16 < -40$, is false. To make it true, we must change the direction of the inequality symbol.

$$16 > -40 \qquad \text{True}$$

NOW TRY ANSWER
3. $(-\infty, 1]$

As these examples suggest, multiplying each side of an inequality by a *negative* number requires reversing the direction of the inequality symbol. The same is true for dividing by a negative number because division is defined in terms of multiplication.

> ### Multiplication Property of Inequality
>
> Let A, B, and C represent real numbers, where $C \neq 0$.
>
> **(a)** If C is *positive*, then the inequalities
>
> $$A < B \quad \text{and} \quad AC < BC \quad \text{are equivalent.}^*$$
>
> **(b)** If C is *negative*, then the inequalities
>
> $$A < B \quad \text{and} \quad AC > BC \quad \text{are equivalent.}^*$$
>
> That is, each side of an inequality may be multiplied (or divided) by the same *positive* number without changing the direction of the inequality symbol. *If the multiplier is negative, we must reverse the direction of the inequality symbol.*
>
> *This also applies to $A \leq B, A > B,$ and $A \geq B.$

Because division is defined in terms of multiplication, the multiplication property also applies when dividing each side of an inequality by the same number.

NOW TRY
EXERCISE 4

Solve each inequality, and graph the solution set.

(a) $8x \geq -40$

(b) $-20x > -60$

EXAMPLE 4   Using the Multiplication Property of Inequality

Solve each inequality, and graph the solution set.

(a) $5x \leq -30$

Divide each side by 5. *Because $5 > 0$, do not reverse the direction of the inequality symbol.*

$$5x \leq -30$$

$$\frac{5x}{5} \leq \frac{-30}{5} \qquad \text{Divide by 5.}$$

$$x \leq -6$$

Check that the solution set is the interval $(-\infty, -6]$, graphed in **FIGURE 14**.

FIGURE 14

(b) $-4x \leq 32$

Divide each side by -4. *Because $-4 < 0$, reverse the direction of the inequality symbol.*

$$-4x \leq 32$$

$$\frac{-4x}{-4} \geq \frac{32}{-4} \qquad \begin{array}{l}\text{Divide by } -4. \\ \text{Reverse the direction of the symbol.}\end{array}$$

Reverse the inequality symbol when dividing by a *negative* number. $x \geq -8$

NOW TRY ANSWERS

4. (a) $[-5, \infty)$

(b) $(-\infty, 3)$

Check the solution set. **FIGURE 15** shows the graph of the solution set, $[-8, \infty)$.

FIGURE 15

NOW TRY

To solve a linear inequality in one variable, use the following steps.

Solving a Linear Inequality in One Variable

Step 1   **Simplify each side separately.** Use the distributive property as needed.
- Clear any parentheses.
- Clear any fractions or decimals.
- Combine like terms.

Step 2   **Isolate the variable terms on one side.** Use the addition property of inequality so that all terms with variables are on one side of the inequality and all constants (numbers) are on the other side.

Step 3   **Isolate the variable.** Use the multiplication property of inequality to obtain an inequality in one of the following forms, where k is a constant (number).

$$\text{variable} < k, \quad \text{variable} \leq k, \quad \text{variable} > k, \quad \text{or} \quad \text{variable} \geq k$$

Remember: Reverse the direction of the inequality symbol only when multiplying or dividing each side of an inequality by a negative number.

NOW TRY
EXERCISE 5

Solve and graph the solution set.

$$5 - 2(x - 4) \leq 11 - 4x$$

EXAMPLE 5   Solving a Linear Inequality

Solve $-3(x + 4) + 2 \geq 7 - x$, and graph the solution set.

Step 1 $-3(x + 4) + 2 \geq 7 - x$

$-3x - 3(4) + 2 \geq 7 - x$ Distributive property

$-3x - 12 + 2 \geq 7 - x$ Multiply.

$-3x - 10 \geq 7 - x$ (*)   Combine like terms.

Step 2 $-3x - 10 + x \geq 7 - x + x$ Add x.

$-2x - 10 \geq 7$ Combine like terms.

$-2x - 10 + 10 \geq 7 + 10$ Add 10.

$-2x \geq 17$ Combine like terms.

Step 3 $\dfrac{-2x}{-2} \leq \dfrac{17}{-2}$ Divide by -2. Change $\geq$ to $\leq$.

> Be sure to reverse the direction of the inequality symbol.

$$x \leq -\frac{17}{2}$$

FIGURE 16 shows the graph of the solution set, $\left(-\infty, -\dfrac{17}{2}\right]$.

NOW TRY ANSWER
5. $(-\infty, -1]$

FIGURE 16

NOW TRY

NOTE In Step 2 of **Example 5,** if we add $3x$ (instead of x) to both sides of the inequality, we obtain the following sequence of equivalent inequalities.

$-3x - 10 \geq 7 - x$	See (*) of Example 5.
$-3x - 10 + 3x \geq 7 - x + 3x$	Add $3x$.
$-10 \geq 2x + 7$	Combine like terms.
$-10 - 7 \geq 2x + 7 - 7$	Subtract 7.
$-17 \geq 2x$	Combine like terms.
$-\dfrac{17}{2} \geq x$	Divide by 2.
$x \leq -\dfrac{17}{2}$	Rewrite. The same solution results.

The symbol points to x in each case.

NOW TRY EXERCISE 6
Solve and graph the solution set.

$$\frac{3}{4}(x - 2) + \frac{1}{2} > \frac{1}{5}(x - 8)$$

EXAMPLE 6 Solving a Linear Inequality with Fractions

Solve $-\frac{2}{3}(x - 3) - \frac{1}{2} < \frac{1}{2}(5 - x)$, and graph the solution set.

$$-\frac{2}{3}(x - 3) - \frac{1}{2} < \frac{1}{2}(5 - x)$$

Step 1 $\qquad -\frac{2}{3}x + 2 - \frac{1}{2} < \frac{5}{2} - \frac{1}{2}x \qquad$ Clear parentheses.

$$6\left(-\frac{2}{3}x + 2 - \frac{1}{2}\right) < 6\left(\frac{5}{2} - \frac{1}{2}x\right) \qquad$$ To clear the fractions, multiply by 6, the LCD.

$$6\left(-\frac{2}{3}x\right) + 6(2) + 6\left(-\frac{1}{2}\right) < 6\left(\frac{5}{2}\right) + 6\left(-\frac{1}{2}x\right) \qquad$$ Distributive property

$$-4x + 12 - 3 < 15 - 3x \qquad$$ Multiply.

$$-4x + 9 < 15 - 3x \qquad$$ Combine like terms.

Step 2 $\qquad -4x + 9 + 3x < 15 - 3x + 3x \qquad$ Add $3x$.

$$-x + 9 < 15 \qquad$$ Combine like terms.

$$-x + 9 - 9 < 15 - 9 \qquad$$ Subtract 9.

$$-x < 6 \qquad$$ Combine like terms.

Step 3 $\qquad -1(-x) > -1(6) \qquad$ Multiply by -1.
Change $<$ to $>$.

Reverse the inequality symbol when multiplying by a *negative* number.

$$x > -6$$

Check that the solution set is $(-6, \infty)$. See the graph in **FIGURE 17**.

NOW TRY ANSWER
6. $\left(-\frac{12}{11}, \infty\right)$

FIGURE 17

NOW TRY

OBJECTIVE 4 Solve linear inequalities with three parts.

Some applications involve a **three-part inequality** such as

$$3 < x + 2 < 8,$$

where $x + 2$ is *between* 3 and 8.

<table>
<tr><td>

NOW TRY
EXERCISE 7

Solve and graph the solution set.

$$-1 < x - 2 < 3$$

</td></tr>
</table>

EXAMPLE 7 Solving a Three-Part Inequality

Solve $3 < x + 2 < 8$, and graph the solution set.

$$3 < \quad x + 2 \quad < 8$$

$$3 - 2 < \quad x + 2 - 2 < 8 - 2 \quad \text{Subtract 2 from all three parts.}$$

$$1 < \quad x \quad < 6$$

Thus, x must be between 1 and 6 so that $x + 2$ will be between 3 and 8. The solution set, $(1, 6)$, is graphed in **FIGURE 18**.

FIGURE 18   NOW TRY

⚠ **CAUTION** *In three-part inequalities, the order of the parts is important.* For example, do not write $8 < x + 2 < 3$ because this would imply that $8 < 3$, a false statement. *Write three-part inequalities so that the symbols point in the same direction, and both point toward the lesser number.*

<table>
<tr><td>

NOW TRY
EXERCISE 8

Solve and graph the solution set.

$$-2 < -4x - 5 \le 7$$

</td></tr>
</table>

EXAMPLE 8 Solving a Three-Part Inequality

Solve $-2 \le -3x - 1 \le 5$ and graph the solution set.

$$-2 \le \quad -3x - 1 \quad \le 5$$

$$-2 + 1 \le \quad -3x - 1 + 1 \le 5 + 1 \qquad \text{Add 1 to each part.}$$

$$-1 \le \quad -3x \quad \le 6$$

$$\frac{-1}{-3} \ge \quad \frac{-3x}{-3} \quad \ge \frac{6}{-3} \qquad \begin{array}{l}\text{Divide each part by } -3.\\ \text{Reverse the direction of the}\\ \text{inequality symbols.}\end{array}$$

$$\frac{1}{3} \ge \quad x \quad \ge -2$$

$$-2 \le \quad x \quad \le \frac{1}{3} \qquad \begin{array}{l}\text{Rewrite in the}\\ \text{order on the}\\ \text{number line.}\end{array}$$

Check that the solution set is $\left[-2, \frac{1}{3}\right]$, as shown in **FIGURE 19**.

FIGURE 19   NOW TRY

▼ **Solution Sets of Equations and Inequalities**

Equation or Inequality	Typical Solution Set	Graph of Solution Set
Linear equation $5x + 4 = 14$	$\{2\}$	
Linear inequality $5x + 4 < 14$	$(-\infty, 2)$	
$5x + 4 > 14$	$(2, \infty)$	
Three-part inequality $-1 \leq 5x + 4 \leq 14$	$[-1, 2]$	

OBJECTIVE 5 Solve applied problems using linear inequalities.

▼ **Words and Phrases That Suggest Inequality**

Word Statement	Interpretation	Example	Inequality
a exceeds b.	$a > b$	Juan's age j exceeds 21 yr.	$j > 21$
a is at least b.	$a \geq b$	Juan is at least 21 yr old.	$j \geq 21$
a is no less than b.	$a \geq b$	Juan is no less than 21 yr old.	$j \geq 21$
a is at most b.	$a \leq b$	Mia's age m is at most 10 yr.	$m \leq 10$
a is no more than b.	$a \leq b$	Mia is no more than 10 yr old.	$m \leq 10$

In **Example 9,** we use the six problem-solving steps from **Section 1.3,** changing Step 3 from

"Write an equation"   to   "Write an inequality."

NOW TRY EXERCISE 9

A local health club charges a $40 one-time enrollment fee, plus $35 per month for a membership. Sara can spend no more than $355 on this exercise expense. What is the *maximum* number of months that Sara can belong to this health club?

EXAMPLE 9 Using a Linear Inequality to Solve a Rental Problem

A rental company charges $20 to rent a chain saw, plus $9 per hr. Tom can spend no more than $65 to clear some logs from his yard. What is the maximum amount of time he can use the rented saw?

Step 1   **Read** the problem again.

Step 2   **Assign a variable.** Let $x =$ the number of hours he can rent the saw.

Step 3   **Write an inequality.** He must pay $20, plus $9x$, to rent the saw for x hours, and this amount must be *no more than* $65.

Cost of renting	is no more than	65 dollars.
$20 + 9x$	$\leq$	65

Step 4   **Solve.**

$$9x \leq 45 \qquad \text{Subtract 20.}$$
$$x \leq 5 \qquad \text{Divide by 9.}$$

Step 5   **State the answer.** He can use the saw for a maximum of 5 hr. (Of course, he may use it for less time, as indicated by the inequality $x \leq 5$.)

Step 6   **Check.** If Tom uses the saw for 5 hr, he will spend

$$20 + 9(5) = 65 \text{ dollars,} \quad \text{the maximum amount.}$$

NOW TRY

NOW TRY ANSWER
9. 9 months

NOW TRY EXERCISE 10

Joel has scores of 82, 97, and 93 on his first three exams. What score must he earn on the fourth exam to keep an average of at least 90?

EXAMPLE 10   Finding an Average Test Score

Martha has scores of 88, 86, and 90 on her first three algebra tests. An average score of at least 90 will earn an A in the class. What possible scores on her fourth test will earn her an A average?

Let x = the score on the fourth test. Her average score must be at least 90. To find the average of four numbers, add them and then divide by 4.

$$\underbrace{\frac{88 + 86 + 90 + x}{4}}_{\text{Average}} \underbrace{\geq}_{\substack{\text{is at}\\\text{least}}} \underbrace{90}_{90.}$$

$$\frac{264 + x}{4} \geq 90 \qquad \text{Add the scores.}$$

$$264 + x \geq 360 \qquad \text{Multiply by 4.}$$

$$x \geq 96 \qquad \text{Subtract 264.}$$

She must score 96 or more on her fourth test.

CHECK $\dfrac{88 + 86 + 90 + 96}{4} = \dfrac{360}{4} = 90,$ the minimum score.   ✓

NOW TRY ANSWER

10. at least 88

A score of 96 or more will give an average of at least 90, as required.   **NOW TRY**

1.5 Exercises

FOR EXTRA HELP

▶ MyMathLab®

▶ *Complete solution available in MyMathLab*

Concept Check   *Match each inequality in Column I with the correct graph or interval in Column II.*

I

1. $x \leq 3$

2. $x > 3$

3. $x < 3$

4. $x \geq 3$

5. $-3 \leq x \leq 3$

6. $-3 < x < 3$

II

A.

B.

C. $(3, \infty)$

D. $(-\infty, 3]$

E. $(-3, 3)$

F. $[-3, 3]$

Concept Check   *Work each problem involving inequalities.*

7. A high level of LDL cholesterol ("bad cholesterol") in the blood increases a person's risk of heart disease. The table shows how LDL levels affect risk.

    If x represents the LDL cholesterol number, write a linear inequality or three-part inequality for each category. Use x as the variable.

(a) Optimal

(b) Near optimal/above optimal

(c) Borderline high

(d) High   **(e)** Very high

LDL Cholesterol	Risk Category
Less than 100	Optimal
100–129	Near optimal/above optimal
130–159	Borderling high
160–189	High
190 and above	Very high

Source: Cholesterol & Triglycerides Health Center, WebMD, published by WebMD, © 2014.

8. A high level of triglycerides in the blood also increases a person's risk of heart disease. The table shows how triglyceride levels affect risk.

   If x represents the triglycerides number, write a linear inequality or three-part inequality for each category. Use x as the variable.

Triglycerides	Risk Category
Less than 100	Normal
100–199	Mildly high
200–499	High
500 or higher	Very high

Source: Cholesterol & Triglycerides Health Center, WebMD, published by WebMD, © 2014.

(a) Normal   **(b)** Mildly high

(c) High   **(d)** Very high

Solve each inequality. Give the solution set in both interval and graph forms. See Examples 1–6.

▶ **9.** $x - 4 \geq 12$ **10.** $x - 3 \geq 7$ **11.** $3k + 1 > 22$ **12.** $5x + 6 < 76$

▶ **13.** $4x < -16$ **14.** $2x > -10$ **15.** $-\dfrac{3}{4}x \geq 30$ **16.** $-\dfrac{2}{3}x \leq 12$

17. $-1.3x \geq -5.2$ **18.** $-2.5x \leq -1.25$ **19.** $5x + 2 \leq -48$ **20.** $4x + 1 \leq -31$

21. $\dfrac{5x - 6}{8} < 8$ **22.** $\dfrac{3x - 1}{4} > 5$ **23.** $\dfrac{2x - 5}{-4} > 5$ **24.** $\dfrac{3x - 2}{-5} < 6$

▶ **25.** $6x - 4 \geq -2x$ **26.** $2x - 8 \geq -2x$ **27.** $x - 2(x - 4) \leq 3x$

28. $x - 3(x + 1) \leq 4x$ ▶ **29.** $-(4 + r) + 2 - 3r < -14$ **30.** $-(9 + x) - 5 + 4x \geq 4$

31. $-3(x - 6) > 2x - 2$ **32.** $-2(x + 4) \leq 6x + 16$

33. $\dfrac{2}{3}(3x - 1) \geq \dfrac{3}{2}(2x - 3)$ **34.** $\dfrac{7}{5}(10x - 1) < \dfrac{2}{3}(6x + 5)$

▶ **35.** $-\dfrac{1}{4}(p + 6) + \dfrac{3}{2}(2p - 5) < 10$ **36.** $\dfrac{3}{5}(t - 2) - \dfrac{1}{4}(2t - 7) \leq 3$

37. $3(2x - 4) - 4x < 2x + 3$ **38.** $7(4 - x) + 5x < 2(16 - x)$

39. $8\left(\dfrac{1}{2}x + 3\right) < 8\left(\dfrac{1}{2}x - 1\right)$ **40.** $10\left(\dfrac{1}{5}x + 2\right) < 10\left(\dfrac{1}{5}x + 1\right)$

41. *Concept Check*   Which one is the graph of $-2 < x$?   Of $-x > 2$?

A.   **B.**   **C.**   **D.**

42. *Concept Check*   A student solved the following inequality as shown.

$$4x \geq -64$$

$$\dfrac{4x}{4} \leq \dfrac{-64}{4}$$

$$x \leq -16 \qquad \text{Solution set: } (-\infty, -16]$$

WHAT WENT WRONG?   Give the correct solution set.

Solve each inequality. Give the solution set in both interval and graph forms. See Examples 7 and 8.

43. $-4 < x - 5 < 6$ **44.** $-1 < x + 1 < 8$ **45.** $-9 \leq x + 5 \leq 15$

46. $-4 \leq x + 3 \leq 10$ **47.** $-6 \leq 2x + 4 \leq 16$ **48.** $-15 < 3x + 6 < -12$

49. $-19 \leq 3x - 5 \leq 1$ **50.** $-16 < 3x + 2 < -10$ ▶ **51.** $4 \leq -9x + 5 < 8$

52. $4 \leq -2x + 3 < 8$ **53.** $-8 \leq -4x + 2 \leq 6$ **54.** $-12 \leq -6x + 3 \leq 15$

55. $-1 \leq \dfrac{2x - 5}{6} \leq 5$ **56.** $-3 \leq \dfrac{3x + 1}{4} \leq 3$

Give, in interval notation, the unknown numbers in each description.

57. A number is between 0 and 1.

58. A number is between -3 and -2.

59. Six times a number is between -12 and 12.

60. Half a number is between -3 and 2.

61. When 1 is added to twice a number, the result is greater than or equal to 7.

62. If 8 is subtracted from a number, then the result is at least 5.

63. One third of a number is added to 6, giving a result of at least 3.

64. Three times a number, minus 5, is no more than 7.

Solve each problem. ***See Examples 9 and 10.***

▶ **65.** Faith earned scores of 90 and 82 on her first two tests in English literature. What score must she make on her third test to keep an average of 84 or greater?

66. Greg scored 92 and 96 on his first two tests in "Methods in Teaching Mathematics." What score must he make on his third test to keep an average of 90 or greater?

▶ **67.** Amber is signing up for cell phone service. She must decide between Plan A, which costs $54.99 per month with a free phone included, and Plan B, which costs $49.99 per month, but would require her to buy a phone for $129. Under either plan, Amber does not expect to go over the included number of monthly minutes. After how many months would Plan B be a better deal?

68. Newlyweds Bryce and Lauren need to rent a truck to move their belongings to their new apartment. They can rent a truck of the size they need from U-Haul for $29.95 per day plus 28 cents per mile or from Budget Truck Rentals for $34.95 per day plus 25 cents per mile. After how many miles (to the nearest mile) would the Budget rental be a better deal than the U-Haul one?

69. The average monthly precipitation for Dallas, TX, for October, November, and December is 3.47 in. If 2.88 in. falls in October and 3.13 in. falls in November, how many inches must fall in December so that the average monthly precipitation for these months exceeds 3.47 in.? (*Source:* www.weather.com)

70. The average monthly precipitation for Honolulu, HI, for October, November, and December is 3.11 in. If 2.98 in. falls in October and 3.05 in. falls in November, how many inches must fall in December so that the average monthly precipitation for these months exceeds 3.11 in.? (*Source:* www.weather.com)

71. A body mass index (BMI) between 19 and 25 is considered healthy. Use the formula

$$\text{BMI} = \frac{704 \times (\text{weight in pounds})}{(\text{height in inches})^2}$$

to find the weight range w, to the nearest pound, that gives a healthy BMI for each height. (*Source: Washington Post.*)

(a) 72 in.   **(b)** 63 in.   **(c)** Your height in inches

72. To achieve the maximum benefit from exercising, the heart rate, in beats per minute, should be in the target heart rate (THR) zone. For a person aged A, the formula is as follows.

$$0.7(220 - A) \leq \text{THR} \leq 0.85(220 - A)$$

Find the THR to the nearest whole number for each age. (*Source:* Hockey, R. V., *Physical Fitness: The Pathway to Healthful Living,* Times Mirror/Mosby College Publishing.)

(a) 35   **(b)** 55   **(c)** Your age

A product will produce a profit only when the revenue R from selling the product exceeds the cost C of producing it. In Exercises 73 and 74, find the least whole number of units x that must be sold for the business to show a profit for the item described.

73. Peripheral Visions, Inc., finds that the cost of producing x studio-quality DVDs is $C = 20x + 100$, while the revenue produced from them is $R = 24x$ (C and R in dollars).

74. Speedy Delivery finds that the cost of making x deliveries is $C = 3x + 2300$, while the revenue produced from them is $R = 5.50x$ (C and R in dollars).

STUDY SKILLS

Using Study Cards

You may have used "flash cards" in other classes. In math, "study cards" can help you remember terms and definitions, procedures, and concepts. Use study cards to do the following.

- Help you understand and learn the material

- Quickly review when you have a few minutes

- Review before a quiz or test

One of the advantages of study cards is that you learn while you are making them.

Vocabulary Cards

Put the word and a page reference on the front of the card. On the back, write the definition, an example, any related words, and a sample problem (if appropriate).

Procedure ("Steps") Cards

Write the name of the procedure on the front of the card. Then write each step in words. On the back of the card, put an example showing each step.

Make a vocabulary card and a procedure card for material you are learning now.

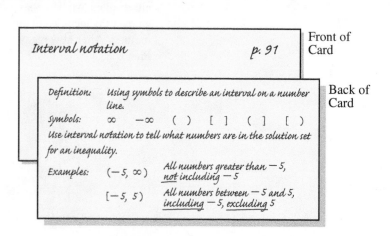

1.6   Set Operations and Compound Inequalities

VOCABULARY

☐ intersection
☐ compound inequality
☐ union

OBJECTIVE 1 Recognize set intersection and union.

Consider the two sets A and B defined as follows.

$$A = \{1, 2, 3\}, \qquad B = \{2, 3, 4\}$$

The set of all elements that belong to both A **and** B, called their *intersection* and symbolized $A \cap B$, is given by

$$A \cap B = \{2, 3\}. \qquad \text{Intersection}$$

The set of all elements that belong to either A **or** B, or both, called their *union* and symbolized $A \cup B$, is given by

$$A \cup B = \{1, 2, 3, 4\}. \qquad \text{Union}$$

OBJECTIVE 2 Find the intersection of two sets.

The intersection of two sets is defined with the word *and*.

Intersection of Sets

For any two sets A and B, the intersection of A and B, symbolized $A \cap B$, is defined as follows.

$$A \cap B = \{x \mid x \text{ is an element of } A \text{ and } x \text{ is an element of } B\}$$

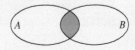

**NOW TRY
EXERCISE 1**

Let $A = \{2, 4, 6, 8\}$ and $B = \{0, 2, 6, 8\}$.
Find $A \cap B$.

EXAMPLE 1 **Finding the Intersection of Two Sets**

Let $A = \{1, 2, 3, 4\}$ and $B = \{2, 4, 6\}$. Find $A \cap B$.

The set $A \cap B$ contains those elements that belong to both A *and* B.

$$A \cap B = \{1, 2, 3, 4\} \cap \{2, 4, 6\}$$
$$= \{2, 4\}$$

NOW TRY

OBJECTIVE 3 Solve compound inequalities with the word *and*.

A **compound inequality** consists of two inequalities linked by a connective word.

$$x + 1 \le 9 \quad \text{and} \quad x - 2 \ge 3$$
$$2x > 4 \quad \text{or} \quad 3x - 6 < 5$$

Compound inequalities

Solving a Compound Inequality with *and*

Step 1 Solve each inequality individually.

Step 2 Because the inequalities are joined with *and,* the solution set of the compound inequality will include all numbers that satisfy both inequalities in Step 1 (the *intersection* of the solution sets).

NOW TRY ANSWER
1. $\{2, 6, 8\}$

**NOW TRY
EXERCISE 2**

Solve the compound inequality, and graph the solution set.

$x - 2 \le 5$ and $x + 5 \ge 9$

| EXAMPLE 2 | **Solving a Compound Inequality with *and*** |

Solve the compound inequality, and graph the solution set.

$$x + 1 \le 9 \quad \text{and} \quad x - 2 \ge 3$$

Step 1   Solve each inequality individually.

$$x + 1 \le 9 \qquad \text{and} \qquad x - 2 \ge 3$$
$$x + 1 - 1 \le 9 - 1 \quad \text{and} \quad x - 2 + 2 \ge 3 + 2$$
$$x \le 8 \qquad \text{and} \qquad x \ge 5$$

Step 2   The solution set will include all numbers that satisfy *both* inequalities in Step 1 at the same time. The compound inequality is true whenever $x \le 8$ and $x \ge 5$ are both true. See the graphs in **FIGURE 20**.

The set of points where the graphs "overlap" represents the intersection.

FIGURE 20

The intersection of the two graphs in **FIGURE 20** is the solution set. **FIGURE 21** shows this solution set, $[5, 8]$.

FIGURE 21

NOW TRY

**NOW TRY
EXERCISE 3**

Solve and graph.

$-4x - 1 < 7$ and

$3x + 4 \ge -5$

| EXAMPLE 3 | **Solving a Compound Inequality with *and*** |

Solve the compound inequality, and graph the solution set.

$$-3x - 2 > 5 \quad \text{and} \quad 5x - 1 \le -21$$

Step 1   Solve each inequality individually.

$$-3x - 2 > 5 \qquad \text{and} \qquad 5x - 1 \le -21$$

| Remember to reverse the direction of the inequality symbol. | $-3x > 7$ | and | $5x \le -20$ |

$$x < -\frac{7}{3} \qquad \text{and} \qquad x \le -4$$

The graphs of $x < -\frac{7}{3}$ and $x \le -4$ are shown in **FIGURE 22**.

FIGURE 22

Step 2   Now find all values of x that are less than $-\frac{7}{3}$ and also less than or equal to -4. As shown in **FIGURE 23**, the solution set is $(-\infty, -4]$.

FIGURE 23

NOW TRY

NOW TRY ANSWERS

2. $[4, 7]$

3. $(-2, \infty)$

**NOW TRY
EXERCISE 4**

Solve and graph.

$x - 7 < -12$ and

$\quad\quad 2x + 1 > 5$

EXAMPLE 4 Solving a Compound Inequality with *and*

Solve the compound inequality, and graph the solution set.

$$x + 2 < 5 \quad \text{and} \quad x - 10 > 2$$

Step 1 Solve each inequality individually.

$$x + 2 < 5 \quad \text{and} \quad x - 10 > 2$$
$$x < 3 \quad \text{and} \quad\quad x > 12$$

The graphs of $x < 3$ and $x > 12$ are shown in **FIGURE 24**.

FIGURE 24

Step 2 There is no number that is both less than 3 *and* greater than 12, so the given compound inequality has no solution. The solution set is $\varnothing$. See **FIGURE 25**.

FIGURE 25   NOW TRY

OBJECTIVE 4 Find the union of two sets.

The union of two sets is defined with the word *or*.

Union of Sets

For any two sets A and B, the **union** of A and B, symbolized $A \cup B$, is defined as follows.

$$A \cup B = \{x \mid x \text{ is an element of } A \text{ or } x \text{ is an element of } B\}$$

**NOW TRY
EXERCISE 5**

Let $A = \{5, 10, 15, 20\}$ and $B = \{5, 15, 25\}$.
Find $A \cup B$.

EXAMPLE 5 Finding the Union of Two Sets

Let $A = \{1, 2, 3, 4\}$ and $B = \{2, 4, 6\}$. Find $A \cup B$.

Begin by listing all the elements of set A: 1, 2, 3, 4. Then list any additional elements from set B. In this case the elements 2 and 4 are already listed, so the only additional element is 6.

$$A \cup B = \{1, 2, 3, 4\} \cup \{2, 4, 6\}$$
$$= \{1, 2, 3, 4, 6\}$$

The union consists of all elements in either A *or* B (or both).   NOW TRY

NOW TRY ANSWERS
4. $\varnothing$
5. $\{5, 10, 15, 20, 25\}$

NOTE Although the elements 2 and 4 appeared in both sets A and B in **Example 5,** they are written only once in $A \cup B$.

OBJECTIVE 5 Solve compound inequalities with the word *or*.

Solving a Compound Inequality with *or*

Step 1   Solve each inequality individually.

Step 2   Because the inequalities are joined with *or,* the solution set of the compound inequality includes all numbers that satisfy either one of the two inequalities in Step 1 (the *union* of the solution sets).

NOW TRY
EXERCISE 6

Solve and graph.

$-12x \le -24$ or $x + 9 < 8$

EXAMPLE 6   **Solving a Compound Inequality with *or***

Solve the compound inequality, and graph the solution set.

$$6x - 4 < 2x \quad \text{or} \quad -3x \le -9$$

Step 1   Solve each inequality individually.

$$6x - 4 < 2x \quad \text{or} \quad -3x \le -9$$

$$4x < 4$$

Remember to reverse the inequality symbol.

$$x < 1 \quad \text{or} \quad x \ge 3$$

The graphs of these two inequalities are shown in **FIGURE 26**.

The set of points in either of the graphs represents the union.

FIGURE 26

Step 2   Because the inequalities are joined with *or,* find the union of the two solution sets. The union is the disjoint interval in **FIGURE 27**.

$$(-\infty, 1) \cup [3, \infty)$$

FIGURE 27

Always pay particular attention to the end points of the solution sets and whether parentheses, brackets, or one of each should be used.   **NOW TRY**

⊘ CAUTION   When inequalities are used to write the solution set in **Example 6,** it *must* be written using two separate inequalities.

$$x < 1 \quad \text{or} \quad x \ge 3,$$

Writing $3 \le x < 1$, which translates using *and,* would imply that

$$3 \le 1, \quad \text{which is } \textbf{\textit{FALSE.}}$$

NOW TRY ANSWER

6. $(-\infty, -1) \cup [2, \infty)$

NOW TRY
EXERCISE 7
Solve and graph.

$-x + 2 < 6$ or $6x - 8 \geq 10$

EXAMPLE 7 Solving a Compound Inequality with *or*

Solve the compound inequality, and graph the solution set.

$$-4x + 1 \geq 9 \quad \text{or} \quad 5x + 3 \leq -12$$

Step 1 Solve each inequality individually.

$$-4x + 1 \geq 9 \qquad \text{or} \qquad 5x + 3 \leq -12$$
$$-4x \geq 8 \qquad \text{or} \qquad 5x \leq -15$$
$$x \leq -2 \qquad \text{or} \qquad x \leq -3$$

The graphs of these two inequalities are shown in **FIGURE 28**.

FIGURE 28

Step 2 We take the union to obtain $(-\infty, -2]$. See **FIGURE 29**.

FIGURE 29

NOW TRY

NOW TRY
EXERCISE 8
Solve and graph.

$$8x - 4 \geq 20 \quad \text{or}$$
$$-2x + 1 > -9$$

EXAMPLE 8 Solving a Compound Inequality with *or*

Solve the compound inequality, and graph the solution set.

$$-2x + 5 \geq 11 \quad \text{or} \quad 4x - 7 \geq -27$$

Step 1 Solve each inequality individually.

$$-2x + 5 \geq 11 \quad \text{or} \quad 4x - 7 \geq -27$$
$$-2x \geq 6 \quad \text{or} \quad 4x \geq -20$$
$$x \leq -3 \quad \text{or} \quad x \geq -5$$

The graphs of these two inequalities are shown in **FIGURE 30**.

FIGURE 30

Step 2 By taking the union, we obtain every real number as a solution because every real number satisfies at least one of the two inequalities. The set of all real numbers is written in interval notation as $(-\infty, \infty)$ and graphed as in **FIGURE 31**.

FIGURE 31

NOW TRY

NOW TRY ANSWERS

7. $(-4, \infty)$

8. $(-\infty, \infty)$

NOW TRY
EXERCISE 9

In **Example 9**, list the elements of each set.

(a) The set of countries to which exports were greater than $100,000 million and from which imports were less than $400,000 million

(b) The set of countries to which exports were less than $200,000 million or from which imports were greater than $250,000 million

EXAMPLE 9 Applying Intersection and Union

The five top U.S. trading partners for 2012 are listed in the table. Amounts are in millions of dollars. (*Source:* U.S. Census Bureau.)

Country	U.S. Exports to Country	U.S. Imports from Country
Canada	292,540	323,937
China	110,484	425,579
Mexico	215,931	277,570
Japan	69,955	146,392
Germany	48,797	108,708

List the elements of the following sets.

(a) The set of countries to which exports were greater than $200,000 million *and* from which imports were less than $300,000 million

The only country that satisfies both conditions is Mexico, so the set is

$$\{Mexico\}.$$

(b) The set of countries to which exports were less than $100,000 million *or* from which imports were greater than $200,000 million

Here, any country that satisfies at least one of the conditions is in the set. This set includes all five countries:

$$\{Canada, China, Mexico, Japan, Germany\}. \qquad \text{NOW TRY} $$

NOW TRY ANSWERS
9. **(a)** {Canada, Mexico}
   (b) {Canada, China, Mexico, Japan, Germany}

1.6 Exercises

FOR EXTRA HELP   ▶ MyMathLab°

▶ *Complete solution available in MyMathLab*

Concept Check   *Decide whether each statement is* true *or* false. *If it is false, explain why.*

1. The union of the solution sets of $x + 1 = 6$, $x + 1 < 6$, and $x + 1 > 6$ is $(-\infty, \infty)$.

2. The intersection of the sets $\{x \mid x \geq 9\}$ and $\{x \mid x \leq 9\}$ is $\varnothing$.

3. The union of the sets $(-\infty, 7)$ and $(7, \infty)$ is $\{7\}$.

4. The intersection of the sets $(-\infty, 7]$ and $[7, \infty)$ is $\{7\}$.

5. The intersection of the set of rational numbers and the set of irrational numbers is $\{0\}$.

6. The union of the set of rational numbers and the set of irrational numbers is the set of real numbers.

Let $A = \{1, 2, 3, 4, 5, 6\}$, $B = \{1, 3, 5\}$, $C = \{1, 6\}$, *and* $D = \{4\}$. *Find each set.* **See Examples 1 and 5.**

▶ 7. $B \cap A$ **8.** $A \cap B$ **9.** $A \cap D$ **10.** $B \cap C$

11. $B \cap \varnothing$ **12.** $A \cap \varnothing$ **▶ 13.** $A \cup B$ **14.** $B \cup D$

Concept Check   *Two sets are specified by graphs. Graph the intersection of the two sets.*

15.

16.

17.

18.

Solve each compound inequality. Give the solution set in both interval and graph forms. **See Examples 2–4.**

19. $x < 2$ and $x > -3$

20. $x < 5$ and $x > 0$

21. $x \le 2$ and $x \le 5$

22. $x \ge 3$ and $x \ge 6$

▶ **23.** $x \le 3$ and $x \ge 6$

24. $x \le -1$ and $x \ge 3$

▶ **25.** $x - 3 \le 6$ and $x + 2 \ge 7$

26. $x + 5 \le 11$ and $x - 3 \ge -1$

27. $-3x > 3$ and $x + 3 > 0$

28. $-3x < 3$ and $x + 2 < 6$

▶ **29.** $3x - 4 \le 8$ and $-4x + 1 \ge -15$

30. $7x + 6 \le 48$ and $-4x \ge -24$

Concept Check   *Two sets are specified by graphs. Graph the union of the two sets.*

31.

32.

33.

34.

Solve each compound inequality. Give the solution set in both interval and graph forms. **See Examples 6–8.**

▶ **35.** $x \le 1$ or $x \le 8$

36. $x \ge 1$ or $x \ge 8$

37. $x \ge -2$ or $x \ge 5$

38. $x \le -2$ or $x \le 6$

39. $x \ge -2$ or $x \le 4$

40. $x \ge 5$ or $x \le 7$

▶ **41.** $x + 2 > 7$ or $1 - x > 6$

42. $x + 1 > 3$ or $x + 4 < 2$

43. $x + 1 > 3$ or $-4x + 1 > 5$

44. $3x < x + 12$ or $x + 1 > 10$

▶ **45.** $4x + 1 \ge -7$ or $-2x + 3 \ge 5$

46. $3x + 2 \le -7$ or $-2x + 1 \le 9$

Concept Check   *Express each set in simplest interval form. (Hint: Graph each set and look for the intersection or union.)*

47. $(-\infty, -1] \cap [-4, \infty)$

48. $[-1, \infty) \cap (-\infty, 9]$

49. $(-\infty, -6] \cap [-9, \infty)$

50. $(5, 11] \cap [6, \infty)$

51. $(-\infty, 3) \cup (-\infty, -2)$

52. $[-9, 1] \cup (-\infty, -3)$

53. $[3, 6] \cup (4, 9)$

54. $[-1, 2] \cup (0, 5)$

*Solve each compound inequality. Give the solution set in both interval and graph forms. **See Examples 2–4 and 6–8.***

55. $x < -1$ and $x > -5$

56. $x > -1$ and $x < 7$

57. $x < 4$ or $x < -2$

58. $x < 5$ or $x < -3$

59. $-3x \le -6$ or $-3x \ge 0$

60. $2x - 6 \le -18$ and $2x \ge -18$

61. $x + 1 \ge 5$ and $x - 2 \le 10$

62. $-8x \le -24$ or $-5x \ge 15$

Average expenses for full-time resident college students at 4-year institutions during the 2011–2012 academic year are shown in the table.

▼ **College Expenses (in Dollars)**

Type of Expense	Public Schools (in-state)	Private Schools
Tuition and fees	7701	23,479
Board rates	4052	4591
Dormitory charges	5036	5646

Source: National Center for Education Statistics.

*Refer to the table, and list the elements of each set. **See Example 9.***

63. The set of expenses that are less than $8000 for public schools *and* are greater than $15,000 for private schools

64. The set of expenses that are greater than $4000 for public schools *and* are less than $5000 for private schools

65. The set of expenses that are less than $8000 for public schools *or* are greater than $15,000 for private schools

66. The set of expenses that are greater than $15,000 *or* are between $7000 and $8000

RELATING CONCEPTS   For Individual or Group Work   (Exercises 67–72)

*The figures represent the backyards of neighbors Luigi, Maria, Than, and Joe. Find the area and the perimeter of each yard. Suppose that each resident has 150 ft of fencing and enough sod to cover 1400 ft^2 of lawn. Give the name or names of the residents whose yards satisfy each description. **Work Exercises 67–72 in order.***

67. The yard can be fenced *and* the yard can be sodded.

68. The yard can be fenced *and* the yard cannot be sodded.

69. The yard cannot be fenced *and* the yard can be sodded.

70. The yard cannot be fenced *and* the yard cannot be sodded.

71. The yard can be fenced *or* the yard can be sodded.

72. The yard cannot be fenced *or* the yard can be sodded.

STUDY SKILLS

Using Study Cards Revisited

We introduced study cards previously. Another type of study card follows.

Practice Quiz Cards

Write a problem with direction words (like *solve, simplify*) on the front of the card, and work the problem on the back. Make one for each type of problem you learn. Use the card when you review for a quiz or test.

Make a practice quiz card for material you are learning now.

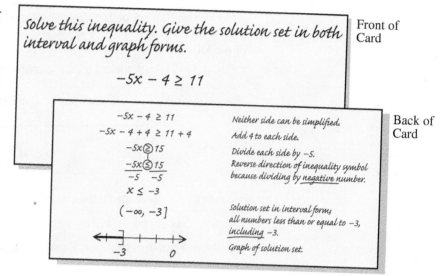

Front of Card

Solve this inequality. Give the solution set in both interval and graph forms.

$$-5x - 4 \geq 11$$

Back of Card

$-5x - 4 \geq 11$ Neither side can be simplified.
$-5x - 4 + 4 \geq 11 + 4$ Add 4 to each side.
$-5x \geq 15$ Divide each side by -5.
$\dfrac{-5x}{-5} \leq \dfrac{15}{-5}$ Reverse direction of inequality symbol because dividing by negative number.
$x \leq -3$

$(-\infty, -3]$ Solution set in interval form; all numbers less than or equal to -3, including -3.

Graph of solution set.

1.7 Absolute Value Equations and Inequalities

OBJECTIVES

1. Use the distance definition of absolute value.
2. Solve equations of the form $|ax + b| = k$, for $k > 0$.
3. Solve inequalities of the form $|ax + b| < k$ and of the form $|ax + b| > k$, for $k > 0$.
4. Solve absolute value equations that involve rewriting.
5. Solve equations of the form $|ax + b| = |cx + d|$.
6. Solve special cases of absolute value equations and inequalities.
7. Solve an application involving relative error.

Suppose the government of a country decides that it will comply with a restriction on greenhouse gas emissions *within* 3 years of 2020. This means that the *difference* between the year it will comply and 2020 is less than 3, *without regard to sign*. We state this mathematically as follows, where x represents the year in which it complies.

$$|x - 2020| < 3 \qquad \text{Absolute value inequality}$$

We can intuitively reason that the year must be between 2017 and 2023, and thus $2017 < x < 2023$ makes this inequality true.

OBJECTIVE 1 Use the distance definition of absolute value.

In **Section R.1,** we saw that the absolute value of a number x, written $|x|$, represents the undirected distance from x to 0 on a number line. For example, the solutions of $|x| = 4$ are 4 and -4, as shown in **FIGURE 32**.

4 units from 0   4 units from 0

$x = -4$ or $x = 4$

FIGURE 32

Because absolute value represents distance from 0, we interpret the solutions of $|x| > 4$ to be all numbers that are *more* than four units from 0 on a number line. The set $(-\infty, -4) \cup (4, \infty)$ fits this description. **FIGURE 33** on the next page shows the graph of the solution set of $|x| > 4$. The graph consists of two separate intervals, which means $x < -4$ *or* $x > 4$.

FIGURE 33

The solution set of $|x| < 4$ consists of all numbers that are *less* than 4 units from 0 on a number line. This is represented by all numbers *between* -4 and 4. This set of numbers is given by $(-4, 4)$, as shown in **FIGURE 34**. Here, the graph shows that $-4 < x < 4$, which means $x > -4$ *and* $x < 4$.

FIGURE 34

Absolute value equations and inequalities generally take the form

$$|ax + b| = k, \qquad |ax + b| > k, \qquad \text{or} \qquad |ax + b| < k,$$

where k is a positive number. From **FIGURES 32–34**, we see that

$|x| = 4$ has the same solution set as $x = -4$ or $x = 4$,

$|x| > 4$ has the same solution set as $x < -4$ or $x > 4$,

$|x| < 4$ has the same solution set as $x > -4$ and $x < 4$.

> This is equivalent to $-4 < x < 4$.

Solving Absolute Value Equations and Inequalities

Let k be a positive real number, and p and q be real numbers.

Case 1 To solve $|ax + b| = k$, solve the following compound equation.

$$ax + b = k \quad \text{or} \quad ax + b = -k$$

The solution set is usually of the form $\{p, q\}$, which includes two numbers.

Case 2 To solve $|ax + b| > k$*, solve the following compound inequality.

$$ax + b > k \quad \text{or} \quad ax + b < -k$$

The solution set is of the form $(-\infty, p) \cup (q, \infty)$, which is a disjoint interval.

Case 3 To solve $|ax + b| < k$**, solve the following three-part inequality.

$$-k < ax + b < k$$

The solution set is of the form (p, q), which is a single interval.

---

*This also applies to $|ax + b| \geq k$. The solution set *includes* the endpoints, using brackets rather than parentheses.

**This also applies to $|ax + b| \leq k$. The solution set *includes* the endpoints, using brackets rather than parentheses.

NOTE   It is acceptable to write the compound statements in Cases 1 and 2 of the preceding box as follows. These forms produce the same results.

$$ax + b = k \quad \text{or} \quad -(ax + b) = k \qquad \text{Alternative for Case 1}$$

$$ax + b > k \quad \text{or} \quad -(ax + b) > k \qquad \text{Alternative for Case 2}$$

OBJECTIVE 2   Solve equations of the form $|ax + b| = k$, for $k > 0$.

Remember that because absolute value refers to distance from the origin, an absolute value equation will have two parts.

**NOW TRY
EXERCISE 1**
Solve $|4x - 1| = 11$.

EXAMPLE 1   Solving an Absolute Value Equation (Case 1)

Solve $|2x + 1| = 7$. Graph the solution set.

For $|2x + 1|$ to equal 7, $2x + 1$ must be 7 units from 0 on a number line. This can happen only when $2x + 1 = 7$ or $2x + 1 = -7$. This is Case 1 in the box on the preceding page. Solve this compound equation as follows.

$$2x + 1 = 7 \quad \text{or} \quad 2x + 1 = -7$$
$$2x = 6 \quad \text{or} \quad 2x = -8 \qquad \text{Subtract 1.}$$
$$x = 3 \quad \text{or} \quad x = -4 \qquad \text{Divide by 2.}$$

CHECK
$$|2x + 1| = 7$$

$$|2(3) + 1| \overset{?}{=} 7 \qquad \text{Let } x = 3. \qquad |2(-4) + 1| \overset{?}{=} 7 \qquad \text{Let } x = -4.$$
$$|6 + 1| \overset{?}{=} 7 \qquad\qquad\qquad\qquad |-8 + 1| \overset{?}{=} 7$$
$$|7| \overset{?}{=} 7 \qquad\qquad\qquad\qquad\qquad |-7| \overset{?}{=} 7$$
$$7 = 7 \; \checkmark \quad \text{True} \qquad\qquad\qquad 7 = 7 \; \checkmark \quad \text{True}$$

The solution set is $\{-4, 3\}$. The graph is shown in **FIGURE 35**.

FIGURE 35

NOW TRY

OBJECTIVE 3   Solve inequalities of the form $|ax + b| < k$ and of the form $|ax + b| > k$, for $k > 0$.

EXAMPLE 2   Solving an Absolute Value Inequality (Case 2)

Solve $|2x + 1| > 7$. Graph the solution set.

By Case 2 in the box on the preceding page, this absolute value inequality is rewritten as

$$2x + 1 > 7 \quad \text{or} \quad 2x + 1 < -7$$

because $2x + 1$ must represent a number that is *more* than 7 units from 0 on either side of a number line. Now solve the compound inequality.

$$2x + 1 > 7 \quad \text{or} \quad 2x + 1 < -7$$
$$2x > 6 \quad \text{or} \quad 2x < -8 \qquad \text{Subtract 1.}$$
$$x > 3 \quad \text{or} \quad x < -4 \qquad \text{Divide by 2.}$$

NOW TRY ANSWER
1. $\left\{-\frac{5}{2}, 3\right\}$

**NOW TRY
EXERCISE 2**

Solve $|4x - 1| > 11$.

CHECK The excluded endpoints -4 and 3 are correct because from **Example 1** we know that the solutions of the related equation are -4 and 3. We now choose a test point in each of the three intervals $(-\infty, -4)$, $(-4, 3)$, and $(3, \infty)$.

For $(-\infty, -4)$, let $x = -5$.

$$|2x + 1| > 7$$
$$|2(-5) + 1| \overset{?}{>} 7$$
$$|-9| \overset{?}{>} 7$$
$$9 > 7 \; \checkmark \; \text{True}$$

For $(-4, 3)$, let $x = 0$.

$$|2x + 1| > 7$$
$$|2(0) + 1| \overset{?}{>} 7$$
$$|1| \overset{?}{>} 7$$
$$1 > 7 \qquad \text{False}$$

For $(3, \infty)$, let $x = 4$.

$$|2x + 1| > 7$$
$$|2(4) + 1| \overset{?}{>} 7$$
$$|9| \overset{?}{>} 7$$
$$9 > 7 \; \checkmark \; \text{True}$$

The solution set, $(-\infty, -4) \cup (3, \infty)$, is a disjoint interval. See **FIGURE 36**.

FIGURE 36

NOW TRY

**NOW TRY
EXERCISE 3**

Solve $|4x - 1| < 11$.

EXAMPLE 3 Solving an Absolute Value Inequality (Case 3)

Solve $|2x + 1| < 7$. Graph the solution set.

The expression $2x + 1$ must represent a number that is less than 7 units from 0 on either side of a number line. That is, $2x + 1$ must be between -7 and 7. As Case 3 in the earlier box shows, this is written as a three-part inequality.

$$-7 < 2x + 1 < 7$$
$$-8 < \quad 2x \quad < 6 \qquad \text{Subtract 1 from each part.}$$
$$-4 < \quad x \quad < 3 \qquad \text{Divide each part by 2.}$$

Check that the solution set is $(-4, 3)$. The graph is the open interval in **FIGURE 37**.

FIGURE 37

NOW TRY

Look back at **FIGURES 35, 36, AND 37**, with the graphs of

$$|2x + 1| = 7, \quad |2x + 1| > 7, \quad \text{and} \quad |2x + 1| < 7.$$

If we find the union of the three sets, we obtain the set of all real numbers. For any value of x, $|2x + 1|$ will satisfy *one and only one* of the following: It is equal to 7, greater than 7, or less than 7.

⚠ CAUTION Remember the following when solving absolute value equations and inequalities.

1. The methods described apply when the constant is alone on one side of the equation or inequality and is *positive*.

2. Absolute value equations $|ax + b| = k$ and inequalities of the form $|ax + b| > k$ translate into "or" compound statements.

3. Absolute value inequalities of the form $|ax + b| < k$ translate into "and" compound statements, which may be written as three-part inequalities.

4. An "or" statement *cannot* be written in three parts. It would be **incorrect** to write $-7 > 2x + 1 > 7$ in **Example 2**, because this would imply that $-7 > 7$, which is *false*.

NOW TRY ANSWERS

2. $\left(-\infty, -\frac{5}{2}\right) \cup (3, \infty)$

3. $\left(-\frac{5}{2}, 3\right)$

NOW TRY EXERCISE 4

Solve $|7 - 4x| \geq 7$.

Solve $|5 - 2x| \geq 5$.

Case 2 is applied. Notice that the endpoints are included because equality is part of the symbol $\geq$.

$$5 - 2x \geq 5 \quad \text{or} \quad 5 - 2x \leq -5$$

$$-2x \geq 0 \quad \text{or} \quad -2x \leq -10 \qquad \text{Subtract 5.}$$

$$x \leq 0 \quad \text{or} \quad x \geq 5 \qquad \begin{array}{l}\text{Divide by } -2. \text{ Reverse the} \\ \text{direction of the inequality symbols.}\end{array}$$

Check that the solution set is $(-\infty, 0] \cup [5, \infty)$. See **FIGURE 38**.

FIGURE 38

NOW TRY

OBJECTIVE 4 Solve absolute value equations that involve rewriting.

NOW TRY EXERCISE 5

Solve $|10x - 2| - 2 = 12$.

EXAMPLE 5 Solving an Absolute Value Equation That Requires Rewriting

Solve $|x + 3| + 5 = 12$.

Isolate the absolute value expression on one side of the equality symbol.

$$|x + 3| + 5 = 12$$

$$|x + 3| + 5 - 5 = 12 - 5 \qquad \text{Subtract 5.}$$

$$|x + 3| = 7 \qquad \text{Combine like terms.}$$

Now use the method shown in **Example 1** for Case 1 to solve $|x + 3| = 7$.

$$x + 3 = 7 \quad \text{or} \quad x + 3 = -7$$

$$x = 4 \quad \text{or} \quad x = -10 \qquad \text{Subtract 3.}$$

CHECK $\qquad\qquad |x + 3| + 5 = 12$

$$\begin{array}{ll} |4 + 3| + 5 \stackrel{?}{=} 12 & \text{Let } x = 4. \\ |7| + 5 \stackrel{?}{=} 12 \\ 12 = 12 \ \checkmark \quad \text{True} \end{array} \Bigg| \begin{array}{ll} |-10 + 3| + 5 \stackrel{?}{=} 12 & \text{Let } x = -10. \\ |-7| + 5 \stackrel{?}{=} 12 \\ 12 = 12 \ \checkmark \quad \text{True} \end{array}$$

The check confirms that the solution set is $\{-10, 4\}$.

NOW TRY

NOW TRY EXERCISE 6

Solve each inequality.

(a) $|x - 1| - 4 \leq 2$

(b) $|x - 1| - 4 \geq 2$

NOW TRY ANSWERS

4. $(-\infty, 0] \cup \left[\frac{7}{2}, \infty\right)$ **5.** $\left\{-\frac{6}{5}, \frac{8}{5}\right\}$

6. **(a)** $[-5, 7]$

(b) $(-\infty, -5] \cup [7, \infty)$

EXAMPLE 6 Solving Absolute Value Inequalities That Require Rewriting

Solve each inequality.

(a) $\qquad |x + 3| + 5 \geq 12$

$$|x + 3| \geq 7 \qquad \text{(Case 2)}$$

$$x + 3 \geq 7 \quad \text{or} \quad x + 3 \leq -7$$

$$x \geq 4 \quad \text{or} \qquad x \leq -10$$

The solution set is $(-\infty, -10] \cup [4, \infty)$.

(b) $\qquad |x + 3| + 5 \leq 12$

$$|x + 3| \leq 7 \qquad \text{(Case 3)}$$

$$-7 \leq x + 3 \leq 7$$

$$-10 \leq \quad x \quad \leq 4$$

The solution set is $[-10, 4]$.

NOW TRY

OBJECTIVE 5 Solve equations of the form $|ax + b| = |cx + d|$.

If two expressions have the same absolute value, they must either be equal or be negatives of each other.

> ### Solving $|ax + b| = |cx + d|$
>
> To solve an absolute value equation of the form
> $$|ax + b| = |cx + d|,$$
> solve the following compound equation.
> $$ax + b = cx + d \quad \text{or} \quad ax + b = -(cx + d)$$

NOW TRY
EXERCISE 7

Solve

$$|3x - 4| = |5x + 12|.$$

EXAMPLE 7   Solving an Equation Involving Two Absolute Values

Solve $|x + 6| = |2x - 3|$.

This equation is satisfied either if $x + 6$ and $2x - 3$ are equal to each other, or if $x + 6$ and $2x - 3$ are negatives of each other.

$$\begin{array}{rcl}
x + 6 = 2x - 3 & \text{or} & x + 6 = -(2x - 3) \\
x + 9 = 2x & \text{or} & x + 6 = -2x + 3 \\
9 = x & \text{or} & 3x = -3 \\
x = 9 & \text{or} & x = -1
\end{array}$$

CHECK $|x + 6| = |2x - 3|$

$\|9 + 6\| \stackrel{?}{=} \|2(9) - 3\|$ Let $x = 9$.	$\|-1 + 6\| \stackrel{?}{=} \|2(-1) - 3\|$ Let $x = -1$.
$\|15\| \stackrel{?}{=} \|18 - 3\|$	$\|5\| \stackrel{?}{=} \|-2 - 3\|$
$\|15\| \stackrel{?}{=} \|15\|$	$\|5\| \stackrel{?}{=} \|-5\|$
$15 = 15$ ✓ True	$5 = 5$ ✓ True

The check confirms that the solution set is $\{-1, 9\}$.

NOW TRY

OBJECTIVE 6 Solve special cases of absolute value equations and inequalities.

When an absolute value equation or inequality involves a *negative constant or 0* alone on one side, use the properties of absolute value to solve the equation or inequality.

> ### Special Cases of Absolute Value
>
> *Case 1*   The absolute value of an expression can never be negative—that is, $|a| \geq 0$ for all real numbers a.
>
> *Case 2*   The absolute value of an expression equals 0 only when the expression is equal to 0.

EXAMPLE 8   Solving Special Cases of Absolute Value Equations

Solve each equation.

(a) $|5x - 3| = -4$

NOW TRY ANSWER

7. $\{-8, -1\}$

See Case 1 in the preceding box. *The absolute value of an expression can never be negative,* so there are no solutions for this equation. The solution set is $\varnothing$.

**NOW TRY
EXERCISE 8**

Solve each equation.

(a) $|3x - 8| = -2$

(b) $|7x + 12| = 0$

(b) $|7x - 3| = 0$

See Case 2 in the preceding box. The expression $|7x - 3|$ will equal 0 *only if* $7x - 3 = 0$.

$$7x - 3 = 0$$

$$7x = 3 \quad \text{Add 3.}$$

> Check by substituting in the original equation.

$$x = \frac{3}{7} \quad \text{Divide by 7.}$$

The solution set $\left\{\frac{3}{7}\right\}$ consists of only one element.   **NOW TRY**

**NOW TRY
EXERCISE 9**

Solve each inequality.

(a) $|x| > -10$

(b) $|4x + 1| + 5 < 4$

(c) $|x - 2| - 3 \leq -3$

 EXAMPLE 9   Solving Special Cases of Absolute Value Inequalities

Solve each inequality.

(a) $|x| \geq -4$

The absolute value of a number is always greater than or equal to 0. Thus, $|x| \geq -4$ is true for *all* real numbers. The solution set is $(-\infty, \infty)$.

(b)
$$|x + 6| - 3 < -5$$

$$|x + 6| < -2 \quad \text{Add 3 to each side.}$$

There is no number whose absolute value is less than -2, so this inequality has no solution. The solution set is $\varnothing$.

(c)
$$|x - 7| + 4 \leq 4$$

$$|x - 7| \leq 0 \quad \text{Subtract 4 from each side.}$$

The value of $|x - 7|$ will never be less than 0. However, $|x - 7|$ will equal 0 when $x = 7$. Therefore, the solution set is $\{7\}$.   **NOW TRY**

OBJECTIVE 7   Solve an application involving relative error.

Absolute value is used to find the **relative error,** or **tolerance,** in a measurement. If x_t represents the expected measurement and x represents the actual measurement, then the relative error in x equals the absolute value of the difference of x_t and x, divided by x_t.

$$\text{relative error in } x = \left|\frac{x_t - x}{x_t}\right|$$

In quality control situations, the relative error must often be less than some predetermined amount.

EXAMPLE 10   Solving an Application Involving Relative Error

Suppose a machine filling *quart* milk cartons is set for a relative error that *is no greater than* 0.05 oz. How many ounces may a filled carton contain?

Here $x_t = 32$ oz (because 1 qt = 32 oz), the relative error = 0.05 oz, and we must find x, given the following condition.

$$\left|\frac{32 - x}{32}\right| \leq 0.05 \quad \textit{Is no greater than translates as } \leq.$$

NOW TRY ANSWERS

8. (a) $\varnothing$ **(b)** $\left\{-\frac{12}{7}\right\}$

9. (a) $(-\infty, \infty)$ **(b)** $\varnothing$ **(c)** $\{2\}$

NOW TRY EXERCISE 10

Suppose a machine filling *quart* milk cartons is set for a relative error that *is no greater than* 0.032 oz. How many ounces may a filled carton contain?

$$\left|\frac{32 - x}{32}\right| \le 0.05$$

$$-0.05 \le \frac{32 - x}{32} \le 0.05 \qquad \text{(Case 3)}$$

$$-1.6 \le 32 - x \le 1.6 \qquad \text{Multiply by 32.}$$

$$-33.6 \le \quad -x \quad \le -30.4 \qquad \text{Subtract 32.}$$

$$33.6 \ge \quad x \quad \ge 30.4 \qquad \begin{array}{l}\text{Multiply by } -1, \text{ and reverse the}\\ \text{direction of the inequality symbols.}\end{array}$$

$$30.4 \le \quad x \quad \le 33.6 \qquad \text{Rewrite.}$$

NOW TRY ANSWER

10. between 30.976 and 33.024 oz, inclusive

The filled carton may contain between 30.4 and 33.6 oz, inclusive.   **NOW TRY**

1.7 Exercises

  MyMathLab®

 Complete solution available in MyMathLab

Concept Check   Match each absolute value equation or inequality in Column I with the graph of its solution set in Column II.

3. *Concept Check*   How many solutions will $|ax + b| = k$ have for each situation?

(a) $k = 0$ (b) $k > 0$ (c) $k < 0$

4. *Concept Check*   Explain when to use *and* and when to use *or* for solving an absolute value equation or inequality of the form $|ax + b| = k$, $|ax + b| < k$, or $|ax + b| > k$, where k is a positive number.

Solve each equation. See Example 1.

5. $|x| = 12$ **6.** $|x| = 14$ **7.** $|4x| = 20$ **8.** $|5x| = 30$

9. $|x - 3| = 9$ **10.** $|x - 5| = 13$ **11.** $|2x - 1| = 11$ **12.** $|2x + 3| = 19$

13. $|4x - 5| = 17$ **14.** $|5x - 1| = 21$ **15.** $|2x + 5| = 14$ **16.** $|2x - 9| = 18$

17. $|-3x + 8| = 1$ **18.** $|-6x + 5| = 4$ **19.** $\left|12 - \frac{1}{2}x\right| = 6$

20. $\left|14 - \frac{1}{3}x\right| = 8$ **21.** $|0.5x| = 6$ **22.** $|0.3x| = 9$

23. $\left|\frac{1}{2}x + 3\right| = 2$ **24.** $\left|\frac{2}{3}x - 1\right| = 5$ **25.** $\left|1 + \frac{3}{4}x\right| = 7$

26. $\left|2 - \frac{5}{2}x\right| = 14$ **27.** $|0.02x - 1| = 2.50$ **28.** $|0.04x - 3| = 5.96$

Solve each inequality, and graph the solution set. See Example 2.

29. $|x| > 3$ **30.** $|x| > 5$ **31.** $|x| \geq 4$

32. $|x| \geq 6$ **33.** $|r + 5| \geq 20$ **34.** $|x + 4| \geq 8$

35. $|5x + 2| > 10$ **36.** $|4x + 1| \geq 21$ **37.** $|3 - x| > 5$

38. $|5 - x| > 3$ **39.** $|-5x + 3| \geq 12$ **40.** $|-2x - 4| \geq 5$

41. *Concept Check*   The graph of the solution set of $|2x + 1| = 9$ is given here.

Without actually doing the algebraic work, graph the solution set of each inequality, referring to the graph shown.

   (a) $|2x + 1| < 9$ **(b)** $|2x + 1| > 9$

42. *Concept Check*   The graph of the solution set of $|3x - 4| < 5$ is given here.

Without actually doing the algebraic work, graph the solution set of the following, referring to the graph shown.

   (a) $|3x - 4| = 5$ **(b)** $|3x - 4| > 5$

Solve each inequality, and graph the solution set. See Example 3. (Hint: Compare the answers with those in Exercises 29–40.)

43. $|x| \leq 3$ **44.** $|x| \leq 5$ **45.** $|x| < 4$

46. $|x| < 6$ **47.** $|r + 5| < 20$ **48.** $|x + 4| < 8$

49. $|5x + 2| \leq 10$ **50.** $|4x + 1| < 21$ **51.** $|3 - x| \leq 5$

52. $|5 - x| \leq 3$ **53.** $|-5x + 3| < 12$ **54.** $|-2x - 4| < 5$

In Exercises 55–78, decide which method of solution applies, and find the solution set. In Exercises 55–66, graph the solution set. See Examples 1–4.

55. $|-4 + x| > 9$ **56.** $|-3 + x| > 8$ **57.** $|3x + 2| < 11$

58. $|2x - 1| < 7$ **59.** $|7 + 2x| = 5$ **60.** $|9 - 3x| = 3$

61. $|3x - 1| \leq 11$ **62.** $|2x - 6| \leq 6$ **63.** $|-6x - 6| \leq 1$

64. $|-2x - 6| \leq 5$ **65.** $|-8 + x| \leq 5$ **66.** $|-4 + x| \leq 9$

67. $|10 - 12x| \geq 4$ **68.** $|8 - 10x| \geq 2$ **69.** $|3(x - 1)| = 8$

70. $|7(x - 2)| = 4$ **71.** $|0.1x - 1| > 3$ **72.** $|0.1x + 1| > 2$

73. $|x + 2| = 5 - 2$ **74.** $|x + 3| = 12 - 2$ **75.** $3|x - 6| = 9$

76. $5|x - 4| = 5$ **77.** $|2 - 0.2x| = 2$ **78.** $|5 - 0.5x| = 4$

Solve each equation or inequality. See Examples 5 and 6.

79. $|x| - 1 = 4$ **80.** $|x| + 3 = 10$ **81.** $|x + 4| + 1 = 2$

82. $|x + 5| - 2 = 12$ **83.** $|2x + 1| + 3 > 8$ **84.** $|6x - 1| - 2 > 6$

85. $|x + 5| - 6 \leq -1$ **86.** $|x - 2| - 3 \leq 4$

87. $|0.1x - 2.5| + 0.3 \geq 0.8$

88. $|0.5x - 3.5| + 0.2 \geq 0.6$

89. $\left|\dfrac{1}{2}x + \dfrac{1}{3}\right| + \dfrac{1}{4} = \dfrac{3}{4}$

90. $\left|\dfrac{2}{3}x + \dfrac{1}{6}\right| + \dfrac{1}{2} = \dfrac{5}{2}$

Solve each equation. ***See Example 7.***

▶ **91.** $|3x + 1| = |2x + 4|$ **92.** $|7x + 12| = |x - 8|$ **93.** $\left|x - \dfrac{1}{2}\right| = \left|\dfrac{1}{2}x - 2\right|$

94. $\left|\dfrac{2}{3}x - 2\right| = \left|\dfrac{1}{3}x + 3\right|$ **95.** $|6x| = |9x + 1|$ **96.** $|13x| = |2x + 1|$

97. $|2x - 6| = |2x + 11|$ **98.** $|3x - 1| = |3x + 9|$

Solve each equation or inequality. ***See Examples 8 and 9.***

▶ **99.** $|x| \geq -10$ **100.** $|x| \geq -15$ ▶ **101.** $|12t - 3| = -8$

102. $|13x + 1| = -3$ **103.** $|4x + 1| = 0$ **104.** $|6x - 2| = 0$

105. $|2x - 1| = -6$ **106.** $|8x + 4| = -4$ **107.** $|x + 5| > -9$

108. $|x + 9| > -3$ **109.** $|7x + 3| \leq 0$ **110.** $|4x - 1| \leq 0$

111. $|5x - 2| = 0$ **112.** $|7x + 4| = 0$ **113.** $|x - 2| + 3 \geq 2$

114. $|x - 4| + 5 \geq 4$ **115.** $|10x + 7| + 3 < 1$ **116.** $|4x + 1| - 2 < -5$

In Exercises 117–120, determine the number of ounces a filled 32 oz carton may contain for the given relative error. ***See Example 10.***

117. no greater than 0.04 oz

118. no greater than 0.03 oz

119. no greater than 0.025 oz

120. no greater than 0.015 oz

In later courses in mathematics, it is sometimes necessary to find an interval in which x must lie in order to keep y within a given difference of some number. For example, suppose

$$y = 2x + 1$$

and we want y to be within 0.01 unit of 4. This criterion can be written as

$$|y - 4| < 0.01.$$

Solving this inequality shows that x must lie in the interval (1.495, 1.505) to satisfy the requirement.

   In Exercises 121–124, find the open interval in which x must lie in order for the given condition to hold.

121. $y = 2x + 1$, and the difference of y and 1 is less than 0.1.

122. $y = 4x - 6$, and the difference of y and 2 is less than 0.02.

123. $y = 4x - 8$, and the difference of y and 3 is less than 0.001.

124. $y = 5x + 12$, and the difference of y and 4 is less than 0.0001.

Work each problem.

125. Dr. Mosely has determined that 99% of the babies he has delivered have weighed x pounds, where

$$|x - 8.3| < 1.5.$$

What range of weights corresponds to this inequality?

126. The Celsius temperatures x on Mars approximately satisfy the inequality

$$|x + 85| \leq 55.$$

What range of temperatures corresponds to this inequality?

127. The recommended daily intake (RDI) of calcium for females aged 19–50 is 1000 mg. Actual needs vary from person to person. Write this statement as an absolute value inequality, with x representing the RDI, to express the RDI plus or minus 100 mg, and solve the inequality. (*Source:* National Academy of Sciences—Institute of Medicine.)

128. The average clotting time of blood is 7.45 sec, with a variation of plus or minus 3.6 sec. Write this statement as an absolute value inequality, with x representing the time, and solve the inequality.

RELATING CONCEPTS For Individual or Group Work **(Exercises 129–132)**

The 10 tallest buildings in Houston, Texas, are listed along with their heights.

Building	Height (in feet)
JPMorgan Chase Tower	1002
Wells Fargo Plaza	992
Williams Tower	901
Bank of America Center	780
Texaco Heritage Plaza	762
Enterprise Plaza	756
Centerpoint Energy Plaza	741
Continental Center I	732
Fulbright Tower	725
One Shell Plaza	714

Source: World Almanac and Book of Facts.

Use this information to **work Exercises 129–132 in order.**

129. To find the average of a group of numbers, we add the numbers and then divide by the number of numbers added. Use a calculator to find the average of the heights.

130. Let k represent the average height of these buildings. If a height x satisfies the inequality

$$|x - k| < t,$$

then the height is said to be within t feet of the average. Using the result from **Exercise 129**, list the buildings that are within 50 ft of the average.

131. Repeat **Exercise 130**, but list the buildings that are within 95 ft of the average.

132. (a) Write an absolute value inequality that describes the height of a building that is *not* within 95 ft of the average.

(b) Solve the inequality from part (a).

(c) Use the result of part (b) to list the buildings that are not within 95 ft of the average.

(d) Confirm that the answer to part (c) makes sense by comparing it with the answer to **Exercise 131.**

SUMMARY EXERCISES   Solving Linear and Absolute Value Equations and Inequalities

Solve each equation or inequality. Give the solution set in set notation for equations and in interval notation for inequalities.

1. $4x + 1 = 49$

2. $|x - 1| = 6$

3. $6x - 9 = 12 + 3x$

4. $3x + 7 = 9 + 8x$

5. $|x + 3| = -4$

6. $2x + 1 \leq x$

7. $8x + 2 \geq 5x$

8. $4(x - 11) + 3x = 20x - 31$

9. $2x - 1 = -7$

10. $|3x - 7| - 4 = 0$

11. $6x - 5 \leq 3x + 10$

12. $|5x - 8| + 9 \geq 7$

13. $9x - 3(x + 1) = 8x - 7$

14. $|x| \geq 8$

15. $9x - 5 \geq 9x + 3$

16. $13x - 5 > 13x - 8$

17. $|x| < 5.5$

18. $4x - 1 = 12 + x$

19. $\dfrac{2}{3}x + 8 = \dfrac{1}{4}x$

20. $-\dfrac{5}{8}x \geq -20$

21. $\dfrac{1}{4}x < -6$

22. $\dfrac{1}{2} \leq \dfrac{2}{3}x \leq \dfrac{5}{4}$

23. $\dfrac{3}{5}x - \dfrac{1}{10} = 2$

24. $\dfrac{x}{6} - \dfrac{3x}{5} = x - 86$

25. $x + 9 + 7x = 4(3 + 2x) - 3$

26. $6 - 3(2 - x) < 2(1 + x) + 3$

27. $-6 \leq \dfrac{3}{2} - x \leq 6$

28. $\dfrac{x}{4} - \dfrac{2x}{3} = -10$

29. $|5x + 1| \leq 0$

30. $5x - (3 + x) \geq 2(3x + 1)$

31. $-2 \leq 3x - 1 \leq 8$

32. $-1 \leq 6 - x \leq 5$

33. $|7x - 1| = |5x + 3|$

34. $|x + 2| = |x + 4|$

35. $|1 - 3x| \geq 4$

36. $7x - 3 + 2x = 9x - 8x$

37. $-(x + 4) + 2 = 3x + 8$

38. $|x - 1| < 7$

39. $|2x - 3| > 11$

40. $|5 - x| < 4$

41. $|x - 1| \geq -6$

42. $|2x - 5| = |x + 4|$

43. $8x - (1 - x) = 3(1 + 3x) - 4$

44. $8x - (x + 3) = -(2x + 1) - 12$

45. $|x - 5| = |x + 9|$

46. $|x + 2| < -3$

47. $2x + 1 > 5$ or $3x + 4 < 1$

48. $1 - 2x \geq 5$ and $7 + 3x \geq -2$

---

1. $\{12\}$ **2.** $\{-5, 7\}$

3. $\{7\}$ **4.** $\left\{-\dfrac{2}{5}\right\}$

5. $\varnothing$ **6.** $(-\infty, -1]$

7. $\left[-\dfrac{2}{3}, \infty\right)$ **8.** $\{-1\}$

9. $\{-3\}$ **10.** $\left\{1, \dfrac{11}{3}\right\}$

11. $(-\infty, 5]$ **12.** $(-\infty, \infty)$

13. $\{2\}$

14. $(-\infty, -8] \cup [8, \infty)$

15. $\varnothing$ **16.** $(-\infty, \infty)$

17. $(-5.5, 5.5)$ **18.** $\left\{\dfrac{13}{3}\right\}$

19. $\left\{-\dfrac{96}{5}\right\}$ **20.** $(-\infty, 32]$

21. $(-\infty, -24)$ **22.** $\left[\dfrac{3}{4}, \dfrac{15}{8}\right]$

23. $\left\{\dfrac{7}{2}\right\}$ **24.** $\{60\}$

25. $\{$all real numbers$\}$

26. $(-\infty, 5)$

27. $\left[-\dfrac{9}{2}, \dfrac{15}{2}\right]$ **28.** $\{24\}$

29. $\left\{-\dfrac{1}{5}\right\}$ **30.** $\left(-\infty, -\dfrac{5}{2}\right]$

31. $\left[-\dfrac{1}{3}, 3\right]$ **32.** $[1, 7]$

33. $\left\{-\dfrac{1}{6}, 2\right\}$ **34.** $\{-3\}$

35. $(-\infty, -1] \cup \left[\dfrac{5}{3}, \infty\right)$

36. $\left\{\dfrac{3}{8}\right\}$

37. $\left\{-\dfrac{5}{2}\right\}$ **38.** $(-6, 8)$

39. $(-\infty, -4) \cup (7, \infty)$

40. $(1, 9)$

41. $(-\infty, \infty)$ **42.** $\left\{\dfrac{1}{3}, 9\right\}$

43. $\{$all real numbers$\}$

44. $\left\{-\dfrac{10}{9}\right\}$

45. $\{-2\}$ **46.** $\varnothing$

47. $(-\infty, -1) \cup (2, \infty)$

48. $[-3, -2]$

STUDY SKILLS

Reviewing a Chapter

Your textbook provides material to help you prepare for quizzes or tests in this course. Refer to a **Chapter Summary** as you read through the following techniques.

Chapter Reviewing Techniques

- **Review the Key Terms and New Symbols.** Make a study card for each. Include a definition, an example, a sketch (if appropriate), and a section or page reference.

- **Take the Test Your Word Power quiz** to check your understanding of new vocabulary. The answers immediately follow.

- **Read the Quick Review.** Pay special attention to the headings. Study the explanations and examples given for each concept. Try to think about the whole chapter.

- **Reread your lecture notes.** Focus on what your instructor has emphasized in class, and review that material in your text.

- **Look over your homework.** Pay special attention to any trouble spots.

- **Work the Review Exercises.** They are grouped by section.

  ▸ Answers are included in the margin for quick reference.

  ▸ Pay attention to direction words, such as *simplify, solve,* and *evaluate*.

  ▸ Are your answers exact and complete? Did you include the correct labels, such as $, cm^2, ft, etc.?

  ▸ Make study cards for difficult problems.

- **Work the Mixed Review Exercises.** They are in mixed-up order. Check your answers in the margin.

- **Take the Chapter Test under test conditions.**

  ▸ Time yourself.

  ▸ Use a calculator or notes (if your instructor permits them on tests).

  ▸ Take the test in one sitting.

  ▸ Show all your work.

  ▸ Check your answers in the margin. Section references are provided.

Reviewing a chapter will take some time. Avoid rushing through your review in one night. Use the suggestions over a few days or evenings to better understand the material and remember it longer.

Follow these reviewing techniques to prepare for your next test.

1. How much time did you spend reviewing for your test? Was it enough?

2. How did the reviewing techniques work for you?

3. What will you do differently when reviewing for your next test?

Chapter 1	Summary

Key Terms

1.1

linear (first-degree)
    equation in one variable
solution
solution set
equivalent equations
conditional equation
identity
contradiction

1.2

mathematical model
formula
percent
percent increase
percent decrease

1.4

consecutive integers
consecutive even integers
consecutive odd integers

1.5

inequality
interval
linear inequality in one
    variable
equivalent inequalities
three-part inequality

1.6

intersection
compound inequality
union

1.7

absolute value equation
absolute value inequality

New Symbols

$\%$	percent	$-\infty$	negative infinity	(a, b)	interval notation for $a < x < b$
$1°$	one degree	$(-\infty, \infty)$	the set of real numbers	$[a, b]$	interval notation for $a \leq x \leq b$
∞	infinity				

$\cap$	set intersection
$\cup$	set union

Test Your Word Power

See how well you have learned the vocabulary in this chapter.

1. An **equation** is
   A. an algebraic expression
   B. an expression that contains fractions
   C. an expression that uses any of the four basic operations or the operation of raising to powers or taking roots on any collection of variables and numbers formed according to the rules of algebra
   D. a statement that two algebraic expressions are equal.

2. An **inequality** is
   A. a statement that two algebraic expressions are equal
   B. a point on a number line
   C. an equation with no solutions
   D. a statement consisting of algebraic expressions related by $<, \leq, >,$ or $\geq$.

3. **Interval notation** is
   A. a point on a number line
   B. a special notation for describing a point on a number line
   C. a way to use symbols to describe an interval on a number line
   D. a notation to describe unequal quantities.

4. The **intersection** of two sets A and B is the set of elements that belong
   A. to both A and B
   B. to either A or B, or both
   C. to either A or B, but not both
   D. to just A.

5. The **union** of two sets A and B is the set of elements that belong
   A. to both A and B
   B. to either A or B, or both
   C. to either A or B, but not both
   D. to just B.

ANSWERS

1. D; *Examples:* $2a + 3 = 7, 3y = -8, x^2 = 4$ **2.** D; *Examples:* $x < 5, 7 + 2k \geq 11, -5 < 2z - 1 \leq 3$
3. C; *Examples:* $(-\infty, 5], (1, \infty), [-3, 3)$ **4.** A; *Example:* If $A = \{2, 4, 6, 8\}$ and $B = \{1, 2, 3\}$, then $A \cap B = \{2\}$.
5. B; *Example:* Using the sets A and B from Answer 4, $A \cup B = \{1, 2, 3, 4, 6, 8\}$.

Quick Review

CONCEPTS	EXAMPLES

1.1 Linear Equations in One Variable

Solving a Linear Equation in One Variable

Step 1 Simplify each side separately.

- Clear any parentheses.
- Clear any fractions or decimals.
- Combine like terms.

Step 2 Isolate the variable terms on one side.

Step 3 Isolate the variable.

Step 4 Check.

Solve $4(8 - 3x) = 32 - 8(x + 2)$.

$32 - 12x = 32 - 8x - 16$	Distributive property
$32 - 12x = 16 - 8x$	Combine like terms.
$32 - 12x + 12x = 16 - 8x + 12x$	Add $12x$.
$32 = 16 + 4x$	Combine like terms.
$32 - 16 = 16 + 4x - 16$	Subtract 16.
$16 = 4x$	Combine like terms.
$\dfrac{16}{4} = \dfrac{4x}{4}$	Divide by 4.
$4 = x$	

The solution set is $\{4\}$. This can be checked by substituting 4 for x in the original equation.

1.2 Formulas and Percent

Solving a Formula for a Specified Variable (Solving a Literal Equation)

Step 1 Clear any parentheses and fractions.

Step 2 Isolate all terms with the specified variable.

Step 3 Isolate the specified variable.

Solve $\mathcal{A} = \dfrac{1}{2}bh$ for h.

$$\mathcal{A} = \frac{1}{2}bh$$

$2\mathcal{A} = 2\left(\dfrac{1}{2}bh\right)$	Multiply by 2.
$2\mathcal{A} = bh$	
$\dfrac{2\mathcal{A}}{b} = h,$ or $h = \dfrac{2\mathcal{A}}{b}$	Divide by b.

1.3 Applications of Linear Equations

Solving an Applied Problem

Step 1 Read the problem.

Step 2 Assign a variable.

How many liters of 30% alcohol solution and 80% alcohol solution must be mixed to obtain 100 L of 50% alcohol solution?

Let x = number of liters of 30% solution needed.

Then $100 - x$ = number of liters of 80% solution needed.

Liters of Solution	Percent (as a decimal)	Liters of Pure Alcohol
x	0.30	$0.30x$
$100 - x$	0.80	$0.80(100 - x)$
100	0.50	$0.50(100)$

Step 3 Write an equation.

From the last column of the table, the equation is

$$0.30x + 0.80(100 - x) = 0.50(100).$$

CONCEPTS	EXAMPLES

Step 4   Solve the equation.

$$0.30x + 0.80(100 - x) = 0.50(100) \qquad \text{Equation from Step 3}$$

$$0.30x + 80 - 0.80x = 50 \qquad \text{Distributive property; Multiply.}$$

$$100(0.30x + 80 - 0.80x) = 100(50) \qquad \text{Multiply by 100.}$$

$$30x + 8000 - 80x = 5000 \qquad \text{Distributive property; Multiply.}$$

$$-50x + 8000 = 5000 \qquad \text{Combine like terms.}$$

$$-50x = -3000 \qquad \text{Subtract 8000.}$$

$$x = 60 \qquad \text{Divide by } -50.$$

Step 5   State the answer.

The solution of the equation is 60.

60 L of 30% solution and $100 - 60 = 40$ L of 80% solution are needed.

Step 6   Check.

$$0.30(60) + 0.80(100 - 60) = 50 \text{ is true.}$$

1.4   Further Applications of Linear Equations

To solve a uniform motion problem, draw a sketch and make a table. Use the formula

$$d = rt \quad \text{or} \quad rt = d.$$

Two cars start from towns 400 mi apart and travel toward each other. They meet after 4 hr. Find the rate of each car if one travels 20 mph faster than the other.

Let $x =$ rate of the slower car in miles per hour.

Then $x + 20 =$ rate of the faster car.

Use the information in the problem and $d = rt$ to complete a table.

	Rate	Time	Distance
Slower Car	x	4	4x
Faster Car	x + 20	4	4(x + 20)
			400 ← Total

A sketch shows that the sum of the distances, $4x$ and $4(x + 20)$, must be 400.

$$4x + 4(x + 20) = 400$$

$$4x + 4x + 80 = 400 \qquad \text{Distributive property}$$

$$8x + 80 = 400 \qquad \text{Combine like terms.}$$

$$8x = 320 \qquad \text{Subtract 80.}$$

$$x = 40 \qquad \text{Divide by 8.}$$

The slower car travels 40 mph, and the faster car travels $40 + 20 = 60$ mph.

$$4(40) + 4(40 + 20) = 400 \text{ is true.}$$

CONCEPTS	EXAMPLES

1.5 Linear Inequalities in One Variable

Solving a Linear Inequality in One Variable

Step 1 Simplify each side separately.

Step 2 Isolate the variable terms on one side.

Step 3 Isolate the variable (x) to write the inequality in one of these forms.

$$x < k, \quad x \le k, \quad x > k, \quad \text{or} \quad x \ge k$$

If an inequality is multiplied or divided by a negative number, the direction of the inequality symbol must be reversed.

Solve each inequality.

$$3(x + 2) - 5x \le 12$$

$3x + 6 - 5x \le 12$	Distributive property
$-2x + 6 \le 12$	Combine like terms.
$-2x + 6 - 6 \le 12 - 6$	Subtract 6.
$-2x \le 6$	Combine like terms.
$\dfrac{-2x}{-2} \ge \dfrac{6}{-2}$	Divide by -2. Change $\le$ to $\ge$.
$x \ge -3$	

The solution set $[-3, \infty)$ is graphed here.

To solve a three-part inequality, work with all three parts at the same time.

$$-4 < \quad 2x + 3 \quad \le 7$$
$$-4 - 3 < 2x + 3 - 3 \le 7 - 3 \qquad \text{Subtract 3.}$$
$$-7 < \quad 2x \quad \le 4$$
$$\dfrac{-7}{2} < \quad \dfrac{2x}{2} \quad \le \dfrac{4}{2} \qquad \text{Divide by 2.}$$
$$-\dfrac{7}{2} < \quad x \quad \le 2$$

The solution set $\left(-\dfrac{7}{2}, 2\right]$ is graphed here.

1.6 Set Operations and Compound Inequalities

Solving a Compound Inequality

Step 1 Solve each inequality in the compound inequality individually.

Step 2 If the inequalities are joined with *and*, then the solution set is the intersection of the two individual solution sets.

If the inequalities are joined with *or*, then the solution set is the union of the two individual solution sets.

Solve each compound inequality.

$$x + 1 > 2 \quad \text{and} \quad 2x < 6$$
$$x > 1 \quad \text{and} \quad x < 3$$

The solution set is $(1, 3)$.

$$2(x + 3) - 2 \le 4 \quad \text{or} \quad -4x \le -16$$
$$2x + 6 - 2 \le 4 \quad \text{or} \quad \dfrac{-4x}{-4} \ge \dfrac{-16}{-4}$$
$$2x + 4 \le 4 \quad \text{or} \quad x \ge 4$$
$$x \le 0$$

The solution set is $(-\infty, 0] \cup [4, \infty)$.

CONCEPTS	EXAMPLES

1.7 **Absolute Value Equations and Inequalities**

Solving Absolute Value Equations and Inequalities
Let k be a positive number.

To solve $|ax + b| = k$, solve the following compound equation.

$$ax + b = k \quad \text{or} \quad ax + b = -k$$

To solve $|ax + b| > k$, solve the following compound inequality.

$$ax + b > k \quad \text{or} \quad ax + b < -k$$

To solve $|ax + b| < k$, solve the following compound inequality.

$$-k < ax + b < k$$

To solve an absolute value equation of the form

$$|ax + b| = |cx + d|,$$

solve the following compound equation.

$$ax + b = cx + d \quad \text{or} \quad ax + b = -(cx + d)$$

Solve each equation or inequality.

$$|x - 7| = 3$$
$$x - 7 = 3 \quad \text{or} \quad x - 7 = -3$$
$$x = 10 \quad \text{or} \quad x = 4 \qquad \text{Add 7.}$$

The solution set is $\{4, 10\}$.

$$|x - 7| > 3$$
$$x - 7 > 3 \quad \text{or} \quad x - 7 < -3$$
$$x > 10 \quad \text{or} \quad x < 4 \qquad \text{Add 7.}$$

The solution set is $(-\infty, 4) \cup (10, \infty)$.

$$|x - 7| < 3$$
$$-3 < x - 7 < 3$$
$$4 < \quad x \quad < 10 \qquad \text{Add 7.}$$

The solution set is $(4, 10)$.

$$|x + 2| = |2x - 6|$$
$$x + 2 = 2x - 6 \quad \text{or} \quad x + 2 = -(2x - 6)$$
$$x = 8 \qquad \text{or} \quad x + 2 = -2x + 6$$
$$3x = 4$$
$$x = \frac{4}{3}$$

The solution set is $\left\{\frac{4}{3}, 8\right\}$.

Chapter 1   Review Exercises

1.1 *Solve each equation.*

1. $\left\{-\dfrac{9}{5}\right\}$ 2. $\{16\}$

3. $\left\{-\dfrac{7}{5}\right\}$ 4. $\varnothing$

1. $-(8 + 3x) + 5 = 2x + 6$

2. $-\dfrac{3}{4}x = -12$

3. $\dfrac{2x + 1}{3} - \dfrac{x - 1}{4} = 0$

4. $5(2x - 3) = 6(x - 1) + 4x$

5. {all real numbers}; identity

6. ∅; contradiction

7. {0}; conditional equation

8. {all real numbers}; identity

9. $L = \dfrac{V}{HW}$

10. $b = \dfrac{2\mathscr{A} - Bh}{h}$, or $b = \dfrac{2\mathscr{A}}{h} - B$

11. $c = P - a - b - B$

12. $y = -\dfrac{4}{7}x + \dfrac{9}{7}$

13. 6 ft   **14.** 3.0%

15. 6.5%   **16.** 25°

17. $775.3 billion

18. $92.0 billion

19. $9 - \dfrac{1}{3}x$ **20.** $\dfrac{4x}{x+9}$

21. length: 13 m; width: 8 m

22. 17 in., 17 in., 19 in.

Solve each equation. Then tell whether the equation is a conditional equation, *an* identity, *or a* contradiction.

5. $10x - 3(2x - 4) = 4(x + 3)$

6. $13x - (x + 7) = 12x - 13$

7. $x + 6(x - 1) - (4 - x) = -10$

8. $5 + 3(2x + 6) = 5 + 3(2x + 6)$

1.2   *Solve for the specified variable.*

9. $V = LWH$ for L

10. $\mathscr{A} = \dfrac{1}{2}h(b + B)$ for b

11. $P = a + b + c + B$ for c

12. $4x + 7y = 9$ for y

1.2, 1.3   *Solve each problem.*

13. A rectangular solid has a volume of 180 ft³. Its length is 6 ft and its width is 5 ft. Find its height.

14. The number of students attending colleges and universities in the United States dropped from about 20.1 million in the fall of 2011 to 19.5 million in the fall of 2013. To the nearest tenth of a percent, what was the percent decrease? (*Source:* National Student Clearinghouse Research Center.)

15. Find the annual simple-interest rate that Halina is earning if the principal of $30,000 earns $7800 interest in 4 yr.

16. If the Fahrenheit temperature is 77°, what is the corresponding Celsius temperature?

In 2012, total U.S. government spending was about $3540 billion (or $3.54 trillion). The circle graph shows how the spending was divided.

2012 U.S. Government Spending

Medicare/health programs 23.1%

National defense 19.2%

Income security 15.3%

Other 17.9%

Education & social services 2.6%

Social Security 21.9%

Source: U.S. Office of Management and Budget.

17. About how much was spent on Social Security?

18. About how much did the U.S. government spend on education and social services in 2012?

Translate each verbal phrase into a mathematical expression, using x as the variable.

19. One-third of a number, subtracted from 9

20. The product of 4 and a number, divided by 9 more than the number

Solve each problem.

21. The length of a rectangle is 3 m less than twice the width. The perimeter of the rectangle is 42 m. Find the length and width of the rectangle.

22. In a triangle with two sides of equal length, the third side measures 15 in. less than the sum of the two equal sides. The perimeter of the triangle is 53 in. Find the lengths of the three sides.

23. A candy clerk has three times as many kilograms of chocolate creams as peanut clusters. The clerk has 48 kg of the two candies altogether. How many kilograms of peanut clusters does the clerk have?

24. How many liters of a 20% solution of a chemical should be mixed with 15 L of a 50% solution to obtain a 30% mixture?

25. How much water should be added to 30 L of a 40% acid solution to reduce it to a 30% solution?

26. Eric invested some money at 6% and $4000 less than that amount at 4%. Find the amount invested at each rate if his total annual interest income was $840.

Liters of Solution	Percent (as a decimal)	Liters of Pure Acid
	0.40	
x		
	0.30	

Principal (in dollars)	Rate (as a decimal)	Interest (in dollars)
x	0.06	
	0.04	

1.4 *Solve each problem.*

27. A clerk has $3.50 in dimes and quarters in her cash drawer. The number of dimes is 1 less than twice the number of quarters. How many of each denomination are there?

28. When Jim emptied his pockets one evening, he found he had 19 nickels and dimes with a total value of $1.55. How many of each denomination did he have?

29. Which choice is the best *estimate* for the average rate for a trip of 405 mi that lasted 8.2 hr?

   A. 50 mph   **B.** 30 mph   **C.** 60 mph   **D.** 40 mph

30. A driver averaged 53 mph and took 10 hr to travel from Memphis to Chicago. What is the distance between Memphis and Chicago?

31. A small plane traveled from Warsaw to Rome, averaging 164 mph. The trip took 2 hr. What is the distance from Warsaw to Rome?

32. A passenger train and a freight train leave a town at the same time and go in opposite directions. They travel at rates of 60 mph and 75 mph, respectively. How long will it take for them to be 297 mi apart?

	Rate	Time	Distance
Passenger Train	60	x	
Freight Train	75	x	

33. Two cars leave small towns 230 km apart at the same time, traveling directly toward one another. One car travels 15 km per hr slower than the other car. They pass one another 2 hr later. What are their rates?

	Rate	Time	Distance
Faster car	x	2	
Slower car	x − 15	2	

34. An 85-mi trip to the beach took Susan 2 hr. During the second hour, a rainstorm caused her to average 7 mph less than she traveled during the first hour. Find her average rate for the first hour.

35. Find the measure of each angle in the triangle.

36. Find the measure of each marked angle.

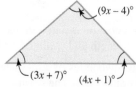

37. $(-9, \infty)$ **38.** $(-\infty, -3]$

39. $\left(\dfrac{3}{2}, \infty\right)$ **40.** $[-3, \infty)$

41. $[3, 5)$ **42.** $\left(\dfrac{59}{31}, \infty\right)$

43. (a) $x < 6.75$
   (b) $6.75 \le x \le 7.25$
   (c) $x > 7.25$

44. 38 m or less

45. 31 tickets or less (but at least 15)

46. any score greater than or equal to 61

47. $\{a, c\}$ **48.** $\{a\}$

49. $\{a, c, e, f, g\}$

50. $\{a, b, c, d, e, f, g\}$

`1.5` *Solve each inequality. Give the solution set in interval form.*

37. $-\dfrac{2}{3}x < 6$

38. $-5x - 4 \ge 11$

39. $\dfrac{6x + 3}{-4} < -3$

40. $5 - (6 - 4x) \ge 2x - 7$

41. $8 \le 3x - 1 < 14$

42. $\dfrac{5}{3}(x - 2) + \dfrac{2}{5}(x + 1) > 1$

Solve each problem.

43. Dr. Paul Donohue writes a syndicated column in which readers question him on a variety of health topics. Reader C. J. wrote, "Many people say they can weigh more because they have a large frame. How is frame size determined?" Here is Dr. Donohue's response:

> *"For a man, a wrist circumference between 6.75 and 7.25 in. [inclusive] indicates a medium frame. Anything above is a large frame and anything below, a small frame."*

(*Source:* Dr. Donohue, © 2004. Used by permission of North America Syndicate.)

Using x to represent wrist circumference in inches, write an inequality or a three-part inequality that represents wrist circumference for a male with the following.

(a) a small frame   **(b)** a medium frame   **(c)** a large frame

44. The perimeter of a rectangular playground must be no greater than 120 m. One dimension of the playground must be 22 m. Find the possible lengths of the other dimension of the playground.

22 m

45. A group of college students wants to buy tickets to attend a performance of *Motown the Musical* at the Lunt-Fontanne Theatre in New York City. They can buy student mezzanine seats for a group rate of $51 per ticket for 15 tickets or more. If they have $1600 available to spend, how many tickets can they purchase at this price? (*Source:* www.broadway.com)

46. To pass algebra, a student must have an average of at least 70 on five tests. On the first four tests, a student has scores of 75, 79, 64, and 71. What possible scores on the fifth test would guarantee the student a passing grade in the class?

`1.6`   *Let* $A = \{a, b, c, d\}$, $B = \{a, c, e, f\}$, *and* $C = \{a, e, f, g\}$. *Find each set.*

47. $A \cap B$ **48.** $A \cap C$ **49.** $B \cup C$ **50.** $A \cup C$

51. $(6, 9)$

52. $(8, 14)$

53. $(-\infty, -3] \cup (5, \infty)$

54. $(-\infty, \infty)$

55. $\varnothing$

56. $(-\infty, -2] \cup [7, \infty)$

57. $(-3, 4)$ **58.** $(-\infty, 2)$

59. $(4, \infty)$ **60.** $(1, \infty)$

61. $\{-7, 7\}$ **62.** $\{-11, 7\}$

63. $\left\{-\dfrac{1}{3}, 5\right\}$ **64.** $\varnothing$

65. $\{0, 7\}$ **66.** $\left\{-\dfrac{3}{2}, \dfrac{1}{2}\right\}$

67. $\left\{-\dfrac{3}{4}, \dfrac{1}{2}\right\}$ **68.** $\left\{-\dfrac{1}{2}\right\}$

69. $(-14, 14)$ **70.** $[-1, 13]$

71. $[-3, -2]$ **72.** $(-\infty, \infty)$

73. $\varnothing$ **74.** $(-\infty, \infty)$

Solve each compound inequality. Give the solution set in both interval and graph forms.

51. $x > 6$ and $x < 9$

52. $x + 4 > 12$ and $x - 2 < 12$

53. $x > 5$ or $x \le -3$

54. $x \ge -2$ or $x < 2$

55. $x - 4 > 6$ and $x + 3 \le 10$

56. $-5x + 1 \ge 11$ or $3x + 5 \ge 26$

Express each set in simplest interval form.

57. $(-3, \infty) \cap (-\infty, 4)$

58. $(-\infty, 6) \cap (-\infty, 2)$

59. $(4, \infty) \cup (9, \infty)$

60. $(1, 2) \cup (1, \infty)$

1.7 *Solve each equation.*

61. $|x| = 7$

62. $|x + 2| = 9$

63. $|3x - 7| = 8$

64. $|x - 4| = -12$

65. $|2x - 7| + 4 = 11$

66. $|4x + 2| - 7 = -3$

67. $|3x + 1| = |x + 2|$

68. $|2x - 1| = |2x + 3|$

Solve each inequality.

69. $|x| < 14$

70. $|-x + 6| \le 7$

71. $|2x + 5| \le 1$

72. $|x + 1| \ge -3$

73. $|3 - 4x| + 7 < -4$

74. $|-8 - 3x| - 7 > -8$

Chapter 1   Mixed Review Exercises

1. $(-2, \infty)$ **2.** $k = \dfrac{6r - bt}{a}$

3. $[-2, 3)$ **4.** $\{0\}$

5. $(-\infty, \infty)$ **6.** $(-\infty, 2]$

7. $\left\{-\dfrac{7}{3}, 1\right\}$ **8.** $\{300\}$

9. $[-16, 10]$ **10.** $\left(-\infty, \dfrac{14}{17}\right)$

11. $\left(-3, \dfrac{7}{2}\right)$ **12.** $(-\infty, 1]$

13. $\left(-\infty, -\dfrac{13}{5}\right) \cup (3, \infty)$

14. $(-\infty, \infty)$

15. $\left\{-4, -\dfrac{2}{3}\right\}$ **16.** $\{30\}$

17. $\left\{1, \dfrac{11}{3}\right\}$ **18.** $\varnothing$

19. $(6, 8)$

20. $(-\infty, -2] \cup [7, \infty)$

Solve.

1. $5 - (6 - 4x) > 2x - 5$

2. $ak + bt = 6r$ for k

3. $x + 4 < 7$ and $x + 5 \ge 3$

4. $\dfrac{4x + 2}{4} + \dfrac{3x - 1}{8} = \dfrac{x + 6}{16}$

5. $|3x + 6| \ge 0$

6. $-5x \ge -10$

7. $|3x + 2| + 4 = 9$

8. $0.05x + 0.03(1200 - x) = 42$

9. $|x + 3| \le 13$

10. $\dfrac{3}{4}(x - 2) - \dfrac{1}{3}(5 - 2x) < -2$

11. $-4 < 3 - 2x < 9$

12. $-0.3x + 2.1(x - 4) \le -6.6$

13. $|5x - 1| > 14$

14. $x \ge -2$ or $x < 4$

15. $|x - 1| = |2x + 3|$

16. $\dfrac{3x}{5} - \dfrac{x}{2} = 3$

17. $|3x - 7| = 4$

18. $5(2x - 7) = 2(5x + 3)$

19. $-5x < -30$ and $-7x > -56$

20. $-5x + 1 \ge 11$ or $3x + 5 \ge 26$

21. 10 ft   **22.** 46, 47, 48
23. any amount greater than or
equal to $1100
24. 5 L
25. 1 hr

Solve each problem.

21. A newspaper recycling collection bin is in the shape of a box 1.5 ft wide and 5 ft long. If the volume of the bin is 75 ft³, find the height.

22. The sum of the first and third of three consecutive integers is 47 more than the second integer. What are the integers?

23. To qualify for a company pension plan, an employee must average at least $1000 per month in earnings. During the first four months of the year, an employee made $900, $1200, $1040, and $760. What possible amounts earned during the fifth month will qualify the employee?

24. How many liters of a 20% solution of a chemical should be mixed with 10 L of a 50% solution to obtain a 40% mixture?

25. An automobile averaged 45 mph for the first part of a trip and 50 mph for the second part. If the entire trip took 4 hr and covered 195 mi, for how long was the rate 45 mph?

| Chapter 1 | Test | FOR EXTRA HELP | *Step-by-step test solutions are found on the Chapter Test Prep Videos available in* MyMathLab® *or on* You Tube. |

▶ *View the complete solutions to all Chapter Test exercises in MyMathLab.*

[1.1]
1. $\{-19\}$ **2.** $\{5\}$
3. (a) ∅; contradiction
(b) {all real numbers}; identity
(c) {0}; conditional equation
(d) {all real numbers}; identity

[1.2]
4. $h = \dfrac{3V}{b}$

5. $y = \dfrac{3}{2}x + 3$

[1.3, 1.4]
6. 2.668 hr
7. 1.25%   **8.** 42.9%
9. $8000 at 1.5%; $20,000 at 2.5%
10. faster car: 60 mph;
slower car: 45 mph
11. 40°, 40°, 100°

Solve each equation.

1. $3(2x - 2) - 4(x + 6) = 3x + 8 + x$ **2.** $0.08x + 0.06(x + 9) = 1.24$

3. Solve each equation. Then tell whether the equation is a *conditional equation*, an *identity*, or a *contradiction*.

(a) $3x - (2 - x) + 4x + 2 = 8x + 3$ (b) $\dfrac{x}{3} + 7 = \dfrac{5x}{6} - 2 - \dfrac{x}{2} + 9$

(c) $-4(2x - 6) = 5x + 24 - 7x$ (d) $\dfrac{x + 6}{10} + \dfrac{x - 4}{15} = \dfrac{x + 2}{6}$

4. Solve $V = \dfrac{1}{3}bh$ for h.   **5.** Solve $-3x + 2y = 6$ for y.

Solve each problem.

6. The 2013 Indianapolis 500 (mile) race was won by Tony Kanaan, who averaged 187.433 mph. What was his time to the nearest thousandth of an hour? (*Source: World Almanac and Book of Facts.*)

7. A certificate of deposit pays $456.25 in simple interest for 1 yr on a principal of $36,500. What is the rate of interest?

8. A total of 160.0 billion items were sent through the U.S. Mail in a recent year. Of these, 68.7 billion items were first-class mail. What percent of the items, to the nearest tenth, were pieces of first-class mail? (*Source:* U.S. Postal Service.)

9. Tyler invested some money at 1.5% simple interest and some at 2.5% simple interest. The total amount of his investments was $28,000, and the interest he earned during the first year was $620. How much did he invest at each rate?

10. Two cars leave from the same point at the same time, traveling in opposite directions. One travels 15 mph slower than the other. After 6 hr, they are 630 mi apart. Find the rate of each car.

11. Find the measure of each angle in the triangle.

Solve each inequality. Give the solution set in both interval and graph forms.

12. $4 - 6(x + 3) \leq -2 - 3(x + 6) + 3x$ **13.** $-\dfrac{4}{7}x > -16$

14. $-1 < 3x - 4 < 2$ **15.** $-6 \leq \dfrac{4}{3}x - 2 \leq 2$

16. Which one of the following inequalities is equivalent to $x < -3$?

   A. $-3x < 9$ **B.** $-3x > -9$ **C.** $-3x > 9$ **D.** $-3x < -9$

17. Justin must have an average of at least 80 on the four tests in a course to get a B. He had scores of 83, 76, and 79 on the first three tests. What possible scores on the fourth test would guarantee him a B in the course?

18. Let $A = \{1, 2, 5, 7\}$ and $B = \{1, 5, 9, 12\}$. Find each set.

   (a) $A \cap B$ **(b)** $A \cup B$

Solve each compound or absolute value equation or inequality.

19. $3x \geq 6$ and $x < 9$ **20.** $-4x \leq -24$ or $4x < 12$

21. $|4x + 3| \leq 7$ **22.** $|5 - 6x| > 12$

23. $|3x - 9| = 6$ **24.** $|-3x + 4| - 4 < -1$

25. $|7 - x| \leq -1$ **26.** $|3x - 2| + 1 = 8$ **27.** $|3 - 5x| = |2x + 8|$

28. If $k < 0$, what is the solution set of each of the following?

   (a) $|8x - 5| < k$ **(b)** $|8x - 5| > k$ **(c)** $|8x - 5| = k$

2

Linear Equations, Graphs, and Functions

The concept of steepness, or grade, is mathematically interpreted using *slope*, one of the topics of this chapter.

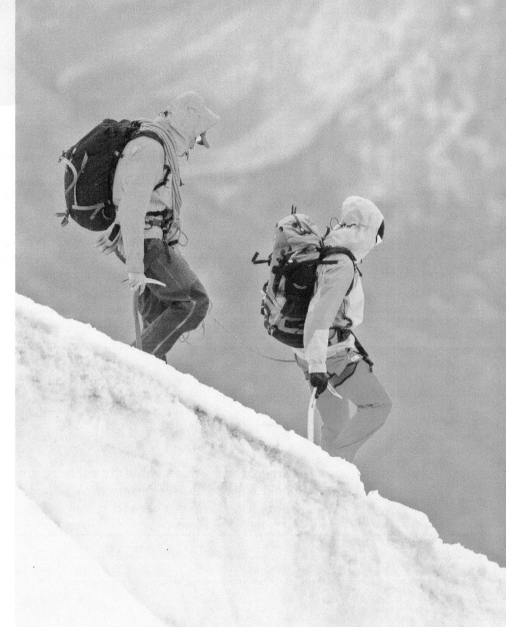

2.1 Linear Equations in Two Variables

OBJECTIVES

1. Interpret a line graph.
2. Plot ordered pairs.
3. Find ordered pairs that satisfy a given equation.
4. Graph lines.
5. Find x- and y-intercepts.
6. Recognize equations of horizontal and vertical lines.
7. Use the midpoint formula.

VOCABULARY

☐ ordered pair
☐ origin
☐ x-axis
☐ y-axis
☐ rectangular (Cartesian) coordinate system
☐ components
☐ plot
☐ coordinate
☐ quadrant
☐ table of ordered pairs (table of values)
☐ graph of an equation
☐ first-degree equation
☐ linear equation in two variables
☐ x-intercept
☐ y-intercept

René Descartes (1596–1650)

OBJECTIVE 1 Interpret a line graph.

The line graph in **FIGURE 1** shows personal spending (in billions of dollars) on medical care in the United States from 2005 through 2012. About how much was spent on medical care in 2010?

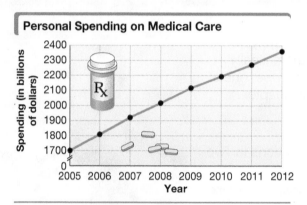

Source: Centers for Medicare & Medicaid Services.

FIGURE 1

The line graph in **FIGURE 1** presents information based on a method for locating a point in a plane developed by René Descartes, a 17th-century French mathematician. According to legend, Descartes was lying in bed ill watching a fly crawl about on the ceiling near a corner of the room. It occurred to him that the location of the fly could be described by determining its distances from the two adjacent walls. (See the figure at the right.)

Locating a fly on a ceiling

We use this insight to plot points and graph linear equations in two variables whose graphs are straight lines.

OBJECTIVE 2 Plot ordered pairs.

Each of the pairs of numbers $(3, 2)$, $(-5, 6)$, and $(4, -1)$ is an example of an **ordered pair**—that is, a pair of numbers written within parentheses in which the order of the numbers is important. We graph an ordered pair by using two perpendicular number lines that intersect at their 0 points, as shown in **FIGURE 2**. The common 0 point is the **origin.**

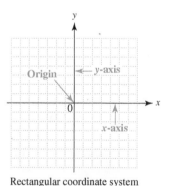

Rectangular coordinate system

FIGURE 2

The position of any point in this coordinate plane is determined by referring to the horizontal number line, or **x-axis,** and the vertical number line, or **y-axis.** The x-axis and the y-axis make up a **rectangular** (or **Cartesian,** for Descartes) **coordinate system.**

The numbers in an ordered pair (x, y) are its **components.** The first component indicates position relative to the x-axis, and the second component indicates position relative to the y-axis. For example, to locate, or **plot,** the point on the graph that corresponds to the ordered pair $(3, 2)$, we move three units from 0 to the right along the x-axis and then two units up parallel to the y-axis. See **FIGURE 3.** The numbers in an ordered pair are the **coordinates** of the corresponding point.

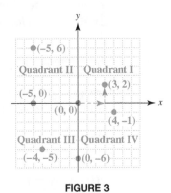

FIGURE 3

We can apply this method of locating ordered pairs to the line graph in **FIGURE 1.** We move along the horizontal axis to a year and then up parallel to the vertical axis to approximate spending for that year. Thus, we can write the ordered pair $(2010, 2200)$ to indicate that in 2010, personal spending on medical care was about $2200 billion.

⚠ CAUTION   The parentheses used to represent an ordered pair are also used to represent an open interval **(Section 1.5).** The context of the discussion tells whether ordered pairs or open intervals are being represented.

The four regions of the graph, shown in **FIGURE 3,** are **quadrants I, II, III,** and **IV,** reading counterclockwise from the upper right quadrant. *The points on the x-axis and y-axis do not belong to any quadrant.*

OBJECTIVE 3 Find ordered pairs that satisfy a given equation.

Each solution of an equation with two variables, such as

$$2x + 3y = 6, \quad \text{Equation with two variables } x \text{ and } y$$

includes two numbers, one for each variable. We write the solutions as ordered pairs. *(If x and y are used as the variables, the x-value is given first.)* For example, we can show that $(6, -2)$ is a solution of $2x + 3y = 6$ by substitution.

$$2x + 3y = 6$$
$$2(6) + 3(-2) \overset{?}{=} 6 \qquad \text{Let } x = 6, y = -2.$$
$$12 - 6 \overset{?}{=} 6 \qquad \text{Multiply.}$$
$$6 = 6 \checkmark \qquad \text{True}$$

Use parentheses to avoid errors.

Because the ordered pair $(6, -2)$ makes the equation true, it is a solution.

On the other hand, $(5, 1)$ is *not* a solution of the equation $2x + 3y = 6$.

$$2x + 3y = 6$$

$$2(5) + 3(1) \stackrel{?}{=} 6 \qquad \text{Let } x = 5, y = 1.$$

$$10 + 3 \stackrel{?}{=} 6 \qquad \text{Multiply.}$$

$$13 = 6 \qquad \text{False}$$

To find ordered pairs that satisfy an equation, select a number for one of the variables, substitute it into the equation for that variable, and solve for the other variable.

Because any real number could be selected for one variable and would lead to a real number for the other variable, an equation with two variables such as $2x + 3y = 6$ has an infinite number of solutions.

NOW TRY
EXERCISE 1

Complete each ordered pair for $2x - y = 4$.

$(0, \underline{\quad})$, $(\underline{\quad}, 0)$,
$(4, \underline{\quad})$, $(\underline{\quad}, 2)$

Then write the results as a table of ordered pairs.

EXAMPLE 1   Completing Ordered Pairs and Making a Table

In parts (a)–(d), complete each ordered pair for $2x + 3y = 6$. Then, in part (e), write the results as a table of ordered pairs.

(a) $(0, \underline{\quad})$

$$2x + 3y = 6$$
$$2(0) + 3y = 6 \qquad \text{Let } x = 0.$$
$$3y = 6 \qquad \text{Multiply. Add.}$$
$$y = 2 \qquad \text{Divide by 3.}$$

The ordered pair is $(0, 2)$.

(b) $(\underline{\quad}, 0)$

$$2x + 3y = 6$$
$$2x + 3(0) = 6 \qquad \text{Let } y = 0.$$
$$2x = 6 \qquad \text{Multiply. Add.}$$
$$x = 3 \qquad \text{Divide by 2.}$$

The ordered pair is $(3, 0)$.

(c) $(-3, \underline{\quad})$

$$2x + 3y = 6$$
$$2(-3) + 3y = 6 \qquad \text{Let } x = -3.$$
$$-6 + 3y = 6 \qquad \text{Multiply.}$$
$$3y = 12 \qquad \text{Add 6.}$$
$$y = 4 \qquad \text{Divide by 3.}$$

The ordered pair is $(-3, 4)$.

(d) $(\underline{\quad}, -4)$

$$2x + 3y = 6$$
$$2x + 3(-4) = 6 \qquad \text{Let } y = -4.$$
$$2x - 12 = 6 \qquad \text{Multiply.}$$
$$2x = 18 \qquad \text{Add 12.}$$
$$x = 9 \qquad \text{Divide by 2.}$$

The ordered pair is $(9, -4)$.

(e) We write a **table of ordered pairs** (or **table of values**) for these results as shown.

x	y	Ordered Pairs
0	2	← Represents (0, 2) from part (a)
3	0	← Represents (3, 0) from part (b)
−3	4	← Represents (−3, 4) from part (c)
9	−4	← Represents (9, −4) from part (d)

NOW TRY

NOW TRY ANSWER

1. $(0, -4), (2, 0), (4, 4), (3, 2)$

x	y
0	−4
2	0
4	4
3	2

OBJECTIVE 4   Graph lines.

The **graph of an equation** is the set of points corresponding to *all* ordered pairs that satisfy the equation. It gives a "picture" of the equation.

To graph $2x + 3y = 6$, we plot the ordered pairs found in **Objective 3** and **Example 1**. These points, plotted in **FIGURE 4(a)** on the next page, appear to lie on a straight line. If the infinite number of ordered pairs that satisfy the equation $2x + 3y = 6$ were graphed, they would form the straight line shown in **FIGURE 4(b)**.

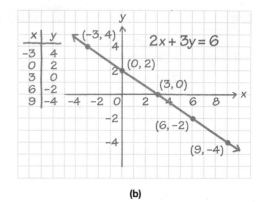

(a)   (b)

FIGURE 4

The equation $2x + 3y = 6$ is a **first-degree equation** because it has no term with a variable to a power greater than 1.

The graph of any first-degree equation in two variables is a straight line.

Because first-degree equations with two variables have straight-line graphs, they are called ***lin****ear equations in two variables.*

Linear Equation in Two Variables

A **linear equation in two variables** (here x and y) can be written in the form

$$Ax + By = C,$$

where A, B, and C are real numbers and A and B are not both 0. This form is called **standard form.**

OBJECTIVE 5 Find x- and y-intercepts.

A straight line is determined if any two different points on the line are known. Therefore, finding two different points is sufficient to graph the line.

Two useful points for graphing are the x- and y-intercepts. The **x-intercept** is the point (if any) where the line intersects the x-axis. The **y-intercept** is the point (if any) where the line intersects the y-axis.* See **FIGURE 5**.

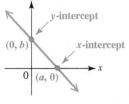

FIGURE 5

• The y-value of the point where the line intersects the x-axis is always 0.

• The x-value of the point where the line intersects the y-axis is always 0.

This suggests a method for finding the x- and y-intercepts.

Finding Intercepts

When graphing the equation of a line, find the intercepts as follows.

Let $y = 0$ to find the x-intercept.

Let $x = 0$ to find the y-intercept.

---

*Some texts define an intercept as a number, not a point. For example, "y-intercept $(0, 4)$" would be given as "y-intercept 4."

NOW TRY
EXERCISE 2
Find the x- and y-intercepts, and graph the equation.

$$x - 2y = 4$$

EXAMPLE 2   Finding Intercepts

Find the x- and y-intercepts of $4x - y = -3$, and graph the equation.

To find the x-intercept, let $y = 0$.

$$4x - y = -3$$
$$4x - 0 = -3 \qquad \text{Let } y = 0.$$
$$4x = -3 \qquad \text{Subtract.}$$
$$x = -\frac{3}{4} \qquad \text{Divide by 4.}$$

The x-intercept is $\left(-\frac{3}{4}, 0\right)$.

To find the y-intercept, let $x = 0$.

$$4x - y = -3$$
$$4(0) - y = -3 \qquad \text{Let } x = 0.$$
$$-y = -3 \qquad \text{Multiply. Subtract.}$$
$$y = 3 \qquad \text{Multiply by } -1.$$

The y-intercept is $(0, 3)$.

To guard against errors when graphing the equation, it is a good idea to find a third point. We arbitrarily choose $x = -2$, and substitute this value in the equation to find the corresponding value of y.

$$4x - y = -3$$
$$4(-2) - y = -3 \qquad \text{Let } x = -2.$$
$$-8 - y = -3 \qquad \text{Multiply.}$$
$$-y = 5 \qquad \text{Add 8.}$$
$$y = -5 \qquad \text{Multiply by } -1.$$

The ordered pair $(-2, -5)$ lies on the graph. We plot the three ordered pairs and draw a line through them. See **FIGURE 6**.

x	y
$-\frac{3}{4}$	0
0	3
-2	-5

Find a third point as a check.

A linear equation with both x and y variables will have both x- and y-intercepts. Its graph will be a "slanted" line.

FIGURE 6

NOW TRY

EXAMPLE 3   Graphing a Line That Passes through the Origin

Graph $x + 2y = 0$.

Find the x-intercept.

$$x + 2y = 0$$
$$x + 2(0) = 0 \qquad \text{Let } y = 0.$$
$$x + 0 = 0 \qquad \text{Multiply.}$$
$$x = 0 \qquad \text{x-intercept is } (0, 0).$$

Find the y-intercept.

$$x + 2y = 0$$
$$0 + 2y = 0 \qquad \text{Let } x = 0.$$
$$2y = 0 \qquad \text{Add.}$$
$$y = 0 \qquad \text{y-intercept is } (0, 0).$$

NOW TRY ANSWER
2. x-intercept: $(4, 0)$;
    y-intercept: $(0, -2)$

Both intercepts are the *same* point, $(0, 0)$, which means that the graph passes through the origin. To find a second point, we choose any nonzero number for x or y and solve for the other variable. We arbitrarily choose $x = 4$.

NOW TRY
EXERCISE 3
Graph $2x + 3y = 0$.

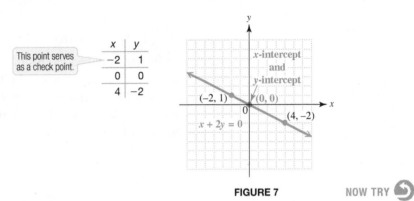

$$x + 2y = 0$$

Choosing a multiple of 2 for x makes dividing by 2 in the last step easier.

$$4 + 2y = 0 \qquad \text{Let } x = 4.$$
$$2y = -4 \qquad \text{Subtract 4.}$$
$$y = -2 \qquad \text{Divide by 2.}$$

This gives the ordered pair $(4, -2)$. As a final check, substitute 1 for y in the equation and verify that $(-2, 1)$ also lies on the line. The graph is shown in **FIGURE 7**.

x	y
-2	1
0	0
4	-2

This point serves as a check point.

FIGURE 7

NOW TRY

OBJECTIVE 6 Recognize equations of horizontal and vertical lines.

A line parallel to the x-axis will not have an x-intercept. Similarly, a line parallel to the y-axis will not have a y-intercept. This is why we included the phrase "if any" when we introduced intercepts.

NOW TRY
EXERCISE 4
Graph each equation.
(a) $y = -2$ **(b)** $x + 3 = 0$

EXAMPLE 4 Graphing Horizontal and Vertical Lines

Graph each equation.

(a) $y = 2$ (This equation can be written as $0x + y = 2$.)

Because y *always* equals 2, there is no value of x corresponding to $y = 0$, and the graph has no x-intercept. One value where $y = 2$ is on the y-axis, so the y-intercept is $(0, 2)$. Plot any two other points with y-coordinate 2, such as $(-1, 2)$ and $(3, 2)$.

The graph is shown in **FIGURE 8**. It is a horizontal line.

x	y
-1	2
0	2
3	2

FIGURE 8

x	y
-1	-4
-1	0
-1	5

FIGURE 9

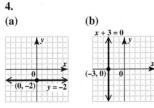
(b) $x + 1 = 0$ (This equation can be written as $x = -1$ or $x + 0y = -1$.)

Because x *always* equals -1, there is no value of y that makes $x = 0$, and the graph has no y-intercept. One value where $x = -1$ is on the x-axis, so the x-intercept is $(-1, 0)$. Plot any two other points with x-coordinate -1, such as $(-1, -4)$ and $(-1, 5)$.

The graph is shown in **FIGURE 9**. It is a vertical line. NOW TRY

> ❗ **CAUTION**   A linear equation that has only *one* variable x or y will have a vertical or horizontal line as its graph.
>
> 1. An equation with only the variable x will always intersect the *x-axis* and thus will be **vertical.** It has the form $x = a$. The vertical line with equation $x = 0$ is the *y*-axis.
>
> 2. An equation with only the variable y will always intersect the *y-axis* and thus will be **horizontal.** It has the form $y = b$. The horizontal line with equation $y = 0$ is the *x*-axis.

OBJECTIVE 7   Use the midpoint formula.

If the coordinates of the endpoints of a line segment are known, then the coordinates of the *midpoint* of the segment can be found.

   FIGURE 10 shows a line segment PQ with endpoints $P(-8, 4)$ and $Q(3, -2)$. R is the point with the same *x*-coordinate as P and the same *y*-coordinate as Q. So the coordinates of R are $(-8, -2)$.

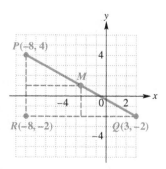

FIGURE 10

   The *x*-coordinate of the midpoint M of PQ is the same as the *x*-coordinate of the midpoint of RQ. Because RQ is horizontal, the *x*-coordinate of its midpoint is the *average* (or *mean*) of the *x*-coordinates of its endpoints.

$$\frac{1}{2}(-8 + 3) = -2.5$$

The *y*-coordinate of M is the average (or *mean*) of the *y*-coordinates of the midpoint of PR.

$$\frac{1}{2}(4 + (-2)) = 1$$

The midpoint of PQ is $M(-2.5, 1)$.
   This discussion leads to the *midpoint formula.*

Midpoint Formula

The midpoint M of a line segment PQ with endpoints (x_1, y_1) and (x_2, y_2) is found as follows.

$$M = \left(\frac{x_1 + x_2}{2}, \frac{y_1 + y_2}{2} \right)$$

The two nonspecific points (x_1, y_1) and (x_2, y_2) use **subscript notation.** Read (x_1, y_1) as **"x-sub-one, y-sub-one."**

NOW TRY EXERCISE 5

Find the midpoint of line segment PQ with endpoints $P(2, -5)$ and $Q(-4, 7)$.

EXAMPLE 5 Finding the Coordinates of a Midpoint

Find the midpoint of line segment PQ with endpoints $P(4, -3)$ and $Q(6, -1)$.

$$(x_1, \ y_1) \qquad (x_2, \ y_2)$$

$$P(4, -3) \quad \text{and} \quad Q(6, -1) \qquad \text{Label the points.}$$

$$M = \left(\frac{x_1 + x_2}{2}, \frac{y_1 + y_2}{2}\right) \qquad \text{Midpoint formula}$$

We are finding the average of the x-coordinates and the average of the y-coordinates.

$$= \left(\frac{4 + 6}{2}, \frac{-3 + (-1)}{2}\right) \qquad \text{Substitute.}$$

$$= \left(\frac{10}{2}, \frac{-4}{2}\right) \qquad \text{Add in the numerators.}$$

$$= (5, -2) \leftarrow \text{Midpoint of segment } PQ \qquad \text{NOW TRY} \ \text{}$$

NOTE When graphing with a graphing calculator, we "set up" a rectangular coordinate system. In the screen in **FIGURE 11**, which shows the **standard viewing window,** minimum x- and y-values are -10 and maximum x- and y-values are 10. The **scale** on each axis, here 1, determines the distance between the tick marks.

Standard viewing window
FIGURE 11

FIGURE 12

To graph an equation such as $4x - y = -3$, we use the intercepts $(-0.75, 0)$ and $(0, 3)$ to determine an appropriate window. Here, we choose the standard viewing window. We solve the equation for y to obtain $y = 4x + 3$ and enter it into the calculator. The graph in **FIGURE 12** also gives the x-intercept at the bottom of the screen.

NOW TRY ANSWER
5. $(-1, 1)$

2.1 Exercises

FOR EXTRA HELP MyMathLab®

● Complete solution available in MyMathLab

Concept Check *Fill in each blank with the correct response.*

1. The point with coordinates $(0, 0)$ is the _____ of a rectangular coordinate system.

2. For any value of x, the point $(x, 0)$ lies on the _____-axis. For any value of y, the point $(0, y)$ lies on the _____-axis.

3. To find the x-intercept of a line, we let _____ equal 0 and solve for _____. To find the y-intercept, we let _____ equal 0 and solve for _____.

4. The equation $y = 4$ has a _____ line as its graph, while $x = 4$ has a _____ line as its graph.

5. To graph a straight line, we must find a minimum of _____ points. The points $(3, \_\_\_)$ and $(\_\_\_, 4)$ lie on the graph of $2x - 3y = 0$.

6. The equation of the x-axis is _____. The equation of the y-axis is _____.

Solve each problem by locating ordered pairs on the graphs. **See Objective 1.**

7. The graph indicates personal spending in billions of dollars on medical care in the United States.

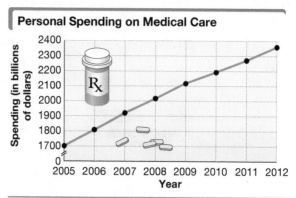

Source: Centers for Medicare & Medicaid Services.

(a) If (x, y) represents a point on the graph, what does x represent? What does y represent?

(b) Estimate spending in 2012.

(c) Write an ordered pair (x, y) that represents approximate spending in 2012.

(d) In what year was spending about $2000 billion?

8. The graph shows the percentage of Americans who moved in selected years.

Source: U.S. Census Bureau.

(a) If the ordered pair (x, y) represents a point on the graph, what does x represent? What does y represent?

(b) Estimate the percentage of Americans who moved in 2013.

(c) Write an ordered pair (x, y) that gives the approximate percentage of Americans who moved in 2013.

(d) What does the ordered pair $(1960, 20)$ mean in the context of this graph?

Name the quadrant, if any, in which each point is located. **See Objective 2.**

9. (a) $(1, 6)$ **(b)** $(-4, -2)$ **10. (a)** $(-2, -10)$ **(b)** $(4, 8)$
    (c) $(-3, 6)$ **(d)** $(7, -5)$ **(c)** $(-9, 12)$ **(d)** $(3, -9)$
    (e) $(-3, 0)$ **(f)** $(0, -0.5)$ **(e)** $(0, -8)$ **(f)** $(2.3, 0)$

11. *Concept Check*   Use the given information to determine the quadrants in which the point (x, y) may lie.

    (a) $xy > 0$ **(b)** $xy < 0$ **(c)** $\dfrac{x}{y} < 0$ **(d)** $\dfrac{x}{y} > 0$

12. *Concept Check*   What must be true about the value of at least one of the coordinates of any point that lies along an axis?

Plot each point in a rectangular coordinate system. **See Objective 2.**

13. $(2, 3)$ **14.** $(-1, 2)$ **15.** $(-3, -2)$ **16.** $(1, -4)$ **17.** $(0, 5)$
18. $(-2, -4)$ **19.** $(-2, 4)$ **20.** $(3, 0)$ **21.** $(-2, 0)$ **22.** $(3, -3)$

In the following exercises, (a) complete the given table for each equation and then (b) graph the equation. See Example 1 and FIGURE 4.

23. $y = x - 4$

x	y
0	
1	
2	
3	
4	

24. $y = x + 3$

x	y
0	
1	
2	
3	
4	

▶ **25.** $x - y = 3$

x	y
0	
	0
5	
2	

26. $x - y = 5$

x	y
0	
	0
1	
3	

27. $x + 2y = 5$

x	y
0	
	0
2	
	2

28. $x + 3y = -5$

x	y
0	
	0
1	
	-1

29. $4x - 5y = 20$

x	y
0	
	0
2	
	-3

30. $6x - 5y = 30$

x	y
0	
	0
3	
	-2

31. $y = -2x + 3$

x	y
0	
1	
2	
3	

32. $y = -3x + 1$

x	y
0	
1	
2	
3	

33. *Concept Check*   Consider the patterns formed in the tables for **Exercises 23 and 31.** Fill in each blank with the appropriate number.

   (a) In **Exercise 23,** for every increase in x by 1 unit, y increases by _____ unit(s).

   (b) In **Exercise 31,** for every increase in x by 1 unit, y decreases by _____ unit(s).

   (c) Based on the results in parts (a) and (b), make a conjecture about a similar pattern for $y = 2x + 4$. Then test this conjecture.

34. *Concept Check*   Which of the following equations have a graph that is a horizontal line?   A vertical line?

   A. $x - 6 = 0$ **B.** $x + y = 0$ **C.** $y + 3 = 0$ **D.** $y = -10$ **E.** $x + 1 = 5$

Find the x- and y-intercepts. Then graph each equation. See Examples 2–4.

▶ **35.** $2x + 3y = 12$ **36.** $5x + 2y = 10$ **37.** $x - 3y = 6$

38. $x - 2y = -4$ **39.** $5x + 6y = -10$ **40.** $3x - 7y = 9$

41. $\frac{2}{3}x - 3y = 7$ **42.** $\frac{5}{7}x + \frac{6}{7}y = -2$ ▶ **43.** $y = 5$

44. $y = -3$ **45.** $x = 2$ **46.** $x = -3$

▶ **47.** $x + 4 = 0$ **48.** $x - 4 = 0$ **49.** $y + 2 = 0$

50. $y - 5 = 0$ ▶ **51.** $x + 5y = 0$ **52.** $x - 3y = 0$

53. $2x = 3y$ **54.** $4y = 3x$ **55.** $-\frac{2}{3}y = x$ **56.** $-\frac{3}{4}y = x$

Each table of values gives several points that lie on a line.

(a) What is the x-intercept of the line?   The y-intercept?

(b) Which equation in choices A–D corresponds to the given table of values?

(c) Graph the equation.

57.

x	y
−4	−3
−2	0
0	3
2	6

A. $3x + 2y = 6$

B. $3x - 2y = -6$

C. $3x + 2y = -6$

D. $3x - 2y = 6$

58.

x	y
−1	6
0	4
1	2
2	0

A. $2x - y = 4$

B. $2x + y = -4$

C. $2x + y = 4$

D. $2x - y = -4$

59.

x	y
−2	−1
0	−1
2	−1
4	−1

A. $y = -1$

B. $y = 1$

C. $x = 1$

D. $x = -1$

60.

x	y
6	−1
6	0
6	1
6	2

A. $x = -6$

B. $y = 0$

C. $y = 6$

D. $x = 6$

Concept Check   Match each equation with its graph in choices A–D. (Coordinates of the points shown are integers.)

61. $x + 3y = 3$

62. $x - 3y = -3$

63. $x - 3y = 3$

64. $x + 3y = -3$

*Find the midpoint of each segment with the given endpoints. **See Example 5.***

▶ **65.** $(-8, 4)$ and $(-2, -6)$

66. $(5, 2)$ and $(-1, 8)$

67. $(3, -6)$ and $(6, 3)$

68. $(-10, 4)$ and $(7, 1)$

69. $(-9, 3)$ and $(9, 8)$

70. $(4, -3)$ and $(-1, 3)$

71. $(2.5, 3.1)$ and $(1.7, -1.3)$

72. $(6.2, 5.8)$ and $(1.4, -0.6)$

Extending Skills   Find the midpoint of each segment with the given endpoints.

73. $\left(\dfrac{1}{2}, \dfrac{1}{3}\right)$ and $\left(\dfrac{3}{2}, \dfrac{5}{3}\right)$

74. $\left(\dfrac{21}{4}, \dfrac{2}{5}\right)$ and $\left(\dfrac{7}{4}, \dfrac{3}{5}\right)$

75. $\left(-\dfrac{1}{3}, \dfrac{2}{7}\right)$ and $\left(-\dfrac{1}{2}, \dfrac{1}{14}\right)$

76. $\left(\dfrac{3}{5}, -\dfrac{1}{3}\right)$ and $\left(\dfrac{1}{2}, -\dfrac{7}{2}\right)$

Extending Skills   Segment PQ has the given coordinates for one endpoint P and for its midpoint M. Find the coordinates of the other endpoint Q. (Hint: Represent Q by (x, y) and write two equations using the midpoint formula, one involving x and the other involving y. Then solve for x and y.)

77. $P(5, 8)$, $M(8, 2)$

78. $P(7, 10)$, $M(5, 3)$

79. $P(1.5, 1.25)$, $M(3, 1)$

80. $P(2.5, 1.75)$, $M(3, 2)$

STUDY SKILLS

Managing Your Time

Many college students juggle a difficult schedule and multiple responsibilities, including school, work, and family demands.

Time Management Tips

- **Read the syllabus for each class.** Understand class policies, such as attendance, late homework, and make-up tests. Find out how you are graded.

- **Make a semester or quarter calendar.** Put test dates and major due dates for *all* your classes on the *same* calendar. Try using a different color pen for each class.

- **Make a weekly schedule.** After you fill in your classes and other regular responsibilities, block off some study periods. Aim for 2 hours of study for each 1 hour in class.

- **Choose a regular study time and place** (such as the campus library). Routine helps.

- **Keep distractions to a minimum.** Get the most out of the time you have set aside for studying by limiting interruptions. Turn off your cell phone. Take a break from social media. Avoid studying in front of the TV.

- **Make "to-do" lists.** Number tasks in order of importance. Cross off tasks as you complete them.

- **Break big assignments into smaller chunks.** Make deadlines for each smaller chunk so that you stay on schedule.

- **Take breaks when studying.** Do not try to study for hours at a time. Take a 10-minute break each hour or so.

- **Ask for help when you need it.** Talk with your instructor during office hours. Make use of the learning center, tutoring center, counseling office, or other resources available at your school.

Think through and answer each question.

1. Evaluate when and where you are currently studying. Are the places you named quiet and comfortable? Are you studying when you are most alert?

2. How many hours do you have available for studying this week?

3. Which two or three of the above suggestions will you try this week to improve your time management?

4. Once the week is over, evaluate how these suggestions worked. What will you do differently next week?

2.2 The Slope of a Line

Slope (steepness) is used in many practical ways. The slope (or *grade*) of a highway is often given as a percent. For example, a 10% $\left(\text{or } \frac{10}{100} = \frac{1}{10}\right)$ slope means that the highway rises 1 unit for every 10 horizontal units. Stairs and roofs have slopes too, as shown in **FIGURE 13**.

(not to scale)

Slope (or grade) is $\frac{1}{10}$.

Slope is $\frac{7}{9}$.

Slope (or pitch) is $\frac{1}{3}$.

FIGURE 13

Slope is the ratio of vertical change, or **rise**, to horizontal change, or **run**. A simple way to remember this is to think, *"Slope is rise over run."*

OBJECTIVE 1   Find the slope of a line given two points on the line.

To obtain a formal definition of the slope of a line, we designate two different points on the line as (x_1, y_1) and (x_2, y_2). See **FIGURE 14**.

FIGURE 14

As we move along the line in **FIGURE 14** from (x_1, y_1) to (x_2, y_2), the y-value changes (vertically) from y_1 to y_2, an amount equal to $y_2 - y_1$. As y changes from y_1 to y_2, the value of x changes (horizontally) from x_1 to x_2 by the amount $x_2 - x_1$.

> **NOTE**   The Greek letter **delta, Δ,** is used in mathematics to denote "change in," so Δy and Δx represent the change in y and the change in x, respectively.

The ratio of the change in y to the change in x $\left(\text{"rise over run," or } \frac{\text{rise}}{\text{run}}\right)$ is the *slope* of the line, with the letter m traditionally used for slope.

Slope Formula

The **slope m** of the line passing through the distinct points (x_1, y_1) and (x_2, y_2) is defined as follows.

$$m = \frac{\text{rise}}{\text{run}} = \frac{\text{change in } y}{\text{change in } x} = \frac{\Delta y}{\Delta x} = \frac{y_2 - y_1}{x_2 - x_1} \quad (\text{where } x_1 \neq x_2)$$

**NOW TRY
EXERCISE 1**

Find the slope of the line
passing through the points
$(2, -6)$ and $(-3, 5)$.

EXAMPLE 1 Finding the Slope of a Line

Find the slope of the line passing through the points $(2, -1)$ and $(-5, 3)$.

Label the points, and then apply the slope formula.

$$(x_1,\ y_1) \qquad\qquad (x_2,\ y_2)$$
$$\downarrow\ \downarrow \qquad\qquad\quad \downarrow\ \downarrow$$
$$(2, -1) \quad \text{and} \quad (-5, 3)$$

$$\text{slope } m = \frac{y_2 - y_1}{x_2 - x_1} = \frac{3 - (-1)}{-5 - 2} \qquad \text{Substitute.}$$

$$= \frac{4}{-7}, \quad \text{or} \quad -\frac{4}{7} \qquad \text{Subtract; } \frac{a}{-b} = -\frac{a}{b}$$

The slope is $-\frac{4}{7}$. See **FIGURE 15**.

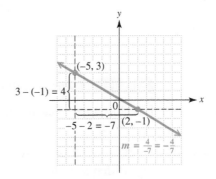

FIGURE 15

The same slope is obtained if we label the points in reverse order. *It makes no difference which point is identified as (x_1, y_1) or (x_2, y_2).*

$$(x_2,\ y_2) \qquad\qquad (x_1,\ y_1)$$
$$\downarrow\ \downarrow \qquad\qquad\quad \downarrow\ \downarrow$$
$$(2, -1) \quad \text{and} \quad (-5, 3) \quad \boxed{\text{y-values are in the numerator, x-values in the denominator.}}$$

$$\text{slope } m = \frac{y_2 - y_1}{x_2 - x_1} = \frac{-1 - 3}{2 - (-5)} \qquad \text{Substitute.}$$

$$= \frac{-4}{7}, \quad \text{or} \quad -\frac{4}{7} \qquad \text{Subtract; } \frac{-a}{b} = -\frac{a}{b} \quad \text{NOW TRY} \ \circlearrowleft$$

Example 1 suggests the following important ideas regarding slope.

1. The slope is the same no matter which point we consider first.

2. Using similar triangles from geometry, we can show that the slope is the same no matter which two different points on the line we choose.

⚠ CAUTION *When calculating slope, remember that the change in y (rise) is the numerator and the change in x (run) is the denominator.*

Correct	Incorrect
$\dfrac{y_2 - y_1}{x_2 - x_1}$	$\dfrac{\cancel{x_2 - x_1}}{\cancel{y_2 - y_1}} \ \text{or} \ \dfrac{y_2 - y_1}{x_1 - x_2} \ \text{or} \ \dfrac{\cancel{y_1 - y_2}}{\cancel{x_2 - x_1}}$

Be careful to subtract the y-values and the x-values in the same order.

OBJECTIVE 2 Find the slope of a line given an equation of the line.

When an equation of a line is given, one way to find its slope is to use the definition of slope with two different points on the line.

NOW TRY
EXERCISE 2
Find the slope of the line
$3x - 7y = 21$.

EXAMPLE 2 Finding the Slope of a Line

Find the slope of the line $4x - y = -8$.

The intercepts can be used as the two points needed to find the slope. Let $y = 0$ to find that the x-intercept is $(-2, 0)$. Then let $x = 0$ to find that the y-intercept is $(0, 8)$. Use these two points in the slope formula.

$$\text{slope } m = \frac{y_2 - y_1}{x_2 - x_1} = \frac{8 - 0}{0 - (-2)} \qquad \begin{matrix} (x_1, y_1) = (-2, 0) \\ (x_2, y_2) = (0, 8) \end{matrix}$$

$$= \frac{8}{2} \qquad \text{Subtract.}$$

$$= 4 \qquad \text{Divide.} \qquad \text{NOW TRY}$$

NOW TRY
EXERCISE 3
Find the slope of each line.
(a) $x = 4$ **(b)** $y - 6 = 0$

EXAMPLE 3 Applying the Slope Concept to Horizontal and Vertical Lines

Find the slope of each line.

(a) $y = 2$

The graph of $y = 2$ is a horizontal line. See **FIGURE 16**. To find the slope, select two different points on the line, such as $(3, 2)$ and $(-1, 2)$, and apply the slope formula.

$$m = \frac{2 - 2}{-1 - 3} = \frac{0}{-4} = 0 \qquad \begin{matrix} (x_1, y_1) = (3, 2) \\ (x_2, y_2) = (-1, 2) \end{matrix}$$

In this case, the *rise* is 0, so the slope is 0.

FIGURE 16   FIGURE 17

(b) $x + 1 = 0$

The graph of $x + 1 = 0$, or $x = -1$, is a vertical line. See **FIGURE 17**. Two points that satisfy the equation $x = -1$ are $(-1, 5)$ and $(-1, -4)$. We use these points and the slope formula.

$$m = \frac{-4 - 5}{-1 - (-1)} = \frac{-9}{0} \qquad \begin{matrix} (x_1, y_1) = (-1, 5) \\ (x_2, y_2) = (-1, -4) \end{matrix}$$

Here the *run* is 0. Because division by 0 is undefined, the slope is undefined. This is why the definition of slope includes the restriction that $x_1 \neq x_2$.   **NOW TRY**

NOW TRY ANSWERS
2. $\frac{3}{7}$
3. (a) undefined   **(b)** 0

Example 3 illustrates the following important concepts.

> ### Horizontal and Vertical Lines
>
> - An equation of the form $y = b$ always intersects the y-axis at the point $(0, b)$. A line with this equation is horizontal and has slope 0.
> - An equation of the form $x = a$ always intersects the x-axis at the point $(a, 0)$. A line with this equation is vertical and has undefined slope.

The slope of a line can also be found directly from its equation. Consider the equation $4x - y = -8$ from **Example 2.** Solve this equation for y.

$$4x - y = -8 \qquad \text{Equation from Example 2}$$

Going forward, we combine these steps.
$$-y = -8 - 4x \qquad \text{Subtract } 4x.$$
$$-y = -4x - 8 \qquad \text{Commutative property}$$
$$y = 4x + 8 \qquad \text{Multiply by } -1.$$

The slope, 4, found with the slope formula in **Example 2** is the same number as the coefficient of x in the equation $y = 4x + 8$. We will see in the next section that this is true in general, *as long as the equation is solved for y.*

NOW TRY EXERCISE 4

Find the slope of the graph of $5x - 4y = 7$.

> **EXAMPLE 4**   Finding the Slope from an Equation

Find the slope of the graph of $3x - 5y = 8$.

Solve the equation for y.

$$3x - 5y = 8 \quad \boxed{\text{Solve for } y.}$$

$$-5y = -3x + 8 \qquad \text{Subtract } 3x.$$

$$\frac{-5y}{-5} = \frac{-3x + 8}{-5} \qquad \text{Divide each side by } -5.$$

$$\boxed{\frac{-3x}{-5} = \frac{-3}{-5} \cdot \frac{x}{1} = \frac{3}{5}x} \quad y = \frac{3}{5}x - \frac{8}{5} \qquad \frac{a+b}{c} = \frac{a}{c} + \frac{b}{c}$$

The slope is given by the coefficient of x, so the slope is $\frac{3}{5}$.   **NOW TRY**

NOTE   We can solve the standard form of a linear equation $Ax + By = C$ (where $B \neq 0$) for y to show that, in general, **the slope of a line in this form is $-\frac{A}{B}$.**

$$Ax + By = C \qquad \text{Standard form (Section 2.1)}$$

$$By = -Ax + C \qquad \text{Subtract } Ax.$$

$$y = -\frac{A}{B}x + \frac{C}{B} \qquad \text{Divide each term by } B.$$

The slope is given by the coefficient of x, $-\frac{A}{B}$. In the equation $3x - 5y = 8$ from **Example 4,** $A = 3$ and $B = -5$, so the slope is

$$-\frac{A}{B} = -\frac{3}{-5} = \frac{3}{5}. \qquad \text{The same slope results.}$$

NOW TRY EXERCISE 5

Graph the line passing through $(-4, 1)$ that has slope $-\frac{2}{3}$.

OBJECTIVE 3 Graph a line given its slope and a point on the line.

EXAMPLE 5   Using the Slope and a Point to Graph Lines

Graph each line described.

(a) With slope $\frac{2}{3}$ and y-intercept $(0, -4)$

Begin by plotting the point $P(0, -4)$, as shown in **FIGURE 18**. Then use the geometric interpretation of slope to find a second point.

$$m = \frac{\text{change in } y}{\text{change in } x} = \frac{2 \leftarrow \text{rise}}{3 \leftarrow \text{run}}$$

We move 2 units *up* from $(0, -4)$ and then 3 units to the *right* to locate another point on the graph, $R(3, -2)$. The line through $P(0, -4)$ and R is the required graph.

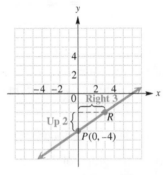

FIGURE 18   FIGURE 19

(b) Through $(3, 1)$ with slope -4

Start by plotting the point $P(3, 1)$, as shown in **FIGURE 19**. Find a second point R on the line by writing the slope -4 as $\frac{-4}{1}$ and using the geometric interpretation of slope.

$$m = \frac{\text{change in } y}{\text{change in } x} = \frac{-4 \leftarrow \text{rise}}{1 \leftarrow \text{run}}$$

We move 4 units *down* from $(3, 1)$ and then 1 unit to the *right* to locate this second point $R(4, -3)$. The line through $P(3, 1)$ and R is the required graph.

The slope -4 also could be written as

$$m = \frac{\text{change in } y}{\text{change in } x} = \frac{4}{-1}.$$

In this case, the second point R is located 4 units *up* and 1 unit to the *left*. Verify that this approach also produces the line in **FIGURE 19**.   NOW TRY

NOW TRY ANSWER

5.

In **Example 5(a),** the slope of the line is the *positive* number $\frac{2}{3}$. The graph of the line in **FIGURE 18** slants up (rises) from left to right. The line in **Example 5(b)** has *negative* slope -4. As **FIGURE 19** shows, its graph slants down (falls) from left to right. These facts illustrate the following generalization.

Orientation of a Line in the Plane

A positive slope indicates that the line slants *up* (rises) from left to right.

A negative slope indicates that the line slants *down* (falls) from left to right.

FIGURE 20 summarizes the four cases for slopes of lines.

Slopes of lines
FIGURE 20

OBJECTIVE 4 Use slopes to determine whether two lines are parallel, perpendicular, or neither.

Recall that the slope of a line measures its steepness and that parallel lines have equal steepness.

Slopes of Parallel Lines

Two nonvertical lines with the same slope are parallel.

Two nonvertical parallel lines have the same slope.

NOW TRY
EXERCISE 6
Is the line passing through
$(2, 5)$ and $(4, 8)$ parallel to
the line passing through $(2, 0)$
and $(-1, -2)$?

EXAMPLE 6   Determining Whether Two Lines Are Parallel

Are the lines L_1, passing through $(-2, 1)$ and $(4, 5)$, and L_2, passing through $(3, 0)$ and $(0, -2)$, parallel?

$$\text{Slope of } L_1: \quad m_1 = \frac{5 - 1}{4 - (-2)} = \frac{4}{6} = \frac{2}{3} \quad \begin{array}{l}(x_1, y_1) = (-2, 1) \\ (x_2, y_2) = (4, 5)\end{array}$$

$$\text{Slope of } L_2: \quad m_2 = \frac{-2 - 0}{0 - 3} = \frac{-2}{-3} = \frac{2}{3} \quad \begin{array}{l}(x_1, y_1) = (3, 0) \\ (x_2, y_2) = (0, -2)\end{array}$$

Because the slopes are equal, the two lines are parallel.   NOW TRY

To see how the slopes of perpendicular lines are related, consider a nonvertical line with slope $\frac{a}{b}$. If this line is rotated 90°, the vertical change and the horizontal change are interchanged and the slope is $-\frac{b}{a}$, because the horizontal change is now negative. See **FIGURE 21**. Thus, the slopes of perpendicular lines have product -1 and are negative reciprocals of each other.

For example, if the slopes of two lines are $\frac{3}{4}$ and $-\frac{4}{3}$, then the lines are perpendicular because

$$\frac{3}{4}\left(-\frac{4}{3}\right) = -1.$$

FIGURE 21

NOW TRY ANSWER
6. no

Slopes of Perpendicular Lines

If neither is vertical, perpendicular lines have slopes that are negative reciprocals—that is, their product is -1. Also, lines with slopes that are negative reciprocals are perpendicular.

A line with slope 0 is perpendicular to a line with undefined slope.

NOW TRY
EXERCISE 7

Are the lines with these equations perpendicular?

$$x + 2y = 7$$
$$2x = y - 4$$

EXAMPLE 7   Determining Whether Two Lines Are Perpendicular

Are the lines with equations $2y = 3x - 6$ and $2x + 3y = -6$ perpendicular?

Find the slope of each line by solving each equation for y.

$2y = 3x - 6$	$2x + 3y = -6$
$y = \dfrac{3}{2}x - 3$ Divide by 2.	$3y = -2x - 6$ Subtract $2x$.
$\uparrow$ Slope	$y = -\dfrac{2}{3}x - 2$ Divide by 3.
	$\uparrow$ Slope

The slopes are negative reciprocals because their product is $\dfrac{3}{2}\left(-\dfrac{2}{3}\right) = -1$. The lines are perpendicular.

NOW TRY

NOTE   In **Example 7,** alternatively, we could have found the slope of each line using intercepts and the slope formula. The graph of $2y = 3x - 6$ has x-intercept $(2, 0)$ and y-intercept $(0, -3)$.

$$m = \frac{0 - (-3)}{2 - 0} = \frac{3}{2} \qquad \text{The same slope results.}$$
$$\text{See Example 7.}$$

Find the intercepts of the graph of $2x + 3y = -6$ and use them to confirm the slope $-\frac{2}{3}$. Because the slopes are negative reciprocals, the lines are perpendicular.

NOW TRY
EXERCISE 8

Determine whether the lines with these equations are *parallel, perpendicular,* or *neither.*

$$2x - y = 4$$
$$2x + y = 6$$

EXAMPLE 8   Determining Whether Two Lines Are Parallel, Perpendicular, or Neither

Determine whether the lines with equations $2x - 5y = 8$ and $2x + 5y = 8$ are *parallel, perpendicular,* or *neither.*

Find the slope of each line by solving each equation for y.

$2x - 5y = 8$	$2x + 5y = 8$
$-5y = -2x + 8$ Subtract $2x$.	$5y = -2x + 8$ Subtract $2x$.
$y = \dfrac{2}{5}x - \dfrac{8}{5}$ Divide by -5.	$y = -\dfrac{2}{5}x + \dfrac{8}{5}$ Divide by 5.
$\uparrow$ Slope	$\uparrow$ Slope

The slopes, $\frac{2}{5}$ and $-\frac{2}{5}$, are not equal, and they are not negative reciprocals because their product is $-\frac{4}{25}$, *not* -1. Thus, the two lines are *neither* parallel nor perpendicular.

NOW TRY

NOW TRY ANSWERS
7. yes
8. neither

OBJECTIVE 5 Solve problems involving average rate of change.

The slope formula applied to any two points on a line gives the **average rate of change** in y per unit change in x, where the value of y depends on the value of x.

For example, suppose the height of a boy increased from 60 to 68 in. between the ages of 12 and 16, as shown in **FIGURE 22**.

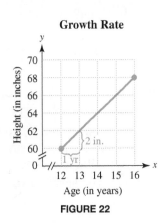

Growth Rate

FIGURE 22

$$\text{Change in height } y \rightarrow \frac{68 - 60}{16 - 12} = \frac{8}{4} = 2 \text{ in.}$$

Change in age $x \longrightarrow$ Boy's average growth rate (or average change in height) *per year*

The boy may actually have grown more than 2 in. during some years and less than 2 in. during other years. If we plotted ordered pairs (age, height) for those years and drew a line connecting any two of the points, the average rate of change would likely be slightly different than that found above. However, using the data for ages 12 and 16, the boy's *average* change in height was 2 in. per year over these years.

**NOW TRY
EXERCISE 9**

There were approximately 40 million digital cable TV customers in 2008. Using this number for 2008 and the number for 2012 from the graph in **FIGURE 23**, find the average rate of change from 2008 to 2012. How does it compare with the average rate of change found in **Example 9?**

EXAMPLE 9 Interpreting Slope as Average Rate of Change

The graph in **FIGURE 23** shows the number of digital cable TV customers in the United States from 2007 to 2012. Find the average rate of change in number of customers per year.

Source: SNL Kagan.

FIGURE 23

To find the average rate of change, we need two pairs of data. From the graph, we have the ordered pairs (2007, 37) and (2012, 47). We use the slope formula.

$$\text{average rate of change} = \frac{47 - 37}{2012 - 2007} = \frac{10}{5} = 2$$

A positive slope indicates an increase.

This means that the number of digital TV customers *increased* by an average of 2 million customers per year from 2007 to 2012.

NOW TRY ANSWER

9. 1.75 million customers per year; It is less than the average rate of change from 2007 to 2012.

NOW TRY

**NOW TRY
EXERCISE 10**

In 2010, sales of digital camcorders in the United States totaled $1150 million. In 2013, sales totaled $137 million. Find the average rate of change in sales of digital camcorders per year, to the nearest million dollars. (*Source:* Consumer Electronics Association.)

EXAMPLE 10   **Interpreting Slope as Average Rate of Change**

In 2006, there were 65 million basic cable TV customers in the United States. There were 56 million such customers in 2012. Find the average rate of change in the number of customers per year. (*Source:* SNL Kagan.)

To use the slope formula, we let one ordered pair be (2006, 65) and the other be (2012, 56).

$$\text{average rate of change} = \frac{56 - 65}{2012 - 2006} = \frac{-9}{6} = -1.5$$

 A negative slope indicates a decrease.

The graph in **FIGURE 24** confirms that the line through the ordered pairs falls from left to right and therefore has negative slope. Thus, the number of basic cable TV customers *decreased* by an average of 1.5 million customers per year from 2006 to 2012.

The negative sign in -1.5 denotes the *decrease*. (We say "The number of customers decreased by 1.5 million per year." It is *incorrect* to say "The number of customers decreased by -1.5 million per year.")

Basic Cable TV Customers

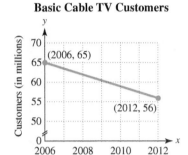

FIGURE 24

NOW TRY ANSWER
10. $-$\$338 million per year

NOW TRY

2.2 Exercises

FOR EXTRA HELP   ▶ MyMathLab°

▶ *Complete solution available in MyMathLab*

Concept Check   *Answer each question.*

1. A hill rises 30 ft for every horizontal 100 ft. Which of the following express its slope (or grade)? (There are several correct choices.)

A. 0.3   **B.** $\frac{3}{10}$ **C.** $3\frac{1}{3}$

D. $\frac{30}{100}$ **E.** $\frac{10}{3}$ **F.** 30%

2. If a walkway rises 2 ft for every 24 ft on the horizontal, which of the following express its slope (or grade)? (There are several correct choices.)

A. 12%   **B.** $\frac{2}{24}$ **C.** $\frac{1}{12}$

D. 12   **E.** $8.\overline{3}\%$ **F.** $\frac{24}{2}$

3. A ladder leaning against a wall has slope 3. How many feet in the horizontal direction correspond to a rise of 15 ft?

4. A hill has slope 0.05. How many feet in the vertical direction correspond to a run of 50 ft?

(not to scale)

5. *Concept Check* Match each situation in parts (a)–(d) with the most appropriate graph in choices A–D.

   (a) Sales rose sharply during the first quarter, leveled off during the second quarter, and then rose slowly for the rest of the year.

   (b) Sales fell sharply during the first quarter and then rose slowly during the second and third quarters before leveling off for the rest of the year.

   (c) Sales rose sharply during the first quarter and then fell to the original level during the second quarter before rising steadily for the rest of the year.

   (d) Sales fell during the first two quarters of the year, leveled off during the third quarter, and rose during the fourth quarter.

A.   **B.**   **C.**   **D.**

6. *Concept Check* Using the given axes, draw a graph that illustrates the following description.

   Profits for a business were $10 million in 2010. They rose sharply from 2010 through 2012, remained constant from 2012 through 2014, and then fell slowly from 2014 through 2015.

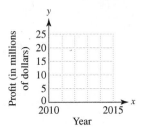

Concept Check *Determine the slope of each line segment in the given figure.*

   7. *AB*   **8.** *BC*   **9.** *CD*

   10. *DE*   **11.** *EF*   **12.** *FG*

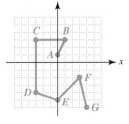

13. If *A* and *F* were joined by a line segment in the figure, what would be its slope?

14. If *B* and *D* were joined by a line segment in the figure, what would be its slope?

15. *Concept Check* On the basis of the figure shown here, determine which line satisfies the given description.

   (a) The line has positive slope.

   (b) The line has negative slope.

   (c) The line has slope 0.

   (d) The line has undefined slope.

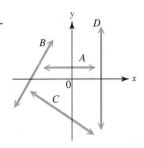

16. *Concept Check*   Which forms of the slope formula are correct? Explain.

A. $m = \dfrac{y_1 - y_2}{x_2 - x_1}$ **B.** $m = \dfrac{y_1 - y_2}{x_1 - x_2}$ **C.** $m = \dfrac{x_2 - x_1}{y_2 - y_1}$ **D.** $m = \dfrac{y_2 - y_1}{x_2 - x_1}$

Evaluate each expression for m, applying the slope formula. See Example 1.

17. $m = \dfrac{6 - 2}{5 - 3}$

18. $m = \dfrac{5 - 7}{-4 - 2}$

19. $m = \dfrac{4 - (-1)}{-3 - (-5)}$

20. $m = \dfrac{-6 - 0}{0 - (-3)}$

21. $m = \dfrac{-5 - (-5)}{3 - 2}$

22. $m = \dfrac{-2 - (-2)}{4 - (-3)}$

23. $m = \dfrac{3 - 8}{-2 - (-2)}$

24. $m = \dfrac{5 - 6}{-8 - (-8)}$

In the following exercises, (a) find the slope of the line passing through each pair of points, if possible, and (b) based on the slope, indicate whether the line rises *from left to right, falls from left to right, is* horizontal, *or is* vertical. *See Examples 1 and 3 and* FIGURE 20.

25. $(-2, -3)$ and $(-1, 5)$ **26.** $(-4, 1)$ and $(-3, 4)$ ▶ **27.** $(-4, 1)$ and $(2, 6)$

28. $(-3, -3)$ and $(5, 6)$ **29.** $(2, 4)$ and $(-4, 4)$ **30.** $(-6, 3)$ and $(2, 3)$

31. $(-2, 2)$ and $(4, -1)$ **32.** $(-3, 1)$ and $(6, -2)$ **33.** $(5, -3)$ and $(5, 2)$

34. $(4, -1)$ and $(4, 3)$ **35.** $(1.5, 2.6)$ and $(0.5, 3.6)$ **36.** $(3.4, 4.2)$ and $(1.4, 10.2)$

Extending Skills   *Find the slope of the line passing through the given pair of points.*

$\left(Hint: \dfrac{\frac{a}{b}}{\frac{c}{d}} = \dfrac{a}{b} \div \dfrac{c}{d} \right)$

37. $\left(\dfrac{1}{6}, \dfrac{1}{2} \right)$ and $\left(\dfrac{5}{6}, \dfrac{9}{2} \right)$

38. $\left(\dfrac{3}{4}, \dfrac{1}{3} \right)$ and $\left(\dfrac{5}{4}, \dfrac{10}{3} \right)$

39. $\left(-\dfrac{2}{9}, \dfrac{5}{18} \right)$ and $\left(\dfrac{1}{18}, -\dfrac{5}{9} \right)$

40. $\left(-\dfrac{4}{5}, \dfrac{9}{10} \right)$ and $\left(-\dfrac{3}{10}, \dfrac{1}{5} \right)$

Each table of values gives several points that line on a line. Find the slope of the line.

41.

x	y
−1	8
0	6
2	2
3	0

42.

x	y
−3	6
−1	0
0	−3
2	−9

43.

x	y
−6	−4
−3	0
0	4
3	8

44.

x	y
−5	−4
0	−2
5	0
10	2

Use the geometric interpretation of slope ("rise over run") to find the slope of each line. (Coordinates of the points shown are integers.)

45.

46.

47.

48.

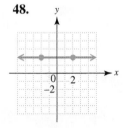

Find the slope of each line in three ways by doing the following.

(a) *Give any two points that lie on the line, and use them to determine the slope. **See Example 2.***

(b) *Solve the equation for y, and identify the slope from the equation. **See Example 4.***

(c) *For the form $Ax + By = C$, calculate $-\frac{A}{B}$. **See the Note following Example 4.***

49. $2x - y = 8$ **50.** $3x - y = -6$ **51.** $3x + 4y = 12$

52. $6x + 5y = 30$ **53.** $x + y = -3$ **54.** $x - y = 4$

*Find the slope of each line, and sketch its graph. **See Examples 1–4.***

▶ **55.** $x + 2y = 4$ **56.** $x + 3y = -6$ ▶ **57.** $5x - 2y = 10$

58. $4x - y = 4$ **59.** $y = 4x$ **60.** $y = -3x$

▶ **61.** $x - 3 = 0$ **62.** $x + 2 = 0$ ▶ **63.** $y = -5$

64. $y = -4$ **65.** $2y = 3$ **66.** $3x = 4$

*Graph each line described. **See Example 5.***

67. Through $(-4, 2)$; $m = \frac{1}{2}$ **68.** Through $(-2, -3)$; $m = \frac{5}{4}$

▶ **69.** *y*-intercept $(0, -2)$; $m = -\frac{2}{3}$ **70.** *y*-intercept $(0, -4)$; $m = -\frac{3}{2}$

71. Through $(-1, -2)$; $m = 3$ **72.** Through $(-2, -4)$; $m = 4$

73. $m = 0$; through $(2, -5)$ **74.** $m = 0$; through $(5, 3)$

75. Undefined slope; through $(-3, 1)$ **76.** Undefined slope; through $(-4, 1)$

77. *Concept Check*   If a line has slope $-\frac{4}{9}$, then any line parallel to it has slope _____ , and any line perpendicular to it has slope _____ .

78. *Concept Check*   If a line has slope 0.2, then any line parallel to it has slope _____ , and any line perpendicular to it has slope _____ .

Determine whether each pair of lines is parallel, perpendicular, *or* neither. ***See Examples 6–8.***

▶ **79.** The line passing through $(15, 9)$ and $(12, -7)$ and the line passing through $(8, -4)$ and $(5, -20)$

80. The line passing through $(4, 6)$ and $(-8, 7)$ and the line passing through $(-5, 5)$ and $(7, 4)$

▶ **81.** $x + 4y = 7$ and $4x - y = 3$ **82.** $2x + 5y = -7$ and $5x - 2y = 1$

83. $4x - 3y = 6$ and $3x - 4y = 2$ **84.** $2x + y = 6$ and $x - y = 4$

85. $x = 6$ and $6 - x = 8$ **86.** $3x = y$ and $2y - 6x = 5$

87. $4x + y = 0$ and $5x - 8 = 2y$ **88.** $2x + 5y = -8$ and $6 + 2x = 5y$

89. $2x = y + 3$ and $2y + x = 3$ **90.** $4x - 3y = 8$ and $4y + 3x = 12$

Extending Skills   Solve each problem.

91. When designing the TD Bank North Garden in Boston, architects designed the ramps leading up to the entrances so that circus elephants would be able to walk up the ramps. The maximum grade (or slope) that an elephant will walk on is 13%. Suppose that such a ramp was constructed with a horizontal run of 150 ft. What would be the maximum vertical rise the architects could use?

150 ft

92. The upper deck at U.S. Cellular Field in Chicago has produced, among other complaints, displeasure with its steepness. It is 160 ft from home plate to the front of the upper deck and 250 ft from home plate to the back. The top of the upper deck is 63 ft above the bottom. What is its slope? (Consider the slope as a positive number here.)

Find and interpret the average rate of change illustrated in each graph. **See Objective 5 and FIGURE 22.**

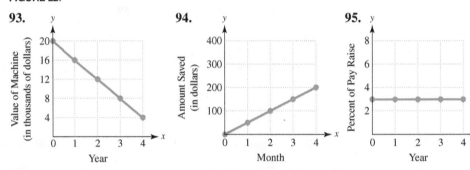

93.

94.

95.

96. *Concept Check*   If the graph of a linear equation rises from left to right, then the average rate of change is (*positive / negative*). If the graph of a linear equation falls from left to right, then the average rate of change is (*positive / negative*).

Solve each problem. **See Examples 9 and 10.**

97. The graph shows the number of wireless subscriber connections (that is, active devices, including smartphones, feature phones, tablets, etc.) in millions in the United States for the years 2007 to 2012.

Wireless Subscriber Connections

Source: CTIA.

(a) In the context of this graph, what does the ordered pair (2012, 326) mean?

(b) Use the given ordered pairs to find the slope of the line.

(c) Interpret the slope in the context of this problem.

98. The graph shows the percent of households in the United States that were wireless-only households for the years 2007 to 2012.

Wireless-Only Households

Source: CTIA.

(a) In the context of this graph, what does the ordered pair (2012, 38) mean?

(b) Use the given ordered pairs to find the slope of the line.

(c) Interpret the slope in the context of this problem.

99. The graph shows the number of drive-in movie theaters in the United States from 2005 through 2012.

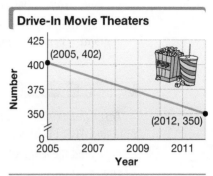

Drive-In Movie Theaters

Source: www.drive-ins.com

(a) Use the given ordered pairs to find the average rate of change in the number of drive-in theaters per year during this period. Round the answer to the nearest whole number.

(b) Explain how a negative slope is interpreted in this situation.

100. The graph shows the number of U.S. travelers to Canada (in thousands) from 2000 through 2011.

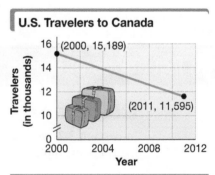

U.S. Travelers to Canada

Source: U.S. Department of Commerce.

(a) Use the given ordered pairs to find the average rate of change in the number of U.S. travelers to Canada per year during this period. Round the answer to the nearest thousand.

(b) Explain how a negative slope is interpreted in this situation.

101. The average price of a gallon of gasoline in 1980 was $1.22. In 2012, the average price was $3.70. Find and interpret the average rate of change in the price of a gallon of gasoline per year to the nearest cent. (*Source:* Energy Information Administration.)

102. The average price of a movie ticket in 1990 was $4.23. In 2012, the average price was $7.96. Find and interpret the average rate of change in the price of a movie ticket per year to the nearest cent. (*Source:* Motion Picture Association of America.)

103. In 2010, the number of digital cameras sold in the United States totaled 7246 thousand. There were 1670 thousand sold in 2013. Find and interpret the average rate of change in the number of digital cameras sold per year to the nearest thousand. (*Source:* Consumer Electronics Association.)

104. In 2010, sales of desktop computers in the United States totaled $7390 million. In 2013, sales were $6876 million. Find and interpret the average rate of change in sales of desktop computers per year to the nearest million dollars. (*Source:* Consumer Electronics Association.)

Extending Skills Use your knowledge of the slopes of parallel and perpendicular lines.

105. Show that $(-13, -9)$, $(-11, -1)$, $(2, -2)$, and $(4, 6)$ are the vertices of a parallelogram. (*Hint:* A parallelogram is a four-sided figure with opposite sides parallel.)

106. Is the figure with vertices at $(-11, -5)$, $(-2, -19)$, $(12, -10)$, and $(3, 4)$ a parallelogram? Is it a rectangle? (*Hint:* A rectangle is a parallelogram with a right angle.)

RELATING CONCEPTS For Individual or Group Work (Exercises 107–112)

Three points that lie on the same straight line are said to be **collinear.** *Consider the points* $A(3, 1)$, $B(6, 2)$, *and* $C(9, 3)$. **Work Exercises 107–112 in order.**

107. Find the slope of segment AB.

108. Find the slope of segment BC.

109. Find the slope of segment AC.

110. If slope of segment AB = slope of segment BC = slope of segment AC, then A, B, and C are collinear. Use the results of **Exercises 107–109** to show that this statement is satisfied.

111. Use the slope formula to determine whether the points $(1, -2)$, $(3, -1)$, and $(5, 0)$ are collinear.

112. Repeat **Exercise 111** for the points $(0, 6)$, $(4, -5)$, and $(-2, 12)$.

2.3 Writing Equations of Lines

OBJECTIVES

1. Write an equation of a line given its slope and y-intercept.
2. Graph a line using its slope and y-intercept.
3. Write an equation of a line given its slope and a point on the line.
4. Write an equation of a line given two points on the line.
5. Write equations of horizontal and vertical lines.
6. Write an equation of a line parallel or perpendicular to a given line.
7. Write an equation of a line that models real data.

VOCABULARY
☐ scatter diagram

OBJECTIVE 1 Write an equation of a line given its slope and y-intercept.

In **Section 2.2,** we found the slope of a line from its equation by solving the equation for y. For example, we found that the slope of the line with equation

$$y = 4x + 8$$

is 4, the coefficient of x. *What does the number 8 represent?*

To answer this question, suppose a line has slope m and y-intercept $(0, b)$. We can find an equation of this line by choosing another point (x, y) on the line, as shown in **FIGURE 25**, and applying the slope formula.

$$m = \frac{y - b}{x - 0} \quad \leftarrow \text{Change in } y$$
$$\leftarrow \text{Change in } x$$

$$m = \frac{y - b}{x} \quad \text{Subtract.}$$

$$mx = y - b \quad \text{Multiply by } x.$$

$$mx + b = y \quad \text{Add } b.$$

$$\boldsymbol{y = mx + b} \quad \text{Interchange sides.}$$

FIGURE 25

This last equation is the *slope-intercept form* of the equation of a line, because we can identify the slope m and y-intercept $(0, b)$ at a glance. In the line with equation $y = 4x + 8$, the number 8 indicates that the y-intercept is $(0, 8)$.

The **slope-intercept form** of the equation of a line with slope m and y-intercept $(0, b)$ is

$$y = mx + b.$$

Slope $\nearrow$ $\nwarrow$ $(0, b)$ is the y-intercept.

NOW TRY EXERCISE 1

Write an equation of the line with slope $\frac{2}{3}$ and y-intercept $(0, 1)$.

EXAMPLE 1   Writing an Equation of a Line

Write an equation of the line with slope $-\frac{4}{5}$ and y-intercept $(0, -2)$.

Here, $m = -\frac{4}{5}$ and $b = -2$. Substitute these values into the slope-intercept form.

$y = mx + b$ Slope-intercept form

$y = -\dfrac{4}{5}x + (-2)$ Let $m = -\frac{4}{5}$ and $b = -2$.

$y = -\dfrac{4}{5}x - 2$ Definition of subtraction   **NOW TRY**

NOTE   Every linear equation (of a nonvertical line) has a *unique* (one and only one) slope-intercept form. In **Section 2.6,** we introduce *linear functions,* which are defined using slope-intercept form. Also, this form is used when graphing a line with a graphing calculator.

OBJECTIVE 2   Graph a line using its slope and y-intercept.

We first saw this approach in **Example 5(a)** of **Section 2.2.**

EXAMPLE 2   Graphing Lines Using Slope and y-Intercept

Graph each line using the slope and y-intercept.

(a) $y = 3x - 6$ (In slope-intercept form)

Here, $m = 3$ and $b = -6$. Plot the y-intercept $(0, -6)$. The slope 3 can be interpreted geometrically as follows.

$$m = \frac{\text{rise}}{\text{run}} = \frac{\text{change in } y}{\text{change in } x} = \frac{3}{1}$$

From $(0, -6)$, move 3 units *up* and 1 unit to the *right,* and plot a second point at $(1, -3)$. Join the two points with a straight line. See **FIGURE 26.**

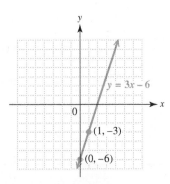

FIGURE 26

NOW TRY ANSWER

1. $y = \frac{2}{3}x + 1$

**NOW TRY
EXERCISE 2**
Graph the line using the slope and y-intercept.
$$4x + 3y = 6$$

(b) $3y + 2x = 9$ (*Not* in slope-intercept form)

Write the equation in slope-intercept form by solving for y.

$$3y + 2x = 9$$

$$3y = -2x + 9 \qquad \text{Subtract } 2x.$$

$$y = -\frac{2}{3}x + 3 \qquad \text{Divide by 3.}$$

Slope ⬈   ⬈ y-intercept is $(0, 3)$.

To graph this equation, plot the y-intercept $(0, 3)$. The slope can be interpreted as either $\frac{-2}{3}$ or $\frac{2}{-3}$. Using $\frac{-2}{3}$, begin at $(0, 3)$ and move 2 units *down* and 3 units to the *right* to locate the point $(3, 1)$. The line through these two points is the required graph. See **FIGURE 27**. (Verify that the point obtained using $\frac{2}{-3}$ as the slope is also on this line.)

FIGURE 27

NOW TRY

OBJECTIVE 3 Write an equation of a line given its slope and a point on the line.

Let m represent the slope of a line and (x_1, y_1) represent a given point on the line. Let (x, y) represent any other point on the line. See **FIGURE 28**.

$$m = \frac{y - y_1}{x - x_1} \qquad \text{Slope formula}$$

$$m(x - x_1) = y - y_1 \qquad \text{Multiply each side by } x - x_1.$$

$$y - y_1 = m(x - x_1) \qquad \text{Interchange sides.}$$

This last equation is the *point-slope form* of the equation of a line.

FIGURE 28

Point-Slope Form

The **point-slope form** of the equation of a line with slope m passing through the point (x_1, y_1) is

Slope
↓
$$y - y_1 = m(x - x_1).$$
⬐ Given point ⬎

NOW TRY ANSWER
2.

NOW TRY
EXERCISE 3

Write an equation of the line with slope $-\frac{1}{5}$ passing through the point $(5, -3)$.

EXAMPLE 3 **Writing an Equation of a Line Given Its Slope and a Point**

Write an equation of the line with slope $\frac{1}{3}$ passing through the point $(-2, 5)$.

Method 1 Use point-slope form with $(x_1, y_1) = (-2, 5)$ and $m = \frac{1}{3}$.

$$y - y_1 = m(x - x_1) \qquad \text{Point-slope form}$$

$$y - 5 = \frac{1}{3}[x - (-2)] \qquad \text{Let } y_1 = 5, \, m = \frac{1}{3}, \text{ and } x_1 = -2.$$

$$y - 5 = \frac{1}{3}(x + 2) \qquad \text{Definition of subtraction}$$

$$y - 5 = \frac{1}{3}x + \frac{2}{3} \qquad (*) \quad \text{Distributive property}$$

Slope-intercept form $\rightarrow y = \frac{1}{3}x + \frac{17}{3} \qquad 5 = \frac{15}{3}; \text{ Add } \frac{15}{3}.$

Method 2 Use slope-intercept form with $(x, y) = (-2, 5)$ and $m = \frac{1}{3}$.

$$y = mx + b \qquad \text{Slope-intercept form}$$

$$5 = \frac{1}{3}(-2) + b \qquad \text{Let } y = 5, \, m = \frac{1}{3}, \text{ and } x = -2.$$

Solve for b. $\quad 5 = -\frac{2}{3} + b \qquad \text{Multiply.}$

$$\frac{17}{3} = b, \quad \text{or} \quad b = \frac{17}{3} \qquad 5 = \frac{15}{3}; \text{ Add } \frac{2}{3}.$$

Substitute to obtain the equation $y = \frac{1}{3}x + \frac{17}{3}$, as above. **NOW TRY**

In **Section 2.1,** we defined *standard form* for a linear equation.

$$\boldsymbol{Ax + By = C} \qquad \text{Standard form}$$

Here A, B, and C are real numbers and A and B are not both 0. (In most cases in this book, A, B, and C are rational numbers.) For consistency, we give answers so that A, B, and C are integers with greatest common factor 1, and $A \geq 0$. (If $A = 0$, then we give $B > 0$.) For example, the equation in **Example 3** is written in standard form as follows.

$$y - 5 = \frac{1}{3}x + \frac{2}{3} \qquad \text{Equation (*) from \textbf{Example 3}}$$

$$3y - 15 = x + 2 \qquad \text{Multiply each term by 3.}$$

$$-x + 3y = 17 \qquad \text{Subtract } x. \text{ Add 15.}$$

Standard form $\rightarrow x - 3y = -17 \qquad \text{Multiply by } -1.$

NOTE "Standard form" is not standard among texts. A linear equation can be written in many different, equally correct ways. For example, $2x + 3y = 8$ can be written as

$$2x = 8 - 3y, \quad 3y = 8 - 2x, \quad x + \frac{3}{2}y = 4, \quad \text{and} \quad 4x + 6y = 16.$$

We prefer the standard form $2x + 3y = 8$ over any multiples of each side, such as $4x + 6y = 16$. (To write $4x + 6y = 16$ in this preferred form, divide each side by 2.)

NOW TRY ANSWER
3. $y = -\frac{1}{5}x - 2$

**NOW TRY
EXERCISE 4**

Write an equation of the line passing through the points $(3, -4)$ and $(-2, -1)$. Give the final answer in standard form.

OBJECTIVE 4 Write an equation of a line given two points on the line.

EXAMPLE 4 Writing an Equation of a Line Given Two Points

Write an equation of the line passing through the points $(-4, 3)$ and $(5, -7)$. Give the final answer in standard form.

First find the slope using the slope formula.

$$m = \frac{-7 - 3}{5 - (-4)} = -\frac{10}{9}$$

Use either $(-4, 3)$ or $(5, -7)$ as (x_1, y_1) in the point-slope form of the equation of a line. We choose $(-4, 3)$, so $-4 = x_1$ and $3 = y_1$.

$y - y_1 = m(x - x_1)$	Point-slope form
$y - 3 = -\dfrac{10}{9}[x - (-4)]$	Let $y_1 = 3$, $m = -\frac{10}{9}$, and $x_1 = -4$.
$y - 3 = -\dfrac{10}{9}(x + 4)$	Definition of subtraction
$y - 3 = -\dfrac{10}{9}x - \dfrac{40}{9}$	Distributive property
$9y - 27 = -10x - 40$	Multiply each term by 9.
Standard form $\longrightarrow 10x + 9y = -13$	Add 10x. Add 27.

Verify that if $(5, -7)$ were used, the same equation would result.   **NOW TRY**

NOTE   Once the slope is found in **Example 4,** the equation of the line could also be determined using Method 2 from **Example 3.**

OBJECTIVE 5 Write equations of horizontal and vertical lines.

A horizontal line has slope 0. Using point-slope form, we can find the equation of a horizontal line through the point (a, b).

$y - y_1 = m(x - x_1)$	Point-slope form
$y - b = 0(x - a)$	$y_1 = b$, $m = 0$, $x_1 = a$
$y - b = 0$	Multiplication property of 0
Horizontal line $\longrightarrow$ $y = b$	Add b.

Point-slope form does not apply to a vertical line because the slope of a vertical line is undefined. A vertical line through the point (a, b) has equation $x = a.$

Equations of Horizontal and Vertical Lines

A **horizontal line** through the point (a, b) has equation $y = b.$

A **vertical line** through the point (a, b) has equation $x = a.$

NOW TRY
EXERCISE 5

Write an equation of the line passing through the point $(4, -4)$ that satisfies the given condition.

(a) The line has undefined slope.

(b) The line has slope 0.

EXAMPLE 5 Writing Equations of Horizontal and Vertical Lines

Write an equation of the line passing through the point $(-3, 3)$ that satisfies the given condition.

(a) The line has slope 0.

Because the slope is 0, this is a horizontal line. A horizontal line through the point (a, b) has equation $y = b$. In $(-3, 3)$, the y-coordinate is 3, so the equation is $y = 3$.

(b) The line has undefined slope.

This is a vertical line because the slope is undefined. A vertical line through the point (a, b) has equation $x = a$. In $(-3, 3)$, the x-coordinate is -3, so the equation is $x = -3$.

Both lines are graphed in **FIGURE 29**.

FIGURE 29

NOW TRY

OBJECTIVE 6 Write an equation of a line parallel or perpendicular to a given line.

Recall that parallel lines have the same slope and perpendicular lines have slopes that are negative reciprocals.

EXAMPLE 6 Writing Equations of Parallel or Perpendicular Lines

Write an equation of the line passing through the point $(-3, 6)$ that satisfies the given condition. Give final answers in slope-intercept form.

(a) The line is parallel to the line $2x + 3y = 6$.

We can find the slope of the given line by solving for y.

$$2x + 3y = 6$$
$$3y = -2x + 6 \qquad \text{Subtract } 2x.$$
$$y = -\frac{2}{3}x + 2 \qquad \text{Divide by 3.}$$

↑
└ Slope

The slope of the line is given by the coefficient of x, so $m = -\frac{2}{3}$. See **FIGURE 30**.

FIGURE 30

The required equation of the line through $(-3, 6)$ and parallel to $2x + 3y = 6$ must also have slope $-\frac{2}{3}$. To find this equation, we use the point-slope form with $(x_1, y_1) = (-3, 6)$ and $m = -\frac{2}{3}$.

$$y - 6 = -\frac{2}{3}[x - (-3)] \qquad \begin{array}{l} y_1 = 6,\ m = -\frac{2}{3}, \\ x_1 = -3 \end{array}$$

$$y - 6 = -\frac{2}{3}(x + 3) \qquad \text{Definition of subtraction}$$

$$y - 6 = -\frac{2}{3}x - 2 \qquad \text{Distributive property}$$

$$y = -\frac{2}{3}x + 4 \qquad \text{Add 6.}$$

FIGURE 31

NOW TRY ANSWERS
5. (a) $x = 4$ (b) $y = -4$

We did not clear the fraction because we want the final equation in slope-intercept form—that is, solved for y. Both lines are shown in **FIGURE 31**.

NOW TRY
EXERCISE 6

Write an equation of the line passing through the point $(6, -1)$ that satisfies the given condition. Give final answers in slope-intercept form.

(a) The line is parallel to the line $3x - 5y = 7$.

(b) The line is perpendicular to the line $3x - 5y = 7$.

(b) The line is perpendicular to the line $2x + 3y = 6$.

In part (a), we wrote the equation $2x + 3y = 6$ in slope-intercept form.

$$y = -\frac{2}{3}x + 2$$

— Slope

To be perpendicular to the line $2x + 3y = 6$, a line must have slope $\frac{3}{2}$, the negative reciprocal of $-\frac{2}{3}$.

We use $(-3, 6)$ and slope $\frac{3}{2}$ in the point-slope form to find the equation of the perpendicular line shown in **FIGURE 32**.

$$y - 6 = \frac{3}{2}[x - (-3)] \qquad y_1 = 6,\ m = \frac{3}{2},\ x_1 = -3$$

$$y - 6 = \frac{3}{2}(x + 3) \qquad \text{Definition of subtraction}$$

$$y - 6 = \frac{3}{2}x + \frac{9}{2} \qquad \text{Distributive property}$$

$$y = \frac{3}{2}x + \frac{21}{2} \qquad \text{Add } 6 = \frac{12}{2}.$$

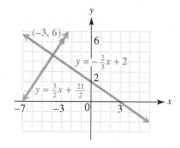

FIGURE 32

Again, we did not clear the fractions because we want the final equation in slope-intercept form.

NOW TRY

▼ **Summary of Forms of Linear Equations**

Equation	Description	When to Use
$y = mx + b$	**Slope-Intercept Form** Slope is m. y-intercept is $(0, b)$.	The slope and y-intercept can be easily identified and used to quickly graph the equation.
$y - y_1 = m(x - x_1)$	**Point-Slope Form** Slope is m. Line passes through (x_1, y_1).	This form is ideal for finding the equation of a line if the slope and a point on the line or two points on the line are known.
$Ax + By = C$	**Standard Form** (A, B, and C integers, $A \geq 0$) Slope is $-\frac{A}{B}$ $(B \neq 0)$. x-intercept is $\left(\frac{C}{A}, 0\right)$ $(A \neq 0)$. y-intercept is $\left(0, \frac{C}{B}\right)$ $(B \neq 0)$.	The x- and y-intercepts can be found quickly and used to graph the equation. The slope must be calculated.
$y = b$	**Horizontal Line** Slope is 0. y-intercept is $(0, b)$.	If the graph intersects only the y-axis, then y is the only variable in the equation.
$x = a$	**Vertical Line** Slope is undefined. x-intercept is $(a, 0)$.	If the graph intersects only the x-axis, then x is the only variable in the equation.

NOW TRY ANSWERS

6. (a) $y = \frac{3}{5}x - \frac{23}{5}$

(b) $y = -\frac{5}{3}x + 9$

OBJECTIVE 7 Write an equation of a line that models real data.

If a given set of data changes at a fairly constant rate, the data may fit a linear pattern, where the rate of change is the slope of the line.

**NOW TRY
EXERCISE 7**

A cell phone plan costs $100 for the telephone plus $85 per month for service. Write an equation that gives the cost y in dollars for x months of cell phone service using this plan.

EXAMPLE 7 Writing a Linear Equation to Describe Real Data

A local gasoline station is selling 89-octane gas for $3.50 per gal.

(a) Write an equation that describes the cost y to buy x gallons of gas.

The total cost is determined by the number of gallons we buy multiplied by the price per gallon (in this case, $3.50). As the gas is pumped, two sets of numbers spin by: the number of gallons pumped and the cost of that number of gallons.

The table illustrates this situation.

Number of Gallons Pumped	Cost of This Number of Gallons
0	0($3.50) = $ 0.00
1	1($3.50) = $ 3.50
2	2($3.50) = $ 7.00
3	3($3.50) = $10.50
4	4($3.50) = $14.00

If we let x denote the number of gallons pumped, then the total cost y in dollars can be found using the following linear equation.

Total cost ⟶   ⟵ Number of gallons
$$y = 3.50x$$

Theoretically, there are infinitely many ordered pairs (x, y) that satisfy this equation, but here we are limited to nonnegative values for x because we cannot have a negative number of gallons. In this situation, there is also a practical maximum value for x, which varies from one car to another—the size of the gas tank.

(b) A car wash at this gas station costs an additional $3.00. Write an equation that defines the cost of gas and a car wash.

The cost will be $3.50x + 3.00$ dollars for x gallons of gas and a car wash.

$$y = 3.5x + 3 \qquad \text{Final 0's need not be included.}$$

(c) Interpret the ordered pairs $(5, 20.5)$ and $(10, 38)$ in relation to the equation from part (b).

$(5, 20.5)$ indicates that 5 gal of gas and a car wash cost $20.50.

$(10, 38)$ indicates that 10 gal of gas and a car wash cost $38.00.

NOW TRY

NOTE In **Example 7(a),** the ordered pair $(0, 0)$ satisfied the equation $y = 3.50x$, so the linear equation has the form

$$y = mx, \quad \text{where } b = 0.$$

If a realistic situation involves an initial charge b plus a charge per unit, m, as in the equation $y = 3.5x + 3$ in **Example 7(b),** then the equation has the form

$$y = mx + b, \quad \text{where } b \neq 0.$$

NOW TRY ANSWER
7. $y = 85x + 100$

NOW TRY
EXERCISE 8

Refer to **Example 8.**

(a) Using the data values for the years 2009 and 2012, write an equation that models the data.

(b) Use the equation from part (a) to approximate the cost of tuition and fees in 2011.

EXAMPLE 8   Writing an Equation of a Line That Models Data

Average annual tuition and fees for in-state students at public two-year colleges are shown in the table for selected years and graphed as ordered pairs of points in the **scatter diagram** in **FIGURE 33**, where $x = 0$ represents 2009, $x = 1$ represents 2010, and so on, and y represents the cost in dollars.

Year	Cost (in dollars)
2009 ($x = 0$)	2787
2010 ($x = 1$)	2938
2011 ($x = 2$)	3074
2012 ($x = 3$)	3216
2013 ($x = 4$)	3264

Source: The College Board.

FIGURE 33

(a) Write an equation that models the data.

Because the points in **FIGURE 33** lie approximately on a straight line, we can write a linear equation that models the relationship between year x and cost y. We choose two data points, $(0, 2787)$ and $(4, 3264)$, to find the slope of the line.

$$m = \frac{3264 - 2787}{4 - 0} = \frac{477}{4} = 119.25$$

The slope 119.25 indicates that the cost of tuition and fees increased by about \$119 per year from 2009 to 2013. We use this slope and the y-intercept $(0, 2787)$ to write an equation of the line in slope-intercept form.

$$y = 119.25x + 2787$$

(b) Use the equation from part (a) to approximate the cost of tuition and fees in 2014.

The value $x = 5$ corresponds to the year 2014.

$y = 119.25x + 2787$ Equation from part (a)

$y = 119.25(5) + 2787$ Substitute 5 for x.

$y = 3383.25$ Multiply, and then add.

According to the model, average tuition and fees for in-state students at public two-year colleges in 2014 were about \$3383.   NOW TRY

NOTE   Choosing different data points in **Example 8** would result in a slightly different line (particularly in regard to its slope) and, hence, a slightly different equation. However, all such equations should yield similar results. See **Now Try Exercise 8.**

NOW TRY ANSWERS

8. (a) $y = 143x + 2787$
   (b) \$3073

NOW TRY
EXERCISE 9

Refer to **Example 9.**

(a) Use the ordered pairs $(8, 243)$ and $(12, 263)$ to write an equation that models the data.

(b) Use the equation from part (a) to estimate retail spending on prescription drugs in 2015.

EXAMPLE 9 Writing an Equation of a Line That Models Data

Retail spending (in billions of dollars) on prescription drugs in the United States is shown in the graph in **FIGURE 34**.

Source: Centers for Medicare & Medicaid Services.

FIGURE 34

(a) Write an equation that models the data.

The data increase linearly—that is, a straight line through the tops of any two bars in the graph would be close to the top of each bar. To model the relationship between year x and spending on prescription drugs y, we let $x = 7$ represent 2007, $x = 8$ represent 2008, and so on. The given data for 2007 and 2012 can be written as the ordered pairs $(7, 236)$ and $(12, 263)$.

$$m = \frac{263 - 236}{12 - 7} = \frac{27}{5} = 5.4 \qquad \text{Find the slope of the line through } (7, 236) \text{ and } (12, 263).$$

Thus, spending increased by about \$5.4 billion per year. To write an equation, we substitute this slope and the point $(7, 236)$ into the point-slope form.

$$y - y_1 = m(x - x_1) \qquad \text{Point-slope form}$$

$$y - 236 = 5.4(x - 7) \qquad (x_1, y_1) = (7, 236); m = 5.4$$

> Either point can be used here. $(12, 263)$ provides the same answer.

$$y - 236 = 5.4x - 37.8 \qquad \text{Distributive property}$$

$$y = 5.4x + 198.2 \qquad \text{Add 236.}$$

Retail spending y (in billions of dollars) on prescription drugs in the United States in year x can be approximated by the equation $y = 5.4x + 198.2$.

(b) Use the equation from part (a) to estimate retail spending on prescription drugs in the United States in 2015. (Assume a constant rate of change.)

Because we let $x = 7$ represent 2007, $x = 15$ represents 2015.

$$y = 5.4x + 198.2 \qquad \text{Equation from part (a)}$$

$$y = 5.4(15) + 198.2 \qquad \text{Substitute 15 for } x.$$

$$y = 279.2 \qquad \text{Multiply, and then add.}$$

About \$279 billion was spent on prescription drugs in 2015. **NOW TRY**

NOW TRY ANSWERS
9. (a) $y = 5x + 203$
  (b) \$278 billion

2.3 Exercises

▶ MyMathLab®

▶ *Complete solution available in MyMathLab*

Concept Check   *Provide the appropriate response.*

1. The following equations all represent the same line. Which one is in standard form as specified in this section?

   A. $3x - 2y = 5$ **B.** $2y = 3x - 5$ **C.** $\frac{3}{5}x - \frac{2}{5}y = 1$ **D.** $3x = 2y + 5$

2. Which equation is in point-slope form?

   A. $y = 6x + 2$ **B.** $4x + y = 9$ **C.** $y - 3 = 2(x - 1)$ **D.** $2y = 3x - 7$

3. Which equation in **Exercise 2** is in slope-intercept form?

4. Write the equation $y + 2 = -3(x - 4)$ in slope-intercept form.

5. Write the equation from **Exercise 4** in standard form.

6. Write the equation $10x - 7y = 70$ in slope-intercept form.

Concept Check   *Match each equation with the graph that it most closely resembles. (Hint: Determining the signs of m and b will help in each case.)*

7. $y = 2x + 3$ **A.**   **B.**   **C.**

8. $y = -2x + 3$

9. $y = -2x - 3$

10. $y = 2x - 3$ **D.**   **E.**   **F.**

11. $y = 2x$

12. $y = -2x$ **G.**   **H.**   **I.**

13. $y = 3$

14. $y = -3$

Write an equation in slope-intercept form of the line that satisfies the given conditions. See Example 1.

15. $m = 5; b = 15$ 16. $m = 2; b = 12$

17. $m = -\frac{2}{3}; b = \frac{4}{5}$ 18. $m = -\frac{5}{8}; b = -\frac{1}{3}$

19. Slope 1; y-intercept $(0, -1)$ 20. Slope -1; y-intercept $(0, -3)$

▶ 21. Slope $\frac{2}{5}$; y-intercept $(0, 5)$ 22. Slope $-\frac{3}{4}$; y-intercept $(0, 7)$

Write an equation in slope-intercept form of the line shown in each graph. (Coordinates of the points shown are integers.)

23.   24.   25.   26.

Each table of values gives several points that lie on a line. Write an equation in slope-intercept form of the line.

27.	x	y
	−2	−8
	0	−4
	1	−2
	3	2

28.	x	y
	−2	−3
	0	3
	2	9
	3	12

29.	x	y
	−5	6
	0	3
	5	0
	10	−3

30.	x	y
	−4	5
	−2	0
	0	−5
	2	−10

For each equation, (a) write it in slope-intercept form, (b) give the slope of the line, (c) give the y-intercept, and (d) graph the line. See Example 2.

31. $-x + y = 4$ **32.** $-x + y = 6$ ▶ **33.** $6x + 5y = 30$

34. $3x + 4y = 12$ **35.** $4x - 5y = 20$ **36.** $7x - 3y = 3$

37. $x + 2y = -4$ **38.** $x + 3y = -9$

Write an equation of the line that satisfies the given conditions. Give the equation (a) in slope-intercept form and (b) in standard form. See Example 3 and the discussion on standard form.

39. Through $(5, 8)$; slope -2 **40.** Through $(12, 10)$; slope 1

▶ **41.** Through $(-2, 4)$; slope $-\frac{3}{4}$ **42.** Through $(-1, 6)$; slope $-\frac{5}{6}$

43. Through $(-5, 4)$; slope $\frac{1}{2}$ **44.** Through $(7, -2)$; slope $\frac{1}{4}$

45. *x*-intercept $(3, 0)$; slope 4 **46.** *x*-intercept $(-2, 0)$; slope -5

47. Through $(2, 6.8)$; slope 1.4 **48.** Through $(6, -1.2)$; slope 0.8

Write an equation of the line passing through the given points. Give the final answer in standard form. See Example 4.

▶ **49.** $(3, 4)$ and $(5, 8)$ **50.** $(5, -2)$ and $(-3, 14)$ **51.** $(6, 1)$ and $(-2, 5)$

52. $(-2, 5)$ and $(-8, 1)$ **53.** $(2, 5)$ and $(1, 5)$ **54.** $(-2, 2)$ and $(4, 2)$

55. $(7, 6)$ and $(7, -8)$ **56.** $(13, 5)$ and $(13, -1)$

57. $\left(\frac{1}{2}, -3\right)$ and $\left(-\frac{2}{3}, -3\right)$ **58.** $\left(-\frac{4}{9}, -6\right)$ and $\left(\frac{12}{7}, -6\right)$

59. $\left(-\frac{2}{5}, \frac{2}{5}\right)$ and $\left(\frac{4}{3}, \frac{2}{3}\right)$ **60.** $\left(\frac{3}{4}, \frac{8}{3}\right)$ and $\left(\frac{2}{5}, \frac{2}{3}\right)$

Write an equation of the line that satisfies the given conditions. See Example 5.

▶ **61.** Through $(9, 5)$; slope 0 **62.** Through $(-4, -2)$; slope 0

63. Through $(9, 10)$; undefined slope   **64.** Through $(-2, 8)$; undefined slope

65. Through $\left(-\frac{3}{4}, -\frac{3}{2}\right)$; slope 0 **66.** Through $\left(-\frac{5}{8}, -\frac{9}{2}\right)$; slope 0

67. Through $(-7, 8)$; horizontal   **68.** Through $(2, -7)$; horizontal

69. Through $(0.5, 0.2)$; vertical   **70.** Through $(0.1, 0.4)$; vertical

Write an equation of the line that satisfies the given conditions. Give the equation (a) in slope-intercept form and (b) in standard form. See Example 6.

▶ **71.** Through $(7, 2)$; parallel to $3x - y = 8$ **72.** Through $(4, 1)$; parallel to $2x + 5y = 10$

73. Through $(-2, -2)$; parallel to $-x + 2y = 10$

74. Through $(-1, 3)$; parallel to $-x + 3y = 12$

▶ **75.** Through $(8, 5)$; perpendicular to $2x - y = 7$

76. Through $(2, -7)$; perpendicular to $5x + 2y = 18$

77. Through $(-2, 7)$; perpendicular to $x = 9$

78. Through $(8, 4)$; perpendicular to $x = -3$

Write an equation in the form $y = mx$ for each situation. Then give the three ordered pairs associated with the equation for x-values 0, 5, and 10. **See Example 7(a).**

79. x represents the number of hours traveling at 45 mph, and y represents the distance traveled (in miles).

80. x represents the number of t-shirts sold at $26 each, and y represents the total cost of the t-shirts (in dollars).

81. x represents the number of gallons of gas sold at $3.75 per gal, and y represents the total cost of the gasoline (in dollars).

82. x represents the number of days a DVD movie is rented at $4.50 per day, and y represents the total charge for the rental (in dollars).

83. x represents the number of credit hours taken at Kirkwood Community College at $140 per credit hour, and y represents the total tuition paid for the credit hours (in dollars). (*Source:* www.kirkwood.edu)

84. x represents the number of tickets to a performance of *Jersey Boys* at the Des Moines Civic Center purchased at $125 per ticket, and y represents the total paid for the tickets (in dollars). (*Source:* Ticketmaster.)

For each situation, do the following.

(a) Write an equation in the form $y = mx + b$.

(b) Find and interpret the ordered pair associated with the equation for $x = 5$.

(c) Answer the question posed in the problem.

See Examples 7(b) and 7(c).

85. A ticket for the Diving Board Tour, featuring Elton John, costs $149. A parking pass costs $15. Let x represent the number of tickets and y represent the cost in dollars. How much does it cost for 2 tickets and a parking pass? (*Source:* Ticketmaster.)

86. Resident tuition at Broward College is $105.90 per credit hour. There is also a $20 health science application fee. Let x represent the number of credit hours and y represent the cost in dollars. How much does it cost for a student in health science to take 15 credit hours? (*Source:* www.broward.edu)

87. A health club membership costs $99, plus $41 per month. Let x represent the number of months and y represent the cost in dollars. How much does the first year's membership cost? (*Source:* Midwest Athletic Club.)

88. An Executive VIP/Gold membership to a health club costs $159, plus $57 per month. Let x represent the number of months and y represent the cost in dollars. How much does a one-year membership cost? (*Source:* Midwest Athletic Club.)

89. A wireless plan includes unlimited talk and text plus 2 GB of data for $95 per month. There is a $36 activation fee. Let x represent the number of months and y represent the cost in dollars. Over a two-year contract, how much will this plan cost? (*Source:* AT&T.)

90. Another wireless plan includes unlimited talk and text plus 4 GB of data for $110 per month. There is a $36 activation fee and a $99 charge for an Apple iPhone 5c. Let x represent the number of months and y represent the cost in dollars. Over a two-year contract, how much will this plan cost? (*Source*: AT&T.)

91. There is a $30 fee to rent a chain saw, plus $6 per day. Let x represent the number of days the saw is rented and y represent the charge to the user in dollars. If the total charge is $138, for how many days is the saw rented?

92. A rental car costs $50, plus $0.45 per mile. Let x represent the number of miles driven and y represent the total charge to the renter in dollars. How many miles was the car driven if the renter paid $127.85?

Solve each problem. In part (a), give equations in slope-intercept form. **See Examples 8 and 9.**

93. Total sales of portable media/MP3 players in the United States (in millions of dollars) are shown in the graph, where the year 2010 corresponds to $x = 0$.

(a) Use the ordered pairs from the graph to write an equation that models the data. Interpret the slope in the context of this problem.

(b) Use the equation from part (a) to approximate sales of portable media/MP3 players in the United States in 2011, the year data was unavailable.

Media/MP3 Player Sales

*Data for this year is unavailable.
Source: Consumer Electronics Association.

94. Total sales of smartphones in the United States (in billions of dollars) are shown in the graph, where the year 2010 corresponds to $x = 0$.

(a) Use the ordered pairs from the graph to write an equation that models the data. (Round the slope to the nearest tenth.) Interpret the slope in the context of this problem.

(b) Use the equation from part (a) to approximate smartphone sales in the United States in 2011, the year data was unavailable.

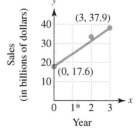

Smartphone Sales

*Data for this year is unavailable.
Source: Consumer Electronics Association.

95. Expenditures for home health care in the United States are shown in the graph.

(a) Use the information given for the years 2008 and 2012, letting $x = 8$ represent 2008 and $x = 12$ represent 2012, and letting y represent spending (in billions of dollars), to write an equation that models the data.

(b) Use the equation from part (a) to approximate the amount spent on home health care in 2011 to the nearest tenth. How does the result compare with the actual value, $74.0 billion?

Spending on Home Health Care

Source: Centers for Medicare & Medicaid Services.

96. The number of pieces of first class mail delivered in the United States is shown in the graph.

First Class Mail

Source: U.S. Postal Service.

(a) Use the information given for the years 2007 and 2012, letting $x = 7$ represent 2007 and $x = 12$ represent 2012, and letting y represent the number of pieces of mail (in billions), to write an equation that models the data.

(b) Use the equation from part (a) to approximate the number of pieces of first class mail delivered in 2010 to the nearest tenth. How does this result compare to the actual value, 78.2 billion?

RELATING CONCEPTS   For Individual or Group Work   **(Exercises 97–104)**

*In **Section 1.2,** we worked with formulas. **Work Exercises 97–104 in order,** to see how the formula that relates Celsius and Fahrenheit temperatures is derived.*

97. There is a linear relationship between Celsius and Fahrenheit temperatures.

When $C = 0°$, $F = $ _____°.

When $C = 100°$, $F = $ _____°.

98. Think of ordered pairs of temperatures (C, F), where C and F represent corresponding Celsius and Fahrenheit temperatures. The equation that relates the two scales has a straight-line graph that contains the two points determined in **Exercise 97.** What are these two points?

99. Find the slope of the line described in **Exercise 98.**

100. Use the slope found in **Exercise 99** and one of the two points determined earlier, and write an equation that gives F in terms of C. (*Hint:* Use the point-slope form, where C replaces x and F replaces y.)

101. To obtain another form of the formula, use the equation found in **Exercise 100** and solve for C in terms of F.

102. Use the equation from **Exercise 100** to find the Fahrenheit temperature when $C = 30$.

103. Use the equation from **Exercise 101** to find the Celsius temperature when $F = 50$.

104. For what temperature does $F = C$? (Use the photo to confirm this temperature.)

STUDY SKILLS

Taking Math Tests

Techniques To Improve Your Test Score	Comments
Come prepared with a pencil, eraser, paper, and calculator, if allowed.	Working in pencil lets you erase, keeping your work neat and readable.
Scan the entire test, note the point values of different problems, and plan your time accordingly.	To do 20 problems in 50 minutes, allow $50 \div 20 = 2.5$ minutes per problem. Spend less time on easier problems.
Do a "knowledge dump" when you get the test. Write important notes, such as formulas, in a corner of the test.	Writing down tips and information that you've learned at the beginning allows you to relax later.
Read directions carefully, and circle any significant words. When you finish a problem, reread the directions. Did you do what was asked?	Pay attention to announcements written on the board or made by your instructor. Ask questions if you don't understand.
Show all your work. Many teachers give partial credit if some steps are correct, even if the final answer is wrong. *Write neatly.*	If your teacher can't read your writing, you won't get credit for it. If you need more space to work, ask to use extra paper.
Write down anything that might help solve a problem: a formula, a diagram, etc. If you still can't solve it, circle the problem and come back to it later. Do *not* erase anything you wrote down.	If you know even a little bit about the problem, write it down. The answer may come to you as you work on it, or you may get partial credit. Don't spend too long on any one problem.
If you can't solve a problem, make a guess. Do not change it unless you find an obvious mistake.	Have a good reason for changing an answer. Your first guess is usually your best bet.
Check that the answer to an application problem is reasonable and makes sense. Reread the problem to make sure that you have answered the question.	Use common sense. Can the father really be seven years old? Would a month's rent be $32,140? Remember to label your answer if needed: $, years, inches, etc.
Check for careless errors. Rework the problem without looking at your previous work. Compare the two answers.	Reworking the problem from the beginning forces you to rethink it. If possible, use a different method to solve the problem.

Think through and answer each question.

1. What two or three tips will you try when you take your next math test?

2. How did the tips you selected work for you when you took your math test?

3. What will you do differently when taking your next math test?

SUMMARY EXERCISES   Finding Slopes and Equations of Lines

1. $-\dfrac{3}{5}$ 2. 0

3. 1 4. $\dfrac{3}{7}$

5. undefined   6. $-\dfrac{4}{7}$

7. (a) B (b) F (c) A
(d) C (e) E (f) D

8. C is in standard form;
A: $4x + y = -7$;
B: $3x - 4y = -12$;
D: $x + 2y = 0$;
E: $3x - y = 5$
F: $5x - 3y = 15$

9. (a) $y = -\dfrac{5}{6}x + \dfrac{13}{3}$
(b) $5x + 6y = 26$

10. (a) $y = -8$ (b) $y = -8$

11. (a) $y = -3x + 10$
(b) $3x + y = 10$

12. (a) $y = -\dfrac{5}{2}x + 2$
(b) $5x + 2y = 4$

13. (a) $y = -\dfrac{7}{9}$ (b) $9y = -7$

14. (a) $y = \dfrac{2}{3}x + 8$
(b) $2x - 3y = -24$

15. (a) $y = -\dfrac{5}{2}x$
(b) $5x + 2y = 0$

16. (a) $y = 3x + 11$
(b) $3x - y = -11$

17. (a) $y = \dfrac{2}{3}x + \dfrac{14}{3}$
(b) $2x - 3y = -14$

18. (a) $y = 2x - 10$
(b) $2x - y = 10$

Find the slope of each line, if possible.

1. Through $(3, -3)$ and $(8, -6)$

2. Through $(4, -5)$ and $(-1, -5)$

3. $y = x - 5$

4. $3x - 7y = 21$

5. $x - 4 = 0$

6. $4x + 7y = 3$

7. *Concept Check*   Match the description in Column I with its equation in Column II.

I	II
(a) Slope -0.5, $b = -2$	**A.** $y = -\dfrac{1}{2}x$
(b) x-intercept $(4, 0)$, y-intercept $(0, 2)$	**B.** $y = -\dfrac{1}{2}x - 2$
(c) Passes through $(4, -2)$ and $(0, 0)$	**C.** $x - 2y = 2$
(d) $m = \dfrac{1}{2}$, passes through $(-2, -2)$	**D.** $y = 2x$
(e) $m = \dfrac{1}{2}$, passes through the origin	**E.** $x = 2y$
(f) Slope 2, $b = 0$	**F.** $x + 2y = 4$

8. *Concept Check*   Which equation is written in standard form as specified in the text?

A. $y = -4x - 7$ **B.** $-3x + 4y = 12$ **C.** $x - 6y = 3$

D. $\dfrac{1}{2}x + y = 0$ **E.** $6x - 2y = 10$ **F.** $3y - 5x = -15$

Write the equations not written in standard form in that form.

*For each line described, write an equation of the line **(a)** in slope-intercept form and **(b)** in standard form.*

9. Through $(-2, 6)$ and $(4, 1)$

10. Through $(5, -8)$, $m = 0$

11. Through $(4, -2)$ with slope -3

12. Through $(4, -8)$ and $(-4, 12)$

13. Through $\left(\dfrac{3}{4}, -\dfrac{7}{9}\right)$; perpendicular to $x = \dfrac{2}{3}$

14. Through $(-3, 6)$ with slope $\dfrac{2}{3}$

15. Through the origin; perpendicular to $2x - 5y = 6$

16. Through $(-2, 5)$; parallel to $3x - y = 4$

17. Through $(-4, 2)$; parallel to the line through $(3, 9)$ and $(6, 11)$

18. Through $(4, -2)$; perpendicular to the line through $(3, 7)$ and $(5, 6)$

2.4 Linear Inequalities in Two Variables

VOCABULARY
☐ linear inequality in two variables
☐ boundary line

OBJECTIVE 1 Graph linear inequalities in two variables.

In **Section 1.5,** we graphed linear inequalities in one variable on a number line. In this section, we graph linear inequalities in two variables on a rectangular coordinate system.

> **Linear Inequality in Two Variables**
>
> A **linear inequality in two variables** (here x and y) can be written in the form
>
> $$Ax + By < C, \quad Ax + By \leq C, \quad Ax + By > C, \quad \text{or} \quad Ax + By \geq C,$$
>
> where A, B, and C are real numbers and A and B are not both 0.

Consider the graph in **FIGURE 35**. The graph of the line $x + y = 5$ divides the points in the rectangular coordinate system into three sets of points.

1. Those points that lie **on** the line itself and satisfy the equation $x + y = 5$, such as $(0, 5)$, $(2, 3)$, and $(5, 0)$;

2. Those points that lie in the region *above* the line and satisfy the inequality $x + y > 5$, such as $(5, 3)$ and $(2, 4)$;

3. Those points that lie in the region *below* the line and satisfy the inequality $x + y < 5$, such as $(0, 0)$ and $(-3, -1)$.

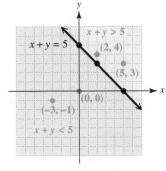

FIGURE 35

The graph of the line $x + y = 5$ is the **boundary line** for the two inequalities

$$x + y > 5 \quad \text{and} \quad x + y < 5.$$

A graph of a linear inequality in two variables is a region in the real number plane that may or may not include the boundary line.

To graph a linear inequality in two variables, follow these steps.

> **Graphing a Linear Inequality in Two Variables**
>
> **Step 1** **Draw the graph of the straight line that is the boundary.**
>
> • Make the line solid if the inequality involves $\leq$ or $\geq$.
>
> • Make the line dashed if the inequality involves $<$ or $>$.
>
> **Step 2** **Choose a test point.** Choose any point not on the line, and substitute the coordinates of that point in the inequality.
>
> **Step 3** **Shade the appropriate region.** Shade the region that includes the test point if it satisfies the original inequality. Otherwise, shade the region on the other side of the boundary line.

NOW TRY
EXERCISE 1

Graph $-x + 2y \geq 4$.

EXAMPLE 1   Graphing a Linear Inequality

Graph $3x + 2y \geq 6$.

Step 1   First graph the boundary line $3x + 2y = 6$, which has intercepts $(2, 0)$ and $(0, 3)$, as shown in **FIGURE 36**.

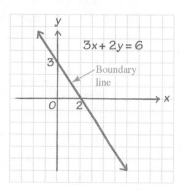

FIGURE 36

Step 2   The graph of the inequality $3x + 2y \geq 6$ includes the points of the boundary line $3x + 2y = 6$ (because the inequality symbol $\geq$ includes equality) and either the points *above* that line or the points *below* it. To decide which, select any point *not* on the boundary line to use as a test point. Substitute the values from the test point for x and y in the inequality.

$$3x + 2y > 6$$ We are testing the region.

$(0, 0)$ is a convenient test point.

$$3(0) + 2(0) \stackrel{?}{>} 6$$ Let $x = 0$ and $y = 0$.

$$0 > 6$$ False

Step 3   Because the result is false, $(0, 0)$ does *not* satisfy the inequality. The solution set includes all points in the region on the *other* side of the line. See **FIGURE 37**.

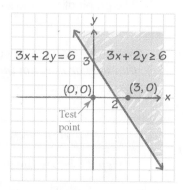

FIGURE 37

As a further check, select a test point in the shaded region, such as $(3, 0)$, and confirm that it does indeed satisfy the inequality. See **FIGURE 37**.

NOW TRY

NOW TRY ANSWER

1.

⚠ CAUTION   When drawing the boundary line in Step 1, be careful to draw a solid line if the inequality includes equality ($\leq$, $\geq$) or a dashed line if equality is not included ($<$, $>$).

If an inequality is written in the form $y > mx + b$ or $y < mx + b$, then the inequality symbol indicates which region to shade.

> If $y > mx + b$, then shade above the boundary line.
>
> If $y < mx + b$, then shade below the boundary line.

This method works only if the inequality is solved for y.

! **CAUTION** A common error in using the method just described is to use the original inequality symbol when deciding which region to shade. *Be sure to use the inequality symbol found in the inequality after it is solved for y.*

🔄 **NOW TRY
EXERCISE 2**
Graph $3x - 2y < 0$.

> **EXAMPLE 2** **Graphing a Linear Inequality with Boundary Passing through the Origin**

Graph $3x - 4y > 0$.

First graph the boundary line. The *x*- and *y*-intercepts are the same point, $(0, 0)$. Thus, this line passes through the origin. Two other points on the line are $(4, 3)$ and $(-4, -3)$. The points of the boundary line do *not* belong to the inequality

$$3x - 4y > 0$$

(because the inequality symbol is $>$, *not* $\geq$). For this reason, the line is dashed. See **FIGURE 38**.

To use the method explained above, we solve the inequality for *y*.

$3x - 4y > 0$	Original inequality
$-4y > -3x$	Subtract $3x$.
$y < \dfrac{3}{4}x$	Divide by -4. Change $>$ to $<$.

Use this equivalent inequality to decide which region to shade.

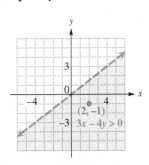

FIGURE 38

Because the *is less than* symbol occurs **when the original inequality is solved for y,** shade the region *below* the boundary line.

CHECK As a further check, choose a test point not on the line, which rules out the origin. We choose $(2, -1)$.

$$3x - 4y > 0 \quad \text{Original inequality}$$

$$3(2) - 4(-1) \overset{?}{>} 0 \quad \text{Let } x = 2 \text{ and } y = -1.$$

$$6 + 4 \overset{?}{>} 0 \quad \text{Multiply.}$$

$$10 > 0 \ \checkmark \quad \text{True}$$

NOW TRY ANSWER
2.

This result agrees with the decision to shade below the line. The solution set, graphed in **FIGURE 38**, includes only those points in the shaded region (and *not* those on the line).

NOW TRY 🔄

**NOW TRY
EXERCISE 3**

Graph $x + 2 > 0$.

EXAMPLE 3   Graphing a Linear Inequality

Graph $x - 3 < 1$.

We graph $x - 3 = 1$, which is equivalent to $x = 4$, as a dashed vertical line passing through the point $(4, 0)$. To determine which region to shade, we choose $(0, 0)$ as a test point.

$$x - 3 < 1$$
$$0 - 3 \overset{?}{<} 1 \qquad \text{Let } x = 0.$$
$$-3 < 1 \qquad \text{True}$$

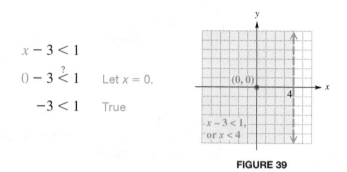

FIGURE 39

Because a true statement results, we shade the region containing $(0, 0)$. See **FIGURE 39**.

NOW TRY

OBJECTIVE 2   Graph the intersection of two linear inequalities.

A pair of inequalities joined with the word **and** is interpreted as the intersection of the solution sets of the inequalities.

> *The graph of the intersection of two or more inequalities is the region of the plane where all points satisfy all of the inequalities at the same time.*

EXAMPLE 4   Graphing the Intersection of Two Inequalities

Graph $2x + 4y \geq 5$ and $x \geq 1$.

To begin, we graph each of the two inequalities $2x + 4y \geq 5$ and $x \geq 1$ separately, as shown in **FIGURES 40(a) AND (b)**. Then we use heavy shading to identify the intersection of the graphs, as shown in **FIGURE 40(c)**.

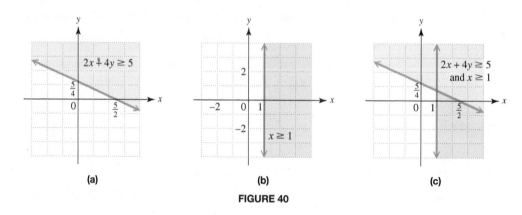

(a)   (b)   (c)

FIGURE 40

In practice, the graphs in **FIGURES 40(a) AND (b)** are graphed on the same axes.

NOW TRY ANSWER

3.

NOW TRY EXERCISE 4

Graph $x + y < 3$ and $y \le 2$.

CHECK Using **FIGURE 40(c)**, we can choose a test point from each of the four regions formed by the intersection of the boundary lines.

$$(2, 1), \quad (0, 2), \quad (0, 0), \quad \text{and} \quad (2, -1) \quad \text{Possible test points}$$

Heavily shaded region · Blue shaded region · Unshaded region · Red shaded region

Verify that only ordered pairs in the heavily shaded region satisfy *both* inequalities. Ordered pairs in the other regions satisfy only one of the inequalities or neither of them. ✓

NOW TRY

OBJECTIVE 3 Graph the union of two linear inequalities.

When two inequalities are joined by the word *or,* we must find the union of the graphs of the inequalities.

> ***The graph of the union of two inequalities includes all of the points that satisfy either inequality.***

NOW TRY EXERCISE 5

Graph $3x - 5y < 15$ or $x > 4$.

EXAMPLE 5 Graphing the Union of Two Inequalities

Graph $2x + 4y \ge 5$ or $x \ge 1$.

The graphs of the two inequalities are shown in **FIGURES 40(a) AND (b)** in **Example 4** on the preceding page. The graph of the union includes all points in *either* inequality, as shown in **FIGURE 41**.

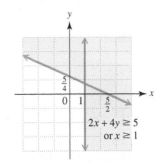

FIGURE 41

NOW TRY

NOW TRY ANSWERS

4.   5.

2.4 Exercises

FOR EXTRA HELP   ▶ MyMathLab®

▶ *Complete solution available in MyMathLab*

Concept Check Decide whether each ordered pair is a solution of the given inequality.

1. $x - 2y \le 4$
 (a) $(0, 0)$ (b) $(2, -1)$
 (c) $(7, 1)$ (d) $(0, 2)$

2. $x + y > 0$
 (a) $(0, 0)$ (b) $(-2, 1)$
 (c) $(2, -1)$ (d) $(-4, 6)$

3. $x - 5 > 0$
 (a) $(0, 0)$ (b) $(5, 0)$
 (c) $(-1, 3)$ (d) $(6, 2)$

4. $y \le 1$
 (a) $(0, 0)$ (b) $(3, 1)$
 (c) $(2, -1)$ (d) $(-3, 3)$

Concept Check   In each statement, fill in the first blank with either solid *or* dashed. *Fill in the second blank with either* above *or* below.

5. The boundary of the graph of $y \leq -x + 2$ will be a _____ line, and the shading will be _____ the line.

6. The boundary of the graph of $y < -x + 2$ will be a _____ line, and the shading will be _____ the line.

7. The boundary of the graph of $y > -x + 2$ will be a _____ line, and the shading will be _____ the line.

8. The boundary of the graph of $y \geq -x + 2$ will be a _____ line, and the shading will be _____ the line.

Concept Check   *Refer to the given graph, and complete each statement with the correct inequality symbol* $<, \leq, >$, *or* $\geq$.

9. x _____ 4   **10.** y _____ -3 **11.** y _____ $3x - 2$ **12.** y _____ $-x + 3$

Graph each linear inequality in two variables. **See Examples 1–3.**

▶ **13.** $x + y \leq 2$ **14.** $x + y \leq -3$ ▶ **15.** $4x - y < 4$

16. $3x - y < 3$ **17.** $x + 3y \geq -2$ **18.** $x + 4y \geq -3$

19. $y < \dfrac{1}{2}x + 3$ **20.** $y < \dfrac{1}{3}x - 2$ **21.** $y \geq -\dfrac{2}{5}x + 2$

22. $y \geq -\dfrac{3}{2}x + 3$ **23.** $2x + 3y \geq 6$ **24.** $3x + 4y \geq 12$

25. $5x - 3y > 15$ **26.** $4x - 5y > 20$ **27.** $x + y > 0$

28. $x + 2y > 0$ **29.** $x - 3y \leq 0$ **30.** $x - 5y \leq 0$

31. $y < x$ **32.** $y \leq 4x$ **33.** $x + 3 \geq 0$

34. $x - 1 \leq 0$ **35.** $y + 5 < 2$ **36.** $y - 1 > 3$

Extending Skills   *Complete each of the following to write an inequality for the graph shown.*

37. Determine the following for the boundary line.

Slope: _____

y-intercept: _____

Equation: $y =$ _____

The boundary line here is (*solid* / *dashed*), and the region (*above* / *below*) it is shaded.

The inequality symbol to indicate this is ($< / \leq / > / \geq$).

Inequality for the graph: y _____

38. Determine the following for the boundary line.

Slope: _____

y-intercept: _____

Equation: $y =$ _____

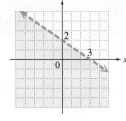

The boundary line here is (*solid* / *dashed*), and the region (*above* / *below*) it is shaded.

The inequality symbol to indicate this is ($<$ / $\leq$ / $>$ / $\geq$).

Inequality for the graph: y _____

Graph each compound inequality. See Example 4.

39. $x + y \leq 1$ and $x \geq 1$

40. $x - y \geq 2$ and $x \geq 3$

41. $2x - y \geq 2$ and $y < 4$

42. $3x - y \geq 3$ and $y < 3$

43. $x + y > -5$ and $y < -2$

44. $6x - 4y < 10$ and $y > 2$

*Extending Skills   Use the method described in **Section 1.7** to write each inequality as a compound inequality, and graph its solution set in the rectangular coordinate plane.*

45. $|x| < 3$

46. $|y| < 5$

47. $|x + 1| < 2$

48. $|y - 3| < 2$

Graph each compound inequality. See Example 5.

49. $x - y \geq 1$ or $y \geq 2$

50. $x + y \leq 2$ or $y \geq 3$

51. $x - 2 > y$ or $x < 1$

52. $x + 3 < y$ or $x > 3$

53. $3x + 2y < 6$ or $x - 2y > 2$

54. $x - y \geq 1$ or $x + y \leq 4$

RELATING CONCEPTS For Individual or Group Work (Exercises 55–60)

Linear programming is a method for finding the optimal (best possible) solution that meets all the conditions for a problem such as the following.

> *A factory can have* no more than 200 *workers on a shift, but must have* at least 100 *and must manufacture* at least 3000 *units at minimum cost. How many workers should be on a shift in order to produce the required units at minimal cost?*

*Let x represent the number of workers and y represent the number of units manufactured. **Work Exercises 55–60 in order.***

55. Write three inequalities expressing the problem conditions.

56. Graph the inequalities from **Exercise 55** using the axes at the right, and shade the intersection.

57. The cost per worker is $50 per day and the cost to manufacture 1 unit is $100. Write an equation in x, y, and C representing the total daily cost C.

58. Find values of x and y for several points in or on the boundary of the shaded region. Include any "corner points," where C is maximized or minimized.

59. Of the values of x and y found in **Exercise 58,** which ones give the least value when substituted in the cost equation from **Exercise 57?**

60. What does the answer in **Exercise 59** mean in terms of the given problem?

2.5 Introduction to Relations and Functions

VOCABULARY

□ relation
□ function
□ dependent variable
□ independent variable
□ domain
□ range

OBJECTIVE 1 Define and identify relations and functions.

Consider the relationship illustrated in the following table between number of hours worked and paycheck amount for an hourly worker.

Number of Hours Worked	Paycheck Amount (in dollars)	Ordered Pairs
5	40	⟶ (5, 40)
10	80	⟶ (10, 80)
20	160	⟶ (20, 160)
40	320	⟶ (40, 320)

The data from the table can be represented by a set of ordered pairs.

$$\{(5, 40), (10, 80), (20, 160), (40, 320)\}$$

Number of hours worked ↑   ↑ Paycheck amount in dollars

Each first component of the ordered pairs represents a number of hours worked, and each second component represents the corresponding paycheck amount. Such a set of ordered pairs is a *relation*.

Relation

A **relation** is any set of ordered pairs.

NOW TRY EXERCISE 1

Write the relation as a set of ordered pairs.

Year	Average Gas Price per Gallon (in dollars)
2000	1.56
2005	2.34
2010	2.84
2015	3.39

Source: Energy Information Administration.

EXAMPLE 1 Writing Ordered Pairs for a Relation

Write the relation as a set of ordered pairs.

Number of Gallons of Gas	Cost (in dollars)
0	0
1	3.50
2	7.00
3	10.50
4	14.00

This table is from Section 2.3, Example 7.

The data in the table defines a relation between number of gallons of gas and cost and can be written as the following set of ordered pairs.

$$\{(0, 0), (1, 3.50), (2, 7.00), (3, 10.50), (4, 14.00)\}$$

Number of gallons of gas ↑   ↑ Cost in dollars

NOW TRY

A *function* is a special kind of relation.

NOW TRY ANSWER
1. $\{(2000, 1.56), (2005, 2.34),$
    $(2010, 2.84), (2015, 3.39)\}$

> ## Function
>
> A **function** is a relation in which, for each distinct value of the first component of the ordered pairs, there is *exactly one value* of the second component.

NOW TRY
EXERCISE 2

Determine whether each relation defines a function.

(a) $\{(1, 5), (3, 5), (5, 5)\}$

(b) $\{(-1, -3), (0, 2), (-1, 6)\}$

EXAMPLE 2 Determining Whether Relations Are Functions

Determine whether each relation defines a function.

(a) $F = \{(1, 2), (-2, 4), (3, -1)\}$

Look at the ordered pairs that define this relation.

> For $x = 1$, there is only one value of y, 2.
>
> For $x = -2$, there is only one value of y, 4.
>
> For $x = 3$, there is only one value of y, -1.

Relation F is a function—for each distinct x-value, there is *exactly one y-value.*

(b) $G = \{(-2, -1), (-1, 0), (0, 1), (1, 2), (2, 2)\}$

Relation G is also a function. Although the last two ordered pairs have the same y-value (1 is paired with 2, and 2 is paired with 2), this does not violate the definition of a function. The first components (x-values) are distinct, and each is paired with only one second component (y-value).

(c) $H = \{(-4, 1), (-2, 1), (-2, 0)\}$

In relation H, the last two ordered pairs have the *same* x-value paired with *two different* y-values (-2 is paired with both 1 and 0). H is a relation, but *not* a function. *In a function, no two ordered pairs have the same first component and different second components.*

Different y-values

$$\text{Relation } H = \{(-4, 1), (-2, 1), (-2, 0)\} \quad \text{Not a function}$$

Same x-value

NOW TRY

Relations may be defined in several different ways.

- **A relation may be defined as a set of ordered pairs. (See Example 2.)**

$$\text{Relation } F = \{(1, 2), (-2, 4), (3, -1)\} \qquad \text{Function}$$

$$\text{Relation } H = \{(-4, 1), (-2, 1), (-2, 0)\} \qquad \text{Not a function}$$

- **A relation may be defined as a correspondence or *mapping*.**

See **FIGURE 42**. In the mapping for relation F from **Example 2(a),** 1 is mapped to 2, -2 is mapped to 4, and 3 is mapped to -1. Thus, F is a function—each first component of an ordered pair is paired with exactly one second component.

In the mapping for relation H from **Example 2(c),** which is *not* a function, the first component -2 is paired with two different second components.

NOW TRY ANSWERS
2. (a) function
   (b) not a function

Relation F Relation H

F is a function. H is not a function.

FIGURE 42

- **A relation may be defined as a table.**
- **A relation may be defined as a graph.**

  FIGURE 43 includes a table and graph for relation F, which is a function, from **Example 2(a).**

Table for
relation F

Graph of relation F

FIGURE 43

- **A relation may be defined as an equation (or rule).**

  The solutions of an equation give an infinite set of ordered pairs. For example, if the value of y is twice the value of x, the equation is

$$y = 2x.$$

  The infinite number of ordered-pair solutions (x, y) can be represented by the graph in **FIGURE 44.**

  In the equation $y = 2x$, the value of y *depends* on the value of x. Thus, the variable y is the **dependent variable.** The variable x is the **independent variable.**

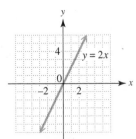

Graph of the relation $y = 2x$

FIGURE 44

Dependent variable $\longrightarrow y = 2x \longleftarrow$ Independent variable

An equation tells how to determine the value of the dependent variable for a specific value of the independent variable.

NOTE   An equation that describes the relationship given at the beginning of this section between number of hours worked and paycheck amount is

$$y = 8x. \quad \text{8 represents the hourly rate, \$8.}$$

Paycheck amount y *depends* on number of hours worked x. Thus, paycheck amount is the dependent variable and number of hours worked is the independent variable.

In a function, there is exactly one value of the dependent variable, the second component, for each value of the independent variable, the first component.

NOTE   Another way to think of a function relationship is to think of the independent variable as an **input** and the dependent variable as an **output.** This **input-output (function) machine** illustrates the relationship between number of hours worked and paycheck amount.

Function machine

OBJECTIVE 2 Find the domain and range.

Domain and Range

For every relation defined by a set of ordered pairs (x, y), there are two important sets of elements.

- The set of all values of the independent variable (x) is the **domain.**

- The set of all values of the dependent variable (y) is the **range.**

**NOW TRY
EXERCISE 3**

Give the domain and range of each relation. Decide whether the relation defines a function.

(a) $\{(2, 2), (2, 5), (4, 8)\}$

(b) The table from **Objective 1**

Number of Hours Worked	Paycheck Amount (in dollars)
5	40
10	80
20	160
40	320

EXAMPLE 3 Finding Domains and Ranges of Relations

Give the domain and range of each relation. Decide whether the relation defines a function.

(a) $\{(3, -1), (4, 2), (4, 5), (6, 8)\}$ Only list 4 once.

Domain: $\{3, 4, 6\}$ Set of x-values

Range: $\{-1, 2, 5, 8\}$ Set of y-values

This relation is not a function because the same x-value 4 is paired with two different y-values, 2 and 5.

(b)

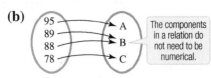

95
89
88
78
→ A
→ B
→ C

The components in a relation do not need to be numerical.

This mapping represents the following set of ordered pairs.

$$\{(95, A), (89, B), (88, B), (78, C)\}$$

Domain: $\{95, 89, 88, 78\}$ Set of first components

Range: $\{A, B, C\}$ Set of second components

The mapping defines a function—each domain value corresponds to exactly one range value.

(c)

x	y
-5	2
0	2
5	2

This table represents the following set of ordered pairs.

$$\{(-5, 2), (0, 2), (5, 2)\}$$

Domain: $\{-5, 0, 5\}$ Set of x-values

Range: $\{2\}$ Set of y-values

NOW TRY ANSWERS
3. **(a)** domain: $\{2, 4\}$;
     range: $\{2, 5, 8\}$;
     not a function
  (b) domain: $\{5, 10, 20, 40\}$;
     range: $\{40, 80, 160, 320\}$;
     function

The table defines a function—each distinct x-value corresponds to exactly one y-value (even though it is the same y-value).   **NOW TRY**

A graph gives a "picture" of a relation and can be used to determine its domain and range.

NOTE   Pay particular attention to the use of color to interpret domain and range in **Example 4**—blue for domain and red for range.

NOW TRY
EXERCISE 4

Give the domain and range of the relation.

EXAMPLE 4   Finding Domains and Ranges from Graphs

Give the domain and range of each relation.

(a)

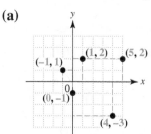

This relation includes the five ordered pairs that are graphed.

$$\{(-1, 1), (0, -1), (1, 2), (4, -3), (5, 2)\}$$

Domain: $\{-1, 0, 1, 4, 5\}$ Set of *x*-values

Range: $\{1, -1, 2, -3\}$ Set of *y*-values

> Only list 2 once.

(b)

The *x*-values of the ordered pairs that form the graph include all numbers between −4 and 4, inclusive, as shown in blue. The *y*-values include all numbers between −6 and 6, inclusive, as shown in red.

Domain: $[-4, 4]$ Use interval notation.

Range: $[-6, 6]$ (Section 1.5)

(c)

The arrowheads on the graphed line indicate that the line extends indefinitely left and right, as well as up and down. Therefore, both the domain, shown in blue, (the set of *x*-values) and the range, shown in red, (the set of *y*-values) include all real numbers.

Domain: $(-\infty, \infty)$ Range: $(-\infty, \infty)$

(d)

The graphed curve extends indefinitely left and right, as well as upward. The domain, shown in blue, includes all real numbers. Because there is a least *y*-value, −3, the range, shown in red, includes all numbers greater than or equal to −3.

Domain: $(-\infty, \infty)$ Range: $[-3, \infty)$

NOW TRY

OBJECTIVE 3   Identify functions defined by graphs and equations.

Because each value of *x* in a function corresponds to only one value of *y*, any vertical line drawn through the graph of a function must intersect the graph in at most one point. This is the *vertical line test* for a function.

FIGURE 45 on the next page illustrates this test with the graphs of two relations.

NOW TRY ANSWER
4. domain: $(-\infty, \infty)$;
    range: $[-2, \infty)$

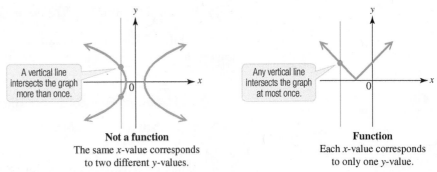

FIGURE 45

Vertical Line Test

If every vertical line intersects the graph of a relation in no more than one point, then the relation represents a function.

NOW TRY EXERCISE 5

Use the vertical line test to determine whether the relation is a function.

EXAMPLE 5   Using the Vertical Line Test

Use the vertical line test to determine whether each relation graphed in **Example 4** is a function. (We repeat the graphs here.)

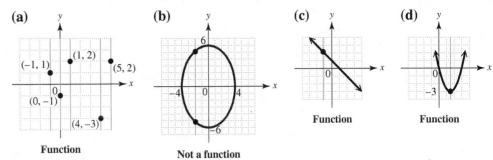

The graphs in (a), (c), and (d) satisfy the vertical line test and represent functions. The graph in (b) fails the vertical line test because a vertical line intersects the graph more than once—that is, the same x-value corresponds to two different y-values. This is not the graph of a function.   NOW TRY

NOTE   Graphs that do not represent functions are still relations. *All equations and graphs represent relations, and all relations have a domain and range.*

If a relation is defined by an equation involving a fraction or a radical, apply these guidelines when finding its domain.

1. **Exclude from the domain any values that make the denominator of a fraction equal to 0.**

   Example: The function $y = \dfrac{1}{x}$ has all real numbers *except* 0 as its domain because division by 0 is undefined.

2. **Exclude from the domain any values that result in an even root of a negative number.**

   Example: The function $y = \sqrt{x}$ has all *nonnegative* real numbers as its domain because the square root of a negative number is not real.

Agreement on Domain

Unless specified otherwise, the domain of a relation is assumed to be all real numbers that produce real numbers when substituted for the independent variable.

NOW TRY
EXERCISE 6

Decide whether each relation defines y as a function of x. Give the domain.

(a) $y = 4x - 3$

(b) $y = \sqrt{2x - 4}$

(c) $y = \dfrac{1}{x - 2}$

(d) $y < 3x + 1$

EXAMPLE 6 Identifying Functions from Their Equations

Decide whether each relation defines y as a function of x. Give the domain.

(a) $y = x + 4$

In this equation, y is found by adding 4 to x. Thus, each value of x corresponds to just one value of y, and the relation defines a function. Because x can be any real number, the domain is $(-\infty, \infty)$.

(b) $y = \sqrt{2x - 1}$

For any choice of x in the domain, there is exactly one corresponding value for y. (The radical is a single nonnegative number.) This equation defines a function. The quantity under the radical symbol cannot be negative—that is, $2x - 1$ *must be greater than or equal to* 0.

$$2x - 1 \geq 0$$

$$2x \geq 1 \qquad \text{Add 1.}$$

$$x \geq \frac{1}{2} \qquad \text{Divide by 2.}$$

The domain of the function is $\left[\frac{1}{2}, \infty\right)$.

(c) $y^2 = x$

The ordered pairs $(16, 4)$ and $(16, -4)$ both satisfy this equation. One value of x, 16, corresponds to two values of y, 4 and -4, so this equation does not define a function. Because x is equal to the square of y, the values of x must always be nonnegative. The domain of the relation is $[0, \infty)$.

(d) $y \leq x - 1$

By definition, y is a function of x if every value of x leads to exactly one value of y. Here, a particular value of x, such as 1, corresponds to many values of y. The ordered pairs

$$(1, 0), \quad (1, -1), \quad (1, -2), \quad (1, -3), \quad \text{and so on}$$

all satisfy the inequality. Thus, this relation does not define a function. Any number can be used for x, so the domain is the set of all real numbers, $(-\infty, \infty)$.

(e) $y = \dfrac{5}{x - 1}$

Given any value of x in the domain, we find y by subtracting 1 and then dividing the result into 5. This process produces exactly one value of y for each value in the domain, so the given equation defines a function.

The domain includes all real numbers except those which make the denominator 0.

NOW TRY ANSWERS
6. (a) yes; $(-\infty, \infty)$
(b) yes; $[2, \infty)$
(c) yes; $(-\infty, 2) \cup (2, \infty)$
(d) no; $(-\infty, \infty)$

$$x - 1 = 0 \qquad \text{Set the denominator equal to 0.}$$

$$x = 1 \qquad \text{Add 1.}$$

The domain includes all real numbers *except* 1, written $(-\infty, 1) \cup (1, \infty)$.

NOW TRY

In summary, we give three variations of the definition of a function.

Variations of the Definition of a Function

1. A **function** is a relation in which, for each distinct value of the first component of the ordered pairs, there is exactly one value of the second component.

2. A **function** is a set of distinct ordered pairs in which no first component is repeated.

3. A **function** is a correspondence (mapping) or an equation (rule) that assigns exactly one range value to each distinct domain value.

2.5 Exercises

FOR EXTRA HELP ▶ MyMathLab®

▶ *Complete solution available in MyMathLab*

Concept Check *Complete each statement. Choices may be used more than once.*

| function | independent variable | vertical line test | relation |
| domain | ordered pairs | dependent variable | range |

1. A(n) _____ is any set of _____ $\{(x, y)\}$.

2. A(n) _____ is a relation in which, for each distinct value of the first component of the _____, there is exactly one value of the second component.

3. In a relation $\{(x, y)\}$, the _____ is the set of x-values, and the _____ is the set of y-values.

4. The relation $\{(0, -2), (2, -1), (2, -4), (5, 3)\}$ (*does / does not*) define a function. The set $\{0, 2, 5\}$ is its _____, and the set $\{-2, -1, -4, 3\}$ is its _____.

5. Consider the function $d = 50t$, where d represents distance and t represents time. The value of d depends on the value of t, so the variable t is the _____, and the variable d is the _____.

6. The _____ is used to determine whether a graph is that of a function. It says that any vertical line can intersect the graph of a(n) _____ in no more than (*zero / one / two*) point(s).

Write each relation as a set of ordered pairs. **See Example 1 and Objective 1.**

7.
x	y
2	-2
2	0
2	1

8.
x	y
-1	-1
0	-1
1	-1

9.
Year	Average Movie Ticket Price (in dollars)
1960	0.76
1980	2.69
2000	5.39
2013	8.38

Source: Motion Picture Association of America.

10.
Year	Average ACT Composite Score
2010	21.0
2011	21.1
2012	21.1
2013	20.9

Source: ACT.

11.

12.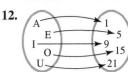

Concept Check   *Express each relation using a different form. (For example, if the given form is a set of ordered pairs, use a graph.) There is more than one correct way to do this.* **See Objective 1.**

13. $\{(0, 2), (2, 4), (4, 6)\}$

14.

x	y
−1	−3
0	−1
1	1
3	3

15.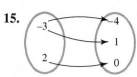

16. *Concept Check*   Does the relation given in **Exercise 15** define a function? Why or why not?

Decide whether each relation defines a function, and give the domain and range. **See Examples 2–5.**

17. $\{(5, 1), (3, 2), (4, 9), (7, 6)\}$

18. $\{(8, 0), (5, 4), (9, 3), (3, 8)\}$

19. $\{(2, 4), (0, 2), (2, 5)\}$

20. $\{(9, -2), (-3, 5), (9, 2)\}$

21. $\{(-3, 1), (4, 1), (-2, 7)\}$

22. $\{(-12, 5), (-10, 3), (8, 3)\}$

23. $\{(1, 1), (1, -1), (0, 0), (2, 4), (2, -4)\}$

24. $\{(2, 5), (3, 7), (4, 9), (5, 11)\}$

25.

26.

27.

x	y
1	5
1	2
1	−1
1	−4

28.

x	y
−4	−4
−4	0
−4	4
−4	8

29.

x	y
4	−3
2	−3
0	−3
−2	−3

30.

x	y
−3	−6
−1	−6
1	−6
3	−6

31.

32.

33.

34.

35.

36.

37.

38.

39.

40.

▶ 41.

42.

43.

44.

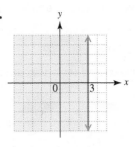

Decide whether each relation defines y as a function of x. (Solve for y first if necessary.) Give the domain. **See Example 6.**

45. $y = -6x$

46. $y = -9x$

▶ 47. $y = 2x - 6$

48. $y = 6x + 8$

49. $y = x^2$

50. $y = x^3$

51. $x = y^6$

52. $x = y^4$

53. $x + y < 4$

54. $x - y < 3$

55. $y = \sqrt{x}$

56. $y = -\sqrt{x}$

57. $y = \sqrt{x - 3}$

58. $y = \sqrt{x - 7}$

59. $y = \sqrt{4x + 2}$

60. $y = \sqrt{2x + 9}$

61. $y = \dfrac{x + 4}{5}$

62. $y = \dfrac{x - 3}{2}$

63. $y = -\dfrac{2}{x}$

64. $y = -\dfrac{6}{x}$

65. $y = \dfrac{2}{x - 4}$

66. $y = \dfrac{7}{x - 2}$

67. $xy = 1$

68. $xy = 3$

Solve each problem.

69. The table shows the percentage of students at 4-year public colleges who graduated within 5 years.

    (a) Does the table define a function?

    (b) What are the domain and range?

    (c) What is the range element that corresponds to 2012? The domain element that corresponds to 43.4?

    (d) Call this function f. Give two ordered pairs that belong to f.

Year	Percentage
2009	44.0
2010	43.4
2011	43.1
2012	42.9
2013	43.1

Source: ACT.

70. The table shows the percentage of full-time college freshmen who said that they frequently smoked cigarettes in the last year.

    (a) Does the table define a function?

    (b) What are the domain and range?

    (c) What is the range element that corresponds to 2012? The domain element that corresponds to 2.8?

    (d) Call this function g. Give two ordered pairs that belong to g.

Year	Percentage
2008	4.4
2009	4.2
2010	3.7
2011	2.8
2012	2.6

Source: Higher Education Research Institute.

STUDY SKILLS

Analyzing Your Test Results

An exam is a learning opportunity—learn from your mistakes. After a test is returned, do the following:

- **Note what you got wrong and why you had points deducted.**

- **Figure out how to solve the problems you missed.** Check your textbook or notes, or ask your instructor. Rework the problems correctly.

- **Keep all quizzes and tests that are returned to you.** Use them to study for future tests and the final exam.

Typical Reasons for Errors on Math Tests

These are test taking errors. They are easy to correct if you read carefully, show all your work, proofread, and double-check units and labels.

1. You read the directions wrong.

2. You read the question wrong or skipped over something.

3. You made a computation error.

4. You made a careless error. (For example, you incorrectly copied a correct answer onto a separate answer sheet.)

5. Your answer is not complete.

6. You labeled your answer wrong. (For example, you labeled an answer "ft" instead of "ft^2.")

7. You didn't show your work.

These are test preparation errors. You must practice the kinds of problems that you will see on tests.

8. You didn't understand a concept.

9. You were unable to set up the problem (in an application).

10. You were unable to apply a procedure.

Below are sample charts for tracking your test taking progress. Refer to the tests you have taken so far in your course, and use the charts to find out if you tend to make certain kinds of errors. Check the appropriate box when you've made an error in a particular category.

Test Taking Errors

Test	Read directions wrong	Read question wrong	Computation error	Not exact or accurate	Not complete	Labeled wrong	Didn't show work
1							
2							
3							

Test Preparation Errors

Test	Didn't understand concept	Didn't set up problem correctly	Couldn't apply concept to new situation
1			
2			
3			

What will you do to avoid these kinds of errors on your next test?

2.6 Function Notation and Linear Functions

OBJECTIVES

1   Use function notation.
2   Graph linear and constant functions.

VOCABULARY

☐ linear function
☐ constant function

OBJECTIVE 1 Use function notation.

When a function f is defined with a rule or an equation using x and y for the independent and dependent variables, we say, "*y is a function of x*" to emphasize that *y depends on x.* We use the notation

$$y = f(x),$$

> The parentheses here do *not* indicate multiplication.

called **function notation,** to express this and read $f(x)$ as "*f of x,*" or "*f at x.*" The letter f is a name for this particular function. For example, if $y = 3x - 5$, we can name this function f and write the following.

$$f(x) = 3x - 5$$

> f is the name of the function.
> x is a value from the domain.
> $f(x)$ is the function value (or y-value) that corresponds to x.

$f(x)$ is just another name for the dependent variable y.

We evaluate a function at different values of x by substituting x-values from the domain into the function.

**NOW TRY
EXERCISE 1**

Let $f(x) = 4x + 3$. Find the value of function f for each value of x.

(a) $x = -2$ **(b)** $x = 0$

EXAMPLE 1   Evaluating a Function

Let $f(x) = 3x - 5$. Find the value of function f for each value of x.

(a) $x = 2$

$$f(x) = 3x - 5$$

> Read $f(2)$ as "f of 2" or "f at 2."

$$f(2) = 3 \cdot 2 - 5 \qquad \text{Replace } x \text{ with 2.}$$
$$f(2) = 6 - 5 \qquad \text{Multiply.}$$
$$f(2) = 1 \qquad \text{Subtract.}$$

Thus, for $x = 2$, the corresponding function value (or y-value) is 1. $f(2) = 1$ is an abbreviation for the statement "If $x = 2$ in the function f, then $y = 1$" and is represented by the ordered pair $(2, 1)$.

(b) $x = -1$

$$f(x) = 3x - 5$$

> Use parentheses to avoid errors.

$$f(-1) = 3(-1) - 5 \qquad \text{Replace } x \text{ with } -1.$$
$$f(-1) = -3 - 5 \qquad \text{Multiply.}$$
$$f(-1) = -8 \qquad \text{Subtract.}$$

Thus, $f(-1) = -8$ and the ordered pair $(-1, -8)$ belongs to f.   NOW TRY

NOW TRY ANSWERS
1. (a) -5 **(b)** 3

⚠ CAUTION   The symbol $f(x)$ *does not* indicate "f times x," but represents the y-value associated with the indicated x-value. As shown in **Example 1(a),** $f(2)$ is the y-value that corresponds to the x-value 2 in f.

These ideas can be illustrated as follows.

Name of the function

Defining expression

$$y = \overset{\text{Name of the function}}{f(x)} = \overbrace{3x - 5}$$

Value of the function   Name of the independent variable

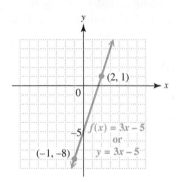

FIGURE 46

NOTE   In the function $f(x) = 3x - 5$ in **Example 1**, $f(2) = 1$ and $f(-1) = -8$ correspond to the ordered pairs $(2, 1)$ and $(-1, -8)$. Because the domain of f is $(-\infty, \infty)$—that is, x can be any real number—this function defines an infinite set of ordered pairs whose graph is a line with slope 3 and y-intercept $(0, -5)$. See **FIGURE 46**. This makes sense because $f(x)$ is another name for y, and

$$f(x) = 3x - 5 \quad \text{is equivalent to} \quad y = 3x - 5.$$

As we will see in **Objective 2**, f is a *linear function*.

**NOW TRY
EXERCISE 2**

Let $f(x) = 2x^2 - 4x + 1$. Find the following.

(a) $f(-2)$ **(b)** $f(a)$

EXAMPLE 2   Evaluating a Function

Let $f(x) = -x^2 + 5x - 3$. Find the following.

(a) $f(4)$

> Do *not* read this as "f times 4." Read it as "f of 4," or "f at 4."

$$f(x) = -x^2 + 5x - 3 \qquad \text{The base in } -x^2 \text{ is } x, \text{ not } (-x).$$

$$f(4) = -4^2 + 5 \cdot 4 - 3 \qquad \text{Replace } x \text{ with 4.}$$

$$f(4) = -16 + 20 - 3 \qquad \text{Apply the exponent. Multiply.}$$

$$f(4) = 1 \qquad \text{Add and subtract.}$$

Thus, $f(4) = 1$, and the ordered pair $(4, 1)$ belongs to f.

(b) $f(q)$

$$f(x) = -x^2 + 5x - 3$$

$$f(q) = -q^2 + 5q - 3 \qquad \text{Replace } x \text{ with } q.$$

The replacement of one variable with another is important in later courses.

NOW TRY

Sometimes letters other than f, such as g, h, or capital letters F, G, and H are used to name functions.

**NOW TRY
EXERCISE 3**

Let $g(x) = 8x - 5$. Find and simplify $g(a - 2)$.

EXAMPLE 3   Evaluating a Function

Let $g(x) = 2x + 3$. Find and simplify $g(a + 1)$.

$$g(x) = 2x + 3$$

$$g(a + 1) = 2(a + 1) + 3 \qquad \text{Replace } x \text{ with } a + 1.$$

$$g(a + 1) = 2a + 2 + 3 \qquad \text{Distributive property}$$

$$g(a + 1) = 2a + 5 \qquad \text{Add.}$$

NOW TRY

NOW TRY ANSWERS
2. (a) 17   **(b)** $2a^2 - 4a + 1$
3. $8a - 21$

NOW TRY
EXERCISE 4

Find $f(-1)$ for each function.

(a) $f = \{(-5, -1), (-3, 2),$
$(-1, 4)\}$

(b) $f(x) = x^2 - 12$

EXAMPLE 4 Evaluating Functions

For each function, find $f(3)$.

(a) $f(x) = 3x - 7$

$f(3) = 3(3) - 7$ Replace x with 3.

$f(3) = 9 - 7$ Multiply.

$f(3) = 2$ Subtract.

(b)

x	$y = f(x)$
6	-12
3	-6
0	0
-3	6

$\leftarrow$ Here, $f(3) = -6$.

(c) $f = \{(-3, 5), (0, 3), (3, 1), (6, -1)\}$

We want $f(3)$, the y-value of the ordered pair whose first component is $x = 3$. As indicated by the ordered pair $(3, 1)$, for $x = 3$, $y = 1$. Thus, $f(3) = 1$.

(d)

The domain element 3 is paired with 5 in the range, so
$$f(3) = 5.$$

NOW TRY

EXAMPLE 5 Finding Function Values from a Graph

Refer to the function graphed in **FIGURE 47**.

(a) Find $f(3)$.

Locate 3 on the x-axis. See **FIGURE 48**. Moving up to the graph of f and over to the y-axis gives 4 for the corresponding y-value. Thus, $f(3) = 4$, which corresponds to the ordered pair $(3, 4)$.

(b) Find $f(0)$.

Refer to **FIGURE 48** to see that $f(0) = 1$.

FIGURE 48

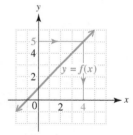

FIGURE 49

(c) For what value of x is $f(x) = 5$?

Because $f(x) = y$, we want the value of x that corresponds to $y = 5$. See **FIGURE 49**, and locate 5 on the y-axis. Moving across to the graph of f and down to the x-axis gives $x = 4$. Thus, $f(4) = 5$, which corresponds to the ordered pair $(4, 5)$.

NOW TRY

If a function f is defined by an equation in x and y instead of function notation, use the following steps to find $f(x)$.

Writing an Equation Using Function Notation

Step 1   Solve the equation for y.

Step 2   Replace y with $f(x)$.

FIGURE 47

NOW TRY
EXERCISE 5

Refer to the function graphed in **FIGURE 47**.

(a) Find $f(-1)$.

(b) For what value of x is
$f(x) = 2$?

NOW TRY ANSWERS

4. (a) 4   **(b)** -11

5. (a) 0   **(b)** 1

**NOW TRY
EXERCISE 6**

Write the equation using function notation $f(x)$. Then find $f(-3)$ and $f(h)$.

$$-4x^2 + y = 5$$

EXAMPLE 6   **Writing Equations Using Function Notation**

Write each equation using function notation $f(x)$. Then find $f(-2)$ and $f(a)$.

(a) $y = x^2 + 1$ ⟵ This equation is already solved for y.   (Step 1)

$f(x) = x^2 + 1$ Replace y with $f(x)$.   (Step 2)

To find $f(-2)$, let $x = -2$.

$$f(x) = x^2 + 1$$

$$f(-2) = (-2)^2 + 1 \qquad \text{Let } x = -2.$$

$$f(-2) = 4 + 1 \qquad\qquad (-2)^2 = -2(-2)$$

$$f(-2) = 5 \qquad\qquad\quad \text{Add.}$$

To find $f(a)$, let $x = a$.

$$f(a) = a^2 + 1$$

(b) $x - 4y = 5$

Step 1 $-4y = -x + 5$ Subtract x.

$$y = \frac{1}{4}x - \frac{5}{4} \qquad \text{Divide by } -4.$$

Step 2 $f(x) = \dfrac{1}{4}x - \dfrac{5}{4}$ Replace y with $f(x)$.

Now find $f(-2)$ and $f(a)$.

$$f(-2) = \frac{1}{4}(-2) - \frac{5}{4} = -\frac{7}{4} \qquad \text{Let } x = -2.$$

$$f(a) = \frac{1}{4}a - \frac{5}{4} \qquad\qquad\qquad \text{Let } x = a. \qquad \text{NOW TRY}$$

OBJECTIVE 2   Graph linear and constant functions.

Linear equations (except for vertical lines with equations of the form $x = a$) define *linear functions.*

Linear Function

A function f that can be written in the form

$$f(x) = ax + b,$$

where a and b are real numbers, is a **linear function.** The value of a is the slope m of the graph of the function. The domain of a linear function is $(-\infty, \infty)$, unless specified otherwise.

A linear function whose graph is a horizontal line has the form

$$f(x) = b \qquad \text{Constant function}$$

and is a **constant function.** While the range of any nonconstant linear function is $(-\infty, \infty)$, the range of a constant function $f(x) = b$ is $\{b\}$.

NOW TRY ANSWER
6. $f(x) = 4x^2 + 5$;
   $f(-3) = 41$;
   $f(h) = 4h^2 + 5$

**NOW TRY
EXERCISE 7**

Graph the function. Give the domain and range.

$$f(x) = \frac{1}{3}x - 2$$

EXAMPLE 7   Graphing Linear and Constant Functions

Graph each function. Give the domain and range.

(a) $f(x) = \dfrac{1}{4}x - \dfrac{5}{4}$ (from Example 6(b))

Slope ⟵┘   └⟶ y-intercept is $\left(0, -\frac{5}{4}\right)$.

To graph this function, plot the y-intercept $\left(0, -\frac{5}{4}\right)$. Use the geometric definition of slope as $\dfrac{\text{rise}}{\text{run}}$ to find a second point on the line. The slope is $\frac{1}{4}$, so we move 1 unit up from $\left(0, -\frac{5}{4}\right)$ and 4 units to the right to the point $\left(4, -\frac{1}{4}\right)$. Draw the straight line through these points. See **FIGURE 50**. The domain and range are both $(-\infty, \infty)$.

FIGURE 50

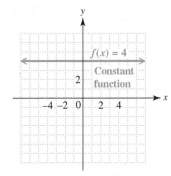

FIGURE 51

NOW TRY ANSWER

7.

domain: $(-\infty, \infty)$;

range: $(-\infty, \infty)$

(b) $f(x) = 4$

The graph of this constant function is the horizontal line containing all points with y-coordinate 4. See **FIGURE 51**. The domain is $(-\infty, \infty)$ and the range is $\{4\}$.

NOW TRY

2.6 Exercises

FOR
EXTRA
HELP

▶ MyMathLab®

▶ *Complete solution available in MyMathLab*

Concept Check   *Work each problem.*

1. To emphasize that "y is a function of x" for a given function f, we use function notation and write $y = $ _____. Here, f is the name of the _____, x is a value from the _____, and $f(x)$ is the function value (or y-value) that corresponds to _____. We read $f(x)$ as "_____."

2. Choose the correct response.

For a function f, the notation $f(3)$ means _____.

A. the variable f times 3, or $3f$.

B. the value of the dependent variable when the independent variable is 3.

C. the value of the independent variable when the dependent variable is 3.

D. f equals 3.

3. Fill in each blank with the correct response.

The equation $2x + y = 4$ has a straight _____ as its graph. One point that lies on the graph is $(3, \text{___})$. If we solve the equation for y and use function notation, we have a(n) _____ function $f(x) = $ _____. For this function, $f(3) = \text{___}$, meaning that the point $(\text{___}, \text{___})$ lies on the graph of the function.

4. Which of the following defines y as a linear function of x?

     A. $y = \dfrac{1}{4}x - \dfrac{5}{4}$ **B.** $y = \dfrac{1}{x}$ **C.** $y = x^2$ **D.** $y = \sqrt{x}$

Let $f(x) = -3x + 4$ and $g(x) = -x^2 + 4x + 1$. Find the following. **See Examples 1–3.**

▶ **5.** $f(0)$ **6.** $g(0)$ **7.** $f(-3)$ **8.** $f(-5)$

   9. $g(-2)$ **10.** $g(-1)$ **11.** $g(3)$ **12.** $g(10)$

   13. $f(100)$ **14.** $f(-100)$ **15.** $f\left(\dfrac{1}{3}\right)$ **16.** $f\left(\dfrac{7}{3}\right)$

   17. $g(0.5)$ **18.** $g(1.5)$ **19.** $f(p)$ **20.** $g(k)$

   21. $f(-x)$ **22.** $g(-x)$ ▶ **23.** $f(x + 2)$ **24.** $f(x - 2)$

   25. $f(2t + 1)$ **26.** $f(3t - 2)$ **27.** $g(\pi)$ **28.** $g(t)$

   29. $f(x + h)$ **30.** $f(a + b)$ **31.** $g\left(\dfrac{p}{3}\right)$ **32.** $g\left(\dfrac{1}{x}\right)$

For each function, find (a) $f(2)$ and (b) $f(-1)$. **See Examples 4, 5(a), and 5(b).**

   33. $f = \{(-2, 2), (-1, -1), (2, -1)\}$ **34.** $f = \{(-1, -5), (0, 5), (2, -5)\}$

▶ **35.** $f = \{(-1, 3), (4, 7), (0, 6), (2, 2)\}$ **36.** $f = \{(2, 5), (3, 9), (-1, 11), (5, 3)\}$

37.

38.

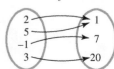

39.

x	$y = f(x)$
2	4
1	1
0	0
−1	1
−2	4

40.

x	$y = f(x)$
8	6
5	3
2	0
−1	−3
−4	−6

41.

42.

43.

44.

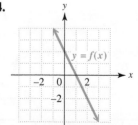

*Refer to the given graph. Find the value of x for each value of f(x). **See Example 5(c).***

45. (a) $f(x) = 3$

(b) $f(x) = -1$

(c) $f(x) = -3$

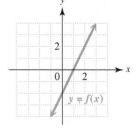

46. (a) $f(x) = 4$

(b) $f(x) = -2$

(c) $f(x) = 0$

*An equation that defines y as a function f of x is given. **(a)** Solve for y in terms of x, and re-place y with function notation f(x). **(b)** Find f(3). **See Example 6.***

▶ **47.** $x + 3y = 12$ **48.** $x - 4y = 8$ **49.** $y + 2x^2 = 3$

50. $y - 3x^2 = 2$ **51.** $4x - 3y = 8$ **52.** $-2x + 5y = 9$

*Graph each linear function. Give the domain and range. **See Example 7.***

▶ **53.** $f(x) = -2x + 5$ **54.** $g(x) = 4x - 1$ **55.** $h(x) = \frac{1}{2}x + 2$

56. $F(x) = -\frac{1}{4}x + 1$ **57.** $G(x) = 2x$ **58.** $H(x) = -3x$

▶ **59.** $g(x) = -4$ **60.** $f(x) = 5$ **61.** $f(x) = 0$ **62.** $f(x) = -2.5$

63. *Concept Check*   What is the name that is usually given to the graph in **Exercise 61?**

64. *Concept Check*   Can the graph of a linear function have an undefined slope? Explain.

Solve each problem.

65. A package weighing x pounds costs $f(x)$ dollars to mail to a given location, where

$$f(x) = 3.75x.$$

(a) Evaluate $f(3)$.

(b) Describe what 3 and the value $f(3)$ mean in part (a), using the terms *independent variable* and *dependent variable*.

(c) How much would it cost to mail a 5-lb package? Then write this question and its answer using function notation.

66. A taxicab driver charges $2.50 per mile.

(a) Fill in the table with the correct response for the price $f(x)$ he charges for a trip of x miles.

(b) The linear function that gives a rule for the amount charged is $f(x) = $ _____.

x	$f(x)$
0	
1	
2	
3	

(c) Graph this function for the domain $\{0, 1, 2, 3\}$.

67. To print t-shirts, there is a $100 set-up fee, plus a $12 charge per t-shirt. Let x represent the number of t-shirts printed and $f(x)$ represent the total charge.

   (a) Write a linear function that models this situation.

   (b) Find $f(125)$. Interpret your answer in the context of this problem.

   (c) Find the value of x if $f(x) = 1000$. Express this situation using function notation, and interpret it in the context of this problem.

68. Rental on a car is $150, plus $0.50 per mile. Let x represent the number of miles driven and $f(x)$ represent the total cost to rent the car.

   (a) Write a linear function that models this situation.

   (b) How much would it cost to drive 250 mi? Interpret this question and answer, using function notation.

   (c) Find the value of x if $f(x) = 400$. Interpret your answer in the context of this problem.

69. The table represents a linear function.

   (a) What is $f(2)$?

   (b) If $f(x) = -2.5$, what is the value of x?

   (c) What is the slope of the line?

   (d) What is the y-intercept of the line?

   (e) Using your answers from parts (c) and (d), write an equation for $f(x)$.

x	$y = f(x)$
0	3.5
1	2.3
2	1.1
3	−0.1
4	−1.3
5	−2.5

70. The table represents a linear function.

   (a) What is $f(2)$?

   (b) If $f(x) = 2.1$, what is the value of x?

   (c) What is the slope of the line?

   (d) What is the y-intercept of the line?

   (e) Using your answers from parts (c) and (d), write an equation for $f(x)$.

x	$y = f(x)$
−1	−3.9
0	−2.4
1	−0.9
2	0.6
3	2.1

71. The graph shows water in a swimming pool over time.

Gallons of Water in a Pool at Time t

   (a) What numbers are possible values of the independent variable? The dependent variable?

   (b) For how long is the water level increasing? Decreasing?

   (c) How many gallons of water are in the pool after 90 hr?

   (d) Call this function f. What is $f(0)$? What does it mean?

   (e) What is $f(25)$? What does it mean?

72. The graph shows electricity use on a summer day.

Electricity Use

   (a) Why is this the graph of a function?

   (b) What is the domain?

   (c) Estimate the number of megawatts used at 8 A.M.

   (d) At what time was the most electricity used? The least electricity?

   (e) Call this function f. What is $f(12)$? What does it mean?

73. Forensic scientists use the lengths of certain bones to calculate the height of a person. Two such bones are the tibia (t), the bone from the ankle to the knee, and the femur (r), the bone from the knee to the hip socket. A person's height (h) in centimeters is determined from the lengths of these bones by using the following functions.

Femur

Tibia

For men: $h(r) = 69.09 + 2.24r$ or $h(t) = 81.69 + 2.39t$

For women: $h(r) = 61.41 + 2.32r$ or $h(t) = 72.57 + 2.53t$

(a) Find the height of a man with a femur measuring 56 cm.

(b) Find the height of a man with a tibia measuring 40 cm.

(c) Find the height of a woman with a femur measuring 50 cm.

(d) Find the height of a woman with a tibia measuring 36 cm.

74. Based on federal regulations, a pool to house sea otters must have a volume that is "the square of the sea otter's average adult length (in meters) multiplied by 3.14 and by 0.91 meter." If x represents the sea otter's average adult length and $f(x)$ represents the volume (in cubic meters) of the corresponding pool size, this formula can be written as the function

$$f(x) = 0.91(3.14)x^2.$$

Find the volume of the pool for each adult sea otter length (in meters). Round answers to the nearest hundredth.

(a) 0.8   (b) 1.0   (c) 1.2   (d) 1.5

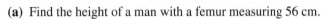

RELATING CONCEPTS For Individual or Group Work **(Exercises 75–82)**

*Refer to the straight-line graph and **work Exercises 75–82 in order.***

75. By just looking at the graph, how can we tell whether the slope is positive, negative, 0, or undefined?

76. Apply the slope formula to find the slope of the line.

77. What is the slope of any line parallel to the line shown? Perpendicular to the line shown?

78. Find the x-intercept of the graph.

79. Find the y-intercept of the graph.

80. Use function notation to write the equation of the line. Use f to designate the function.

81. Find $f(8)$.

82. If $f(x) = -8$, what is the value of x?

Chapter 2	Summary

Key Terms

2.1
ordered pair
origin
x-axis
y-axis
rectangular (Cartesian)
   coordinate system
components
plot
coordinate
quadrant
table of ordered pairs
   (table of values)

graph of an equation
first-degree equation
linear equation in two
   variables
x-intercept
y-intercept

2.2
rise
run
slope

2.3
scatter diagram

2.4
linear inequality in two
   variables
boundary line

2.5
relation
function

dependent variable
independent variable
domain
range

2.6
linear function
constant function

New Symbols

(x, y) ordered pair

(x_1, y_1) subscript notation
   (read "x-sub-one,
   y-sub-one")

Δ Greek letter delta
m slope

$f(x)$ function notation;
   function of x (read
   "f of x" or "f at x")

Test Your Word Power

See how well you have learned the vocabulary in this chapter.

1. An **ordered pair** is a pair of numbers written
   A. in numerical order between brackets
   B. between parentheses or brackets
   C. between parentheses in which order is important
   D. between parentheses in which order does not matter.

2. A **linear equation in two variables** is an equation that can be written in the form
   A. $Ax + By < C$
   B. $ax = b$
   C. $y = x^2$
   D. $Ax + By = C$.

3. An **intercept** is
   A. the point where the x-axis and y-axis intersect
   B. a pair of numbers written between parentheses in which order matters
   C. one of the regions determined by a coordinate system

D. the point where a graph intersects the x-axis or the y-axis.

4. The **slope** of a line is
   A. the measure of the run over the rise of the line
   B. the distance between two points on the line
   C. the ratio of the change in y to the change in x along the line
   D. the horizontal change compared to the vertical change of two points on the line.

5. A **relation** is
   A. a set of ordered pairs
   B. the ratio of the change in y to the change in x along a line
   C. the set of all possible values of the independent variable
   D. all the second components of a set of ordered pairs.

6. A **function** is
   A. a pair of numbers in an ordered pair

B. a set of ordered pairs in which each x-value corresponds to exactly one y-value
   C. a pair of numbers written between parentheses
   D. the set of all ordered pairs that satisfy an equation.

7. The **domain** of a relation is
   A. the set of all possible values of the dependent variable y
   B. a set of ordered pairs
   C. the difference between the x-values
   D. the set of all possible values of the independent variable x.

8. The **range** of a relation is
   A. the set of all possible values of the dependent variable y
   B. a set of ordered pairs
   C. the difference between the y-values
   D. the set of all possible values of the independent variable x.

ANSWERS

1. C; *Examples:* $(0, 3)$, $(3, 8)$, $(4, 0)$ **2.** D; *Examples:* $3x + 2y = 6$, $x = y - 7$ **3.** D; *Example:* In **FIGURE 4(b)** of **Section 2.1**, the x-intercept is $(3, 0)$ and the y-intercept is $(0, 2)$.   **4.** C; *Example:* The line through $(3, 6)$ and $(5, 4)$ has slope $\frac{4 - 6}{5 - 3} = \frac{-2}{2} = -1$.   **5.** A; *Example:* The set $\{(2, 0), (4, 3), (6, 6)\}$ defines a relation.   **6.** B; *Example:* The relation given in Answer 5 is a function.   **7.** D; *Example:* In the relation in Answer 5, the domain is the set of x-values, $\{2, 4, 6\}$.   **8.** A; *Example:* In the relation in Answer 5, the range is the set of y-values, $\{0, 3, 6\}$.

Quick Review

CONCEPTS	EXAMPLES

2.1 Linear Equations in Two Variables

Finding Intercepts

To find the x-intercept, let $y = 0$ and solve for x.

To find the y-intercept, let $x = 0$ and solve for y.

Find the intercepts of the graph of $2x + 3y = 12$.

$$2x + 3(0) = 12 \quad \text{Let } y = 0.$$
$$2x = 12$$
$$x = 6$$

The x-intercept is $(6, 0)$.

$$2(0) + 3y = 12 \quad \text{Let } x = 0.$$
$$3y = 12$$
$$y = 4$$

The y-intercept is $(0, 4)$.

Midpoint Formula

The midpoint M of a line segment PQ with endpoints (x_1, y_1) and (x_2, y_2) is found as follows.

$$M = \left(\frac{x_1 + x_2}{2}, \frac{y_1 + y_2}{2} \right)$$

Find the midpoint of the segment with endpoints $(4, -7)$ and $(-10, -13)$.

$$M = \left(\frac{4 + (-10)}{2}, \frac{-7 + (-13)}{2} \right)$$
$$= (-3, -10)$$

2.2 The Slope of a Line

The slope m of the line passing through the points (x_1, y_1) and (x_2, y_2) is defined as follows.

$$\textbf{slope } m = \frac{\textbf{rise}}{\textbf{run}} = \frac{\textbf{change in } y}{\textbf{change in } x} = \frac{\Delta y}{\Delta x} = \frac{y_2 - y_1}{x_2 - x_1}$$

$$(\text{where } x_1 \neq x_2)$$

Find the slope of the graph of $2x + 3y = 12$.

Use the intercepts $(6, 0)$ and $(0, 4)$ and the slope formula.

$$m = \frac{4 - 0}{0 - 6} = \frac{4}{-6} = -\frac{2}{3} \qquad \begin{array}{l} (x_1, y_1) = (6, 0) \\ (x_2, y_2) = (0, 4) \end{array}$$

A horizontal line has slope 0.

A vertical line has undefined slope.

Parallel lines have equal slopes.

The graph of the horizontal line $y = -5$ has slope $m = 0$.

The graph of the vertical line $x = 3$ has undefined slope.

The lines $y = 2x + 3$ and $4x - 2y = 6$ are parallel. Both have $m = 2$.

$$y = 2x + 3 \qquad\qquad 4x - 2y = 6 \qquad\qquad \text{Solve for } y.$$
$$-2y = -4x + 6$$
$$y = 2x - 3$$

Perpendicular lines, neither of which is vertical, **have slopes that are negative reciprocals** (that is, have a product of -1).

The lines $y = 3x - 1$ and $x + 3y = 4$ are perpendicular. Their slopes are negative reciprocals.

$$y = 3x - 1 \qquad\qquad x + 3y = 4 \qquad\qquad \text{Solve for } y.$$
$$3y = -x + 4$$
$$y = -\frac{1}{3}x + \frac{4}{3}$$

Slope gives the **average rate of change** in y per unit change in x, where the value of y depends on the value of x.

The weight of a young child increased from 30 lb to 60 lb between the ages of 3 and 8. What was the child's average change in weight per year over these years?

$$\frac{60 - 30}{8 - 3} = \frac{30}{5} = 6 \text{ lb per yr}$$

CONCEPTS	EXAMPLES

2.3 Writing Equations of Lines

Slope-Intercept Form

$y = mx + b$

$y = 2x + 3$ $m = 2$, y-intercept is $(0, 3)$.

Point-Slope Form

$y - y_1 = m(x - x_1)$

$y - 3 = 4(x - 5)$ $(5, 3)$ is on the line, $m = 4$.

Standard Form

$Ax + By = C$, where A, B, and C are real numbers and A and B are not both 0. (We give A, B, and C integers, with greatest common factor 1 and $A \geq 0$.)

$2x - 5y = 8$ Standard form

Horizontal Line

$y = b$

$y = 4$ Horizontal line

Vertical Line

$x = a$

$x = -1$ Vertical line

2.4 Linear Inequalities in Two Variables

Graphing a Linear Inequality

Graph $2x - 3y \leq 6$.

Step 1 Draw the graph of the straight line that is the boundary. Make the line solid if the inequality involves $\leq$ or $\geq$. Make the line dashed if the inequality involves $<$ or $>$.

Draw the graph of $2x - 3y = 6$. Use a solid line because of the inclusion of equality in the symbol $\leq$.

Step 2 Choose any point not on the line as a test point. Substitute the coordinates of that point in the inequality.

Choose $(0, 0)$ as a test point.

$2(0) - 3(0) \overset{?}{<} 6$

$0 < 6$ True

Step 3 Shade the region that includes the test point if it satisfies the original inequality. Otherwise, shade the region on the other side of the boundary line.

Shade the region that includes $(0, 0)$.

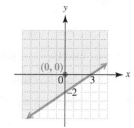

2.5 Introduction to Relations and Functions

A **relation** is any set of ordered pairs. A **function** is a set of ordered pairs such that, for each distinct first component, there is one and only one second component.

The set of first components is the **domain.**

The set of second components is the **range.**

The set of ordered pairs $\{(-1, 4), (0, 6), (1, 4)\}$ defines a function.

Domain: $\{-1, 0, 1\}$ Set of x-values

Range: $\{4, 6\}$ Set of y-values

The equation $y = x^2$ defines a function.

Domain: $(-\infty, \infty)$ Range: $[0, \infty)$

2.6 Function Notation and Linear Functions

$f(x) = x^2 - 7x + 12$

$f(1) = 1^2 - 7(1) + 12$ Let $x = 1$.

$f(1) = 6$

To evaluate a function f, where $f(x)$ defines the range value for a given value of x in the domain, substitute the value wherever x appears.

To write an equation that defines a function f in function notation, follow these steps.

Write $2x + 3y = 12$ using function notation for a function f.

$3y = -2x + 12$ Subtract $2x$.

Step 1 Solve the equation for y.

$y = -\dfrac{2}{3}x + 4$ Divide by 3.

Step 2 Replace y with $f(x)$.

$f(x) = -\dfrac{2}{3}x + 4$ $y = f(x)$

Chapter 2 | Review Exercises

1.

x	y
0	5
$\frac{10}{3}$	0
2	2
$\frac{14}{3}$	-2

2.

x	y
2	-6
5	-3
3	-5
6	-2

3. $(3, 0)$; $(0, -4)$ **4.** $\left(\frac{28}{5}, 0\right)$; $(0, 4)$

5. $(10, 0)$; $(0, 4)$ **6.** $(8, 0)$; $(0, -2)$

7. $(0, 2)$ **8.** $\left(-\frac{9}{2}, \frac{3}{2}\right)$

9. $-\frac{7}{5}$ **10.** $-\frac{1}{2}$

11. 2 **12.** $\frac{3}{4}$

13. undefined **14.** $\frac{2}{3}$

15. $-\frac{1}{3}$ **16.** undefined

17. $-\frac{1}{3}$ **18.** -1

19. positive **20.** negative

21. undefined **22.** 0

23. 12 ft **24.** $938 per year

Exercises (right column):

2.1 *Complete the table of ordered pairs for each equation. Then graph the equation.*

1. $3x + 2y = 10$

x	y
0	
	0
2	
	-2

2. $x - y = 8$

x	y
2	
	-3
3	
	-2

Find the x- and y-intercepts. Then graph each equation.

3. $4x - 3y = 12$ **4.** $5x + 7y = 28$ **5.** $2x + 5y = 20$ **6.** $x - 4y = 8$

Find the midpoint of each segment with the given endpoints.

7. $(-8, -12)$ and $(8, 16)$ **8.** $(0, -5)$ and $(-9, 8)$

2.2 *Find the slope of each line. (In Exercises 17 and 18, coordinates of the points shown are integers.)*

9. Through $(-1, 2)$ and $(4, -5)$ **10.** Through $(0, 3)$ and $(-2, 4)$

11. $y = 2x + 3$ **12.** $3x - 4y = 5$

13. $x = 5$ **14.** Parallel to $3y = 2x + 5$

15. Perpendicular to $3x - y = 4$ **16.** Through $(-1, 5)$ and $(-1, -4)$

17.

18.

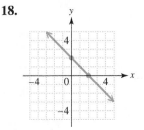

Tell whether the slope of the line is positive, negative, 0, or undefined.

19. **20.** **21.** **22.**

Solve each problem.

23. If the pitch of a roof is $\frac{1}{4}$, how many feet in the horizontal direction correspond to a rise of 3 ft?

24. In 1980, the median family income in the United States was about $21,000 per year. In 2012, it was about $51,017 per year. Find the average rate of change in median family income per year to the nearest dollar during this period. (*Source:* U.S. Census Bureau.)

25. (a) $y = -\frac{1}{3}x - 1$

(b) $x + 3y = -3$

26. (a) $y = -2$

(b) $y = -2$

27. (a) $y = -\frac{4}{3}x + \frac{29}{3}$

(b) $4x + 3y = 29$

28. (a) $y = 3x + 7$

(b) $3x - y = -7$

29. (a) not possible

(b) $x = 2$

30. (a) $y = -9x + 13$

(b) $9x + y = 13$

31. (a) $y = \frac{7}{5}x + \frac{16}{5}$

(b) $7x - 5y = -16$

32. (a) $y = -x + 2$

(b) $x + y = 2$

33. (a) $y = 4x - 29$

(b) $4x - y = 29$

34. (a) $y = -\frac{5}{2}x + 13$

(b) $5x + 2y = 26$

35. $y = 47x + 159$; $723

36. (a) $y = 38x + 2172$;

The revenue from skiing facilities increased by an average of $38 million per year from 2008 to 2012.

(b) $2552 million

37.

38.

39.

40.

41. not a function;
domain: $\{-4, 1\}$;
range: $\{2, -2, 5, -5\}$

42. function;
domain: $\{9, 11, 4, 17, 25\}$;
range: $\{32, 47, 69, 14\}$

43. function;
domain: $[-4, 4]$;
range: $[0, 2]$

44. not a function;
domain: $(-\infty, 0]$;
range: $(-\infty, \infty)$

45. function;
domain: $(-\infty, \infty)$;
linear function

2.3 *Write an equation of the line that satisfies the given conditions. Give the equation (a) in slope-intercept form if possible and (b) in standard form.*

25. Slope $-\frac{1}{3}$; y-intercept $(0, -1)$

26. Slope 0; y-intercept $(0, -2)$

27. Slope $-\frac{4}{3}$; through $(2, 7)$

28. Slope 3; through $(-1, 4)$

29. Vertical; through $(2, 5)$

30. Through $(2, -5)$ and $(1, 4)$

31. Through $(-3, -1)$ and $(2, 6)$

32. The line graphed in **Exercise 18**

33. Through $(7, -1)$; parallel to $4x - y = 3$

34. Through $(4, 3)$; perpendicular to $2x - 5y = 7$

Solve each problem.

35. An Executive Regular/Silver membership to a health club costs $159, plus $47 per month. Let x represent the number of months and y represent the cost. How much will a one-year membership cost? (*Source:* Midwest Athletic Club.)

36. Revenue for skiing facilities in the United States is shown in the graph.

(a) Use the information given for the years 2008 and 2012, letting $x = 8$ represent 2008 and $x = 12$ represent 2012, and letting y represent revenue (in millions of dollars), to write an equation that models the data. Write the equation in slope-intercept form. Interpret the slope.

(b) Use the equation from part (a) to approximate revenue for skiing facilities in 2010.

Source: U.S. Department of Commerce.

2.4 *Graph each inequality or compound inequality.*

37. $3x - 2y \leq 12$

38. $5x - y > 6$

39. $2x + y \leq 1$ and $x \geq 2y$

40. $x \geq 2$ or $y \geq 2$

2.5 *Decide whether each relation defines a function, and give the domain and range.*

41. $\{(-4, 2), (-4, -2), (1, 5), (1, -5)\}$

42.

43.

44.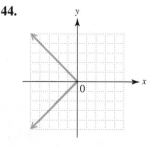

2.5, 2.6 *Decide whether each relation defines y as a function of x. Give the domain. Identify any linear functions.*

45. $y = 3x - 3$

46. $y < x + 2$

47. $y = |x|$

48. $y = \sqrt{4x + 7}$

49. $x = y^2$

50. $y = \frac{7}{x - 6}$

46. not a function;
domain: $(-\infty, \infty)$

47. function;
domain: $(-\infty, \infty)$

48. function;
domain: $\left[-\dfrac{7}{4}, \infty\right)$

49. not a function;
domain: $[0, \infty)$

50. function;
domain: $(-\infty, 6) \cup (6, \infty)$

51. -6 **52.** -8.52
53. -8 **54.** $-2k^2 + 3k - 6$
55. $f(x) = 2x^2$; 18
56. C
57. It is a horizontal line.
58. (a) yes
(b) domain: $\{1960, 1970, 1980,$ $1990, 2000, 2010\}$;
range: $\{69.7, 70.8, 73.7, 75.4,$ $76.8, 78.7\}$
(c) Answers will vary.
Two possible answers are
$(1960, 69.7)$ and $(2010, 78.7)$.
(d) 73.7;
In 1980, life expectancy at
birth was 73.7 yr.
(e) 2000

2.6 *Let* $f(x) = -2x^2 + 3x - 6$. *Find the following.*

51. $f(0)$ **52.** $f(2.1)$ **53.** $f\left(-\dfrac{1}{2}\right)$ **54.** $f(k)$

Solve each problem.

55. The equation $2x^2 - y = 0$ defines y as a function f of x. Write it using function notation, and find $f(3)$.

56. Suppose that $2x - 5y = 7$ defines y as a function f of x. If $y = f(x)$, which one of the following defines the same function?

A. $f(x) = -\dfrac{2}{5}x + \dfrac{7}{5}$ **B.** $f(x) = -\dfrac{2}{5}x - \dfrac{7}{5}$

C. $f(x) = \dfrac{2}{5}x - \dfrac{7}{5}$ **D.** $f(x) = \dfrac{2}{5}x + \dfrac{7}{5}$

57. Describe the graph of a constant function.

58. The table shows life expectancy at birth in the United States for selected years.

(a) Does the table define a function?

(b) What are the domain and range?

(c) Call this function f. Give two ordered pairs that belong to f.

(d) Find $f(1980)$. What does this mean?

(e) If $f(x) = 76.8$, what does x equal?

Year	Life Expectancy at Birth (years)
1960	69.7
1970	70.8
1980	73.7
1990	75.4
2000	76.8
2010	78.7

Source: National Center for Health Statistics.

Chapter 2   Mixed Review Exercises

1. perpendicular
2. parallel

3. -1.8 lb per year;
Per capita consumption of
potatoes decreased by an
average of 1.8 lb per year from
2003 to 2011.
4. $y = -1.8x + 46.8$

Determine whether each pair of lines is parallel, perpendicular, *or* neither.

1. $3x + y = 4$ and $3y = x - 6$ **2.** $4x + 3y = 8$ and $6y = 7 - 8x$

The graph shows per capita consumption of potatoes (in pounds) in the United States from 2003 to 2011.

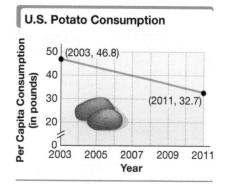

U.S. Potato Consumption

Source: U.S. Department of Agriculture.

3. Use the given ordered pairs to find and interpret the average rate of change in per capita potato consumption per year to the nearest tenth during this period.

4. Write an equation in slope-intercept form that models per capita consumption of potatoes y (in pounds) in year x, where $x = 0$ represents 2003.

5. $y = 3x$
6. $x + 2y = 6$
7. $y = -3$

8. A, B, D
9. D
10. (a) -1 **(b)** -2
  (c) 2
  (d) $(-\infty, \infty); (-\infty, \infty)$

Write an equation of a line (in the form specified, if given) that satisfies the given conditions.

5. $m = 3$; y-intercept $(0, 0)$ (slope-intercept form)

6. Through $(0, 3)$ and $(-2, 4)$ (standard form)

7. Through $(2, -3)$; perpendicular to $x = 2$

Solve each problem.

8. Which equations have a graph with just one intercept?

  A. $x - 6 = 0$ **B.** $x + y = 0$ **C.** $x - y = 4$ **D.** $y = -4$

9. Which inequality has as its graph a dashed boundary line and shading below the line?

  A. $y \geq 4x + 3$ **B.** $y > 4x + 3$ **C.** $y \leq 4x + 3$ **D.** $y < 4x + 3$

10. Refer to the graph of function f.

  (a) Find $f(-2)$.

  (b) Find $f(0)$.

  (c) For what value of x is $f(x) = -3$?

  (d) Give the domain and range.

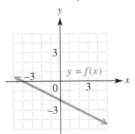

Chapter 2   Test   FOR EXTRA HELP

Step-by-step test solutions are found on the Chapter Test Prep Videos available in MyMathLab® *or on* You Tube™.

▶ *View the complete solutions to all Chapter Test exercises in MyMathLab.*

[2.1]

1. $-\dfrac{10}{3}; -2; 0$

2. $\left(\dfrac{20}{3}, 0\right); (0, -10)$

3. none; $(0, 5)$ **4.** $(2, 0)$; none

[2.2]

5. $\dfrac{1}{2}$

6. It is a vertical line.
7. perpendicular
8. neither
9. -838 farms per yr;
  The number of farms decreased an average of 838 farms per year from 1980 to 2012.

1. Complete the table of ordered pairs for the equation $2x - 3y = 12$.

x	y
1	
3	
	-4

Find the x- and y-intercepts. Then graph each equation.

2. $3x - 2y = 20$ **3.** $y = 5$ **4.** $x = 2$

5. Find the slope of the line passing through the points $(6, 4)$ and $(-4, -1)$.

6. Describe how the graph of a line with undefined slope is situated in a rectangular coordinate system.

Determine whether each pair of lines is parallel, perpendicular, *or* neither.

7. $5x - y = 8$ and $5y = -x + 3$ **8.** $2y = 3x + 12$ and $3y = 2x - 5$

9. In 1980, there were 119,000 farms in Iowa. As of 2012, there were 92,200. Find and interpret the average rate of change in the number of farms per year, to the nearest whole number. (*Source:* U.S. Department of Agriculture.)

Write an equation of the line that satisfies the given conditions. Give the equation **(a)** *in slope-intercept form if possible and* **(b)** *in standard form.*

10. Through $(4, -1)$; $m = -5$ **11.** Through $(-3, 14)$; horizontal

12. Through $(-2, 3)$ and $(6, -1)$ **13.** Through $(5, -6)$; vertical

14. Through $(-7, 2)$; parallel to $3x + 5y = 6$

15. Through $(-7, 2)$; perpendicular to $y = 2x$

[2.3]

10. (a) $y = -5x + 19$

(b) $5x + y = 19$

11. (a) $y = 14$ **(b)** $y = 14$

12. (a) $y = -\dfrac{1}{2}x + 2$

(b) $x + 2y = 4$

13. (a) not possible   **(b)** $x = 5$

14. (a) $y = -\dfrac{3}{5}x - \dfrac{11}{5}$

(b) $3x + 5y = -11$

15. (a) $y = -\dfrac{1}{2}x - \dfrac{3}{2}$

(b) $x + 2y = -3$

16. B

17. (a) $y = 142.75x + 45$

(b) \$901.50

[2.4]

18.   **19.**

[2.5]

20. D   **21.** D

22. domain: $[0, \infty)$;

range: $(-\infty, \infty)$

23. domain: $\{0, -2, 4\}$;

range: $\{1, 3, 8\}$

[2.6]

24. $0; -a^2 + 2a - 1$

25.

domain: $(-\infty, \infty)$;

range: $(-\infty, \infty)$

16. Which line has positive slope and negative y-coordinate for its y-intercept?

A.   **B.**   **C.**   **D.**

17. A ticket to a rock concert costs \$142.75. An advance parking pass costs \$45. Let x represent the number of tickets purchased and y represent the total cost in dollars.

(a) Write an equation in slope-intercept form that represents this situation.

(b) How much does it cost for 6 tickets and a parking pass?

Graph each inequality or compound inequality.

18. $3x - 2y > 6$

19. $y < 2x - 1$ and $x - y < 3$

20. Which one of the following is the graph of a function?

A.   **B.**   **C.** 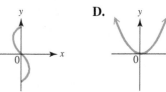   **D.**

21. Which of the following does not define y as a function of x?

A. $\{(0, 1), (-2, 3), (4, 8)\}$ **D.**

x	y
0	1
3	2
0	2
6	3

B. $y = 2x - 6$

C. $y = \sqrt{x + 2}$

Give the domain and range of the relation shown in each of the following.

22. Choice A of **Exercise 20**   **23.** Choice A of **Exercise 21**

24. For $f(x) = -x^2 + 2x - 1$, find $f(1)$ and $f(a)$.

25. Graph the linear function $f(x) = \dfrac{2}{3}x - 1$. Give the domain and range.

| Chapters R–2 | Cumulative Review Exercises |

[R.1]

1. always true   **2.** never true

3. sometimes true;

For example, $3 + (-3) = 0$, but

$3 + (-1) = 2$ and $2 \neq 0$.

[R.2]

4. 4

[R.3]

5. 0.64

6. not a real number

Decide whether each statement is always true, sometimes true, *or* never true. *If the statement is* sometimes true, *give examples for which it is true and for which it is false.*

1. The absolute value of a negative number equals the additive inverse of the number.

2. The sum of two negative numbers is positive.

3. The sum of a positive number and a negative number is 0.

Perform each operation.

4. $-|-2| - 4 + |-3| + 7$ **5.** $(-0.8)^2$ **6.** $\sqrt{-64}$

[R.4]
7. $4x - 3$
8. $2x^2 + 5x + 4$

[R.3]
9. $-\dfrac{19}{2}$ 10. 0
11. -39 12. undefined

[1.1]
13. $\left\{\dfrac{7}{6}\right\}$ 14. $\{-1\}$

[1.4]
15. 6 in.   16. 2 hr

[1.5]
17. $\left(-3, \dfrac{7}{2}\right)$ 18. $(-\infty, 1]$

[1.6]
19. $(6, 8)$
20. $(-\infty, -2] \cup (7, \infty)$

[1.7]
21. $\{0, 7\}$ 22. $(-\infty, \infty)$

[2.1]
23. $(4, 0); \left(0, \dfrac{12}{5}\right)$

[2.2]
24. (a) $-\dfrac{6}{5}$ (b) $\dfrac{5}{6}$

[2.4]
25.

[2.3]
26. (a) $y = -\dfrac{3}{4}x - 1$
   (b) $3x + 4y = -4$
27. (a) $y = -\dfrac{4}{3}x + \dfrac{7}{3}$
   (b) $4x + 3y = 7$

[2.5]
28. domain: $\{14, 91, 75, 23\}$;
   range: $\{9, 70, 56, 5\}$;
   not a function

Simplify each expression.

7. $-(-4x + 3)$

8. $3x^2 - 4x + 4 + 9x - x^2$

9. $\dfrac{(4^2 - 4) - (-1)7}{4 + (-6)}$

10. $\sqrt{25} - 5(-1)^2$

Evaluate each expression for $p = -4$, $q = \frac{1}{2}$, and $r = 16$.

11. $-3(2q - 3p)$

12. $\dfrac{\sqrt{r}}{8p + 2r}$

Solve each equation.

13. $2z - 5 + 3z = 4 - (z + 2)$

14. $\dfrac{3x - 1}{5} + \dfrac{x + 2}{2} = -\dfrac{3}{10}$

Solve each problem.

15. If each side of a square were increased by 4 in., the perimeter would be 8 in. less than twice the perimeter of the original square. Find the length of a side of the original square.

Original square   New square

16. Two planes leave the Dallas–Fort Worth airport at the same time. One travels east at 550 mph, and the other travels west at 500 mph. Assuming no wind, how long will it take for the planes to be 2100 mi apart?

West ← ... Airport ... → East

Solve.

17. $-4 < 3 - 2k < 9$

18. $-0.3x + 2.1(x - 4) \le -6.6$

19. $\dfrac{1}{2}x > 3$ and $\dfrac{1}{3}x < \dfrac{8}{3}$

20. $-5x + 1 \ge 11$ or $3x + 5 > 26$

21. $|2k - 7| + 4 = 11$

22. $|3x + 6| \ge 0$

Solve each problem.

23. Find the x- and y-intercepts of the line with equation $3x + 5y = 12$, and graph the line.

24. Consider the points $A(-2, 1)$ and $B(3, -5)$.
   (a) Find the slope of the line AB.
   (b) Find the slope of a line perpendicular to line AB.

25. Graph the inequality $-2x + y < -6$.

*Write an equation of the line that satisfies the given conditions. Give the equation **(a)** in slope-intercept form if possible and **(b)** in standard form.*

26. Slope $-\dfrac{3}{4}$; y-intercept $(0, -1)$

27. Through $(4, -3)$ and $(1, 1)$

28. Give the domain and range of the relation. Does it define a function?

14 → 9
91 → 70
75 → 56
23 → 5

3

Systems of Linear Equations

Just as the *intersection* of two streets consists of the region common to both, a solution of a *system* of two linear equations (represented graphically by lines) is an ordered pair found in the solution sets of *both* of the individual equations.

3.1 Systems of Linear Equations in Two Variables

VOCABULARY

☐ system of equations
☐ system of linear equations (linear system)
☐ solution set of a linear system
☐ consistent system
☐ independent equations
☐ inconsistent system
☐ dependent equations

In recent years, the number of Americans aged 7 and over participating in hiking has increased, while the number participating in fishing has decreased. These trends can be seen in the graph in **FIGURE 1**. The two straight-line graphs intersect at the time when the two sports had the *same* number of participants.

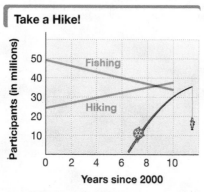

Take a Hike!

$$-1.34x + y = 24.3$$
$$1.55x + y = 49.3$$

Linear system of equations

(Here, $x = 0$ represents 2000, $x = 1$ represents 2001, and so on. y represents millions of participants.)

Source: National Sporting Goods Association.

FIGURE 1

As shown beside **FIGURE 1**, we can use a linear equation to model the graph of the number of people who hiked (red graph) and another linear equation to model the graph of the number of people who fished (blue graph). Such a set of equations is a **system of equations**—in this case, a **system of linear equations,** or a **linear system.**

The point where the graphs in **FIGURE 1** intersect is a solution of each of the individual equations. It is also the solution of the linear system of equations.

OBJECTIVE 1   Decide whether an ordered pair is a solution of a linear system.

The **solution set of a linear system** of equations contains all ordered pairs that satisfy all the equations of the system *at the same time.*

EXAMPLE 1   Deciding Whether an Ordered Pair Is a Solution

Decide whether the given ordered pair is a solution of the given system.

(a) $x + y = 6$
      $4x - y = 14$; $(4, 2)$

Replace x with 4 and y with 2 in each equation of the system.

$$x + y = 6 \qquad\qquad 4x - y = 14$$
$$4 + 2 \stackrel{?}{=} 6 \qquad\qquad 4(4) - 2 \stackrel{?}{=} 14$$
$$6 = 6 \ \checkmark \ \text{True} \qquad\qquad 16 - 2 \stackrel{?}{=} 14$$
$$14 = 14 \ \checkmark \ \text{True}$$

Because $(4, 2)$ makes *both* equations true, $(4, 2)$ is a solution of the system.

**NOW TRY
EXERCISE 1**

Decide whether the ordered pair $(2, 5)$ is a solution of the given system.

(a) $-x + 2y = 8$
$\quad 3x - 2y = 0$

(b) $2x - y = -1$
$\quad 3x + 2y = 16$

(b) $3x + 2y = 11$
$\quad x + 5y = 36$; $\quad (-1, 7)$

$3x + 2y = 11$	$x + 5y = 36$
$3(-1) + 2(7) \overset{?}{=} 11$	$-1 + 5(7) \overset{?}{=} 36$
$-3 + 14 \overset{?}{=} 11$	$-1 + 35 \overset{?}{=} 36$
$11 = 11$ ✓ True	$34 = 36$ False

The ordered pair $(-1, 7)$ is not a solution of the system, because it does not make *both* equations true.

NOW TRY

OBJECTIVE 2 Solve linear systems by graphing.

One way to find the solution set of a linear system of equations is to graph each equation and find the point where the graphs intersect.

**NOW TRY
EXERCISE 2**

Solve the system of equations by graphing.

$3x - 2y = 6$
$\quad x - y = 1$

EXAMPLE 2 Solving a System by Graphing

Solve the system of equations by graphing.

$$x + y = 5 \quad (1)$$
$$2x - y = 4 \quad (2)$$

To graph these linear equations, we plot several points for each line.

$x + y = 5$

The intercepts are a convenient choice.

x	y
0	5
5	0
2	3

$2x - y = 4$

x	y
0	-4
2	0
4	4

Find a third ordered pair as a check.

As shown in **FIGURE 2**, the graph suggests that the point of intersection is the ordered pair $(3, 2)$.

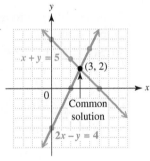

FIGURE 2

To confirm that $(3, 2)$ is a solution of *both* equations, we check by substituting 3 for x and 2 for y in each equation.

NOW TRY ANSWERS
1. (a) not a solution **(b)** solution
2. $\{(4, 3)\}$

CHECK $x + y = 5$ $\quad (1)$	$2x - y = 4$ $\quad (2)$
$3 + 2 \overset{?}{=} 5$	$2(3) - 2 \overset{?}{=} 4$
$5 = 5$ ✓ True	$6 - 2 \overset{?}{=} 4$
	$4 = 4$ ✓ True

Because $(3, 2)$ makes both equations true, $\{(3, 2)\}$ is the solution set of the system.

NOW TRY

There are three possibilities for the number of elements in the solution set of a linear system in two variables.

Graphs of Linear Systems in Two Variables

Case 1 **The two graphs intersect in a single point.** The coordinates of this point give the only solution of the system. Because the system has a solution, it is **consistent.** The equations are *not* equivalent, so they are **independent.** See **FIGURE 3(a)**.

Case 2 **The graphs are parallel lines.** There is no solution common to both equations, so the solution set is $\varnothing$ and the system is **inconsistent.** Because the equations are *not* equivalent, they are **independent.** See **FIGURE 3(b)**.

Case 3 **The graphs are the same line—that is, they coincide.** Because any solution of one equation of the system is a solution of the other, the solution set is an infinite set of ordered pairs representing the points on the line. This type of system is **consistent** because there is a solution. The equations are equivalent, so they are **dependent.** See **FIGURE 3(c)**.

Consistent system Independent equations	Inconsistent system Independent equations	Consistent system Dependent equations
(a)	(b)	(c)

FIGURE 3

OBJECTIVE 3 Solve linear systems (with two equations and two variables) by substitution.

It can be difficult to read exact coordinates, especially if they are not integers, from a graph, so we usually use algebraic methods to solve systems. One such method, the **substitution method,** is well suited for solving linear systems in which one equation is solved or can be easily solved for one variable in terms of the other.

EXAMPLE 3 Solving a System by Substitution

Solve the system.

$$2x - y = 6 \quad \text{(1)}$$
$$x = y + 2 \quad \text{(2)}$$

Because equation (2) is solved for x, we substitute $y + 2$ for x in equation (1).

$$2x - y = 6 \quad \text{(1)}$$
$$2(y + 2) - y = 6 \qquad \text{Let } x = y + 2.$$
$$2y + 4 - y = 6 \qquad \text{Distributive property}$$

> Be sure to use parentheses here.

$$y + 4 = 6 \qquad \text{Combine like terms.}$$
$$y = 2 \qquad \text{Subtract 4.}$$

NOW TRY
EXERCISE 3
Solve the system.

$$x = 3 + 2y$$
$$4x - 3y = 32$$

We found y. Now we solve for x by substituting 2 for y in equation (2).

$$x = y + 2 \qquad \text{(2)}$$
$$x = 2 + 2 \qquad \text{Let } y = 2.$$
$$x = 4 \qquad \text{Add.}$$

> Write the x-value first in the ordered pair.

Thus, $x = 4$ and $y = 2$, giving the ordered pair $(4, 2)$. Check this ordered pair in both equations of the original system.

CHECK

$2x - y = 6 \qquad \text{(1)}$	$x = y + 2 \qquad \text{(2)}$
$2(4) - 2 \overset{?}{=} 6$	$4 \overset{?}{=} 2 + 2$
$8 - 2 \overset{?}{=} 6$	$4 = 4 \ \checkmark \qquad \text{True}$
$6 = 6 \ \checkmark \quad \text{True}$	

Because $(4, 2)$ makes both equations true, the solution set is $\{(4, 2)\}$. **NOW TRY**

Solving a Linear System by Substitution

Step 1 **Solve one equation for either variable.** If one of the equations has a variable term with coefficient 1 or -1, choose it because the substitution method is usually easier.

Step 2 **Substitute** for that variable in the other equation. The result should be an equation with just one variable.

Step 3 **Solve** the equation from Step 2.

Step 4 **Find the other value.** Substitute the result from Step 3 into the equation from Step 1 and solve for the other variable.

Step 5 **Check** the values in *both* of the *original* equations. Then write the solution set as a set containing an ordered pair.

EXAMPLE 4 Solving a System by Substitution

Solve the system.

$$3x + 2y = 13 \qquad \text{(1)}$$
$$4x - y = -1 \qquad \text{(2)}$$

Step 1 First solve one of the equations for either x or y. Because the coefficient of y in equation (2) is -1, it is easiest to solve for y in equation (2).

$$4x - y = -1 \qquad \text{(2)}$$
$$-y = -1 - 4x \qquad \text{Subtract } 4x.$$
$$y = 1 + 4x \qquad \text{Multiply by } -1.$$

Step 2 Substitute $1 + 4x$ for y in equation (1).

$$3x + 2y = 13 \qquad \text{(1)}$$

> Substitute in the *other* equation.

$$3x + 2(1 + 4x) = 13 \qquad \text{Let } y = 1 + 4x.$$

Step 3 Solve for x.
$$3x + 2 + 8x = 13 \qquad \text{Distributive property}$$
$$11x = 11 \qquad \text{Combine like terms. Subtract 2.}$$
$$x = 1 \qquad \text{Divide by 11.}$$

NOW TRY ANSWER
3. $\{(11, 4)\}$

NOW TRY
EXERCISE 4
Solve the system.

$$5x + y = 7$$
$$3x - 2y = 25$$

Step 4   Now find y. From Step 1, $y = 1 + 4x$, so substitute 1 for x.

$$y = 1 + 4(1) \qquad \text{Let } x = 1.$$
$$y = 5 \qquad \text{Multiply. Add.}$$

Step 5   Check the ordered pair $(1, 5)$ in both equations (1) and (2).

CHECK
$$3x + 2y = 13 \qquad (1)$$
$$3(1) + 2(5) \overset{?}{=} 13$$
$$3 + 10 \overset{?}{=} 13$$
$$13 = 13 \quad \checkmark \quad \text{True}$$

$$4x - y = -1 \qquad (2)$$
$$4(1) - 5 \overset{?}{=} -1$$
$$4 - 5 \overset{?}{=} -1$$
$$-1 = -1 \quad \checkmark \quad \text{True}$$

The solution set is $\{(1, 5)\}$.

NOW TRY

EXAMPLE 5   **Solving a System with Fractional Coefficients**

Solve the system.

$$\frac{2}{3}x - \frac{1}{2}y = \frac{7}{6} \qquad (1)$$
$$3x - y = 6 \qquad (2)$$

This system will be easier to solve if we clear the fractions in equation (1).

$$6\left(\frac{2}{3}x - \frac{1}{2}y\right) = 6\left(\frac{7}{6}\right) \qquad \text{Multiply (1) by the LCD, 6.}$$

Remember to multiply *each* term by 6.

$$6 \cdot \frac{2}{3}x - 6 \cdot \frac{1}{2}y = 6 \cdot \frac{7}{6} \qquad \text{Distributive property}$$

$$4x - 3y = 7 \qquad (3)$$

Now the system consists of equations (2) and (3).

This equation is equivalent to equation (1).

$$3x - y = 6 \qquad (2)$$
$$4x - 3y = 7 \qquad (3)$$

To use the substitution method, we solve equation (2) for y.

$$3x - y = 6 \qquad (2)$$
$$-y = 6 - 3x \qquad \text{Subtract } 3x.$$
$$y = 3x - 6 \qquad \text{Multiply by } -1. \text{ Rewrite.}$$

Substitute $3x - 6$ for y in equation (3).

$$4x - 3y = 7 \qquad (3)$$
$$4x - 3(3x - 6) = 7 \qquad \text{Let } y = 3x - 6.$$
$$4x - 9x + 18 = 7 \qquad \text{Distributive property}$$

Be careful with signs.

$$-5x + 18 = 7 \qquad \text{Combine like terms.}$$
$$-5x = -11 \qquad \text{Subtract 18.}$$

NOW TRY ANSWER
4. $\{(3, -8)\}$

$$x = \frac{11}{5} \qquad \text{Divide by } -5.$$

NOW TRY EXERCISE 5

Solve the system.

$$\frac{1}{10}x - \frac{3}{5}y = \frac{2}{5}$$
$$-2x + 3y = 1$$

Now find y using $y = 3x - 6$ (equation (2) solved for y).

$$y = 3\left(\frac{11}{5}\right) - 6 \qquad \text{Let } x = \frac{11}{5}.$$

$$y = \frac{33}{5} - \frac{30}{5} \qquad 6 = \frac{30}{5}$$

$$y = \frac{3}{5} \qquad \text{Subtract fractions.}$$

A check verifies that the solution set is $\left\{\left(\frac{11}{5}, \frac{3}{5}\right)\right\}$. NOW TRY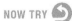

NOTE If an equation in a system contains decimal coefficients, it is best to first clear the decimals by multiplying by 10, 100, or 1000, depending on the number of decimal places. Then solve the system. For example, we multiply *each side* of the equation

$$0.5x + 0.75y = 3.25$$

by 10^2, or 100, to obtain an equivalent equation

$$50x + 75y = 325.$$

OBJECTIVE 4 Solve linear systems (with two equations and two variables) by elimination.

Another algebraic method, the **elimination method,** involves combining the two equations in a system so that one variable is eliminated. This is done using the following logic.

If $a = b$ and $c = d$, then $a + c = b + d$.

NOW TRY EXERCISE 6

Solve the system.

$$8x - 2y = 5$$
$$5x + 2y = -18$$

EXAMPLE 6 Solving a System by Elimination

Solve the system.

$$2x + 3y = -6 \qquad (1)$$
$$4x - 3y = 6 \qquad (2)$$

Notice that adding the equations together will eliminate the variable y.

$$2x + 3y = -6 \qquad (1)$$
$$\underline{4x - 3y = 6} \qquad (2)$$
$$6x = 0 \qquad \text{Add.}$$
$$x = 0 \qquad \text{Solve for } x.$$

To find y, substitute 0 for x in either equation (1) or equation (2).

$$2x + 3y = -6 \qquad (1)$$
$$2(0) + 3y = -6 \qquad \text{Let } x = 0.$$
$$0 + 3y = -6 \qquad \text{Multiply.}$$
$$y = -2 \qquad \text{Add. Divide by 3.}$$

NOW TRY ANSWERS
5. $\{(-2, -1)\}$
6. $\left\{\left(-1, -\frac{13}{2}\right)\right\}$

Check by substituting 0 for x and -2 for y in both equations of the original system to verify that $(0, -2)$ satisfies both equations. It does, so the solution set is $\{(0, -2)\}$.

NOW TRY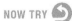

From **Example 6:**

$$2x + 3y = -6 \quad (1)$$
$$\underline{4x - 3y = 6} \quad (2)$$
$$6x = 0$$

By adding the equations in **Example 6** (repeated in the margin), we eliminated the variable y because the coefficients of the y-terms were opposites. In many cases the coefficients will *not* be opposites, and we must transform one or both equations so that the coefficients of one pair of variable terms are opposites.

Solving a Linear System by Elimination

Step 1   Write both equations in standard form $Ax + By = C$.

Step 2   **Transform the equations as needed so that the coefficients of one pair of variable terms are opposites.** Multiply one or both equations by appropriate numbers so that the sum of the coefficients of either the x- or y-terms is 0.

Step 3   **Add** the new equations to eliminate a variable. The sum should be an equation with just one variable.

Step 4   **Solve** the equation from Step 3 for the remaining variable.

Step 5   **Find the other value.** Substitute the result from Step 4 into either of the original equations and solve for the other variable.

Step 6   **Check** the values in *both* of the *original* equations. Then write the solution set as a set containing an ordered pair.

EXAMPLE 7   Solving a System by Elimination

Solve the system.

$$5x - 2y = 4 \quad (1)$$
$$2x + 3y = 13 \quad (2)$$

Step 1   Both equations are in standard form.

Step 2   Suppose that we wish to eliminate the variable x. One way to do this is to multiply equation (1) by 2 and equation (2) by -5.

The goal is to have *opposite* coefficients.

$$10x - 4y = 8 \qquad \text{2 times each side of equation (1)}$$
$$-10x - 15y = -65 \qquad \text{-5 times each side of equation (2)}$$

Step 3   Now add.

$$10x - 4y = 8$$
$$\underline{-10x - 15y = -65}$$
$$-19y = -57 \qquad \text{Add.}$$

Step 4   Solve for y. $\qquad\qquad y = 3 \qquad$ Divide by -19.

Step 5   To find x, substitute 3 for y in either equation (1) or equation (2).

$$2x + 3y = 13 \qquad (2)$$
$$2x + 3(3) = 13 \qquad \text{Let } y = 3.$$
$$2x + 9 = 13 \qquad \text{Multiply.}$$
$$2x = 4 \qquad \text{Subtract 9.}$$
$$x = 2 \qquad \text{Divide by 2.}$$

NOW TRY EXERCISE 7

Solve the system.

$$2x - 5y = 4$$
$$5x + 2y = 10$$

Step 6 To check, substitute 2 for x and 3 for y in both equations (1) and (2).

CHECK

$$5x - 2y = 4 \quad (1) \qquad\qquad 2x + 3y = 13 \quad (2)$$
$$5(2) - 2(3) \stackrel{?}{=} 4 \qquad\qquad 2(2) + 3(3) \stackrel{?}{=} 13$$
$$10 - 6 \stackrel{?}{=} 4 \qquad\qquad\qquad 4 + 9 \stackrel{?}{=} 13$$
$$4 = 4 \ \checkmark \ \text{True} \qquad\qquad 13 = 13 \ \checkmark \ \text{True}$$

The solution set is $\{(2, 3)\}$.

NOW TRY

OBJECTIVE 5 Solve special systems.

As we saw in **FIGURES 3(b) AND (c)**, some systems of linear equations have no solution or an infinite number of solutions.

NOW TRY EXERCISE 8

Solve the system.

$$x - 3y = 7$$
$$-3x + 9y = -21$$

EXAMPLE 8 Solving a System of Dependent Equations

Solve the system.

$$2x - y = 3 \quad (1)$$
$$6x - 3y = 9 \quad (2)$$

We multiply equation (1) by -3 and then add the result to equation (2).

$$-6x + 3y = -9 \qquad \text{-3 times each side of equation (1)}$$
$$\underline{6x - 3y = 9} \qquad (2)$$
$$0 = 0 \qquad \text{True}$$

Adding these equations gives the true statement $0 = 0$. In the original system, we could obtain equation (2) from equation (1) by multiplying equation (1) by 3. Because of this, equations (1) and (2) are equivalent and have the same graph, as shown in **FIGURE 4**. The equations are dependent.

FIGURE 4

The solution set is the set of all points on the line with equation $2x - y = 3$, written in set-builder notation (**Section R.1**) as

$$\{(x, y) \mid 2x - y = 3\}$$

and read "the set of all ordered pairs (x, y), such that $2x - y = 3$." NOW TRY

NOTE When a system has dependent equations and an infinite number of solutions, as in **Example 8,** either equation of the system could be used to write the solution set. *In this book, we use the equation in standard form with coefficients that are integers having greatest common factor 1 and positive coefficient of x.*

NOW TRY ANSWERS
7. $\{(2, 0)\}$
8. $\{(x, y) \mid x - 3y = 7\}$

NOW TRY
EXERCISE 9

Solve the system.

$$-2x + 5y = 6$$
$$6x - 15y = 4$$

EXAMPLE 9   **Solving an Inconsistent System**

Solve the system.

$$x + 3y = 4 \qquad (1)$$
$$-2x - 6y = 3 \qquad (2)$$

Multiply equation (1) by 2, and then add the result to equation (2).

$$2x + 6y = 8 \qquad \text{Equation (1) multiplied by 2}$$
$$\underline{-2x - 6y = 3} \qquad (2)$$
$$0 = 11 \qquad \text{False}$$

The result of the addition step is a false statement, which indicates that the system is inconsistent. As shown in **FIGURE 5**, the graphs of the equations of the system are parallel lines.

There are no ordered pairs that satisfy both equations, so there is no solution for the system. The solution set is $\varnothing$.

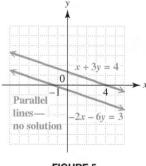

FIGURE 5

NOW TRY

Special Cases of Linear Systems

If both variables are eliminated when a system of linear equations is solved, then the solution sets are determined as follows.

Case 1   There are infinitely many solutions if the resulting statement is *true*. (See **Example 8.**)

Case 2   There is no solution if the resulting statement is *false*. (See **Example 9.**)

Slopes and y-intercepts can be used to decide whether the graphs of a system of equations are parallel lines or whether they coincide.

EXAMPLE 10   **Using Slope-Intercept Form to Determine the Number of Solutions**

Refer to **Examples 8 and 9.** Write each equation in slope-intercept form and then tell how many solutions the system has.

Solve each equation from **Example 8** for y.

$2x - y = 3$	(1)	$6x - 3y = 9$ (2)

$$-y = -2x + 3 \qquad \text{Subtract } 2x.$$
$$y = 2x - 3 \qquad \text{Multiply by } -1.$$

$\underset{\uparrow}{\text{Slope}} \quad \underset{\uparrow}{y\text{-intercept } (0, -3)}$

$\underline{2x - y = 3} \qquad \text{Divide by 3.}$

Solving for y leads to the same result as on the left.

The lines have the same slope and same y-intercept, meaning that they coincide. There are infinitely many solutions.

NOW TRY EXERCISE 10

Write each equation in slope-intercept form and then tell how many solutions the system has.

(a) $2x - 3y = 3$
$4x - 6y = -6$

(b) $5y = -x - 4$
$-10y = 2x + 8$

Solve each equation from **Example 9** for y.

$x + 3y = 4$	(1)	$-2x - 6y = 3$	(2)

$3y = -x + 4$ Subtract x. $-6y = 2x + 3$ Add $2x$.

$y = -\dfrac{1}{3}x + \dfrac{4}{3}$ Divide by 3. $y = -\dfrac{1}{3}x - \dfrac{1}{2}$ Divide by -6; $\dfrac{2}{-6} = -\dfrac{1}{3}$; $\dfrac{3}{-6} = -\dfrac{1}{2}$

Slope y-intercept $\left(0, \dfrac{4}{3}\right)$ Slope y-intercept $\left(0, -\dfrac{1}{2}\right)$

The lines have the same slope, but different y-intercepts, indicating that they are parallel. Thus, the system has no solution.

NOW TRY

NOTE In **Example 2,** we solved the system

$$x + y = 5 \qquad (1)$$
$$2x - y = 4 \qquad (2)$$

by graphing the two lines and finding their point of intersection. We can also do this with a graphing calculator, as shown in **FIGURE 6**. The two lines were graphed by solving each equation for y.

$y = 5 - x$ Equation (1) solved for y

$y = 2x - 4$ Equation (2) solved for y

NORMAL FIX3 AUTO REAL RADIAN MP
CALC INTERSECT

Intersection
X=3   Y=2

FIGURE 6

The coordinates of their point of intersection are displayed at the bottom of the screen, indicating that the solution set is $\{(3, 2)\}$. (Compare this graph with the one in **FIGURE 2**.)

NOW TRY ANSWERS

10. (a) $y = \dfrac{2}{3}x - 1; y = \dfrac{2}{3}x + 1$; no solution

(b) Both are $y = -\dfrac{1}{5}x - \dfrac{4}{5}$; infinitely many solutions

---

3.1 Exercises

FOR EXTRA HELP   MyMathLab®

▶ *Complete solution available in MyMathLab*

Concept Check   *Complete each statement.*

1. If $(4, -3)$ is a solution of a linear system in two variables, then substituting _____ for x and _____ for y leads to true statements in *both* equations.

2. A solution of a system of independent linear equations in two variables is an ordered _____.

3. If solving a system leads to a false statement such as $0 = 3$, the solution set is _____.

4. If solving a system leads to a true statement such as $0 = 0$, the system has _____ equations.

5. If the two lines forming a system have the same slope and different y-intercepts, the system has (*no / one / infinitely many*) solution(s).

6. If the two lines forming a system have different slopes, the system has (*no / one / infinitely many*) solution(s).

7. *Concept Check* Which ordered pair could be a solution of the graphed system of equations? Why?

A. $(4, 4)$

B. $(-4, 4)$

C. $(-4, -4)$

D. $(4, -4)$

8. *Concept Check* Which ordered pair could be a solution of the graphed system of equations? Why?

A. $(4, 0)$

B. $(-4, 0)$

C. $(0, 4)$

D. $(0, -4)$

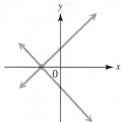

9. *Concept Check* Match each system with the correct graph.

(a) $x + y = 6$
  $x - y = 0$

(b) $x + y = -6$
  $x - y = 0$

(c) $x + y = 0$
  $x - y = -6$

(d) $x + y = 0$
  $x - y = 6$

A.

B.

C.

D.

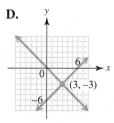

10. *Concept Check* If a system of the following form has a single solution, what must that solution be?

$$Ax + By = 0$$
$$Cx + Dy = 0$$

Decide whether the given ordered pair is a solution of the given system. See Example 1.

11. $x - y = 17$; $(8, -9)$
  $x + y = -1$

12. $x + y = 6$; $(5, 1)$
  $x - y = 4$

13. $3x - 5y = -12$; $(-1, 2)$
  $x - y = 1$

14. $2x - y = 8$; $(5, 2)$
  $3x + 2y = 20$

Solve each system by graphing. See Example 2.

15. $x + y = -5$
  $-2x + y = 1$

16. $x + y = 4$
  $2x - y = 2$

17. $x - 4y = -4$
  $3x + y = 1$

18. $6x - y = 2$
  $x - 2y = 4$

19. $2x + y = 4$
  $3x - y = 6$

20. $2x + 3y = -6$
  $x - 3y = -3$

Solve each system by substitution. If the system is inconsistent or has dependent equations, say so. See Examples 3–5, 8, and 9.

21. $4x + y = 6$
  $y = 2x$

22. $2x - y = 6$
  $y = 5x$

23. $-x - 4y = -14$
  $y = 2x - 1$

24. $-3x - 5y = -17$
  $y = 4x + 8$

25. $3x - 4y = -22$
  $-3x + y = 0$

26. $-3x + y = -5$
  $3x + 6y = 0$

27. $5x - 4y = 9$
  $3 - 2y = -x$

28. $6x - y = -9$
  $4 + 7x = -y$

29. $4x - 5y = -11$
  $x + 2y = 7$

30. $3x - y = 10$
$2x + 5y = 1$

31. $x = 3y + 5$
$x = \dfrac{3}{2}y$

32. $x = 6y - 2$
$x = \dfrac{3}{4}y$

▶ 33. $\dfrac{1}{2}x + \dfrac{1}{3}y = 3$
$-3x + y = 0$

34. $\dfrac{1}{4}x - \dfrac{1}{5}y = 9$
$5x - y = 0$

35. $y = 2x$
$4x - 2y = 0$

36. $x = 3y$
$3x - 9y = 0$

37. $x = 5y$
$5x - 25y = 5$

38. $y = -4x$
$8x + 2y = 4$

39. $y = 0.5x$
$1.5x - 0.5y = 5.0$

40. $y = 1.4x$
$0.5x + 1.5y = 26.0$

41. $\dfrac{1}{2}x - \dfrac{1}{4}y = -5$
$\dfrac{1}{8}x + \dfrac{1}{4}y = 0$

42. $-\dfrac{1}{3}x + \dfrac{2}{5}y = -6$
$-\dfrac{1}{2}x - \dfrac{3}{2}y = 12$

43. $0.4x + 0.2y = 0$
$\dfrac{1}{2}x - \dfrac{1}{3}y = 0$

44. To minimize the amount of work required, tell whether to use the substitution or elimination method to solve each system. Explain. *Do not actually solve.*

(a) $3x + y = -7$
$x - y = -5$

(b) $6x - y = 5$
$y = 11x$

(c) $3x - 2y = 0$
$9x + 8y = 7$

Solve each system by elimination. If the system is inconsistent or has dependent equations, say so. **See Examples 6–9.**

▶ 45. $-2x + 3y = -16$
$2x - 5y = 24$

46. $6x + 5y = -7$
$-6x - 11y = 1$

47. $2x - 5y = 11$
$3x + y = 8$

48. $-2x + 3y = 1$
$-4x + y = -3$

▶ 49. $3x + 4y = -6$
$5x + 3y = 1$

50. $4x + 3y = 1$
$3x + 2y = 2$

▶ 51. $7x + 2y = 6$
$-14x - 4y = -12$

52. $x - 4y = 2$
$4x - 16y = 8$

53. $3x + 3y = 0$
$4x + 2y = 3$

54. $8x + 4y = 0$
$4x - 2y = 2$

▶ 55. $5x - 5y = 3$
$x - y = 12$

56. $2x - 3y = 7$
$-4x + 6y = 14$

57. $x + y = 0$
$2x - 2y = 0$

58. $3x + 3y = 0$
$-2x - y = 0$

59. $x - \dfrac{1}{2}y = 2$
$-x + \dfrac{2}{5}y = -\dfrac{8}{5}$

60. $\dfrac{3}{2}x + y = 3$
$\dfrac{2}{3}x + \dfrac{1}{3}y = 1$

61. $\dfrac{1}{2}x + \dfrac{1}{3}y = \dfrac{49}{18}$
$\dfrac{1}{2}x + 2y = \dfrac{4}{3}$

62. $\dfrac{1}{5}x + \dfrac{1}{7}y = \dfrac{12}{5}$
$\dfrac{1}{10}x + \dfrac{1}{3}y = \dfrac{5}{6}$

Write each equation in slope-intercept form and then tell how many solutions the system has. Do not actually solve. **See Example 10.**

▶ **63.** $3x + 7y = 4$
  $6x + 14y = 3$

64. $-x + 2y = 8$
  $4x - 8y = 1$

65. $2x = -3y + 1$
  $6x = -9y + 3$

66. $5x = -2y + 1$
  $10x = -4y + 2$

Solve each system by the method of your choice. **See Examples 3–9.** *(For Exercises 67–69, see the answers to* **Exercise 44.**)

67. $3x + y = -7$
  $x - y = -5$

68. $6x - y = 5$
  $y = 11x$

69. $3x - 2y = 0$
  $9x + 8y = 7$

70. $3x - 5y = 7$
  $2x + 3y = 30$

71. $2x + 3y = 10$
  $-3x + y = 18$

▶ **72.** $x + y = 10$
  $2x - y = 5$

73. $\dfrac{1}{2}x - \dfrac{1}{8}y = -\dfrac{1}{4}$
  $4x - y = -2$

74. $\dfrac{1}{6}x + \dfrac{1}{3}y = 8$
  $\dfrac{1}{4}x + \dfrac{1}{2}y = 12$

75. $0.3x + 0.2y = 0.4$
  $0.5x + 0.4y = 0.7$

76. $0.2x + 0.5y = 6$
  $0.4x + y = 9$

77. *Concept Check*   Explain why *System A* would be more difficult to solve by substitution than *System B*.

  System A: $3x + 7y = 19$
       $8x - 5y = 4$

  System B: $x + 7y = 8$
       $3x - 2y = 4$

78. *Concept Check*   Make up a system of the following form, where *a*, *b*, *c*, *d*, *e*, and *f* are consecutive integers. Solve the system.

$$ax + by = c$$
$$dx + ey = f$$

Use each graph provided to work Exercises 79–82.

79. The figure shows graphs that represent supply and demand for a certain brand of low-fat frozen yogurt at various prices per half-gallon (in dollars).

  (a) At what price does supply equal demand?

  (b) For how many half-gallons does supply equal demand?

  (c) What are the supply and demand at a price of $2 per half-gallon?

The Fortunes of Frozen Yogurt

80. Sharon compared the monthly payments she would incur for two types of mortgages: fixed rate and variable rate. Her observations led to the following graphs.

  (a) For which years would the monthly payment be more for the fixed-rate mortgage than for the variable-rate mortgage?

  (b) In what year would the payments be the same? What would those payments be?

Mortgage Shopping

81. The graph shows viewers (in millions) in the United States for three television programs from 2009 through 2012.

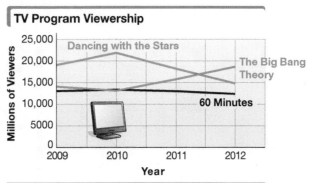

Source: tvbythenumbers.zap2it.com

(a) During what years did the number of viewers for *Dancing with the Stars* exceed that for *The Big Bang Theory?*

(b) Between what two consecutive years did *The Big Bang Theory* first become the most popular program?

(c) In what year were the numbers of viewers of *The Big Bang Theory* and *60 Minutes* approximately equal? What was the approximate number of viewers during that year (to the nearest million)?

(d) Write the answer for part (c) as an ordered pair.

(e) Describe the trends in viewership of the three programs from 2010 through 2012.

82. The graph shows numbers of nuclear weapons possessed by the United States and USSR/Russia from 1950 through 2013.

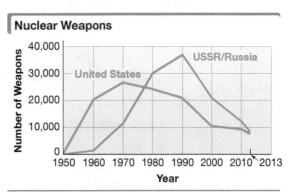

Source: World Almanac and Book of Facts.

(a) In what year were the numbers of nuclear weapons approximately equal?

(b) Approximately how many nuclear weapons did each country possess in that year?

(c) Express the point of intersection of the graphs for U.S. and USSR nuclear weapons as an ordered pair of the form (year, number of nuclear weapons).

(d) Over the entire period 1950–2013, which country possessed the greatest number of nuclear weapons at any one particular time? In what year did that maximum occur, and what was the approximate number of nuclear weapons possessed?

(e) Describe the trend in number of nuclear weapons possessed by the USSR from 1990 through 2013. If a straight line were used to approximate its graph, would the line have a slope that is positive, negative, or 0?

Use the graph shown in **FIGURE 1** *at the beginning of this section (and repeated here) to work Exercises 83–86.*

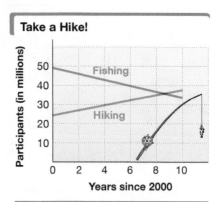

Take a Hike!

Source: National Sporting Goods Association.

83. Which sport was more popular in 2010?

84. Estimate the year in which participation in the two sports was the same. About how many Americans participated in each sport during that year?

85. If $x = 0$ represents 2000 and $x = 10$ represents 2010, the number of participants y in millions in the two sports can be modeled by the linear equations in the following system.

$$-1.34x + y = 24.3 \quad \text{Hiking}$$
$$1.55x + y = 49.3 \quad \text{Fishing}$$

Solve this system. Express values as decimals rounded to the nearest tenth. Write the solution as an ordered pair of the form (year, number of participants).

86. Interpret the answer for **Exercise 85,** rounding down for the year. How does it compare to the estimate from **Exercise 84?**

Extending Skills   The following systems can be solved by elimination. One way to do this is to let $p = \frac{1}{x}$ and $q = \frac{1}{y}$. Substitute, solve for p and q, and then find x and y.$\left(\text{For example, in Exercise 87, } \frac{3}{x} = 3 \cdot \frac{1}{x} = 3p.\right)$
Use this method to solve each system.

87. $\dfrac{3}{x} + \dfrac{4}{y} = \dfrac{5}{2}$

$\dfrac{5}{x} - \dfrac{3}{y} = \dfrac{7}{4}$

88. $\dfrac{2}{x} - \dfrac{5}{y} = \dfrac{3}{2}$

$\dfrac{4}{x} + \dfrac{1}{y} = \dfrac{4}{5}$

89. $\dfrac{2}{x} + \dfrac{3}{y} = \dfrac{11}{2}$

$-\dfrac{1}{x} + \dfrac{2}{y} = -1$

90. $\dfrac{4}{x} - \dfrac{9}{y} = -1$

$-\dfrac{7}{x} + \dfrac{6}{y} = -\dfrac{3}{2}$

Extending Skills   Solve by any method. Assume that a and b represent nonzero constants.

91. $ax + by = c$

$ax - 2by = c$

92. $ax + by = 2$

$-ax + 2by = 1$

93. $2ax - y = 3$

$y = 5ax$

94. $3ax + 2y = 1$

$-ax + y = 2$

STUDY SKILLS

Preparing for Your Math Final Exam

Your math final exam is likely to be a comprehensive exam, which means it will cover material from the entire term. **One way to prepare for it now is by working a set of Cumulative Review Exercises** each time your class finishes a chapter. This continual review will help you remember concepts and procedures as you progress through the course.

Final Exam Preparation Suggestions

1. **Figure out the grade you need to earn on the final exam to get the course grade you want.** Check your course syllabus for grading policies, or ask your instructor if you are not sure.

   How many points do you need to earn on your math final exam to get the grade you want?

2. **Create a final exam week plan.** Set priorities that allow you to spend extra time studying. This may mean making adjustments, in advance, in your work schedule or enlisting extra help with family responsibilities.

   What adjustments do you need to make for final exam week? List two or three here.

3. **Use the following suggestions to guide your studying.**

   - **Begin reviewing several days before the final exam.** DON'T wait until the last minute.

   - **Know exactly which chapters and sections will be covered on the exam.**

   - **Divide up the chapters.** Decide how much you will review each day.

   - **Keep returned quizzes and tests. Use them to review.**

   - **Practice all types of problems. Use the Cumulative Review Exercises** at the end of each chapter in your textbook beginning in Chapter 2. All answers, with section references, are given in the margin.

   - **Review or rewrite your notes** to create summaries of important information.

   - **Make study cards for all types of problems.** Carry the cards with you, and review them whenever you have a few minutes.

   - **Take plenty of short breaks (as you study) to reduce physical and mental stress.** Exercising, listening to music, and enjoying a favorite activity are effective stress busters.

   Finally, *DON'T* stay up all night the night before an exam—*get a good night's sleep.*

Which of these suggestions will you use as you study for your math final exam? List two or three here.

3.2 Systems of Linear Equations in Three Variables

A solution of an equation in three variables, such as

$$2x + 3y - z = 4, \qquad \text{Linear equation in three variables}$$

is an **ordered triple** and is written (x, y, z). For example, the ordered triple $(0, 1, -1)$ is a solution of the preceding equation, because

$$2(0) + 3(1) - (-1) = 4 \qquad \text{is a true statement.}$$

Verify that another solution of this equation is $(10, -3, 7)$.

We now extend the term *linear equation* to equations of the form

$$Ax + By + Cz + \cdots + Dw = K,$$

where not all the coefficients $A, B, C, \ldots, D$ equal 0. For example,

$$2x + 3y - 5z = 7 \quad \text{and} \quad x - 2y - z + 3w = 8$$

are linear equations, the first with three variables and the second with four.

OBJECTIVE 1 Understand the geometry of systems of three equations in three variables.

Consider the solution of a system such as the following.

$$4x + 8y + z = 2$$
$$x + 7y - 3z = -14 \qquad \text{System of linear equations in three variables}$$
$$2x - 3y + 2z = 3$$

Theoretically, a system of this type can be solved by graphing. However, the graph of a linear equation with three variables is a *plane,* not a line. Because visualizing a plane requires three-dimensional graphing, the method of graphing is not practical with these systems. However, it does illustrate the number of solutions possible for such systems, as shown in **FIGURE 7**.

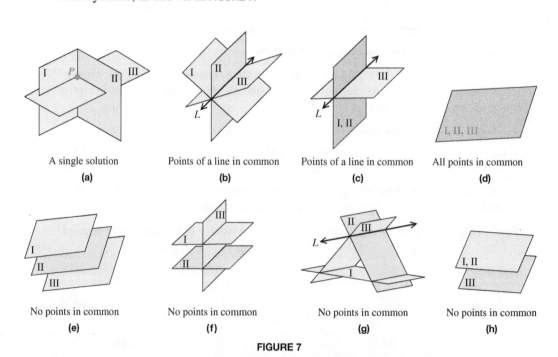

A single solution	Points of a line in common	Points of a line in common	All points in common
(a)	(b)	(c)	(d)

No points in common	No points in common	No points in common	No points in common
(e)	(f)	(g)	(h)

FIGURE 7

FIGURE 7 illustrates the following cases.

Graphs of Linear Systems in Three Variables

Case 1 **The three planes may meet at a single, common point.** This point is the solution of the system. See **FIGURE 7(a)**.

Case 2 **The three planes may have the points of a line in common.** The infinite set of points that satisfy the equation of the line is the solution of the system. See **FIGURES 7(b) AND (c)**.

Case 3 **The three planes may coincide.** The solution of the system is the set of all points on a plane. See **FIGURE 7(d)**.

Case 4 **The planes may have no points common to all three.** There is no solution of the system. See **FIGURES 7(e)–(h)**.

OBJECTIVE 2 Solve linear systems (with three equations and three variables) by elimination.

Because graphing to find the solution set of a system of three equations in three variables is impractical, these systems are solved with an extension of the elimination method from **Section 3.1.**

In the steps that follow, we use the term **focus variable** to identify the first variable to be eliminated in the process. The focus variable will always be present in the **working equation,** which will be used twice to eliminate this variable.

Solving a Linear System in Three Variables*

Step 1 **Select a variable and an equation.** A good choice for the variable, which we call the *focus variable,* is one that has coefficient 1 or -1. Then select an equation, one that contains the focus variable, as the *working equation*.

Step 2 **Eliminate the focus variable.** Use the working equation and one of the other two equations of the original system. The result is an equation in two variables.

Step 3 **Eliminate the focus variable again.** Use the working equation and the remaining equation of the original system. The result is another equation in two variables.

Step 4 **Write the equations in two variables that result from Steps 2 and 3 as a system, and solve it.** Doing this gives the values of two of the variables.

Step 5 **Find the value of the remaining variable.** Substitute the values of the two variables found in Step 4 into the working equation to obtain the value of the focus variable.

Step 6 **Check** the three values in *each* of the *original* equations of the system. Then write the solution set as a set containing an ordered triple.

---

*The authors wish to thank Christine Heinecke Lehmann of Purdue University North Central for her suggestions here.

EXAMPLE 1 Solving a System in Three Variables

Solve the system.

$$4x + 8y + z = 2 \qquad (1)$$
$$x + 7y - 3z = -14 \qquad (2)$$
$$2x - 3y + 2z = 3 \qquad (3)$$

Step 1 Because z in equation (1) has coefficient 1, we choose z as the focus variable and (1) as the working equation. (Another option would be to choose x as the focus variable—it also has coefficient 1—and use (2) as the working equation.)

Focus variable

$$4x + 8y + z = 2 \qquad (1) \leftarrow \text{Working equation}$$

Step 2 Multiply working equation (1) by 3 and add the result to equation (2).

$$12x + 24y + 3z = 6 \qquad \text{Multiply each side of (1) by 3.}$$
$$\underline{x + 7y - 3z = -14 \qquad (2)}$$

Focus variable z was eliminated.

$$13x + 31y = -8 \qquad \text{Add.} \quad (4)$$

Step 3 Multiply working equation (1) by -2 and add the result to remaining equation (3) to again eliminate focus variable z.

$$-8x - 16y - 2z = -4 \qquad \text{Multiply each side of (1) by } -2.$$
$$\underline{2x - 3y + 2z = 3 \qquad (3)}$$

Focus variable z was eliminated.

$$-6x - 19y = -1 \qquad \text{Add.} \quad (5)$$

Step 4 Write the equations in two variables that result in Steps 2 and 3 as a system.

Make sure these equations have the same two variables.

$$13x + 31y = -8 \qquad (4) \quad \text{The result from Step 2}$$
$$-6x - 19y = -1 \qquad (5) \quad \text{The result from Step 3}$$

Now solve this system. We choose to eliminate x.

$$78x + 186y = -48 \qquad \text{Multiply each side of (4) by 6.}$$
$$\underline{-78x - 247y = -13 \qquad \text{Multiply each side of (5) by 13.}}$$
$$-61y = -61 \qquad \text{Add.}$$
$$y = 1 \qquad \text{Divide by } -61.$$

Substitute 1 for y in either equation (4) or (5) to find x.

$$-6x - 19y = -1 \qquad (5)$$
$$-6x - 19(1) = -1 \qquad \text{Let } y = 1.$$
$$-6x - 19 = -1 \qquad \text{Multiply.}$$
$$-6x = 18 \qquad \text{Add 19.}$$
$$x = -3 \qquad \text{Divide by } -6.$$

Step 5 Now substitute the two values we found in Step 4 in working equation (1) to find the value of the remaining variable, focus variable z.

$$4x + 8y + z = 2 \qquad (1)$$
$$4(-3) + 8(1) + z = 2 \qquad \text{Let } x = -3 \text{ and } y = 1.$$
$$-4 + z = 2 \qquad \text{Multiply, and then add.}$$
$$z = 6 \qquad \text{Add 4.}$$

NOW TRY
EXERCISE 1

Solve the system.

$$x - y + 2z = 1$$
$$3x + 2y + 7z = 8$$
$$-3x - 4y + 9z = -10$$

Write the values of x, y, and z in the correct order.

Step 6 It appears that $(-3, 1, 6)$ is the only solution of the system. We must check that this ordered triple satisfies all three original equations of the system. We begin with equation (1).

CHECK

$$4x + 8y + z = 2 \qquad \text{(1)}$$

$$4(-3) + 8(1) + 6 \overset{?}{=} 2 \qquad \text{Substitute.}$$

$$-12 + 8 + 6 \overset{?}{=} 2 \qquad \text{Multiply.}$$

$$2 = 2 \ \checkmark \quad \text{True}$$

Because $(-3, 1, 6)$ also satisfies equations (2) and (3), $\{(-3, 1, 6)\}$ is the solution set. This is Case 1 as shown in **FIGURE 7(a)** at the beginning of this section.

NOW TRY

OBJECTIVE 3 Solve linear systems (with three equations and three variables) in which some of the equations have missing terms.

If a linear system includes an equation that is missing a term or terms, one elimination step can be omitted.

EXAMPLE 2   Solving a System of Equations with Missing Terms

Solve the system.

$$6x - 12y = -5 \qquad \text{(1)} \quad \text{Missing } z$$
$$8y + z = 0 \qquad \text{(2)} \quad \text{Missing } x$$
$$9x - z = 12 \qquad \text{(3)} \quad \text{Missing } y$$

Equation (3) is missing the variable y, so one way to begin is to eliminate y again, using equations (1) and (2).

$$12x - 24y \qquad = -10 \qquad \text{Multiply each side of (1) by 2.}$$

Leave space for the missing terms.

$$\underline{\qquad\quad 24y + 3z = \quad 0} \qquad \text{Multiply each side of (2) by 3.}$$
$$12x \qquad + 3z = -10 \qquad \text{Add. \quad (4)}$$

Use resulting equation (4) in x and z, together with equation (3), $9x - z = 12$, to eliminate z.

$$27x - 3z = \quad 36 \qquad \text{Multiply each side of (3) by 3.}$$
$$\underline{12x + 3z = -10} \qquad \text{(4)}$$
$$39x \qquad = \quad 26 \qquad \text{Add.}$$

$$x = \frac{26}{39} \qquad \text{Divide by 39.}$$

$$x = \frac{2}{3} \qquad \text{Lowest terms}$$

We can find z by substituting this value for x in equation (3).

$$9x - z = 12 \qquad \text{(3)}$$

$$9\left(\frac{2}{3}\right) - z = 12 \qquad \text{Let } x = \tfrac{2}{3}.$$

$$6 - z = 12 \qquad \text{Multiply.}$$

$$z = -6 \qquad \text{Subtract 6. Multiply by } -1.$$

NOW TRY ANSWER
1. $\{(2, 1, 0)\}$

NOW TRY
EXERCISE 2
Solve the system.

$$3x - z = -10$$
$$4y + 5z = 24$$
$$x - 6y = -8$$

We can find y by substituting -6 for z in equation (2).

$$8y + z = 0 \quad \text{(2)}$$

$$8y - 6 = 0 \qquad \text{Let } z = -6.$$

$$8y = 6 \qquad \text{Add 6.}$$

$$y = \frac{6}{8} \qquad \text{Divide by 8.}$$

$$y = \frac{3}{4} \qquad \text{Lowest terms}$$

Check to verify that the solution set is $\left\{\left(\frac{2}{3}, \frac{3}{4}, -6\right)\right\}$. This is also an example of Case 1.

NOW TRY

NOTE   Another way to solve the system in **Example 2** is to begin by eliminating the variable z from equations (2) and (3). The resulting equation together with equation (1) forms a system of two equations in the variables x and y. Try working **Example 2** this way to see that the same solution results.

There are often multiple ways to solve a system of equations. Some ways may involve more work than others.

OBJECTIVE 4 Solve special systems.

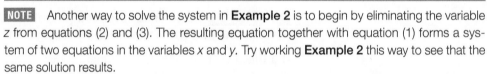

EXAMPLE 3 **Solving a System of Dependent Equations with Three Variables**

NOW TRY
EXERCISE 3
Solve the system.

$$x - 3y + 2z = 10$$
$$-2x + 6y - 4z = -20$$
$$\frac{1}{2}x - \frac{3}{2}y + z = 5$$

Solve the system.

$$2x - 3y + 4z = 8 \quad \text{(1)}$$

$$-x + \frac{3}{2}y - 2z = -4 \quad \text{(2)}$$

$$6x - 9y + 12z = 24 \quad \text{(3)}$$

Multiplying each side of equation (1) by 3 gives equation (3). Multiplying each side of equation (2) by -6 also gives equation (3). Because of this, the equations are dependent.

When solving a system such as this, attempting to eliminate one variable results in elimination of *all* variables, leading to the true statement $0 = 0$. This indicates that all three equations have the same graph, as illustrated in **FIGURE 7(d)**. This is Case 3. The solution set is written as follows.

$$\{(x, y, z) \mid 2x - 3y + 4z = 8\} \qquad \text{Set-builder notation}$$

Although any one of the three equations could be used to write the solution set, we use the equation in standard form with coefficients that are integers with greatest common factor 1, as we did in **Section 3.1**.

NOW TRY

EXAMPLE 4 **Solving an Inconsistent System with Three Variables**

Solve the system.

$$2x - 4y + 6z = 5 \quad \text{(1)}$$

$$-x + 3y - 2z = -1 \quad \text{(2)}$$

$$x - 2y + 3z = 1 \quad \text{(3)}$$

Use as the working equation, with focus variable x.

Eliminate the focus variable, x, using equations (1) and (3).

NOW TRY ANSWERS
2. $\{(-2, 1, 4)\}$
3. $\{(x, y, z) \mid x - 3y + 2z = 10\}$

**NOW TRY
EXERCISE 4**

Solve the system.

$$x - 5y + 2z = 4$$
$$3x + y - z = 6$$
$$-2x + 10y - 4z = 7$$

$$-2x + 4y - 6z = -2 \qquad \text{Multiply each side of (3) by } -2.$$
$$\underline{2x - 4y + 6z = 5} \qquad \text{(1)}$$
$$0 = 3 \qquad \text{False}$$

The resulting false statement indicates that equations (1) and (3) have no common solution. Thus, the system is inconsistent and the solution set is $\emptyset$. The graph of this system would show two planes parallel to one another and a third plane which intersects both, as in **FIGURE 7(f)**. This is Case 4.

NOW TRY

NOTE If a false statement results when adding as in **Example 4,** it is not necessary to go any further with the solution. Because two of the three planes are parallel, it is not possible for the three planes to have any points in common.

**NOW TRY
EXERCISE 5**

Solve the system.

$$x - 3y + 2z = 4$$
$$\frac{1}{3}x - y + \frac{2}{3}z = 7$$
$$\frac{1}{2}x - \frac{3}{2}y + z = 2$$

EXAMPLE 5 Solving Another Special System

Solve the system.

$$2x - y + 3z = 6 \qquad \text{(1)}$$
$$x - \frac{1}{2}y + \frac{3}{2}z = 3 \qquad \text{(2)}$$
$$4x - 2y + 6z = 1 \qquad \text{(3)}$$

Multiplying each side of equation (2) by 2 gives equation (1), so these two equations are dependent. Equations (1) and (3) are not equivalent, however. Multiplying equation (3) by $\frac{1}{2}$ does *not* give equation (1). Instead, we obtain two equations with the same coefficients, but with different constant terms.

The graphs of equations (1) and (3) have no points in common (that is, the planes are parallel). Thus, the system is inconsistent and the solution set is $\emptyset$, as illustrated in **FIGURE 7(h)**. This is another example of Case 4.

NOW TRY

NOW TRY ANSWERS
4. $\emptyset$
5. $\emptyset$

3.2 Exercises

FOR EXTRA HELP   MyMathLab®

Complete solution available in MyMathLab

Concept Check   Answer each of the following.

1. Using your immediate surroundings, give an example of three planes that satisfy the condition.

   (a) They intersect in a single point.

   (b) They do not intersect.

   (c) They intersect in infinitely many points.

2. Suppose that a system has infinitely many ordered triple solutions of the form (x, y, z) such that

   $$x + y + 2z = 1.$$

   Give three specific ordered triples that are solutions of the system.

3. Explain what the following statement means: "The solution set of the following system is $\{(-1, 2, 3)\}$."

   $$2x + y + z = 3$$
   $$3x - y + z = -2$$
   $$4x - y + 2z = 0$$

4. The following two equations have a common solution of $(1, 2, 3)$.

$$x + y + z = 6$$
$$2x - y + z = 3$$

Which equation would complete a system of three linear equations in three variables having solution set $\{(1, 2, 3)\}$?

A. $3x + 2y - z = 1$ **B.** $3x + 2y - z = 4$

C. $3x + 2y - z = 5$ **D.** $3x + 2y - z = 6$

5. What constant should replace the question mark in this system so that the solution set is $\{(1, 1, 1)\}$?

$$2x - 3y + z = 0$$
$$-5x + 2y - z = -4$$
$$x + y + 2z = \,?$$

6. Complete the work of **Example 1** and show that the ordered triple $(-3, 1, 6)$ is also a solution of equations (2) and (3).

$$x + 7y - 3z = -14 \qquad \text{Equation (2)}$$
$$2x - 3y + 2z = 3 \qquad \text{Equation (3)}$$

Solve each system. See Example 1.

▶ 7. $2x - 5y + 3z = -1$
$x + 4y - 2z = 9$
$x - 2y - 4z = -5$

8. $x + 3y - 6z = 1$
$2x - y + z = 7$
$x + 2y + 2z = 14$

9. $3x + 2y + z = 8$
$2x - 3y + 2z = -16$
$x + 4y - z = 20$

10. $-3x + y - z = -10$
$-4x + 2y + 3z = -1$
$2x + 3y - 2z = -5$

11. $2x + 5y + 2z = 0$
$4x - 7y - 3z = 1$
$3x - 8y - 2z = -6$

12. $5x - 2y + 3z = -9$
$4x + 3y + 5z = 4$
$2x + 4y - 2z = 14$

13. $x + 2y + z = 4$
$2x + y - z = -1$
$x - y - z = -2$

14. $x - 2y + 5z = -7$
$-2x - 3y + 4z = -14$
$-3x + 5y - z = -7$

15. $-x + 2y + 6z = 2$
$3x + 2y + 6z = 6$
$x + 4y - 3z = 1$

16. $2x + y + 2z = 1$
$x + 2y + z = 2$
$x - y - z = 0$

17. $x + y - z = -2$
$2x - y + z = -5$
$-x + 2y - 3z = -4$

18. $x + 2y + 3z = 1$
$-x - y + 3z = 2$
$-6x + y + z = -2$

19. $\dfrac{1}{3}x + \dfrac{1}{6}y - \dfrac{2}{3}z = -1$

$-\dfrac{3}{4}x - \dfrac{1}{3}y - \dfrac{1}{4}z = 3$

$\dfrac{1}{2}x + \dfrac{3}{2}y + \dfrac{3}{4}z = 21$

20. $\dfrac{2}{3}x - \dfrac{1}{4}y + \dfrac{5}{8}z = 0$

$\dfrac{1}{5}x + \dfrac{2}{3}y - \dfrac{1}{4}z = -7$

$-\dfrac{3}{5}x + \dfrac{4}{3}y - \dfrac{7}{8}z = -5$

21. $5.5x - 2.5y + 1.6z = 11.83$
$2.2x + 5.0y - 0.1z = -5.97$
$3.3x - 7.5y + 3.2z = 21.25$

22. $6.2x - 1.4y + 2.4z = -1.80$
$3.1x + 2.8y - 0.2z = 5.68$
$9.3x - 8.4y - 4.8z = -34.20$

Solve each system. See Example 2.

23. $2x - 3y + 2z = -1$
$x + 2y + z = 17$
$2y - z = 7$

24. $2x - y + 3z = 6$
$x + 2y - z = 8$
$2y + z = 1$

25. $4x + 2y - 3z = 6$
$x - 4y + z = -4$
$-x + 2z = 2$

26. $2x + 3y - 4z = 4$
$x - 6y + z = -16$
$-x + 3z = 8$

▶ **27.** $2x + y = 6$
$3y - 2z = -4$
$3x - 5z = -7$

28. $4x - 8y = -7$
$4y + z = 7$
$-8x + z = -4$

29. $-5x + 2y + z = 5$
$-3x - 2y - z = 3$
$-x + 6y = 1$

30. $-4x + 3y - z = 4$
$-5x - 3y + z = -4$
$-2x - 3z = 12$

31. $7x - 3z = -34$
$2y + 4z = 20$
$\dfrac{3}{4}x + \dfrac{1}{6}y = -2$

32. $5x - 2z = 8$
$4y + 3z = -9$
$\dfrac{1}{2}x + \dfrac{2}{3}y = -1$

33. $4x - z = -6$
$\dfrac{3}{5}y + \dfrac{1}{2}z = 0$
$\dfrac{1}{3}x + \dfrac{2}{3}z = -5$

34. $5x - z = 38$
$\dfrac{2}{3}y + \dfrac{1}{4}z = -17$
$\dfrac{1}{5}y + \dfrac{5}{6}z = 4$

Solve each system. If the system is inconsistent or has dependent equations, say so. **See Examples 1, 3, 4, and 5.**

▶ **35.** $2x + 2y - 6z = 5$
$-3x + y - z = -2$
$-x - y + 3z = 4$

36. $-2x + 5y + z = -3$
$5x + 14y - z = -11$
$7x + 9y - 2z = -5$

37. $-5x + 5y - 20z = -40$
$x - y + 4z = 8$
$3x - 3y + 12z = 24$

38. $x + 4y - z = 3$
$-2x - 8y + 2z = -6$
$3x + 12y - 3z = 9$

39. $x + 5y - 2z = -1$
$-2x + 8y + z = -4$
$3x - y + 5z = 19$

40. $x + 3y + z = 2$
$4x + y + 2z = -4$
$5x + 2y + 3z = -2$

▶ **41.** $2x + y - z = 6$
$4x + 2y - 2z = 12$
$-x - \dfrac{1}{2}y + \dfrac{1}{2}z = -3$

42. $2x - 8y + 2z = -10$
$-x + 4y - z = 5$
$\dfrac{1}{8}x - \dfrac{1}{2}y + \dfrac{1}{8}z = -\dfrac{5}{8}$

43. $x + y - 2z = 0$
$3x - y + z = 0$
$4x + 2y - z = 0$

44. $2x + 3y - z = 0$
$x - 4y + 2z = 0$
$3x - 5y - z = 0$

▶ **45.** $x - 2y + \dfrac{1}{3}z = 4$
$3x - 6y + z = 12$
$-6x + 12y - 2z = -3$

46. $4x + y - 2z = 3$
$x + \dfrac{1}{4}y - \dfrac{1}{2}z = \dfrac{3}{4}$
$2x + \dfrac{1}{2}y - z = 1$

Extending Skills   *Extend the method of this section to solve each system. Express the solution in the form* (x, y, z, w).

47. $x + y + z - w = 5$
$2x + y - z + w = 3$
$x - 2y + 3z + w = 18$
$-x - y + z + 2w = 8$

48. $3x + y - z + 2w = 9$
$x + y + 2z - w = 10$
$x - y - z + 3w = -2$
$-x + y - z + w = -6$

49. $3x + y - z + w = -3$
$2x + 4y + z - w = -7$
$-2x + 3y - 5z + w = 3$
$5x + 4y - 5z + 2w = -7$

50. $x - 3y + 7z + w = 11$
$2x + 4y + 6z - 3w = -3$
$3x + 2y + z + 2w = 19$
$4x + y - 3z + w = 22$

3.3 Applications of Systems of Linear Equations

Although some problems with two unknowns can be solved using just one variable, it is often easier to use two variables and a system of equations. The following problem, which can be solved with a system, appeared in a Hindu work that dates back to about A.D. 850. (See **Exercise 39.**)

> The mixed price of 9 citrons (a lemonlike fruit) and 7 fragrant wood apples is 107; again, the mixed price of 7 citrons and 9 fragrant wood apples is 101. O you arithmetician, tell me quickly the price of a citron and the price of a wood apple here, having distinctly separated those prices well.

PROBLEM-SOLVING HINT   When solving an applied problem using two variables, it is a good idea to pick letters that correspond to the descriptions of the unknown quantities. In the example above, we could choose *c* to represent the number of citrons, and *w* to represent the number of wood apples.

The following steps are based on the problem-solving method of **Section 1.3.**

Solving an Applied Problem Using a System of Equations

Step 1 **Read** the problem carefully. *What information is given? What is to be found?*

Step 2 **Assign variables** to represent the unknown values. Write down what each variable represents. Make a sketch, diagram, or table, as needed.

Step 3 **Write a system of equations** using both variables.

Step 4 **Solve** the system of equations.

Step 5 **State the answer.** Label it appropriately. *Does it seem reasonable?*

Step 6 **Check** the answer in the words of the *original* problem.

OBJECTIVE 1 Solve geometry problems using two variables.

EXAMPLE 1 Finding the Dimensions of a Soccer Field

A rectangular soccer field may have a width between 50 and 100 yd and a length between 100 and 130 yd. One particular soccer field has a perimeter of 320 yd. Its length measures 40 yd more than its width. What are the dimensions of this field? (*Source:* www.soccer-training-guide.com)

Step 1 **Read** the problem again. We must find the dimensions of the field.

Step 2 **Assign variables.** A sketch may be helpful. See **FIGURE 8** on the next page.

$$\text{Let} \quad L = \text{the length} \quad \text{and} \quad W = \text{the width.}$$

**NOW TRY
EXERCISE 1**

A rectangular parking lot has a length that is 10 ft more than twice its width. The perimeter of the parking lot is 620 ft. What are the dimensions of the parking lot?

FIGURE 8

Step 3 **Write a system of equations.** Because the perimeter is 320 yd, we find one equation by using the perimeter formula.

$$2L + 2W = 320 \qquad 2L + 2W = P$$

For a second equation, use the information given about the width.

$$L = W + 40 \qquad \text{The length is 40 yd more than the width.}$$

These two equations form a system of equations.

$$2L + 2W = 320 \qquad (1)$$
$$L = W + 40 \qquad (2)$$

Step 4 **Solve** the system of equations. Because equation (2), $L = W + 40$, is solved for L, we can substitute $W + 40$ for L in equation (1) and solve for W.

$$2L + 2W = 320 \qquad (1)$$
$$2(W + 40) + 2W = 320 \qquad \text{Let } L = W + 40.$$

> Be sure to use parentheses around $W + 40$.

$$2W + 80 + 2W = 320 \qquad \text{Distributive property}$$
$$4W + 80 = 320 \qquad \text{Combine like terms.}$$
$$4W = 240 \qquad \text{Subtract 80.}$$

> Don't stop here.

$$W = 60 \qquad \text{Divide by 4.}$$

Let $W = 60$ in the equation $L = W + 40$ to find L.

$$L = 60 + 40 = 100$$

Step 5 **State the answer.** The length is 100 yd, and the width is 60 yd. Both dimensions are within the ranges given in the problem.

Step 6 **Check** using the words of the problem. The answer is correct.

$$2(100) + 2(60) = 320 \qquad \text{The perimeter is 320 yd.}$$
$$100 - 60 = 40 \qquad \text{Length is 40 yd more than width.} \qquad \text{NOW TRY} \ \text{}$$

PROBLEM-SOLVING HINT   There is often more than one way to write the equations in a system used to solve an application. In **Example 1,** we might write the second equation as

$$W = L - 40. \qquad (2)$$

In this case, we would substitute $L - 40$ for W in equation (1) to obtain

$$2L + 2(L - 40) = 320 \qquad \text{Let } W = L - 40.$$

and solve for L first (instead of W, as in Step 4 above). The *same* answers result.

NOW TRY ANSWER
1. length: 210 ft; width: 100 ft

**NOW TRY
EXERCISE 2**

For the 2013 season at Six Flags St. Louis, two general admission tickets and three tickets for children cost $239.95. One general admission ticket and four tickets for children cost $224.95. Determine the ticket prices for general admission and for children. (*Source:* www.sixflags.com)

OBJECTIVE 2 Solve money problems using two variables.

EXAMPLE 2   Solving a Problem about Ticket Prices

For the 2012–2013 National Hockey League and National Basketball Association seasons, two hockey tickets and one basketball ticket purchased at their average prices cost $173.01. One hockey ticket and two basketball tickets cost $162.99. What were the average ticket prices for the two sports? (*Source:* Team Marketing Report.)

Step 1   **Read** the problem again. There are two unknowns.

Step 2   **Assign variables.**

$$\text{Let } h = \text{the average price for a hockey ticket}$$
$$\text{and } b = \text{the average price for a basketball ticket.}$$

Step 3   **Write a system of equations.** Because two hockey tickets and one basketball ticket cost a total of $173.01, one equation for the system is

$$2h + b = 173.01.$$

By similar reasoning, the second equation is

$$h + 2b = 162.99.$$

These two equations form a system of equations.

$$2h + b = 173.01 \quad (1)$$
$$h + 2b = 162.99 \quad (2)$$

Step 4   **Solve** the system. To eliminate h, multiply equation (2) by -2 and add.

$$\begin{aligned}
2h + b &= 173.01 \quad &(1) \\
-2h - 4b &= -325.98 \quad &\text{Multiply each side of (2) by } -2. \\
\hline
-3b &= -152.97 \quad &\text{Add.} \\
b &= 50.99 \quad &\text{Divide by } -3.
\end{aligned}$$

To find the value of h, let $b = 50.99$ in equation (2).

$$\begin{aligned}
h + 2b &= 162.99 \quad &(2) \\
h + 2(50.99) &= 162.99 \quad &\text{Let } b = 50.99. \\
h + 101.98 &= 162.99 \quad &\text{Multiply.} \\
h &= 61.01 \quad &\text{Subtract } 101.98.
\end{aligned}$$

Step 5   **State the answer.** The average price for one basketball ticket was $50.99. For one hockey ticket, the average price was $61.01.

Step 6   **Check** that these values satisfy the problem conditions.

$$2(\$61.01) + \$50.99 = \$173.01, \quad \text{as required.}$$
$$\$61.01 + 2(\$50.99) = \$162.99, \quad \text{as required.}$$

NOW TRY

NOW TRY ANSWER
2. general admission: $56.99; children: $41.99

NOTE   In **Example 2,** we could have solved the system using the substitution method.

OBJECTIVE 3 Solve mixture problems using two variables.

We solved mixture problems in **Section 1.3** using one variable. For many mixture problems we can use more than one variable and a system of equations.

EXAMPLE 3 Solving a Mixture Problem

How many ounces each of 5% hydrochloric acid and 20% hydrochloric acid must be combined to obtain 10 oz of solution that is 12.5% hydrochloric acid?

Step 1   **Read** the problem. Two solutions of different strengths are being mixed to obtain a specific amount of a solution with an "in-between" strength.

Step 2   **Assign variables.**

Let $x =$ the number of ounces of 5% solution

and $y =$ the number of ounces of 20% solution.

Use a table to summarize the information from the problem.

Ounces of Solution	Percent (as a decimal)	Ounces of Pure Acid
x	5% = 0.05	0.05x
y	20% = 0.20	0.20y
10	12.5% = 0.125	(0.125)10

Gives equation (1)   Gives equation (2)

Multiply the amount of each solution (given in the first column) by its concentration of acid (given in the second column) to find the amount of acid in that solution (given in the third column).

FIGURE 9 illustrates what is happening in the problem.

Ounces of solution

Ounces of pure acid

x + y = 10 → Gives equation (1)

0.05x 0.20y 0.125(10) → Gives equation (2)

FIGURE 9

Step 3   **Write a system of equations.** When x ounces of 5% solution and y ounces of 20% solution are combined, the total number of ounces is 10.

$$x + y = 10$$

The number of ounces of acid in the 5% solution $(0.05x)$ added to the number of ounces of acid in the 20% solution $(0.20y)$ must equal the total number of ounces of acid in the mixture, which is $(0.125)10$, or 1.25.

$$0.05x + 0.20y = 1.25$$

Notice that these equations can be quickly determined by reading down the table or using the labels in **FIGURE 9.**

Multiply the equation in red by 100 to clear the decimals and obtain an equivalent system of equations.

$$x + y = 10 \quad \text{(1)}$$
$$5x + 20y = 125 \quad \text{(2)}$$

This is the system to solve.

**NOW TRY
EXERCISE 3**
How many liters each of a 15% acid solution and a 25% acid solution should be mixed to obtain 30 L of an 18% acid solution?

Step 4   **Solve** the system. To eliminate x, multiply equation (1), $x + y = 10$, by -5.

$$-5x - 5y = -50 \quad \text{Multiply each side of (1) by } -5.$$
$$\underline{5x + 20y = 125} \quad \text{(2)}$$
$$15y = 75 \quad \text{Add.}$$

Ounces of 20% solution $\longrightarrow y = 5 \quad$ Divide by 15.

Substitute 5 for y in equation (1) to find the value of x.

$$x + y = 10 \quad \text{(1)}$$
$$x + 5 = 10 \quad \text{Let } y = 5.$$

Ounces of 5% solution $\longrightarrow x = 5 \quad$ Subtract 5.

Step 5   **State the answer.** The desired mixture will require 5 oz of the 5% solution and 5 oz of the 20% solution.

Step 6   **Check.**

Total amount of solution: $x + y = 5 \text{ oz} + 5 \text{ oz}$
$$= 10 \text{ oz}, \quad \text{as required.}$$

Total amount of acid: 5% of 5 oz + 20% of 5 oz
$$= 0.05(5) + 0.20(5)$$
$$= 1.25 \text{ oz}$$

Percent of acid in solution:

Total acid $\longrightarrow \dfrac{1.25}{10} = 0.125, \quad$ or   12.5%,   as required.   **NOW TRY**

OBJECTIVE 4 Solve distance-rate-time problems using two variables.

Motion problems require the distance formula $d = rt$, where d is distance, r is rate (or speed), and t is time.

EXAMPLE 4 Solving a Motion Problem

A car travels 250 km in the same time that a truck travels 225 km. If the rate of the car is 8 km per hr faster than the rate of the truck, find both rates.

Step 1   **Read** the problem again. Given the distances traveled, we need to find the rate of each vehicle.

Step 2   **Assign variables.**

Let $x =$ the rate of the car,

and $y =$ the rate of the truck.

As in **Example 3,** a table helps organize the information. Fill in the distance for each vehicle, and the variables for the unknown rates.

	d	r	t
Car	250	x	$\frac{250}{x}$
Truck	225	y	$\frac{225}{y}$

To find the expressions for time, we solved the distance formula $d = rt$ for t. Thus, $\frac{d}{r} = t$.

NOW TRY ANSWER
3. 9 L of the 25% acid solution;
   21 L of the 15% acid solution

**NOW TRY
EXERCISE 4**
On a bicycle ride, Vann
can travel 50 mi in the
same amount of time that
Ivy can travel 40 mi.
Determine both bicyclists'
rates, if Vann's rate is 2 mph
faster than Ivy's.

Step 3   **Write a system of equations.** The car travels 8 km per hr faster than the truck. Because the two rates are x and y,

$$x = y + 8. \quad (1)$$

Both vehicles travel for the *same* time, so the times must be equal.

Time for car $\longrightarrow$ $\dfrac{250}{x} = \dfrac{225}{y}$ $\longleftarrow$ Time for truck

Multiply both sides by xy to obtain an equivalent equation with no variable denominators.

$$xy \cdot \frac{250}{x} = \frac{225}{y} \cdot xy \qquad \text{Multiply by the LCD, } xy.$$

$$\frac{250xy}{x} = \frac{225xy}{y}$$

$$250y = 225x \qquad \text{Divide out the common factors.} \quad (2)$$

We now have a system of linear equations.

$$x = y + 8 \qquad (1)$$
$$250y = 225x \qquad (2)$$

Step 4   **Solve** the system by substitution. Replace x with $y + 8$ in equation (2).

$$250y = 225x \qquad (2)$$

Be sure to use
parentheses
around $y + 8$. $250y = 225(y + 8) \qquad \text{Let } x = y + 8.$

$$250y = 225y + 1800 \qquad \text{Distributive property}$$

$$25y = 1800 \qquad \text{Subtract } 225y.$$

Truck's rate $\rightarrow y = 72$ $\qquad \text{Divide by 25.}$

Let $y = 72$ in the equation $x = y + 8$ to find x.

Car's rate $\rightarrow x = 72 + 8 = 80$

Step 5   **State the answer.** The rate of the car is 80 km per hr, and the rate of the truck is 72 km per hr.

Step 6   **Check.**

$$\text{Car:} \quad t = \frac{d}{r} = \frac{250}{80} = 3.125 \longleftarrow$$

$$\text{Truck:} \quad t = \frac{d}{r} = \frac{225}{72} = 3.125 \longleftarrow$$

Times are equal,
as required.

The rate of the car, 80 km per hr, is 8 km per hour greater than that of the truck, 72 km per hr, as required.   **NOW TRY**

PROBLEM-SOLVING HINT   When solving a problem as in **Example 4,** where one quantity is compared to another (e.g., the car travels 8 km per hr faster than the truck), be sure to translate correctly in terms of the two variables.

**NOW TRY
EXERCISE 5**

In his motorboat, Ed travels 42 mi upstream at top speed in 2.1 hr. Still at top speed, the return trip to the same spot takes only 1.5 hr. Find the rate of Ed's boat in still water and the rate of the current.

Downstream
(with the current)

Upstream
(against the current)

FIGURE 10

EXAMPLE 5 Solving a Motion Problem

While kayaking on the Blackledge River, Rebecca traveled 9 mi upstream (against the current) in 2.25 hr. It only took her 1 hr paddling downstream (with the current) back to the spot where she started. Find Rebecca's kayaking rate in still water and the rate of the current.

Step 1 **Read** the problem. We must find two rates—Rebecca's kayaking rate in still water and the rate of the current.

Step 2 **Assign variables.**

> Let x = Rebecca's kayaking rate in still water
>
> and y = the rate of the current.

When the kayak is traveling *against* the current, the current slows it down. The rate of the kayak is the *difference* between its rate in still water and the rate of the current, which is $(x - y)$ mph.

When the kayak is traveling *with* the current, the current speeds it up. The rate of the kayak is the *sum* of its rate in still water and the rate of the current, which is $(x + y)$ mph.

> Thus, $x - y$ = the rate of the kayak *against* the current,
>
> and $x + y$ = the rate of the kayak *with* the current.

See **FIGURE 10**. Make a table. Use the formula $d = rt$, or $rt = d$.

	r	t	d
Upstream	$x - y$	2.25	$2.25(x - y)$
Downstream	$x + y$	1	$1(x + y)$

The distance is the same in each direction, 9 mi.

Step 3 **Write a system of equations.**

$$2.25(x - y) = 9 \qquad \text{Upstream}$$
$$1(x + y) = 9 \qquad \text{Downstream}$$

Clear parentheses in each equation, and then divide each term in the first equation by 2.25 to obtain an equivalent system.

$$
\begin{aligned}
x - y &= 4 \qquad &(1)\\
x + y &= 9 \qquad &(2)\\
\hline
2x &= 13 \qquad &\text{Add.}
\end{aligned}
$$

Rebecca's rate $\longrightarrow x = 6.5$ Divide by 2.

Step 4 **Solve.**

Substitute 6.5 for x in equation (2) and solve for y.

$$x + y = 9 \qquad (2)$$
$$6.5 + y = 9 \qquad \text{Let } x = 6.5.$$

Rate of current $\longrightarrow y = 2.5$ Subtract 6.5.

Step 5 **State the answer.** Rebecca's rate in still water was 6.5 mph, and the rate of the current was 2.5 mph.

Step 6 **Check.**

> *Distance upstream:* $2.25(6.5 - 2.5) = 9$ True statements result.
>
> *Distance downstream:* $1(6.5 + 2.5) = 9$

NOW TRY

NOW TRY ANSWER
5. boat: 24 mph; current: 4 mph

OBJECTIVE 5 Solve problems with three variables using a system of three equations.

PROBLEM-SOLVING HINT   If an application has *three* unknown quantities, we can use a system of *three* equations to solve it. We extend the method used for two unknowns.

EXAMPLE 6   Solving a Problem Involving Prices

At Panera Bread, a loaf of honey wheat bread costs $2.95, a loaf of sunflower bread costs $2.99, and a loaf of French bread costs $5.79. On a recent day, three times as many loaves of honey wheat bread were sold as sunflower bread. The number of loaves of French bread sold was 5 less than the number of loaves of honey wheat bread sold. Total receipts for these breads were $87.89. How many loaves of each type of bread were sold? (*Source:* Panera Bread menu.)

Step 1   **Read** the problem again. There are three unknowns in this problem.

Step 2   **Assign variables** to represent the three unknowns.

> Let x = the number of loaves of honey wheat bread,
>
> y = the number of loaves of sunflower bread,
>
> and z = the number of loaves of French bread.

Step 3   **Write a system of three equations.** Three times as many loaves of honey wheat bread were sold as sunflower bread.

$$x = 3y, \quad \text{or} \quad x - 3y = 0 \qquad \text{Subtract } 3y. \quad (1)$$

Also, we have the information needed for another equation.

Number of loaves of French	equals	5 less than the number of loaves of honey wheat.
↓	↓	↓
z	$=$	$x - 5$

$$-x + z = -5 \qquad \text{Subtract } x.$$
$$x - z = 5 \qquad \text{Multiply by } -1. \quad (2)$$

Multiplying the cost of a loaf of each kind of bread by the number of loaves of that kind sold and adding gives an equation for the total receipts.

$$2.95x + 2.99y + 5.79z = 87.89$$
$$295x + 299y + 579z = 8789 \qquad \begin{array}{l}\text{Multiply each term by}\\ \text{100 to clear decimals.} \quad (3)\end{array}$$

Step 4   **Solve** the system of three equations.

$$x - 3y = 0 \qquad (1)$$
$$x - z = 5 \qquad (2)$$
$$295x + 299y + 579z = 8789 \qquad (3)$$

Equation (1) is missing the variable z, so one way to begin is to eliminate z again, using equations (2) and (3).

$$
\begin{array}{rll}
579x \qquad\quad - 579z = & 2895 & \text{Multiply (2) by 579.}\\
\underline{295x + 299y + 579z = } & \underline{8789} & (3)\\
874x + 299y \qquad\quad = & 11{,}684 & \text{Add.} \quad (4)
\end{array}
$$

NOW TRY
EXERCISE 6

At Panera Bread, a loaf of white bread costs $3.69, a loaf of cheese bread costs $4.29, and a loaf of whole grain bread costs $7.69. On a recent day, twice as many loaves of white bread were sold as cheese bread. The number of loaves of whole grain bread sold was 3 less than the number of loaves of white bread sold. Total receipts for these breads were $139.23. How many loaves of each type of bread were sold? (*Source:* Panera Bread menu.)

Use resulting equation (4) in x and y, together with equation (1), $x - 3y = 0$, to eliminate x.

$$
\begin{array}{ll}
-874x + 2622y = 0 & \text{Multiply (1) by } -874. \\
\underline{874x + 299y = 11{,}684} & \text{(4)} \\
2921y = 11{,}684 & \text{Add.} \\
y = 4 & \text{Divide by 2921.}
\end{array}
$$

We can find x by substituting this value for y in equation (1).

$$
\begin{array}{ll}
x - 3y = 0 & \text{(1)} \\
x - 3(4) = 0 & \text{Let } y = 4. \\
x - 12 = 0 & \text{Multiply.} \\
x = 12 & \text{Add 12.}
\end{array}
$$

We can find z by substituting this value for x in equation (2).

$$
\begin{array}{ll}
x - z = 5 & \text{(2)} \\
12 - z = 5 & \text{Let } x = 12. \\
z = 7 & \text{Subtract 12. Multiply by } -1.
\end{array}
$$

Thus, $x = 12$, $y = 4$, and $z = 7$.

Step 5 **State the answer.** There were 12 loaves of honey wheat bread, 4 loaves of sunflower bread, and 7 loaves of French bread sold.

Step 6 **Check.** Because $12 = 3 \cdot 4$, the number of loaves of honey wheat bread is three times the number of loaves of sunflower bread. Also, $12 - 7 = 5$, so the number of loaves of French bread is 5 less than the number of loaves of honey wheat bread. Multiply the appropriate cost per loaf by the number of loaves sold and add the results to check that total receipts were $87.89.

 NOW TRY

EXAMPLE 7 Solving a Business Production Problem

A company produces three flat screen television sets: models X, Y, and Z.

- Each model X set requires 2 hr of electronics work, 2 hr of assembly time, and 1 hr of finishing time.

- Each model Y requires 1 hr of electronics work, 3 hr of assembly time, and 1 hr of finishing time.

- Each model Z requires 3 hr of electronics work, 2 hr of assembly time, and 2 hr of finishing time.

There are 100 hr available for electronics, 100 hr available for assembly, and 65 hr available for finishing per week. How many of each model should be produced each week if all available time must be used?

Step 1 **Read** the problem again. There are three unknowns.

Step 2 **Assign variables.** Then organize the information in a table.

$$
\begin{array}{rl}
\text{Let} & x = \text{the number of model X produced per week,} \\
& y = \text{the number of model Y produced per week,} \\
\text{and} & z = \text{the number of model Z produced per week.}
\end{array}
$$

NOW TRY ANSWER
6. 12 loaves of white bread;
6 loaves of cheese bread;
9 loaves of whole grain bread

NOW TRY
EXERCISE 7

Katherine has a quilting shop and makes three kinds of quilts: the lone star quilt, the bandana quilt, and the log cabin quilt.

- Each lone star quilt requires 8 hr of piecework, 4 hr of machine quilting, and 2 hr of finishing.

- Each bandana quilt requires 2 hr of piecework, 2 hr of machine quilting, and 2 hr of finishing.

- Each log cabin quilt requires 10 hr of piecework, 5 hr of machine quilting, and 2 hr of finishing.

Katherine allocates 74 hr for piecework, 42 hr for machine quilting, and 24 hr for finishing quilts each month. How many of each type of quilt should be made each month if all available time must be used?

	Each Model X	Each Model Y	Each Model Z	Totals	
Hours of Electronics Work	2	1	3	100	→ Gives equation (1)
Hours of Assembly Time	2	3	2	100	→ Gives equation (2)
Hours of Finishing Time	1	1	2	65	→ Gives equation (3)

Step 3 **Write a system of three equations.** The x model X sets require $2x$ hours of electronics, the y model Y sets require $1y$ (or y) hours of electronics, and the z model Z sets require $3z$ hours of electronics. There are 100 hr available for electronics. This gives one equation.

$$2x + y + 3z = 100$$

By similar reasoning, we write two more equations using the fact that there are 100 hr available for assembly and 65 hr available for finishing.

$$2x + y + 3z = 100 \qquad \text{Electronics} \quad (1)$$
$$2x + 3y + 2z = 100 \qquad \text{Assembly} \quad (2)$$
$$x + y + 2z = 65 \qquad \text{Finishing} \quad (3)$$

Notice that by reading *across* the table, we can easily determine the coefficients and constants in the equations of the system.

Step 4 **Solve** the system of equations (1), (2), and (3). Because x in equation (3) has coefficient 1, we choose x as the focus variable and (3) as the working equation.

$$2x + y + 3z = 100 \qquad (1)$$
$$\underline{-2x - 2y - 4z = -130} \qquad \text{Multiply (3) by } -2.$$
$$-y - z = -30 \qquad \text{Add.} \quad (4)$$

Eliminate x again, using equations (2) and (3).

$$2x + 3y + 2z = 100 \qquad (2)$$
$$\underline{-2x - 2y - 4z = -130} \qquad \text{Multiply (3) by } -2.$$
$$y - 2z = -30 \qquad \text{Add.} \quad (5)$$

Solve the system of two equations (4) and (5).

$$-y - z = -30 \qquad (4)$$
$$\underline{y - 2z = -30} \qquad (5)$$
$$-3z = -60 \qquad \text{Add.}$$
$$z = 20 \qquad \text{Divide by } -3.$$

We can find y by substituting this value for z in equation (5).

$$y - 2z = -30 \qquad (5)$$
$$y - 2(20) = -30 \qquad \text{Let } z = 20.$$
$$y - 40 = -30 \qquad \text{Multiply.}$$
$$y = 10 \qquad \text{Add 40.}$$

NOW TRY ANSWER
7. lone star quilts: 3;
   bandana quilts: 5;
   log cabin quilts: 4

NOW TRY EXERCISE 7
is on the preceding page.

We can find x by substituting the values for y and z in equation (3).

$$x + y + 2z = 65 \quad \text{(3)}$$

$$x + 10 + 2(20) = 65 \quad \text{Let } y = 10 \text{ and } z = 20.$$

$$x + 50 = 65 \quad \text{Multiply. Add.}$$

$$x = 15 \quad \text{Subtract 50.}$$

Thus, $x = 15$, $y = 10$, and $z = 20$.

Step 5 **State the answer.** The company should produce 15 model X, 10 model Y, and 20 model Z sets per week.

Step 6 **Check** that these values satisfy the conditions of the problem.   NOW TRY

3.3 Exercises

FOR EXTRA HELP   ▶ MyMathLab°

▶ *Complete solution available in MyMathLab*

Concept Check   *Answer each question.*

1. If a container of liquid contains 60 oz of solution, what is the number of ounces of pure acid if the given solution contains the following acid concentrations?

   (a) 10%   **(b)** 25%   **(c)** 40%   **(d)** 50%

2. If $5000 is invested in an account paying simple annual interest, how much interest will be earned during the first year at the following rates?

   (a) 2%   **(b)** 3%   **(c)** 4%   **(d)** 3.5%

3. If one pound of turkey costs $1.89, how much will x pounds cost?

4. If one ticket to the movie *12 Years a Slave* costs $13.50 and y tickets are sold, how much is collected from the sale?

5. If the rate of a boat in still water is 10 mph, and the rate of the current of a river is x mph, what is the rate of the boat in each case?

   (a) The boat is going upstream (that is, against the current, which slows the boat down).

   (b) The boat is going downstream (that is, with the current, which speeds the boat up).

6. The swimming rate of a whale is 25 mph.

   (a) If the whale swims for y hours, what is its distance?

   (b) If the whale travels 10 mi, what is its time?

Solve each problem. See Example 1.

7. During the 2013 Major League Baseball season, the Los Angeles Dodgers played 162 games. They won 22 more games than they lost. What was their win-loss record that year?

8. Refer to **Exercise 7.** During the same 162-game season, the Colorado Rockies lost 14 more games than they won. What was the team's win-loss record?

Team	W	L
L.A. Dodgers	___	___
Arizona	81	70
San Diego	76	86
San Francisco	76	86
Colorado	___	___

Source: Major League Baseball.

▶ 9. Venus and Serena measured a tennis court and found that it was 42 ft longer than it was wide and had a perimeter of 228 ft. What were the length and the width of the tennis court?

10. LeBron and Shaq measured a basketball court and found that the width of the court was 44 ft less than the length. If the perimeter was 288 ft, what were the length and the width of the basketball court?

11. In 2012, the two American telecommunication companies with the greatest revenues were AT&T and Verizon. The two companies had combined revenues of $242.2 billion. AT&T's revenue was $10.6 billion more than that of Verizon. What was the revenue for each company? (*Source:* Verizon and AT&T Annual Reports.)

12. In 2012, U.S. exports to Canada were $76.6 billion more than exports to Mexico. Together, exports to these two countries totaled $508.4 billion. How much were exports to each country? (*Source:* U.S. Census Bureau.)

Find the measures of the angles marked x and y. Remember that (**1**) *the sum of the measures of the angles of a triangle is* 180°, (**2**) *supplementary angles have a sum of* 180°, *and* (**3**) *vertical angles have equal measures.*

13.

14.

The Fan Cost Index (FCI) represents the cost of four average-price tickets (two adult, two child), four small soft drinks, two small beers, four hot dogs, parking for one car, two game programs, and two souvenir caps to a sporting event. (Source: Team Marketing Report.)
   Use the concept of FCI in Exercises 15 and 16. **See Example 2.**

15. For the 2013 season, the FCI prices for the National Hockey League and the National Basketball Association totaled $670.50. The hockey FCI was $39.18 more than that of basketball. What were the FCIs for these sports?

16. In 2013, the FCI prices for Major League Baseball and the National Football League totaled $667.45. The football FCI was $251.85 more than that of baseball. What were the FCIs for these sports?

Solve each problem. **See Example 2.**

17. Leanna is a waitress at Bonefish Grill. During one particular day she sold 15 ribeye steak dinners and 20 grilled salmon dinners, totaling $559.15. Another day she sold 25 ribeye steak dinners and 10 grilled salmon dinners, totaling $582.15. How much did each type of dinner cost? (*Source:* Bonefish Grill Menu.)

18. Two days at Busch Gardens Williamsburg (Virginia) and 3 days at Universal Studios Florida (Orlando) cost $420, while 4 days at Busch Gardens and 2 days at Universal Studios cost $472. (Prices are based on single-day admissions.) What was the cost per day for each park? (*Sources:* Busch Gardens and Universal Studios.)

19. The movie *Saving Mr. Banks* was available in both DVD and Blu-ray formats. The price for 3 DVDs and 2 Blu-ray discs was $77.86, while the price for 2 DVDs and 3 Blu-ray discs was $84.39. How much did each format cost?

20. On the basis of average total costs per day for business travel to New York City and Washington, DC (which include a hotel room, car rental, and three meals), 2 days in New York and 3 days in Washington cost $2936, while 4 days in New York and 2 days in Washington cost $3616. What was the average cost per day in each city? (*Source: Business Travel News.*)

Solve each problem. See Example 3.

▶ 21. How many gallons each of 25% alcohol and 35% alcohol should be mixed to obtain 20 gal of 32% alcohol?

Gallons of Solution	Percent (as a decimal)	Gallons of Pure Alcohol
x	25% = 0.25	
y	35% = 0.35	
20	32% =	

22. How many liters each of 15% acid and 33% acid should be mixed to obtain 120 L of 21% acid?

Liters of Solution	Percent (as a decimal)	Liters of Pure Acid
x	15% = 0.15	
y	33% =	
120	21% =	

23. Pure acid is to be added to a 10% acid solution to obtain 54 L of a 20% acid solution. What amounts of each should be used?

24. A truck radiator holds 36 L of fluid. How much pure antifreeze must be added to a mixture that is 4% antifreeze to fill the radiator with a mixture that is 20% antifreeze?

25. A party mix is made by adding nuts that sell for $2.50 per kg to a cereal mixture that sells for $1 per kg. How much of each should be added to obtain 30 kg of a mix that will sell for $1.70 per kg?

	Number of Kilograms	Price per Kilogram (in dollars)	Value (in dollars)
Nuts	x	2.50	
Cereal	y	1.00	
Mixture		1.70	

26. A fruit drink is made by mixing fruit juices. Such a drink with 50% juice is to be mixed with another drink that is 30% juice to obtain 200 L of a drink that is 45% juice. How much of each should be used?

	Liters of Drink	Percent (as a decimal)	Liters of Pure Juice
50% Juice	x	0.50	
30% Juice	y	0.30	
Mixture		0.45	

27. A total of $3000 is invested, part at 2% simple interest and part at 4%. If the total annual return from the two investments is $100, how much is invested at each rate?

Principal (in dollars)	Rate (as a decimal)	Interest (in dollars)
x	0.02	0.02x
y	0.04	0.04y
3000		100

28. An investor will invest a total of $15,000 in two accounts, one paying 4% annual simple interest and the other 3%. If he wants to earn $550 annual interest, how much should he invest at each rate?

Principal (in dollars)	Rate (as a decimal)	Interest (in dollars)
x	0.04	
y	0.03	
15,000		

*Solve each problem. **See Examples 4 and 5.***

▶ 29. A train travels 150 km in the same time that a plane travels 400 km. If the rate of the plane is 20 km per hr less than three times the rate of the train, find both rates.

	r	t	d
Train	x		150
Plane	y		400

30. A freight train and an express train leave towns 390 km apart, traveling toward one another. The freight train travels 30 km per hr slower than the express train. They pass one another 3 hr later. What are their rates?

	r	t	d
Freight Train	x	3	
Express Train	y	3	

31. A motor scooter travels 20 mi in the same time that a bicycle travels 8 mi. If the rate of the scooter is 5 mph more than twice the rate of the bicycle, find both rates.

32. A plane travels 1000 mi in the same time that a car travels 300 mi. If the rate of the plane is 20 mph greater than three times the rate of the car, find both rates.

33. In his motorboat, Bill travels upstream at top speed to his favorite fishing spot, a distance of 36 mi, in 2 hr. Returning, he finds that the trip downstream, still at top speed, takes only 1.5 hr. Find the rate of Bill's boat and the rate of the current. Let x = the rate of the boat and y = the rate of the current.

	r	t	d
Upstream	x − y	2	
Downstream	x + y		

34. Traveling for 3 hr into a steady head wind, a plane flies 1650 mi. The pilot determines that flying *with* the same wind for 2 hr, he could make a trip of 1300 mi. Find the rate of the plane and the wind speed.

$x − y$ mph
into wind

$x + y$ mph
with wind

Solve each problem. ***See Examples 1–5.***

35. How many pounds of candy that sells for $0.75 per lb must be mixed with candy that sells for $1.25 per lb to obtain 9 lb of a mixture that should sell for $0.96 per lb? (*Source: The Bill Cosby Show.*)

36. The top-grossing tour on the North American concert circuit for 2012 was Madonna, followed by Bruce Springsteen and the E Street Band. Together, they took in $238.4 million from ticket sales. If Springsteen took in $29 million less than Madonna, how much did each band generate? (*Source:* Pollstar.)

37. Tickets to a production of *A Midsummer Night's Dream* at Broward College cost $5 for general admission or $4 with a student ID. If 184 people paid to see a performance and $812 was collected, how many of each type of ticket were sold?

38. At a business meeting at Panera Bread, the bill for two cappuccinos and three house lattes was $17.55. At another table, the bill for one cappuccino and two house lattes was $10.57. How much did each type of beverage cost? (*Source:* Panera Bread menu.)

39. The mixed price of 9 citrons and 7 fragrant wood apples is 107; again, the mixed price of 7 citrons and 9 fragrant wood apples is 101. O you arithmetician, tell me quickly the price of a citron and the price of a wood apple here, having distinctly separated those prices well. (*Source:* Hindu work, A.D. 850.)

40. Braving blizzard conditions on the planet Hoth, Luke Skywalker sets out in his snow speeder for a rebel base 4800 mi away. He travels into a steady head wind and makes the trip in 3 hr. Returning, he finds that the trip back, now with a tailwind, takes only 2 hr. Find the rate of Luke's snow speeder and the speed of the wind.

	r	t	d
Into Head Wind			
With Tailwind			

Solve each problem. ***See Examples 6 and 7.*** *(In Exercises 41–44, remember that the sum of the measures of the angles of a triangle is 180°.)*

41. In the triangle below, $z = x + 10$ and $x + y = 100$. Determine a third equation involving x, y, and z, and then find the measures of the three angles.

42. In the triangle below, x is 10 less than y and 20 less than z. Write a system of equations and find the measures of the three angles.

43. In a certain triangle, the measure of the second angle is 10° greater than three times the first. The third angle measure is equal to the sum of the measures of the other two. Find the measures of the three angles.

44. The measure of the largest angle of a triangle is 12° less than the sum of the measures of the other two. The smallest angle measures 58° less than the largest. Find the measures of the angles.

45. The perimeter of a triangle is 70 cm. The longest side is 4 cm less than the sum of the other two sides. Twice the shortest side is 9 cm less than the longest side. Find the length of each side of the triangle.

46. The perimeter of a triangle is 56 in. The longest side measures 4 in. less than the sum of the other two sides. Three times the shortest side is 4 in. more than the longest side. Find the lengths of the three sides.

47. In the 2014 Winter Olympics in Sochi, Russia, host Russia earned 4 more gold medals than bronze. The number of silver medals earned was 7 less than twice the number of bronze medals. Russia earned a total of 33 medals. How many of each kind of medal did Russia earn? (*Source:* www.sochi.com)

48. In a random sample of Americans of voting age conducted recently, 17% more people identified themselves as Independents than as Republicans, while 6% fewer people identified themselves as Republicans than as Democrats. Of those sampled, 2% did not identify with any of the three categories. What percent of the people in the sample identified themselves with each of the three political affiliations? *(Source: Gallup, Inc.)*

49. Tickets for a Harlem Globetrotters show cost $28 general admission, $43 courtside, or $173 bench seats. Nine times as many general admission tickets were sold as bench tickets, and the number of general admission tickets sold was 55 more than the sum of the number of courtside tickets and bench tickets. Sales of all three kinds of tickets totaled $97,605. How many of each kind of ticket were sold? (*Source:* www.harlemglobetrotters.com)

50. Three kinds of tickets are available for a rock concert: "up close," "in the middle," and "far out." "Up close" tickets cost $10 more than "in the middle" tickets. "In the middle" tickets cost $10 more than "far out" tickets. Twice the cost of an "up close" ticket is $20 more than three times the cost of a "far out" ticket. Find the price of each kind of ticket.

51. A wholesaler supplies college t-shirts to three college bookstores: A, B, and C. The wholesaler recently shipped a total of 800 t-shirts to the three bookstores. Twice as many t-shirts were shipped to bookstore B as to bookstore A, and the number shipped to bookstore C was 40 less than the sum of the numbers shipped to the other two bookstores. How many t-shirts were shipped to each bookstore?

52. An office supply store sells three models of computer desks: A, B, and C. In one month, the store sold a total of 85 computer desks. The number of model B desks was five more than the number of model C desks. The number of model A desks was four more than twice the number of model C desks. How many of each model did the store sell that month?

53. A plant food is to be made from three chemicals. The mix must include 60% of the first and second chemicals. The second and third chemicals must be in the ratio of 4 to 3 by weight. How much of each chemical is needed to make 750 kg of the plant food?

54. How many ounces of 5% hydrochloric acid, 20% hydrochloric acid, and water must be combined to obtain 10 oz of solution that is 8.5% hydrochloric acid if the amount of water used must equal the total amount of the other two solutions?

The National Hockey League uses a point system to determine team standings. A team is awarded 2 points for a win (W), *0 points for a loss in regulation play* (L), *and 1 point for an overtime loss* (OTL). *Use this information to solve each problem.*

55. During the 2012–2013 NHL regular season, the Anaheim Ducks played 48 games. Their wins and overtime losses resulted in a total of 66 points. They had 6 more losses in regulation play than overtime losses. How many wins, losses, and overtime losses did they have that year?

Team	GP	W	L	OTL	Points
Anaheim	48	_____	_____	_____	66
Los Angeles	48	27	16	5	59
San Jose	48	25	16	7	57
Phoenix	48	21	18	9	51
Dallas	48	_____	_____	_____	48

Source: World Almanac and Book of Facts.

56. During the same NHL regular season, the Dallas Stars also played 48 games. Their wins and overtime losses resulted in a total of 48 points. They had 4 more total losses (in regulation play and overtime) than wins. How many wins, losses, and overtime losses did they have that year?

The following exercises are based on the "Bait Box Puzzle," featured in a recent "Ask Marilyn" column in Parade Magazine.

57. There are three kinds of bait boxes—those containing fish, those containing bugs, and those containing worms. Although the bait boxes look alike, each kind has a different weight. Use the information in **FIGURE A** to write a system of three equations, and solve it to determine the weight of each kind of bait box.

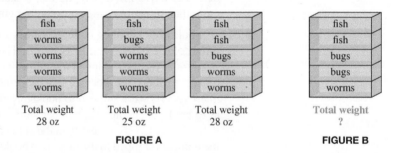

fish	fish	fish	fish
worms	bugs	fish	fish
worms	worms	bugs	bugs
worms	worms	worms	bugs
worms	worms	worms	worms

Total weight 28 oz · Total weight 25 oz · Total weight 28 oz · Total weight ?

FIGURE A · **FIGURE B**

58. Write an equation that describes the situation depicted in **FIGURE B**. Use the same three variables used in **Exercise 57.** Then determine the total weight of the bait boxes in **FIGURE B**.

Chapter 3	Summary

Key Terms

3.1

system of equations
system of linear equations
   (linear system)
solution set of a linear
   system

consistent system
independent equations
inconsistent system
dependent equations

3.2

ordered triple
focus variable
working equation

New Symbol

(x, y, z) ordered triple

Test Your Word Power

See how well you have learned the vocabulary in this chapter.

1. A **system of equations** consists of
   A. at least two equations with
      different variables
   B. two or more equations that have
      an infinite number of solutions
   C. two or more equations that are to
      be solved at the same time
   D. two or more inequalities that are
      to be solved.

2. The **solution set of a system of
   equations** is
   A. all ordered pairs that satisfy one
      equation of the system

   B. all ordered pairs that satisfy all
      the equations of the system at the
      same time
   C. any ordered pair that satisfies one
      or more equations of the system
   D. the set of values that make all the
      equations of the system false.

3. An **inconsistent system** is a system
   of equations
   A. with one solution
   B. with no solution
   C. with an infinite number of solutions
   D. that have the same graph.

4. **Dependent equations**
   A. have different graphs
   B. have no solution
   C. have one solution
   D. are different forms of the same
      equation.

5. A **consistent system** has
   A. no solution
   B. a solution
   C. exactly two solutions
   D. exactly three solutions.

ANSWERS

1. C; *Example:* $\begin{array}{l} 3x - y = 3 \\ 2x + y = 7 \end{array}$ **2.** B; *Example:* The ordered pair $(2, 3)$ satisfies both equations of the system in Answer 1, so $\{(2, 3)\}$ is the solution set
of the system.   **3.** B; *Example:* The equations of two parallel lines form an inconsistent system. Their graphs never intersect, so the system has no solution.
4. D; *Example:* The equations $4x - y = 8$ and $8x - 2y = 16$ are dependent because their graphs are the same line.   **5.** B; *Example:* The system in
Answer 1 is a consistent system.

Quick Review

CONCEPTS	EXAMPLES
3.1 Systems of Linear Equations in Two Variables	
Solving a Linear System by Substitution	Solve by substitution.
Step 1 Solve one of the equations for either variable.	$$4x - y = 7 \qquad (1)$$ $$3x + 2y = 30 \qquad (2)$$ Solve for y in equation (1) to obtain $y = 4x - 7$.

CONCEPTS	**EXAMPLES**

Step 2 Substitute for that variable in the other equation. The result should be an equation with just one variable.	Substitute $4x - 7$ for y in equation (2), and solve for x. $3x + 2y = 30$ (2) $3x + 2(4x - 7) = 30$ Let $y = 4x - 7$. $3x + 8x - 14 = 30$ Distributive property $11x = 44$ Combine like terms. Add 14. $x = 4$ Divide by 11.
Step 3 Solve the equation from Step 2.	
Step 4 Find the value of the other variable by substituting the result from Step 3 into the equation from Step 1.	Substitute 4 for x in the equation $y = 4x - 7$ to find y. $y = 4(4) - 7$ $y = 9$ Multiply. Subtract.
Step 5 Check the values in *both* of the *original* equations. Then write the solution set as a set containing an ordered pair.	Check to verify that $\{(4, 9)\}$ is the solution set.

Solving a Linear System by Elimination

Step 1 Write both equations in standard form.	Solve by elimination. $5x + y = 2$ (1) $2x - 3y = 11$ (2)
Step 2 Transform the equations as needed so that the coefficients of one pair of variable terms are opposites.	To eliminate y, multiply equation (1) by 3 and add the result to equation (2).
Step 3 Add the new equations. The sum should be an equation with just one variable.	$15x + 3y = 6$ 3 times equation (1) $\underline{2x - 3y = 11}$ (2) $17x \quad\quad = 17$ Add.
Step 4 Solve the equation from Step 3.	$x = 1$ Divide by 17.
Step 5 Find the value of the other variable by substituting the result from Step 4 into either of the original equations.	Let $x = 1$ in equation (1), and solve for y. $5(1) + y = 2$ $y = -3$ Multiply. Subtract 5.
Step 6 Check the values in *both* of the *original* equations. Then write the solution set as a set containing an ordered pair.	Check to verify that $\{(1, -3)\}$ is the solution set.

If the result of the addition step (Step 3) is a false statement, such as $0 = 4$, the graphs are parallel lines and *there is no solution. The solution set is* $\varnothing$.	$x - 2y = 6$ $\underline{-x + 2y = -2}$ $0 = 4$ Solution set: $\varnothing$
If the result is a true statement, such as $0 = 0$, the graphs are the same line, and an *infinite number of ordered pairs are solutions. The solution set is written in set-builder notation as* $$\{(x, y) \mid \text{_____}\},$$ *where a form of the equation is written in the blank.*	$x - 2y = 6$ $\underline{-x + 2y = -6}$ $0 = 0$ Solution set: $\{(x, y) \mid x - 2y = 6\}$

CONCEPTS	EXAMPLES

3.2 Systems of Linear Equations in Three Variables

Solving a Linear System in Three Variables

Step 1 Select a focus variable, preferably one with co-efficient 1 or −1, and a working equation.

Solve the system.

$$x + 2y - z = 6 \quad (1)$$
$$x + y + z = 6 \quad (2)$$
$$2x + y - z = 7 \quad (3)$$

We choose z as the focus variable and (2) as the working equation.

Step 2 Eliminate the focus variable, using the working equation and one of the equations of the system.

Add equations (1) and (2).

$$2x + 3y = 12 \quad (4)$$

Step 3 Eliminate the focus variable again, using the working equation and the remaining equation of the system.

Add equations (2) and (3).

$$3x + 2y = 13 \quad (5)$$

Step 4 Solve the system of two equations in two variables formed by the equations from Steps 2 and 3.

Use equations (4) and (5) to eliminate x.

$$-6x - 9y = -36 \qquad \text{Multiply (4) by } -3.$$
$$\underline{6x + 4y = 26} \qquad \text{Multiply (5) by 2.}$$
$$-5y = -10 \qquad \text{Add.}$$
$$y = 2 \qquad \text{Divide by } -5.$$

To find x, substitute 2 for y in equation (4).

$$2x + 3(2) = 12 \qquad \text{Let } y = 2 \text{ in (4).}$$
$$2x + 6 = 12 \qquad \text{Multiply.}$$
$$2x = 6 \qquad \text{Subtract 6.}$$
$$x = 3 \qquad \text{Divide by 2.}$$

Step 5 Find the value of the remaining variable.

Substitute 3 for x and 2 for y in working equation (2).

$$x + y + z = 6 \quad (2)$$
$$3 + 2 + z = 6 \qquad \text{Substitute.}$$
$$z = 1 \qquad \text{Subtract 5.}$$

Step 6 Check the values in *each* of the *original* equations of the system. Then write the solution set as a set containing an ordered triple.

A check of the ordered triple $(3, 2, 1)$ confirms that the solution set is $\{(3, 2, 1)\}$.

3.3 Applications of Systems of Linear Equations

Use the six-step problem-solving method.

Step 1 Read the problem carefully.

Step 2 Assign variables.

Step 3 Write a system of equations.

Step 4 Solve the system.

Step 5 State the answer.

Step 6 Check.

The perimeter of a rectangle is 18 ft. The length is 3 ft more than twice the width. What are the dimensions of the rectangle?

Let $x =$ the length and $y =$ the width. Write a system of equations.

$$2x + 2y = 18 \qquad \text{From the perimeter formula}$$
$$x = 2y + 3 \qquad \text{Length is 3 ft more than twice the width.}$$

Solve to find that

$$x = 7 \quad \text{and} \quad y = 2.$$

The length is 7 ft, and the width is 2 ft. The answer checks because

$$2(7) + 2(2) = 18 \quad \text{and} \quad 2(2) + 3 = 7, \quad \text{as required.}$$

Chapter 3 | Review Exercises

1. (a) 2004–2005
   (b) 30%
2. $\{(2,2)\}$

3. D
4. Answers will vary.
   (a)

   (b)

   (c)

5. $\left\{\left(-\dfrac{8}{9}, -\dfrac{4}{3}\right)\right\}$ 6. $\{(0,4)\}$

7. $\{(2,4)\}$ 8. $\{(2,2)\}$
9. $\{(0,1)\}$ 10. $\{(-1,2)\}$
11. $\{(-6,3)\}$
12. $\{(x,y)\,|\,3x-y=-6\}$; dependent equations
13. $\varnothing$; inconsistent system
14. The two lines have the same slope, 3, but the y-intercepts, $(0,2)$ and $(0,-4)$, are different. Therefore, the lines are parallel, do not intersect, and have no common solution.

3.1

1. The graph shows trends during the years 2002 through 2013 relating broadband vs. dial-up Internet users in the United States.

   (a) Between what years did the percentage of broadband users equal that for dial-up users?

   (b) When the percentage of broadband internet users was equal to that for dial-up internet users, approximately what was that number?

Source: Pew Research Center, © 2013. Used by permission of Pew Research Center.

2. Solve the system by graphing.

$$x + 3y = 8$$
$$2x - y = 2$$

3. Which ordered pair is *not* a solution of the equation $3x + 2y = 6$?

   A. $(2,0)$ **B.** $(0,3)$ **C.** $(4,-3)$ **D.** $(3,-2)$

4. Suppose that two linear equations are graphed on the same set of coordinate axes. Sketch what the graph might look like if the system has the given description.

   (a) The system has a single solution.

   (b) The system has no solution.

   (c) The system has infinitely many solutions.

Solve each system by the substitution method. If a system is inconsistent or has dependent equations, say so.

5. $3x + y = -4$
   $x = \dfrac{2}{3}y$

6. $9x - y = -4$
   $y = x + 4$

7. $-5x + 2y = -2$
   $x + 6y = 26$

Solve each system of equations by the elimination method. If a system is inconsistent or has dependent equations, say so.

8. $5x + y = 12$
   $2x - 2y = 0$

9. $x - 4y = -4$
   $3x + y = 1$

10. $6x + 5y = 4$
    $-4x + 2y = 8$

11. $\dfrac{1}{6}x + \dfrac{1}{6}y = -\dfrac{1}{2}$
    $x - y = -9$

12. $-3x + y = 6$
    $y = 6 + 3x$

13. $5x - 4y = 2$
    $-10x + 8y = 7$

14. Without doing any algebraic work, but answering on the basis of knowledge of the graphs of the two lines, explain why the following system has $\varnothing$ as its solution set.

$$y = 3x + 2$$
$$y = 3x - 4$$

15. $\{(1, 2, 3)\}$

16. $\{(1, -5, 3)\}$

17. $\emptyset$; inconsistent system

18. length: 200 ft;
width: 85 ft

19. New York Yankees: $51.55;
Boston Red Sox: $53.38

20. plane: 300 mph;
wind: 20 mph

21. gold: 24;
silver: 26;
bronze: 32

22. $2-per-lb nuts: 30 lb;
$1-per-lb candy: 70 lb

23. 85°, 60°, 35°

24. $40,000 at 10%;
$100,000 at 6%;
$140,000 at 5%

25. 5 L of 8%;
3 L of 20%;
none of 10%

26. Mantle: 54;
Maris: 61;
Berra: 22

3.2 *Solve each system. If a system is inconsistent or has dependent equations, say so.*

15. $4x - y = 2$
$3y + z = 9$
$x + 2z = 7$

16. $2x + 3y - z = -16$
$x + 2y + 2z = -3$
$-3x + y + z = -5$

17. $3x - y - z = -8$
$4x + 2y + 3z = 15$
$-6x + 2y + 2z = 10$

3.3 *Solve each problem.*

18. A regulation National Hockey League ice rink has perimeter 570 ft. The length of the rink is 30 ft longer than twice the width. What are the dimensions of an NHL ice rink? (*Source:* www.nhl.com)

19. During a recent Major League Baseball season, two New York Yankees tickets and three Boston Red Sox tickets purchased at their average prices cost $263.24. Three Yankees tickets and two Red Sox tickets cost $261.41. Find the average ticket price for a Yankees ticket and a Red Sox ticket. (*Source:* Team Marketing Report.)

20. A plane flies 560 mi in 1.75 hr traveling with the wind. The return trip later against the same wind takes the plane 2 hr. Find the rate of the plane and the wind speed. Let $x =$ the rate of the plane and $y =$ the wind speed.

	r	t	d
With Wind	$x + y$	1.75	
Against Wind		2	

21. In the 2012 Summer Olympics in London, England, Russia earned 8 fewer gold medals than bronze. The number of silver medals earned was 38 less than twice the number of bronze medals. Russia earned a total of 82 medals. How many of each kind of medal did Russia earn? (*Source: World Almanac and Book of Facts.*)

22. For Valentine's Day, Ms. Sweet will mix some $2-per-lb nuts with some $1-per-lb chocolate candy to obtain 100 lb of mix, which she will sell at $1.30 per lb. How many pounds of each should she use?

	Number of Pounds	Price per Pound (in dollars)	Value (in dollars)
Nuts	x		
Chocolate	y		
Mixture	100		

23. The sum of the measures of the angles of a triangle is 180°. The largest angle measures 10° less than the sum of the other two. The measure of the middle-sized angle is the average of the other two. Find the measures of the three angles.

24. Noemi sells real estate. On three recent sales, she made 10% commission, 6% commission, and 5% commission. Her total commissions on these sales were $17,000, and she sold property worth $280,000. If the 5% sale amounted to the sum of the other two, what were the three sales prices?

25. How many liters each of 8%, 10%, and 20% hydrogen peroxide should be mixed together to obtain 8 L of 12.5% solution if the amount of 8% solution used must be 2 L more than the amount of 20% solution used?

26. In the great baseball year of 1961, Yankee teammates Mickey Mantle, Roger Maris, and Yogi Berra combined for 137 home runs. Mantle hit 7 fewer than Maris, and Maris hit 39 more than Berra. What were the home run totals for each player? (*Source:* www.mlb.com)

Chapter 3 | Mixed Review Exercises

Solve by any method.

1. $-7x + 3y = 12$
$5x + 2y = 8$

2. $2x - 5y = 8$
$3x + 4y = 10$

3. $x + 4y = 17$
$-3x + 2y = -9$

4. $x = 7y + 10$
$2x + 3y = 3$

5. $\dfrac{2}{3}x + \dfrac{1}{6}y = \dfrac{19}{2}$
$\dfrac{1}{3}x - \dfrac{2}{9}y = 2$

6. $2x + 5y - z = 12$
$-x + y - 4z = -10$
$-8x - 20y + 4z = 31$

Solve each problem.

7. Which system would be easier to solve using the substitution method? Why?

System A: $5x - 3y = 7$ System B: $7x + 2y = 4$
$2x + 8y = 3$ $y = -3x + 1$

8. Solve each system in **Exercise 7.**

9. To make a 10% acid solution, Jeffrey wants to mix some 5% solution with 10 L of 20% solution. How many liters of 5% solution should he use?

10. In the 2012 Summer Olympics, China, the United States, and Russia won a combined total of 274 medals. China won 16 fewer medals than the United States, while Russia won 22 fewer medals than the United States. How many medals did each country win? (*Source: World Almanac and Book of Facts.*)

1. $\{(0, 4)\}$

2. $\left\{\left(\dfrac{82}{23}, -\dfrac{4}{23}\right)\right\}$

3. $\{(5, 3)\}$ 4. $\{(3, -1)\}$

5. $\{(12, 9)\}$ 6. $\varnothing$

7. *B*; The second equation is already solved for *y*.

8. *System A:* $\left\{\left(\dfrac{65}{46}, \dfrac{1}{46}\right)\right\}$;
   System B: $\{(2, -5)\}$

9. 20 L

10. United States: 104;
    China: 88;
    Russia: 82

Chapter 3 | Test

FOR EXTRA HELP *Step-by-step test solutions are found on the Chapter Test Prep Videos available in* MyMathLab® *or on* YouTube™.

▶ *View the complete solutions to all Chapter Test exercises in MyMathLab.*

Use the graph to work Exercises 1 and 2.

1. (a) Which two cities experienced the most population growth over time?

   (b) Which city experienced a population decline?

   (c) Rank the city populations from least to greatest for the year 2010.

2. (a) In which year did the population of Atlanta equal that of New York? About what was that population to the nearest million?

   (b) Write the answer from part (a) as an ordered pair (year, population).

3. Use a graph to solve the system.
$x + y = 7$
$x - y = 5$

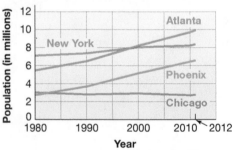

Populations of U.S. Cities

Source: "City Population," by Thomas Brinkhoff, © 2013.

Solve each system. If a system is inconsistent or has dependent equations, say so.

4. $2x - 3y = 24$
$y = -\dfrac{2}{3}x$

5. $3x - y = -8$
$2x + 6y = 3$

6. $12x - 5y = 8$
$3x = \dfrac{5}{4}y + 2$

7. $3x + y = 12$
$2x - y = 3$

8. $-5x + 2y = -4$
$6x + 3y = -6$

9. $3x + 4y = 8$
$8y = 7 - 6x$

[3.1]

1. (a) Atlanta and Phoenix
   (b) Chicago
   (c) Chicago, Phoenix, New York, Atlanta

2. (a) 2000; 8 million
   (b) (2000, 8)

3. $\{(6, 1)\}$

$x + y = 7$
$x - y = 5$
$(6, 1)$

4. $\{(6, -4)\}$

5. $\left\{\left(-\dfrac{9}{4}, \dfrac{5}{4}\right)\right\}$

6. $\{(x, y) \mid 12x - 5y = 8\}$; dependent equations

7. $\{(3, 3)\}$

8. $\{(0, -2)\}$

9. $\varnothing$; inconsistent system

[3.2]

10. $\left\{\left(-\dfrac{2}{3}, \dfrac{4}{5}, 0\right)\right\}$

11. $\{(3, -2, 1)\}$

[3.3]

12. *Iron Man 3:* $409 million;
Man of Steel: $291 million

13. 45 mph, 75 mph

14. 20% solution: 4 L;
50% solution: 8 L

15. AC adaptor: $8;
rechargeable flashlight: $15

16. Orange Pekoe: 60 oz;
Irish Breakfast: 30 oz;
Earl Grey: 10 oz

10. $\begin{aligned} 3x + 5y + 3z &= 2 \\ 6x + 5y + z &= 0 \\ 3x + 10y - 2z &= 6 \end{aligned}$

11. $\begin{aligned} 4x + y + z &= 11 \\ x - y - z &= 4 \\ y + 2z &= 0 \end{aligned}$

Solve each problem.

12. Two top-grossing super hero films, *Iron Man 3* and *Man of Steel,* earned $700 million together. If *Man of Steel* grossed $118 million less than *Iron Man 3,* how much did each film gross? (*Source:* www.the-numbers.com)

13. Two cars start from points 420 mi apart and travel toward each other. They meet after 3.5 hr. Find the average rate of each car if one travels 30 mph slower than the other.

420 mi

14. A chemist needs 12 L of a 40% alcohol solution. She must mix a 20% solution and a 50% solution. How many liters of each will be required to obtain what she needs?

Liters of Solution	Percent (as a decimal)	Liters of Pure Alcohol

15. A local electronics store will sell seven AC adaptors and two rechargeable flashlights for $86, or three AC adaptors and four rechargeable flashlights for $84. What is the price of a single AC adaptor and a single rechargeable flashlight?

16. The owner of a tea shop wants to mix three kinds of tea to make 100 oz of a mixture that will sell for $0.83 per oz. He uses Orange Pekoe, which sells for $0.80 per oz, Irish Breakfast, for $0.85 per oz, and Earl Grey, for $0.95 per oz. If he wants to use twice as much Orange Pekoe as Irish Breakfast, how much of each kind of tea should he use?

Chapters R–3 Cumulative Review Exercises

[R.3]

1. 81 **2.** −81

3. −81 **4.** 0.7

5. −0.7

6. It is not a real number.

7. −199 **8.** 455

[R.4]

9. commutative property

[1.1] **[1.7]**

10. $\left\{-\dfrac{15}{4}\right\}$ **11.** $\left\{\dfrac{2}{3}, 2\right\}$

[1.2]

12. $x = \dfrac{d - by}{a}$

[1.1] **[1.5]**

13. $\{11\}$ **14.** $\left(-\infty, \dfrac{240}{13}\right]$

[1.7]

15. $\left[-2, \dfrac{2}{3}\right]$ **16.** $(-\infty, \infty)$

[1.6]

17. $(-\infty, \infty)$

Evaluate each expression if possible.

1. $(-3)^4$ **2.** -3^4 **3.** $-(-3)^4$

4. $\sqrt{0.49}$ **5.** $-\sqrt{0.49}$ **6.** $\sqrt{-0.49}$

Evaluate for $x = -4$, $y = 3$, and $z = 6$.

7. $|2x| + 3y - z^3$ **8.** $-5(x^3 - y^3)$

9. Which property of real numbers justifies the statement $5 + (3 \cdot 6) = 5 + (6 \cdot 3)$?

Solve each equation.

10. $7(2x + 3) - 4(2x + 1) = 2(x + 1)$ **11.** $|6x - 8| = 4$

12. $ax + by = d$ for x **13.** $0.04x + 0.06(x - 1) = 1.04$

Solve each inequality.

14. $\dfrac{2}{3}x + \dfrac{5}{12}x \le 20$ **15.** $|3x + 2| \le 4$

16. $|12t + 7| \ge 0$ **17.** $2x + 3 > 5$ or $x - 1 \le 6$

[1.2]
18. 2010; 1813; 62.8%; 57.2%

[1.3, 1.4]
19. pennies: 35;
     nickels: 29;
     dimes: 30
20. 46°, 46°, 88°

[2.1]
21. $y = 6$ **22.** $x = 4$

[2.2]
23. $-\dfrac{4}{3}$ **24.** $\dfrac{3}{4}$

[2.3]
25. $4x + 3y = 10$

[2.2]
26.

[2.4]
27.

[2.6]
28. (a) -6
     (b) $a^2 + 3a - 6$

[3.1]
29. $\{(3, -3)\}$
30. $\{(x, y) \mid x - 3y = 7\}$

[3.2]
31. $\{(5, 3, 2)\}$

[3.1]
32. (a) $x = 8$, or 800 items; $3000
     (b) about $400

Solve each problem.

18. A survey measured public recognition of some popular contemporary advertising slogans. Complete the results shown in the table if 2500 people were surveyed.

Slogan (product or company)	Percent Recognition (nearest tenth of a percent)	Actual Number Who Recognized Slogan (nearest whole number)
Please Don't Squeeze the . . . (Charmin)	80.4%	
The Breakfast of Champions (Wheaties)	72.5%	
The King of Beers (Budweiser)		1570
Like a Good Neighbor (State Farm)		1430

Source: Department of Integrated Marketing Communications, Northwestern University.

19. A jar contains only pennies, nickels, and dimes. The number of dimes is one more than the number of nickels, and the number of pennies is six more than the number of nickels. How many of each denomination are in the jar, if the total value is $4.80?

20. Two angles of a triangle have the same measure. The measure of the third angle is 4° less than twice the measure of each of the equal angles. Find the measures of the three angles.

Measures are in degrees.

In Exercises 21–25, point A has coordinates $(-2, 6)$ and point B has coordinates $(4, -2)$.

21. What is the equation of the horizontal line through A?

22. What is the equation of the vertical line through B?

23. What is the slope of line AB?

24. What is the slope of a line perpendicular to line AB?

25. What is the standard form of the equation of line AB?

26. Graph the line having slope $\frac{2}{3}$ and passing through the point $(-1, -3)$.

27. Graph the inequality $-3x - 2y \le 6$.

28. Given that $f(x) = x^2 + 3x - 6$, find **(a)** $f(-3)$ and **(b)** $f(a)$.

Solve by any method.

29. $-2x + 3y = -15$
     $4x - y = 15$

30. $x - 3y = 7$
     $2x - 6y = 14$

31. $x + y + z = 10$
     $x - y - z = 0$
     $-x + y - z = -4$

32. The graph shows a company's costs to produce computer parts and the revenue from the sale of computer parts.

(a) At what production level does the cost equal the revenue? What is the revenue at that point?

(b) Profit is revenue less cost. Estimate the profit on the sale of 1100 parts.

4

Exponents, Polynomials, and Polynomial Functions

Large numbers, such as world population, can be written using *scientific notation,* one of the topics of this chapter.

4.1   Integer Exponents and Scientific Notation

VOCABULARY

☐ exponent (power)
☐ base
☐ exponential expression

Recall that we use exponents to write products of repeated factors.

$$2^5 \quad \text{is defined as} \quad 2 \cdot 2 \cdot 2 \cdot 2 \cdot 2, \quad \text{which equals} \quad 32.$$

In 2^5, the number 5 is the **exponent** (or **power**). It indicates that the **base** 2 appears as a factor five times. The quantity 2^5 is an **exponential expression.** We read 2^5 as **"2 to the fifth power"** or **"2 to the fifth."**

OBJECTIVE 1 Use the product rule for exponents.

Consider the product $2^5 \cdot 2^3$, which can be simplified as follows.

$$\overbrace{2^5 \cdot 2^3 = (2 \cdot 2 \cdot 2 \cdot 2 \cdot 2)(2 \cdot 2 \cdot 2) = 2^8}^{5 + 3 = 8}$$

This result suggests the **product rule for exponents.**

> **Product Rule for Exponents**
>
> If m and n are natural numbers and a is any real number, then
> $$a^m \cdot a^n = a^{m+n}.$$
>
> That is, when multiplying powers of like bases, keep the same base and add the exponents.

To see that the product rule is true, use the definition of an exponent.

$$a^m = \underbrace{a \cdot a \cdot a \cdot \ldots \cdot a}_{a \text{ appears as a factor } m \text{ times.}} \qquad a^n = \underbrace{a \cdot a \cdot a \cdot \ldots \cdot a}_{a \text{ appears as a factor } n \text{ times.}}$$

From this, $\quad a^m \cdot a^n = \underbrace{a \cdot a \cdot a \cdot \ldots \cdot a}_{m \text{ factors}} \cdot \underbrace{a \cdot a \cdot a \cdot \ldots \cdot a}_{n \text{ factors}}$

$$= \underbrace{a \cdot a \cdot a \cdot \ldots \cdot a}_{(m + n) \text{ factors}}$$

$$a^m \cdot a^n = a^{m+n}.$$

NOW TRY
EXERCISE 1

Apply the product rule, if possible, in each case.

(a) $8^5 \cdot 8^4$

(b) $r^7 \cdot r$

(c) $p^2 \cdot q^2$

(d) $(5x^4y^7)(-7xy^3)$

NOW TRY ANSWERS
1. **(a)** 8^9 **(b)** r^8
   (c) The product rule does not apply.
   (d) $-35x^5y^{10}$

EXAMPLE 1   **Using the Product Rule for Exponents**

Apply the product rule for exponents, if possible, in each case.

(a) $3^4 \cdot 3^7$

$= 3^{4+7}$ Keep the same base.

$= 3^{11}$

(b) $5^3 \cdot 5$

$= 5^3 \cdot 5^1$

$= 5^{3+1}$

$= 5^4$

(c) $y^3 \cdot y^8 \cdot y^2$

$= y^{3+8+2}$

$= y^{13}$

(d) $(5y^2)(-3y^4)$

$= 5(-3)y^2y^4$ Commutative property

$= -15y^{2+4}$ Multiply; product rule

$= -15y^6$

(e) $(7p^3q)(2p^5q^2)$

$= 7(2)p^3p^5q^1q^2$

$= 14p^{3+5}q^{1+2}$

$= 14p^8q^3$

(f) $x^2 \cdot y^4$ The product rule does not apply because the bases are not the same.

NOW TRY

⊘ **CAUTION** Be careful not to multiply the bases. In **Example 1(a),**

$$3^4 \cdot 3^7 = 3^{11}, \quad \textbf{\textit{not}} \quad 9^{11}.$$

Keep the same base and add the exponents.

OBJECTIVE 2 Define 0 and negative exponents.

Consider the following, where the product rule is extended to whole numbers.

$$4^2 \cdot 4^0 = 4^{2+0} = 4^2$$

For the product rule to hold, 4^0 must equal 1, so we define a^0 this way for any non-zero real number a.

Zero Exponent

If a is any nonzero real number, then

$$a^0 = 1.$$

The expression 0^0 is undefined.*

**NOW TRY
EXERCISE 2**

Evaluate.

(a) 5^0 **(b)** $(-5x)^0$ $(x \neq 0)$

(c) -5^0 **(d)** $10^0 - 9^0$

EXAMPLE 2 Using 0 as an Exponent

Evaluate.

(a) $6^0 = 1$

(b) $(-6)^0 = 1$
  Here the base is −6.

(c) $-6^0 = -(6)^0 = -1$
  The base is 6, not −6.

(d) $-(-6)^0 = -1$

(e) $5^0 + 12^0$
$= 1 + 1$
$= 2$

(f) $(8k)^0 = 1$ $(k \neq 0)$
Any nonzero quantity raised to the zero power equals 1.   **NOW TRY** ↻

To define a negative exponent, we extend the product rule, as follows.

$$8^2 \cdot 8^{-2} = 8^{2+(-2)} = 8^0 = 1$$

Because their product is 1, it appears that 8^{-2} is the *reciprocal* of 8^2. But we know that $\frac{1}{8^2}$ is the reciprocal of 8^2, and a number can have only one reciprocal. Therefore, **8^{-2} must equal $\frac{1}{8^2}$.**

We can generalize this result.

Negative Exponent

For any natural number n and any nonzero real number a,

$$a^{-n} = \frac{1}{a^n}.$$

With this definition, the expression a^n is meaningful for any integer exponent n and any nonzero real number a.

NOW TRY ANSWERS

2. (a) 1   **(b)** 1   **(c)** −1   **(d)** 0

---

*In advanced courses, 0^0 is called an *indeterminate form.*

! CAUTION   *A negative exponent does not indicate that an expression represents a negative number. Negative exponents lead to reciprocals.*

$$3^{-2} = \frac{1}{3^2} = \frac{1}{9} \quad \text{Not negative} \quad \bigg| \quad -3^{-2} = -\frac{1}{3^2} = -\frac{1}{9} \quad \text{Negative}$$

The base is 3 in both cases. 3^{-2} represents the reciprocal of 3^2.

**NOW TRY
EXERCISE 3**

Write with only positive exponents.

(a) 9^{-4}

(b) $(3y)^{-6}$ $(y \neq 0)$

(c) $-4k^{-3}$ $(k \neq 0)$

(d) Evaluate $4^{-1} + 6^{-1}$.

EXAMPLE 3 **Using Negative Exponents**

In parts (a)–(f), write with only positive exponents.

(a) $2^{-3} = \dfrac{1}{2^3}$ ⟵ This is the *reciprocal* of 2^3.

(b) $6^{-1} = \dfrac{1}{6^1} = \dfrac{1}{6}$ ⟵ This is the *reciprocal* of 6^1, or 6.

(c) $(5z)^{-3} = \dfrac{1}{(5z)^3}$ $(z \neq 0)$

The base is $5z$.
(Notice the parentheses around it.)

(d) $5z^{-3} = 5\left(\dfrac{1}{z^3}\right) = \dfrac{5}{z^3}$ $(z \neq 0)$

The base is z, *not* $5z$.

(e) $-m^{-2} = -\dfrac{1}{m^2}$ $(m \neq 0)$

(What is the base here?)

(f) $(-m)^{-2} = \dfrac{1}{(-m)^2}$ $(m \neq 0)$

(What is the base here?)

In parts (g) and (h), evaluate.

(g) $3^{-1} + 4^{-1}$

$$= \frac{1}{3} + \frac{1}{4} \qquad \text{Definition of negative exponent}$$

$$= \frac{4}{12} + \frac{3}{12} \qquad \frac{1}{3} \cdot \frac{4}{4} = \frac{4}{12}; \frac{1}{4} \cdot \frac{3}{3} = \frac{3}{12}$$

$$= \frac{7}{12} \qquad \frac{a}{c} + \frac{b}{c} = \frac{a+b}{c}$$

(h) $5^{-1} - 2^{-1}$

$$= \frac{1}{5} - \frac{1}{2} \qquad \text{Definition of negative exponent}$$

$$= \frac{2}{10} - \frac{5}{10} \qquad \text{Find a common denominator.}$$

$$= -\frac{3}{10} \qquad \frac{a}{c} - \frac{b}{c} = \frac{a-b}{c}$$

NOW TRY

! CAUTION   Note that $3^{-1} + 4^{-1} \neq (3+4)^{-1}$. The expression $3^{-1} + 4^{-1}$ simplifies to $\frac{7}{12}$, as shown in **Example 3(g)**. The expression $(3+4)^{-1}$ simplifies to 7^{-1}, which equals $\frac{1}{7}$. Similar reasoning can be applied to part (h).

**NOW TRY
EXERCISE 4**

Evaluate.

(a) $\dfrac{1}{5^{-3}}$ **(b)** $\dfrac{10^{-2}}{2^{-5}}$

NOW TRY ANSWERS

3. (a) $\dfrac{1}{9^4}$ **(b)** $\dfrac{1}{(3y)^6}$

(c) $-\dfrac{4}{k^3}$ **(d)** $\dfrac{5}{12}$

4. (a) 125 **(b)** $\dfrac{8}{25}$

EXAMPLE 4 **Using Negative Exponents**

Evaluate.

(a) $\dfrac{1}{2^{-3}} = \dfrac{1}{\frac{1}{2^3}} = 1 \div \dfrac{1}{2^3} = 1 \cdot \dfrac{2^3}{1} = 2^3 = 8$

Multiply by the reciprocal of the divisor.

$\frac{1}{2^{-3}}$ represents the reciprocal of 2^{-3}.
Because $2^{-3} = \frac{1}{8}$, the reciprocal is 8, which agrees with the final answer.

(b) $\dfrac{2^{-3}}{3^{-2}} = \dfrac{\frac{1}{2^3}}{\frac{1}{3^2}} = \dfrac{1}{2^3} \div \dfrac{1}{3^2} = \dfrac{1}{2^3} \cdot \dfrac{3^2}{1} = \dfrac{3^2}{2^3} = \dfrac{9}{8}$

NOW TRY

Example 4 suggests the following generalizations.

Special Rules for Negative Exponents

If $a \neq 0$ and $b \neq 0$, then

$$\frac{1}{a^{-n}} = a^n \quad \text{and} \quad \frac{a^{-n}}{b^{-m}} = \frac{b^m}{a^n}.$$

OBJECTIVE 3 Use the quotient rule for exponents.

We simplify a quotient, such as $\frac{a^8}{a^3}$, in much the same way as a product. (In all quotients of this type, assume that the denominator is not 0.) Consider this example.

$$\frac{a^8}{a^3} = \frac{a \cdot a \cdot a \cdot a \cdot a \cdot a \cdot a \cdot a}{a \cdot a \cdot a} = a \cdot a \cdot a \cdot a \cdot a = a^5$$

Notice that $8 - 3 = 5$. In the same way, we simplify $\frac{a^3}{a^8}$.

$$\frac{a^3}{a^8} = \frac{a \cdot a \cdot a}{a \cdot a \cdot a \cdot a \cdot a \cdot a \cdot a \cdot a} = \frac{1}{a^5} = a^{-5}$$

Here, $3 - 8 = -5$. These examples suggest the **quotient rule for exponents.**

Quotient Rule for Exponents

If a is any nonzero real number and m and n are integers, then

$$\frac{a^m}{a^n} = a^{m-n}.$$

That is, when dividing powers of like bases, keep the same base and subtract the exponent of the denominator from the exponent of the numerator.

NOW TRY EXERCISE 5

Apply the quotient rule, if possible, and write each result with only positive exponents.

(a) $\dfrac{t^8}{t^2}$ $(t \neq 0)$ **(b)** $\dfrac{4^5}{4^{-2}}$

(c) $\dfrac{m^4}{n^3}$ $(n \neq 0)$

EXAMPLE 5 Using the Quotient Rule for Exponents

Apply the quotient rule for exponents, if possible, and write each result with only positive exponents.

Numerator exponent — Denominator exponent

(a) $\dfrac{3^7}{3^2} = 3^{7-2} = 3^5$

Subtraction symbol

(b) $\dfrac{p^6}{p^2} = p^{6-2} = p^4$ $(p \neq 0)$

(c) $\dfrac{k^7}{k^{12}} = k^{7-12} = k^{-5} = \dfrac{1}{k^5}$ $(k \neq 0)$

(d) $\dfrac{2^7}{2^{-3}} = 2^{7-(-3)} = 2^{7+3} = 2^{10}$

> Use parentheses to avoid errors.

(e) $\dfrac{8^{-2}}{8^5} = 8^{-2-5} = 8^{-7} = \dfrac{1}{8^7}$

(f) $\dfrac{6}{6^{-1}} = \dfrac{6^1}{6^{-1}} = 6^{1-(-1)} = 6^2$

(g) $\dfrac{z^{-5}}{z^{-8}} = z^{-5-(-8)} = z^3$ $(z \neq 0)$

> Be careful with signs.

(h) $\dfrac{a^3}{b^4}$ $(b \neq 0)$

> This expression cannot be simplified further.

The quotient rule does not apply because the bases are different.

NOW TRY

OBJECTIVE 4 Use the power rules for exponents.

We can simplify $(3^4)^2$ as follows.

$$(3^4)^2 = 3^4 \cdot 3^4 = 3^{4+4} = 3^8$$

Notice that $4 \cdot 2 = 8$. This example suggests the first **power rule for exponents.** The other two power rules can be demonstrated similarly.

Power Rules for Exponents

If a and b are real numbers and m and n are integers, then

(a) $(a^m)^n = a^{mn}$,   **(b)** $(ab)^m = a^m b^m$,   and   **(c)** $\left(\dfrac{a}{b}\right)^m = \dfrac{a^m}{b^m}$ $(b \neq 0)$.

That is,

(a) To raise a power to a power, multiply exponents.

(b) To raise a product to a power, raise each factor to that power.

(c) To raise a quotient to a power, raise the numerator and the denominator to that power.

NOW TRY EXERCISE 6

Simplify using the power rules.

(a) $(9x)^3$ **(b)** $(-2m^3)^4$

(c) $\left(\dfrac{3x^2}{y^3}\right)^3$ $(y \neq 0)$

EXAMPLE 6   Using the Power Rules for Exponents

Simplify using the power rules.

(a) $(p^8)^3$

$= p^{8 \cdot 3}$ Power rule (a)

$= p^{24}$

(b) $(3y)^4$

$= 3^4 y^4$ Power rule (b)

$= 81y^4$

(c) $\left(\dfrac{2}{3}\right)^4$

$= \dfrac{2^4}{3^4}$ Power rule (c)

$= \dfrac{16}{81}$

(d) $(6p^7)^2$

$= 6^2(p^7)^2$ Power rule (b)

$= 6^2 p^{7 \cdot 2}$ Power rule (a)

$= 36p^{14}$ Square 6. Multiply exponents.

(e) $\left(\dfrac{-2m^5}{z}\right)^3$

$= \dfrac{(-2m^5)^3}{z^3}$ Power rule (c)

$= \dfrac{(-2)^3 m^{5 \cdot 3}}{z^3}$ Power rule (b)

$= -\dfrac{8m^{15}}{z^3}$ $(z \neq 0)$ Simplify.

NOW TRY

The reciprocal of a^n is $\dfrac{1}{a^n}$, which equals $\left(\dfrac{1}{a}\right)^n$. Also, a^n and a^{-n} are reciprocals.

$$a^n \cdot a^{-n} = a^n \cdot \dfrac{1}{a^n} = 1$$ Reciprocals have product 1.

Thus, because both $\left(\dfrac{1}{a}\right)^n$ and a^{-n} are reciprocals of a^n, the following is true.

$$a^{-n} = \left(\dfrac{1}{a}\right)^n$$ a^{-n} represents the reciprocal of a^n.

NOW TRY ANSWERS

6. (a) $729x^3$ **(b)** $16m^{12}$

(c) $\dfrac{27x^6}{y^9}$

This discussion can be generalized.

> **Special Rules for Negative Exponents, Continued**
>
> If $a \neq 0$ and $b \neq 0$ and n is an integer, then
>
> $$a^{-n} = \left(\frac{1}{a}\right)^n \quad \text{and} \quad \left(\frac{a}{b}\right)^{-n} = \left(\frac{b}{a}\right)^n.$$
>
> That is, any nonzero number raised to the negative nth power is equal to the reciprocal of that number raised to the nth power.

NOW TRY
EXERCISE 7
Write with only positive exponents and then evaluate.

(a) $\left(\frac{1}{3}\right)^{-2}$ (b) $\left(\frac{5}{3}\right)^{-3}$

> **EXAMPLE 7** Using Negative Exponents with Fractions

Write with only positive exponents and then evaluate.

(a) $\left(\frac{1}{2}\right)^{-4}$

$= 2^4 \quad \left(\frac{1}{a}\right)^n = a^{-n}$

$= 16$

(b) $\left(\frac{3}{7}\right)^{-2}$

$= \left(\frac{7}{3}\right)^2 \quad \left(\frac{a}{b}\right)^{-n} = \left(\frac{b}{a}\right)^n$

$= \frac{49}{9}$

(c) $\left(\frac{4x}{5}\right)^{-3}$ $(x \neq 0)$

$= \left(\frac{5}{4x}\right)^3 \quad \left(\frac{a}{b}\right)^{-n} = \left(\frac{b}{a}\right)^n$

$= \frac{5^3}{4^3 x^3}$ Power rules (c) and (b)

$= \frac{125}{64x^3}$ Apply the exponents.

In each case, applying the negative exponent involves changing the base to its reciprocal and changing the sign of the exponent.   **NOW TRY**

> **Summary of Definitions and Rules for Exponents**
>
> For all integers m and n and all real numbers a and b, the following hold.
>
> **Product Rule** $a^m \cdot a^n = a^{m+n}$
>
> **Quotient Rule** $\dfrac{a^m}{a^n} = a^{m-n} \quad (a \neq 0)$
>
> **Zero Exponent** $a^0 = 1 \quad (a \neq 0)$
>
> **Negative Exponent** $a^{-n} = \dfrac{1}{a^n} \quad (a \neq 0)$
>
> **Power Rules**   (a) $(a^m)^n = a^{mn}$ (b) $(ab)^m = a^m b^m$
>
> (c) $\left(\dfrac{a}{b}\right)^m = \dfrac{a^m}{b^m} \quad (b \neq 0)$
>
> **Special Rules for Negative Exponents** $\dfrac{1}{a^{-n}} = a^n \quad (a \neq 0)$ $\dfrac{a^{-n}}{b^{-m}} = \dfrac{b^m}{a^n} \quad (a, b \neq 0)$
>
> $a^{-n} = \left(\dfrac{1}{a}\right)^n \quad (a \neq 0)$ $\left(\dfrac{a}{b}\right)^{-n} = \left(\dfrac{b}{a}\right)^n \quad (a, b \neq 0)$

NOW TRY ANSWERS
7. (a) 9 (b) $\frac{27}{125}$

NOW TRY
EXERCISE 8

Simplify. Assume that all variables represent nonzero real numbers.

(a) $x^{-8} \cdot x \cdot x^4$

(b) $(5^{-3})^2$

(c) $\dfrac{p^2 q^{-4}}{p^{-2} q^{-1}}$

(d) $\left(\dfrac{2x^2}{y^2}\right)^3 \left(\dfrac{-5x^{-2}}{y}\right)^{-2}$

OBJECTIVE 5 Simplify exponential expressions.

EXAMPLE 8   Using the Definitions and Rules for Exponents

Simplify each expression so that no negative exponents appear in the final result. Assume that all variables represent nonzero real numbers.

(a) $3^2 \cdot 3^{-5}$

$= 3^{2+(-5)}$ Product rule

$= 3^{-3}$ Add exponents.

$= \dfrac{1}{3^3}$ $a^{-n} = \dfrac{1}{a^n}$

$= \dfrac{1}{27}$ $3^3 = 27$

(b) $x^{-3} \cdot x^{-4} \cdot x^2$

$= x^{-3+(-4)+2}$ Product rule

$= x^{-5}$ Add exponents.

$= \dfrac{1}{x^5}$ $a^{-n} = \dfrac{1}{a^n}$

(c) $(4^{-2})^{-5}$

$= 4^{(-2)(-5)}$ Power rule (a)

$= 4^{10}$ Multiply exponents.

(d) $(x^{-4})^6$

$= x^{(-4)6}$ Power rule (a)

$= x^{-24}$ Multiply exponents.

$= \dfrac{1}{x^{24}}$ $a^{-n} = \dfrac{1}{a^n}$

(e) $\dfrac{x^{-4} y^2}{x^2 y^{-5}}$

$= \dfrac{x^{-4}}{x^2} \cdot \dfrac{y^2}{y^{-5}}$

$= x^{-4-2} \cdot y^{2-(-5)}$ Quotient rule
Subtract exponents.

$= x^{-6} y^7$

$= \dfrac{y^7}{x^6}$ $a^{-n} = \dfrac{1}{a^n}$

(f) $(2^3 x^{-2})^{-2}$

$= (2^3)^{-2} \cdot (x^{-2})^{-2}$ Power rule (b)

$= 2^{-6} x^4$ Power rule (a)

$= \dfrac{x^4}{2^6}$ $a^{-n} = \dfrac{1}{a^n}$

$= \dfrac{x^4}{64}$ $2^6 = 64$

(g) $\left(\dfrac{3x^2}{y}\right)^2 \left(\dfrac{4x^3}{y^{-2}}\right)^{-1}$

$= \dfrac{3^2(x^2)^2}{y^2} \cdot \dfrac{y^{-2}}{4x^3}$ Combination of rules

$= \dfrac{9x^4}{y^2} \cdot \dfrac{y^{-2}}{4x^3}$ $3^2 = 9$;
Power rule (a)

$= \dfrac{9}{4} x^{4-3} y^{-2-2}$ Quotient rule

$= \dfrac{9}{4} x^1 y^{-4}$ Subtract exponents.

$= \dfrac{9x}{4y^4}$ $a^{-n} = \dfrac{1}{a^n}$

(h) $\left(\dfrac{-4m^5 n^4}{24mn^{-7}}\right)^{-2}$

$= \left(\dfrac{m^{5-1} n^{4-(-7)}}{-6}\right)^{-2}$ Quotient rule; divide coefficients.

$= \left(\dfrac{m^4 n^{11}}{-6}\right)^{-2}$ Subtract exponents.

$= \dfrac{(m^4)^{-2}(n^{11})^{-2}}{(-6)^{-2}}$ Power rules (b) and (c)

$= \dfrac{m^{-8} n^{-22}}{(-6)^{-2}}$ Power rule (a)

$= \dfrac{(-6)^2}{m^8 n^{22}}$ $\dfrac{a^{-n}}{b^{-m}} = \dfrac{b^m}{a^n}$

The sign on -6 does *not* change in this step.

$= \dfrac{36}{m^8 n^{22}}$ $(-6)^2 = 36$

NOW TRY

NOW TRY ANSWERS

8. (a) $\dfrac{1}{x^3}$ (b) $\dfrac{1}{5^6}$

(c) $\dfrac{p^4}{q^3}$ (d) $\dfrac{8x^{10}}{25y^4}$

NOTE There is often more than one way to simplify expressions involving negative exponents.

In **Example 8(e),** we began by using the quotient rule. At the right, we simplify the same expression using one of the special rules for exponents. The final result is the same.

$$\frac{x^{-4}y^2}{x^2y^{-5}} \qquad \text{Example 8(e)}$$

$$= \frac{y^5y^2}{x^4x^2} \qquad \text{Use } \frac{a^{-n}}{b^{-m}} = \frac{b^m}{a^n}.$$

$$= \frac{y^7}{x^6} \qquad \text{Product rule}$$

OBJECTIVE 6 Use the rules for exponents with scientific notation.

The number of one-celled organisms that will sustain a whale for a few hours is 400,000,000,000,000, and the shortest wavelength of visible light is approximately 0.0000004 m. It is often simpler to write such numbers in *scientific notation.*

In scientific notation, a number is written with the decimal point after the first nonzero digit and multiplied by a power of 10.

Scientific Notation

A number is written in **scientific notation** when it is expressed in the form

$$a \times 10^n,$$

where $1 \le |a| < 10$ and n is an integer.

$$1 \le |a| < 10$$

It is customary to use $\times$ rather than $\cdot$ for multiplication.

Examples: $\quad 8500 = 8.5 \times 1000 = 8.5 \times 10^3 \qquad$ In scientific notation

$$0.230 \times 10^4 \qquad 46.5 \times 10^{-3} \qquad \textit{Not} \text{ in scientific notation}$$

$$a < 1 \qquad\qquad a > 10$$

To write a positive number in scientific notation, follow these steps.

Converting a Positive Number to Scientific Notation

Step 1 **Position the decimal point.** Place a caret, ^, to the right of the first nonzero digit, where the decimal point will be placed.

Step 2 **Determine the numeral for the exponent.** Count the number of digits from the decimal point to the caret. This number gives the absolute value of the exponent on 10.

Step 3 **Determine the sign for the exponent.** Decide whether multiplying by 10^n should make the result of Step 1 greater or less.

- The exponent should be positive to make the result greater.

- The exponent should be negative to make the result less.

It is helpful to remember the following.

For $n \ge 1,\quad 10^{-n} < 1 \quad$ and $\quad 10^n \ge 10.$

To convert a negative number to scientific notation, temporarily ignore the negative sign and go through the steps in the box above. Then attach a negative sign to the result.

NOW TRY
EXERCISE 9

Write each number in scientific notation.

(a) 7,560,000,000

(b) −0.000000245

EXAMPLE 9 **Writing Numbers in Scientific Notation**

Write each number in scientific notation.

(a) 820,000

> **Step 1** Place a caret to the right of the 8 (the first nonzero digit) to mark the new location of the decimal point.
>
> $$8_\wedge 20,000$$
>
> **Step 2** Count from the decimal point, which is understood to be after the last 0, to the caret.
>
> $$8_\wedge 20,000. \quad \leftarrow \text{Decimal point.}$$
>
> Count 5 places.
>
> **Step 3** Because 8.2 is to be made greater, the exponent on 10 is positive.
>
> $$820,000 = 8.2 \times 10^5$$

(b) 0.0000072

$0.000007_\wedge 2$ Place a caret to the right of the first nonzero digit.

$0.000007_\wedge 2$ Count from left to right.

6 places

Because 7.2 is to be made less, the exponent on 10 is negative.

$$0.0000072 = 7.2 \times 10^{-6}$$

(c) $-0.0004_\wedge 62 = -4.62 \times 10^{-4}$ Remember the negative sign.

Count 4 places.   NOW TRY

Converting a Positive Number from Scientific Notation

Multiplying a positive number by a positive power of 10 makes the number greater, so move the decimal point to the right if n is positive in 10^n.

Multiplying a positive number by a negative power of 10 makes the number less, so move the decimal point to the left if n is negative in 10^n.

If n is 0, leave the decimal point where it is in 10^n.

NOW TRY
EXERCISE 10

Write each number in standard notation.

(a) 4.45×10^{10}

(b) -5.9×10^{-5}

EXAMPLE 10 **Converting from Scientific Notation to Standard Notation**

Write each number in standard notation.

(a) 6.93×10^7

$6.93\underbrace{00000}_{7 \text{ places}}$ Attach 0's as necessary.

We moved the decimal point 7 places to the right. (We had to attach five 0's.)

$$6.93 \times 10^7 = 69,300,000 \quad \text{Insert commas.}$$

Standard notation

(b) 4.7×10^{-3}

$\underbrace{004.7}_{3 \text{ places}}$ Move the decimal point 3 places to the left. Attach 0's as necessary.

$$4.7 \times 10^{-3} = 0.0047 \quad \text{Attach a leading zero.}$$

(c) $-1.083 \times 10^0 = -1.083 \times 1 = -1.083$ NOW TRY

NOW TRY ANSWERS
9. (a) 7.56×10^9
   (b) -2.45×10^{-7}
10. (a) 44,500,000,000
    (b) −0.000059

NOTE *When converting from scientific notation to standard notation, use the exponent to determine the number of places and the direction in which to move the decimal point.*

NOW TRY
EXERCISE 11

Evaluate.

$$\frac{0.00063 \times 400,000}{1400 \times 0.000003}$$

EXAMPLE 11   Using Scientific Notation in Computation

Evaluate.

$$\frac{1,920,000 \times 0.0015}{0.000032 \times 45,000}$$

$$= \frac{1.92 \times 10^6 \times 1.5 \times 10^{-3}}{3.2 \times 10^{-5} \times 4.5 \times 10^4} \qquad \text{Express all numbers in scientific notation.}$$

$$= \frac{1.92 \times 1.5 \times 10^6 \times 10^{-3}}{3.2 \times 4.5 \times 10^{-5} \times 10^4} \qquad \text{Commutative property}$$

$$= \frac{1.92 \times 1.5 \times 10^3}{3.2 \times 4.5 \times 10^{-1}} \qquad \text{Product rule}$$

$$= \frac{1.92 \times 1.5}{3.2 \times 4.5} \times 10^4 \qquad \text{Quotient rule}$$

Don't stop here. $\qquad = 0.2 \times 10^4 \qquad \text{Simplify.}$

$$= (2 \times 10^{-1}) \times 10^4 \qquad \text{Write 0.2 in scientific notation.}$$

$$= 2 \times 10^3 \qquad \text{Product rule}$$

$$= 2000 \qquad \text{Standard notation} \qquad \text{NOW TRY}$$

NOW TRY
EXERCISE 12

The speed of light is approximately 30,000,000,000 cm per sec. How long will it take light to travel 1.2×10^{15} cm?

EXAMPLE 12   Using Scientific Notation to Solve Problems

In 1990, national health care expenditures in the United States were $724 billion. By 2012, health care expenditures were four times this amount. (*Source:* Centers for Medicare & Medicaid Services.)

(a) Write the amount of health care expenditures in 1990 using scientific notation.

$$724 \text{ billion}$$

$$= 724 \times 10^9 \qquad \text{1 billion} = 1,000,000,000 = 10^9$$

$$= (7.24 \times 10^2) \times 10^9 \qquad \text{Write 724 in scientific notation.}$$

$$= 7.24 \times 10^{11} \qquad \text{Product rule; } 10^2 \times 10^9 = 10^{2+9}$$

In 1990, health care expenditures were $\$7.24 \times 10^{11}$.

(b) What were health care expenditures in 2012?

$$(7.24 \times 10^{11}) \times 4 \qquad \text{Multiply the result in part (a) by 4.}$$

$$= (4 \times 7.24) \times 10^{11} \qquad \text{Commutative and associative properties}$$

$$= 28.96 \times 10^{11} \qquad \text{Multiply.}$$

$$= (2.896 \times 10^1) \times 10^{11} \qquad \text{Write 28.96 in scientific notation.}$$

$$= 2.896 \times 10^{12} \qquad \text{Product rule; } 10^1 \times 10^{11} = 10^{12}$$

NOW TRY ANSWERS
11. 60,000
12. 4.0×10^4 sec, or 40,000 sec

Expenditures in 2012 were about $\$2,896,000,000,000$ (almost $3 trillion).

NOW TRY

4.1 Exercises

  MyMathLab®

 Complete solution available in MyMathLab

Concept Check Decide whether each expression has been simplified correctly. If not, correct it.

1. $(ab)^2$
$= ab^2$

2. $(5x)^3$
$= 5^3x^3$

3. $\left(\dfrac{4}{a}\right)^3$
$= \dfrac{4^3}{a}$ $(a \neq 0)$

4. $y^2 \cdot y^6$
$= y^{12}$

5. $x^3 \cdot x^4$
$= x^7$

6. xy^0
$= 0$ $(y \neq 0)$

7. *Concept Check*   A friend evaluated

$$4^5 \cdot 4^2 \quad \text{as} \quad 16^7.$$

WHAT WENT WRONG? Give the correct answer.

8. *Concept Check*   Another friend evaluated

$$\dfrac{6^5}{3^2} \quad \text{as} \quad 2^3, \quad \text{which equals} \quad 8.$$

WHAT WENT WRONG? Give the correct answer.

Apply the product rule for exponents, if possible, in each case. **See Example 1.**

9. $13^4 \cdot 13^8$ **10.** $11^6 \cdot 11^4$ **11.** $8^9 \cdot 8$ **12.** $12 \cdot 12^6$

13. $x^3 \cdot x^5 \cdot x^9$ **14.** $y^4 \cdot y^5 \cdot y^6$ **15.** $(-3w^5)(9w^3)$ **16.** $(-5x^2)(3x^4)$

17. $(2x^2y^5)(9xy^3)$ **18.** $(8s^4t)(3s^3t^5)$ **19.** $r^2 \cdot s^4$ **20.** $p^3 \cdot q^2$

Match the expression in Column I with its equivalent expression in Column II. Choices may be used once, more than once, or not at all. **See Example 2.**

	I		II
21.	**(a)** 9^0	**A.** 0
	(b) -9^0	**B.** 1
	(c) $(-9)^0$	**C.** -1
	(d) $-(-9)^0$	**D.** 9
		E. -9

	I		II
22.	**(a)** $8x^0$	**A.** 0
	(b) $-8x^0$	**B.** 1
	(c) $(8x)^0$	**C.** -1
	(d) $(-8x)^0$	**D.** 8
		E. -8

Evaluate. Assume that all variables represent nonzero real numbers. **See Example 2.**

23. 15^0 **24.** 19^0 **25.** -8^0 **26.** -10^0

27. $(-25)^0$ **28.** $(-30)^0$ **29.** $3^0 + (-3)^0$ **30.** $5^0 + (-5)^0$

31. $-3^0 + 3^0$ **32.** $-5^0 + 5^0$ **33.** $-4^0 - m^0$ **34.** $-8^0 - k^0$

Match the expression in Column I with its equivalent expression in Column II. Choices may be used once, more than once, or not at all. **See Example 3.**

	I		II
35.	**(a)** 5^{-2}	**A.** 25
	(b) -5^{-2}	**B.** $\dfrac{1}{25}$
	(c) $(-5)^{-2}$	**C.** -25
	(d) $-(-5)^{-2}$	**D.** $-\dfrac{1}{25}$

	I		II
36.	**(a)** 4^{-3}	**A.** 64
	(b) -4^{-3}	**B.** -64
	(c) $(-4)^{-3}$	**C.** $\dfrac{1}{64}$
	(d) $-(-4)^{-3}$	**D.** $-\dfrac{1}{64}$

Write each expression with only positive exponents. Assume that all variables represent non-zero real numbers. See Examples 3(a)–(f).

37. 5^{-4} **38.** 7^{-2} **39.** 3^{-5} **40.** 8^{-3}

41. 9^{-1} **42.** 14^{-1} **43.** $(4x)^{-2}$ **44.** $(5t)^{-3}$

45. $4x^{-2}$ **46.** $5t^{-3}$ **47.** $-a^{-3}$ **48.** $-b^{-4}$

49. $(-a)^{-4}$ **50.** $(-b)^{-6}$ **51.** $(-3x)^{-3}$ **52.** $(-2x)^{-5}$

Evaluate. See Examples 3(g) and (h).

53. $5^{-1} + 6^{-1}$ **54.** $2^{-1} + 8^{-1}$ **55.** $8^{-1} - 3^{-1}$

56. $6^{-1} - 4^{-1}$ **57.** $-2^{-1} - 4^{-1}$ **58.** $-3^{-1} - 9^{-1}$

Evaluate. See Example 4.

59. $\dfrac{1}{4^{-2}}$ **60.** $\dfrac{1}{3^{-3}}$ **61.** $\dfrac{2^{-2}}{3^{-3}}$ **62.** $\dfrac{3^{-3}}{2^{-2}}$

Apply the quotient rule for exponents, if possible, and write each result with only positive exponents. Assume that all variables represent nonzero real numbers. See Example 5.

63. $\dfrac{4^8}{4^6}$ **64.** $\dfrac{5^9}{5^7}$ **65.** $\dfrac{x^{12}}{x^8}$ **66.** $\dfrac{y^{14}}{y^{10}}$

67. $\dfrac{r^7}{r^{10}}$ **68.** $\dfrac{y^8}{y^{12}}$ **69.** $\dfrac{6^4}{6^{-2}}$ **70.** $\dfrac{7^5}{7^{-3}}$

71. $\dfrac{6^{-3}}{6^7}$ **72.** $\dfrac{5^{-4}}{5^2}$ **73.** $\dfrac{7}{7^{-1}}$ **74.** $\dfrac{8}{8^{-1}}$

75. $\dfrac{r^{-3}}{r^{-6}}$ **76.** $\dfrac{s^{-4}}{s^{-8}}$ **77.** $\dfrac{x^3}{y^2}$ **78.** $\dfrac{y^5}{t^3}$

Simplify using the power rules. Assume that all variables represent nonzero real numbers. See Example 6.

79. $(x^3)^6$ **80.** $(y^5)^4$ **81.** $\left(\dfrac{3}{5}\right)^3$ **82.** $\left(\dfrac{4}{3}\right)^2$

83. $(4t)^3$ **84.** $(5t)^4$ **85.** $(-6x^2)^3$ **86.** $(-2x^5)^5$

87. $\left(\dfrac{-4m^2}{t}\right)^3$ **88.** $\left(\dfrac{-5n^4}{r^2}\right)^3$ **89.** $\left(\dfrac{-s^3}{t^5}\right)^4$ **90.** $\left(\dfrac{-2a^4}{b^5}\right)^6$

Match the expression in Column I with its equivalent expression in Column II. Choices may be used once, more than once, or not at all. See Example 7.

	I	II		I	II
91. (a)	$\left(\dfrac{1}{3}\right)^{-1}$	**A.** $\dfrac{1}{3}$	**92. (a)**	$\left(\dfrac{2}{5}\right)^{-2}$	**A.** $\dfrac{25}{4}$
(b)	$\left(-\dfrac{1}{3}\right)^{-1}$	**B.** 3	**(b)**	$\left(-\dfrac{2}{5}\right)^{-2}$	**B.** $-\dfrac{25}{4}$
(c)	$-\left(\dfrac{1}{3}\right)^{-1}$	**C.** $-\dfrac{1}{3}$	**(c)**	$-\left(\dfrac{2}{5}\right)^{-2}$	**C.** $\dfrac{4}{25}$
(d)	$-\left(-\dfrac{1}{3}\right)^{-1}$	**D.** -3	**(d)**	$-\left(-\dfrac{2}{5}\right)^{-2}$	**D.** $-\dfrac{4}{25}$

Write with only positive exponents and then evaluate. Assume that all variables represent nonzero real numbers. **See Example 7.**

93. $\left(\dfrac{1}{4}\right)^{-3}$ **94.** $\left(\dfrac{1}{5}\right)^{-2}$ ▶ **95.** $\left(\dfrac{2}{3}\right)^{-3}$ **96.** $\left(\dfrac{3}{2}\right)^{-3}$

97. $\left(\dfrac{4}{5}\right)^{-2}$ **98.** $\left(\dfrac{5}{4}\right)^{-2}$ **99.** $\left(\dfrac{2t}{3}\right)^{-4}$ **100.** $\left(\dfrac{3z}{4}\right)^{-3}$

101. $\left(\dfrac{1}{4x}\right)^{-2}$ **102.** $\left(\dfrac{1}{5x}\right)^{-3}$ **103.** $\left(\dfrac{x}{2}\right)^{-5}$ **104.** $\left(\dfrac{t}{4}\right)^{-4}$

Simplify each expression so that no negative exponents appear in the final result. Assume that all variables represent nonzero real numbers. **See Examples 1–8.**

105. $3^5 \cdot 3^{-6}$ **106.** $4^4 \cdot 4^{-6}$ ▶ **107.** $a^{-3}a^2a^{-4}$ **108.** $k^{-5}k^{-3}k^4$

109. $(5^{-3})^{-2}$ **110.** $(4^{-4})^{-2}$ **111.** $(x^{-4})^3$ **112.** $(x^{-3})^6$

113. $(k^2)^{-3}k^4$ **114.** $(x^3)^{-4}x^5$ **115.** $-4r^{-2}(r^4)^2$ **116.** $-2m^{-1}(m^3)^2$

117. $(5a^{-1})^4(a^2)^{-3}$ **118.** $(3p^{-4})^2(p^3)^{-1}$ **119.** $(z^{-4}x^3)^{-1}$ **120.** $(y^{-2}z^4)^{-3}$

121. $7k^2(-2k)(4k^{-5})^0$ **122.** $3a^2(-5a^{-6})(-2a)^0$ **123.** $\dfrac{(p^{-2})^0}{5p^{-4}}$

124. $\dfrac{(m^4)^0}{9m^{-3}}$ **125.** $\dfrac{m^2n^{-8}}{m^{-6}n^3}$ **126.** $\dfrac{a^{-9}b^6}{a^3b^{-4}}$

127. $\dfrac{(3pq)q^2}{6p^2q^4}$ **128.** $\dfrac{(-8xy)y^3}{4x^5y^4}$ **129.** $\dfrac{4a^5(a^{-1})^3}{(a^{-2})^{-2}}$

130. $\dfrac{12k^{-2}(k^{-3})^{-4}}{6k^5}$ **131.** $\dfrac{(-y^{-4})^2}{6(y^{-5})^{-1}}$ **132.** $\dfrac{2(-m^{-1})^{-4}}{9(m^{-3})^2}$

133. $\dfrac{(2k)^2m^{-5}}{(km)^{-3}}$ **134.** $\dfrac{(3rs)^{-2}}{3^2r^2s^{-4}}$ **135.** $\left(\dfrac{3k^{-2}}{k^4}\right)^{-1} \cdot \dfrac{2}{k}$

136. $\left(\dfrac{7m^{-2}}{m^{-3}}\right)^{-2} \cdot \dfrac{m^3}{4}$ **137.** $\left(\dfrac{2p}{q^2}\right)^3\left(\dfrac{3p^4}{q^{-4}}\right)^{-1}$ **138.** $\left(\dfrac{5z^3}{2a^2}\right)^{-3}\left(\dfrac{8a^{-1}}{15z^{-2}}\right)^{-3}$

139. $\dfrac{2^2y^4(y^{-3})^{-1}}{2^5y^{-2}}$ **140.** $\dfrac{3^{-1}m^4(m^2)^{-1}}{3^2m^{-2}}$ **141.** $\left(\dfrac{5m^4n^{-3}}{m^{-5}n^2}\right)^{-2}$

142. $\left(\dfrac{8x^{-6}y^3}{x^4y^{-4}}\right)^{-2}$ **143.** $\left(\dfrac{-3x^4y^6}{15x^{-6}y^7}\right)^{-3}$ **144.** $\left(\dfrac{-4a^3b^2}{12a^5b^{-4}}\right)^{-3}$

Extending Skills   *Simplify each expression. Assume that all variables represent nonzero real numbers.*

145. $\dfrac{(2k)^2k^3}{k^{-1}k^{-5}}(5k^{-2})^{-3}$ **146.** $\dfrac{(3r^2)^2r^{-5}}{r^{-2}r^3}(2r^{-6})^2$

147. $\dfrac{(2m^2p^3)^2(4m^2p)^{-2}}{(-3mp^4)^{-1}(2m^3p^4)^3}$ **148.** $\dfrac{(-5y^3z^4)^2(2yz^5)^{-2}}{10(y^4z)^3(3y^3z^2)^{-1}}$

149. $\dfrac{(-3y^3x^3)(-4y^4x^2)(x^2)^{-4}}{18x^3y^2(y^3)^3(x^3)^{-2}}$ **150.** $\dfrac{(2m^3x^2)^{-1}(3m^4x)^{-3}}{(m^2x^3)^3(m^2x)^{-5}}$

151. $\left(\dfrac{p^2q^{-1}}{2p^{-2}}\right)^2 \cdot \left(\dfrac{p^3 \cdot 4q^{-2}}{3q^{-5}}\right)^{-1} \cdot \left(\dfrac{pq^{-5}}{q^{-2}}\right)^3$ **152.** $\left(\dfrac{a^6b^{-2}}{2a^{-2}}\right)^{-1} \cdot \left(\dfrac{6a^{-2}}{5b^{-4}}\right)^2 \cdot \left(\dfrac{2b^{-1}a^2}{3b^{-2}}\right)^{-1}$

153. *Concept Check* In scientific notation, a number is written with a decimal point (*before/after*) the first nonzero digit and multiplied by a _____ of 10. A number written in scientific notation is expressed in the form _____ ×_____, where $1 \le |a| < 10$ and n is an integer.

154. *Concept Check* Tell whether each number is written in scientific notation. If it is not, tell why and write the number in scientific notation.

(a) 16.8×10^5 (b) 6×10^{-9} (c) 0.2×10^{-2}

Write each number in scientific notation. See Example 9.

▶ **155.** 530   **156.** 1600   **157.** 0.830   **158.** 0.0072

159. 0.00000692   **160.** 0.875   **161.** −38,500   **162.** −976,000,000

Write the boldfaced numbers in each problem in scientific notation. See Example 9.

163. The annual U.S. budget first passed **$1,000,000,000** in 1917. In 1987, it exceeded **$1,000,000,000,000** for the first time. The budget request for fiscal-year 2014 was **$3,800,000,000,000**. If stacked in dollar bills, this amount would stretch **257,891** mi. (*Source:* Office of Management and Budget.)

164. The largest of the **50** United States is Alaska, with land area of about **365,482,000** acres, while the smallest is Rhode Island, with land area of about **677,000** acres. The total land area of the United States is about **2,271,343,000** acres. (*Source:* General Services Administration.)

Write each number in standard notation. See Example 10.

▶ **165.** 7.2×10^4 **166.** 8.91×10^2 **167.** 2.54×10^{-3} **168.** 5.42×10^{-4}

169. -6×10^4 **170.** -9×10^3 **171.** 1.2×10^{-5} **172.** 2.7×10^{-6}

Evaluate. Give answers in standard notation. See Example 11.

173. $\dfrac{12 \times 10^4}{2 \times 10^6}$ **174.** $\dfrac{16 \times 10^5}{4 \times 10^8}$ **175.** $\dfrac{3 \times 10^{-2}}{12 \times 10^3}$

176. $\dfrac{5 \times 10^{-3}}{25 \times 10^2}$ **177.** $\dfrac{0.05 \times 1600}{0.0004}$ **178.** $\dfrac{0.003 \times 40,000}{0.00012}$

▶ **179.** $\dfrac{20,000 \times 0.018}{300 \times 0.0004}$ **180.** $\dfrac{840,000 \times 0.03}{0.00021 \times 600}$

Calculators can express numbers in scientific notation. The displays often use notation such as

$$\cdot\ 2.5\text{E}5 \quad \text{to represent} \quad 2.5 \times 10^5.$$

Similarly, $2.5\text{E}{-3}$ represents 2.5×10^{-3}. They can also perform operations with numbers entered in scientific notation.

Predict the result the calculator will give for each screen. (Use the usual scientific notation to write the answers.)

181. $\boxed{(1.5\text{E}12)*(5\text{E}^-3)}$ **182.** $\boxed{(3.2\text{E}^-5)*(3\text{E}12)}$

183. $\boxed{(8.4\text{E}14)/(2.1\text{E}^-3)}$ **184.** $\boxed{(2.5\text{E}10)/(2\text{E}^-3)}$

Solve each problem. See Example 12.

185. In 2014, the population of the United States was approximately 317.4 million. (*Source:* U.S. Census Bureau.)

(a) Write the population using scientific notation.

(b) Write $1 trillion, that is, $1,000,000,000,000, using scientific notation.

(c) Using the answers from parts (a) and (b), calculate how much each person in the United States in the year 2014 would have had to contribute in order to make someone a trillionaire. Write this amount in standard notation to the nearest dollar.

186. In 2014, the national debt of the United States was about $17.27 trillion. The U.S. population at that time was approximately 317.4 million. (*Source:* U.S. Census Bureau.)

(a) Write the population using scientific notation.

(b) Write the amount of the national debt using scientific notation.

(c) Using the answers for parts (a) and (b), calculate how much debt this is per American. Write this amount in standard notation to the nearest dollar.

187. In 2013, the population of India was about 1.22×10^{10}, which was 4.0×10^5 times the population of Monaco. What was the population of Monaco? (*Source: World Almanac and Book of Facts.*)

188. In the early years of the Powerball® Lottery, a player would choose five numbers from 1 through 49 and one number from 1 through 42. It can be shown that there are about 8.009×10^7

different ways to do this. Suppose that a group of 2000 persons decided to purchase tickets for all these numbers and each ticket cost $1.00. How much should each person have expected to pay? (*Source:* www.powerball.com)

189. The speed of light is approximately 3×10^{10} cm per sec. How long will it take light to travel 9×10^{12} cm?

190. The average distance from Earth to the sun is 9.3×10^7 mi. How long would it take a rocket, traveling at 2.9×10^3 mph, to reach the sun?

191. A *light-year* is the distance that light travels in one year. Find the number of miles in a light-year if light travels 1.86×10^5 mi per sec.

192. Use the information given in the previous two exercises to find the number of minutes necessary for light from the sun to reach Earth.

193. In 2013, the population of Luxembourg was approximately 5.15×10^5. The population density was 516 people per square mile. (*Source: The World Factbook.*)

(a) Write the population density in scientific notation.

(b) To the nearest square mile, what is the area of Luxembourg?

194. In 2013, the population of Costa Rica was approximately 4.70×10^6. The population density was 92.12 people per square kilometer. (*Source: The World Factbook.*)

(a) Write the population density in scientific notation.

(b) To the nearest square kilometer, what is the area of Costa Rica?

4.2 Adding and Subtracting Polynomials

VOCABULARY

☐ term
☐ algebraic expression
☐ polynomial
☐ numerical coefficient (coefficient)
☐ degree of a term
☐ polynomial in x
☐ descending powers
☐ leading term
☐ leading coefficient
☐ trinomial
☐ binomial
☐ monomial
☐ degree of a polynomial
☐ like terms
☐ negative of a polynomial

OBJECTIVE 1 Know the basic definitions for polynomials.

Recall that a **term** is a number (constant), a variable, or the product of a number and one or more variables raised to powers.

Examples: $4x$, $\dfrac{1}{2}m^5$ $\left(\text{or } \dfrac{m^5}{2}\right)$, $-7z^9$, $6x^2z$, $\dfrac{5}{3x^2}$, $3\sqrt{x}$, and 9 Terms

A term or a sum of two or more terms is an **algebraic expression.** The simplest kind of algebraic expression is a *polynomial.*

> **Polynomial**
>
> A **polynomial** is a term or a finite sum of terms of the form ax^n, where a is a real number, x is a variable, and the exponent n is a whole number.
>
> *Examples:* $12x^9$, $3t - 5$, and $4m^3 - 5m^2 + 8$ Polynomials in x, t, and m

Even though an expression such as $3t - 5$ involves subtraction, it can be written as a sum of terms, here $3t + (-5)$.

Some algebraic expressions that are *not* polynomials follow.

Examples: $x^{-1} + 3x^{-2}$, $\sqrt{9 - x}$, and $\dfrac{1}{x}$ Not polynomials

The first has negative integer exponents, the second involves a variable under a radical, and the third has a variable in the denominator.

For each term ax^n of a polynomial, a is the **numerical coefficient,** or just the **coefficient** of x^n, and the exponent n is the **degree of the term.**

▼ **Terms and Their Coefficients and Degrees**

Term ax^n	Numerical Coefficient	Degree
$12x^9$	12	9
$3x$, or $3x^1$	3	1
-6, or $-6x^0$	-6	0
$-x^4$, or $-1x^4$	-1	4
$\dfrac{x^2}{3} = \dfrac{1x^2}{3} = \dfrac{1}{3}x^2$	$\dfrac{1}{3}$	2

Any nonzero constant has degree 0.

NOTE   The number 0 has no degree because 0 times a variable to any power is 0.

A polynomial containing only the variable x is a **polynomial in x.** A polynomial in one variable is written in **descending powers** of the variable if the exponents on the variable in the terms decrease from left to right.

$$x^5 - 6x^2 + 12x - 5$$

Descending powers of x

Think of $12x$ as $12x^1$ and -5 as $-5x^0$.

When written in descending powers of the variable, the greatest-degree term is written first and is the **leading term** of the polynomial. Its coefficient is the **leading coefficient.**

**NOW TRY
EXERCISE 1**

Write the polynomial in descending powers of the variable. Then give the leading term and the leading coefficient.

$$-2x^3 - 2x^5 + 4x^2 + 7 - x$$

EXAMPLE 1   Writing Polynomials in Descending Powers

Write each polynomial in descending powers of the variable. Then give the leading term and the leading coefficient.

(a) $y - 6y^3 + 8y^5 - 9y^4 + 12$ is written as $8y^5 - 9y^4 - 6y^3 + y + 12$.

(b) $-2 + m + 6m^2 - m^3$ is written as $-m^3 + 6m^2 + m - 2$.

Each leading term is shown in color. In part (a), the leading coefficient is 8, and in part (b) it is -1.

NOW TRY

Some polynomials with a specific number of terms are given special names.

- A polynomial with exactly three terms is a **trinomial.**
- A two-term polynomial is a **binomial.**
- A single-term polynomial is a **monomial.**

Although many polynomials contain only one variable, polynomials may have more than one variable. The degree of a term with more than one variable is the sum of the exponents on the variables. The **degree of a polynomial** is the greatest degree of all of its terms.

▼ **Polynomials and Their Degrees**

Type of Polynomial	Example	Degree
Monomial	7	0 $(7 = 7x^0)$
	$5x^3y^7$	10 $(3 + 7 = 10)$
Binomial	$6 + 2x^3$	3
	$11y + 8$	1 $(y = y^1)$
Trinomial	$t^2 + 11t + 4$	2
	$-3 + 2k^5 + 9z^4$	5
	$x^3y^9 + 12xy^4 + 7xy$	12 (The terms have degrees 12, 5, and 2, and 12 is the greatest.)

NOTE   If a polynomial in a single variable is written in descending powers of that variable, the degree of the polynomial will be the degree of the leading term.

**NOW TRY
EXERCISE 2**

Identify each polynomial as a *monomial, binomial, trinomial,* or *none of these.* Give the degree.

(a) $-4x^3 + 10x^5 + 7$

(b) $-6m^2n^5$

EXAMPLE 2   Classifying Polynomials

Identify each polynomial as a *monomial, binomial, trinomial,* or *none of these.* Give the degree.

(a) $-x^2 + 5x + 1$ This is a trinomial of degree 2.

(b) $\frac{3}{4}xy^4$ $\left(\text{or } \frac{3}{4}x^1y^4\right)$ This is a monomial of degree 5 (because $1 + 4 = 5$).

(c) $7m^9 + 18m^{14}$ This is a binomial of degree 14.

(d) $p^4 - p^2 - 6p - 5$ Polynomials of four terms or more do not have special names, so *none of these* is the answer that applies here. This polynomial has degree 4.

NOW TRY

NOW TRY ANSWERS
1. $-2x^5 - 2x^3 + 4x^2 - x + 7$; $-2x^5$; -2
2. **(a)** trinomial; 5
   (b) monomial; 7

OBJECTIVE 2 Add and subtract polynomials.

We use the distributive property to simplify polynomials by combining like terms.

$$x^3 + 4x^2 + 5x^2 - 1$$
$$= x^3 + (4 + 5)x^2 - 1 \qquad \text{Distributive property}$$
$$= x^3 + 9x^2 - 1 \qquad\qquad \text{Add.}$$

The terms in a polynomial such as $4x + 5x^2$ cannot be combined. *Only terms containing exactly the same variables raised to the same powers may be combined.* Recall that such terms are **like terms**.

⚠ **CAUTION** *Only like terms can be combined.*

🔄 **NOW TRY**
EXERCISE 3
Combine like terms.
(a) $2x^2 - 8x^2 + x^2$
(b) $3p^3 - 2q + p^3 - 5q$
(c) $-x^2t + 4x^2t + 3xt^2 - 7xt^2$

EXAMPLE 3 **Combining Like Terms**

Combine like terms.

(a) $-5y^3 + 8y^3 - y^3$
$$= (-5 + 8 - 1)y^3 \qquad \text{Distributive property}$$
$$= 2y^3 \qquad\qquad\qquad \text{Add and subtract.}$$

(b) $6x + 5y - 9x + 2y$
$$= 6x - 9x + 5y + 2y \qquad \text{Commutative property}$$
$$= -3x + 7y \qquad\qquad\quad \text{Combine like terms.}$$

Because $-3x$ and $7y$ are unlike terms, no further simplification is possible.

(c) $5x^2y - 6xy^2 + 9x^2y + 13xy^2$
$$= 5x^2y + 9x^2y - 6xy^2 + 13xy^2 \qquad \text{Commutative property}$$
$$= 14x^2y + 7xy^2 \qquad\qquad\qquad\quad \text{Combine like terms.} \qquad \text{NOW TRY} 🔄$$

Adding Polynomials

To find the sum of two polynomials, combine like terms.

🔄 **NOW TRY**
EXERCISE 4
Add.
$$(7x^2 - 9x + 4) +$$
$$(x^3 - 3x^2 - 5)$$

EXAMPLE 4 **Adding Polynomials**

Add $(3a^5 - 9a^3 + 4a^2) + (-8a^5 + 8a^3 + 2)$.
$$(3a^5 - 9a^3 + 4a^2) + (-8a^5 + 8a^3 + 2)$$
$$= 3a^5 - 8a^5 - 9a^3 + 8a^3 + 4a^2 + 2 \qquad \begin{array}{l}\text{Commutative and}\\ \text{associative properties}\end{array}$$
$$= -5a^5 - a^3 + 4a^2 + 2 \qquad\qquad\quad \text{Combine like terms.}$$

Alternatively, we can add these two polynomials vertically.

$$3a^5 - 9a^3 + 4a^2 + 0 \qquad \text{Place like terms in columns.}$$
$$\underline{-8a^5 + 8a^3 + 0a^2 + 2} \qquad \text{Using placeholders may help.}$$

The sum is the same. $\quad -5a^5 - a^3 + 4a^2 + 2 \qquad \text{Add in columns.} \qquad \text{NOW TRY} 🔄$

NOW TRY ANSWERS
3. **(a)** $-5x^2$ **(b)** $4p^3 - 7q$
    (c) $3x^2t - 4xt^2$
4. $x^3 + 4x^2 - 9x - 1$

In **Section R.2,** we defined subtraction of real numbers as follows.

$$a - b = a + (-b)$$

That is, we add the first number and the negative (or opposite) of the second. We define the **negative of a polynomial** as that polynomial with the sign of every coefficient changed.

Subtracting Polynomials

To find the difference of two polynomials, add the first polynomial (minuend) and the negative (or opposite) of the *second* polynomial (subtrahend).

NOW TRY
EXERCISE 5
Subtract.

$$(2y^2 - 7y - 4) -$$
$$(8y^2 - 2y + 10)$$

EXAMPLE 5 **Subtracting Polynomials**

Subtract $(-6m^2 - 8m + 5) - (-5m^2 + 7m - 8)$.

Change every sign in the second polynomial (subtrahend) and add.

$$(-6m^2 - 8m + 5) - (-5m^2 + 7m - 8)$$

$$= -6m^2 - 8m + 5 + 5m^2 - 7m + 8 \qquad \text{Definition of subtraction}$$

$$= -6m^2 + 5m^2 - 8m - 7m + 5 + 8 \qquad \text{Rearrange terms.}$$

$$= -m^2 - 15m + 13 \qquad \text{Combine like terms.}$$

CHECK $\quad \underset{\underset{\text{Difference}}{\uparrow}}{(-m^2 - 15m + 13)} + \underset{\underset{\text{Subtrahend}}{\uparrow}}{(-5m^2 + 7m - 8)} = \underset{\underset{\text{Minuend}}{\uparrow}}{-6m^2 - 8m + 5} \;\checkmark$

Alternatively, we can subtract these two polynomials vertically.

$$\begin{array}{r} -6m^2 - 8m + 5 \\ -5m^2 + 7m - 8 \end{array} \qquad \begin{array}{l}\text{Write the subtrahend below} \\ \text{the minuend, lining up like} \\ \text{terms in columns.}\end{array}$$

Change all the signs in the subtrahend and add.

NOW TRY ANSWER
5. $-6y^2 - 5y - 14$

$$\begin{array}{r} -6m^2 - 8m + 5 \\ +5m^2 - 7m + 8 \\ \hline -m^2 - 15m + 13 \end{array} \qquad \begin{array}{l}\text{Change all signs.} \\[4pt] \text{Add in columns.}\end{array}$$

The difference is the same.

NOW TRY 🔄

4.2 Exercises

FOR EXTRA HELP ▶ MyMathLab®

▶ *Complete solution available in MyMathLab*

1. *Concept Check* Which polynomial is a trinomial in descending powers, having degree 6?

A. $5x^6 - 4x^5 + 12$ **B.** $6x^5 - x^6 + 4$

C. $2x + 4x^2 - x^6$ **D.** $4x^6 - 6x^4 + 9x^2 - 8$

2. *Concept Check* Give an example of a polynomial of four terms in the variable x, having degree 5, written in descending powers, and lacking a fourth-degree term.

Give the numerical coefficient and the degree of each term. **See Objective 1.**

3. $7z$ **4.** $3r$ **5.** $-15p^2$ **6.** $-27k^3$ **7.** x^4 **8.** y^6

9. $\dfrac{t}{6}$ **10.** $\dfrac{m}{4}$ **11.** 8 **12.** 2 **13.** $-x^3$ **14.** $-y^9$

Write each polynomial in descending powers of the variable. Then give the leading term and the leading coefficient. **See Example 1.**

▶ **15.** $2x^3 + x - 3x^2 + 4$ **16.** $q^2 + 3q^4 - 2q + 1$ **17.** $4p^3 - 8p^5 + p^7$

18. $3y^2 + y^4 - 2y^3$ **19.** $10 - m^3 - 3m^4$ **20.** $4 - x - 8x^2$

Identify each polynomial as a monomial, binomial, trinomial, *or* none of these. *Give the degree.* **See Example 2.**

21. 25 **22.** 15 **23.** $7m - 22$ **24.** $6x + 15$

▶ **25.** $-7y^6 + 11y^8$ **26.** $12k^2 - 9k^5$ **27.** $-mn^5$ **28.** $-a^3b$

29. $-5m^3 + 6m - 9m^2$ **30.** $4z^2 - 11z + 2$

31. $-6p^4q - 3p^3q^2 + 2pq^3 - q^4$ **32.** $8s^3t - 4s^2t^2 + 2st^3 + 9$

Combine like terms. **See Example 3.**

33. $5z^4 + 3z^4$ **34.** $8r^5 - 2r^5$ ▶ **35.** $-m^3 + 2m^3 + 6m^3$

36. $3p^4 + 5p^4 - 2p^4$ **37.** $x + x + x + x + x$ **38.** $z - z - z + z$

39. $m^4 - 3m^2 + m$ **40.** $5a^5 + 2a^4 - 9a^3$ **41.** $5t + 4s - 6t + 9s$

42. $8p - 9q - 3p + q$ **43.** $2k + 3k^2 + 5k^2 - 7$ **44.** $4x^2 + 2x - 6x^2 - 6$

45. $n^4 - 2n^3 + n^2 - 3n^4 + n^3$ **46.** $2q^3 + 3q^2 - 4q - q^3 + 5q^2$

47. $3ab^2 + 7a^2b - 5ab^2 + 13a^2b$ **48.** $6m^2n - 8mn^2 + 3mn^2 - 7m^2n$

49. $4 - (2 + 3m) + 6m + 9$ **50.** $8 - (3a + 4) + 5a - 3$

51. $6 + 3p - (2p + 1) - (2p + 9)$ **52.** $-8 + 4x - (x - 1) - (11x + 5)$

Add or subtract as indicated. **See Examples 4 and 5.**

▶ **53.** $(5x^2 + 7x - 4) + (3x^2 - 6x + 2)$ **54.** $(4k^3 + k^2 + k) + (2k^3 - 4k^2 - 3k)$

55. $(6t^2 - 4t^4 - t) + (3t^4 - 4t^2 + 5)$ **56.** $(3p^2 + 2p - 5) + (7p^2 - 4p^3 + 3p)$

57. $(y^3 + 3y + 2) + (4y^3 - 3y^2 + 2y - 1)$ **58.** $(2x^5 - 2x^4 + x^3 - 1) + (x^4 - 3x^3 + 2)$

59. $(3r + 8) - (2r - 5)$ **60.** $(2d + 7) - (3d - 1)$

61. $(2a^2 + 3a - 1) - (4a^2 + 5a + 6)$ **62.** $(q^4 - 2q^2 + 10) - (3q^4 + 5q^2 - 5)$

▶ **63.** $(z^5 + 3z^2 + 2z) - (4z^5 + 2z^2 - 5z)$ **64.** $(5t^3 - 3t^2 + 2t) - (4t^3 + 2t^2 + 3t)$

65. Add.
$21p - 8$
$\underline{-9p + 4}$

66. Add.
$15m - \ \ 9$
$\underline{4m + 12}$

67. Add.
$-12p^2 + 4p - 1$
$\underline{3p^2 + 7p - 8}$

68. Add.
$-6y^3 + 8y + 5$
$\underline{9y^3 + 4y - 6}$

69. Subtract.
$12a + 15$
$\underline{7a - \ \ 3}$

70. Subtract.
$-3b + 6$
$\underline{2b - 8}$

71. Subtract.
$6m^2 - 11m + 5$
$\underline{-8m^2 + \ \ 2m - 1}$

72. Subtract.
$-4z^2 + 2z - 1$
$\underline{3z^2 - 5z + 2}$

73. Add.
$12z^2 - 11z + 8$
$5z^2 + 16z - 2$
$\underline{-4z^2 + \ \ 5z - 9}$

74. Add.
$$-6m^3 + 2m^2 + 5m$$
$$8m^3 + 4m^2 - 6m$$
$$-3m^3 + 2m^2 - 7m$$

75. Add.
$$6y^3 - 9y^2 \quad\quad + 8$$
$$4y^3 + 2y^2 + 5y$$

76. Add.
$$-7r^8 + 2r^6 - r^5$$
$$3r^6 \quad\quad + 5$$

77. Subtract.
$$-5a^4 \quad\; + 8a^2 - 9$$
$$6a^3 - \; a^2 + 2$$

78. Subtract.
$$- 2m^3 + 8m^2$$
$$m^4 - \; m^3 \quad\quad + 2m$$

Extending Skills   *Perform the indicated operations.*

79. Subtract $4y^2 - 2y + 3$ from $7y^2 - 6y + 5$.

80. Subtract $-(-4x + 2z^2 + 3m)$ from $\left[\,(2z^2 - 3x + m) + (z^2 - 2m)\,\right]$.

81. $(-4m^2 + 3n^2 - 5n) - \left[\,(3m^2 - 5n^2 + 2n) + (-3m^2) + 4n^2\,\right]$

82. $\left[\,-(4m^2 - 8m + 4m^3) - (3m^2 + 2m + 5m^3)\,\right] + m^2$

83. $\left[\,-(y^4 - y^2 + 1) - (y^4 + 2y^2 + 1)\,\right] + (3y^4 - 3y^2 - 2)$

84. $\left[\,2p - (3p - 6)\,\right] - \left[\,(5p - (8 - 9p)) + 4p\,\right]$

85. $-\left[\,3z^2 + 5z - (2z^2 - 6z)\,\right] + \left[\,(8z^2 - [5z - z^2]) + 2z^2\,\right]$

86. $5k - (5k - \left[\,2k - (4k - 8k)\,\right]) + 11k - (9k - 12k)$

Find the perimeter of each figure. Express it as a polynomial in descending powers of the variable x.

87.

88.

4.3   Polynomial Functions, Graphs, and Composition

OBJECTIVES

1. Recognize and evaluate polynomial functions.
2. Use a polynomial function to model data.
3. Add and subtract polynomial functions.
4. Find the composition of functions.
5. Graph basic polynomial functions.

OBJECTIVE 1   Recognize and evaluate polynomial functions.

In **Chapter 2,** we studied linear (first-degree polynomial) functions $f(x) = ax + b$. Now we consider more general polynomial functions.

> **Polynomial Function**
>
> A **polynomial function of degree n** is defined by
> $$f(x) = a_nx^n + a_{n-1}x^{n-1} + \cdots + a_1x + a_0,$$
> for real numbers $a_n, a_{n-1}, \ldots, a_1$, and a_0, where $a_n \neq 0$ and n is a whole number.

Another way of describing a polynomial function is to say that it is a function defined by a polynomial in one variable, consisting of one or more terms. It is usually written in descending powers of the variable, and its degree is the degree of the polynomial that defines it.

We can evaluate a polynomial function $f(x)$ at different values of the variable x.

VOCABULARY

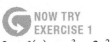

☐ polynomial function
☐ composite function
   (composition of functions)
☐ identity function
☐ squaring function
☐ cubing function

**NOW TRY
EXERCISE 1**
Let $f(x) = x^3 - 2x^2 + 7$.
Find $f(-3)$.

EXAMPLE 1 Evaluating Polynomial Functions

Let $f(x) = 4x^3 - x^2 + 5$. Find each value.

(a) $f(3)$

Read this as "f of 3," not "f times 3."

$f(x) = 4x^3 - x^2 + 5$	Given function
$f(3) = 4(3)^3 - 3^2 + 5$	Substitute 3 for x.
$f(3) = 4(27) - 9 + 5$	Apply the exponents.
$f(3) = 108 - 9 + 5$	Multiply.
$f(3) = 104$	Subtract, and then add.

Thus, $f(3) = 104$ and the ordered pair $(3, 104)$ belongs to f.

(b) $f(-4)$

$f(x) = 4x^3 - x^2 + 5$ *Use parentheses.*	
$f(-4) = 4(-4)^3 - (-4)^2 + 5$	Let $x = -4$.
$f(-4) = 4(-64) - 16 + 5$ *Be careful with signs.*	
$f(-4) = -256 - 16 + 5$	Multiply.
$f(-4) = -267$	Subtract, and then add.

So, $f(-4) = -267$. The ordered pair $(-4, -267)$ belongs to f.   **NOW TRY**

The capital letter P is sometimes used for polynomial functions. The function
$$P(x) = 4x^3 - x^2 + 5$$
yields the same ordered pairs as the function f in **Example 1.**

OBJECTIVE 2 Use a polynomial function to model data.

EXAMPLE 2 Using a Polynomial Model to Approximate Data

**NOW TRY
EXERCISE 2**
Use the function in **Example 2** to approximate the number of public school students in 2010 (to two decimal places).

The number of students enrolled in public schools (grades pre-K–12) in the United States during the years 2000 through 2011 can be modeled by the polynomial function
$$P(x) = -0.02675x^2 + 0.4873x + 47.26,$$
where $x = 0$ corresponds to the year 2000, $x = 1$ corresponds to 2001, and so on, and $P(x)$ is in millions. Use this function to approximate the number of public school students in 2011. (*Source:* National Center for Education Statistics.)

Here $x = 11$ corresponds to 2011, so we find $P(11)$.

$P(x) = -0.02675x^2 + 0.4873x + 47.26$	
$P(11) = -0.02675(11)^2 + 0.4873(11) + 47.26$	Let $x = 11$.
$P(11) \approx 49.38$	Evaluate.

NOW TRY ANSWERS
1. -38
2. 49.46 million

There were about 49.38 million public school students in 2011.   **NOW TRY**

OBJECTIVE 3 Add and subtract polynomial functions.

The operations of addition, subtraction, multiplication, and division are also defined for functions. For example, the graph in **FIGURE 1** shows dollars (in billions) spent for general science and for space/other technologies over a 20-year period.

Science and Space Spending

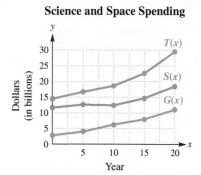

- $G(x)$ represents dollars spent for general science.

- $S(x)$ represents dollars spent for space/other technologies.

- $T(x)$ represents total expenditures for these two categories.

Source: U.S. Office of Management and Budget.

FIGURE 1

The total expenditures function can be found by *adding* the spending functions for the two individual categories.

$$T(x) = G(x) + S(x)$$

As another example, businesses use the equation "profit equals revenue minus cost," which can be written using function notation.

$$P(x) \;=\; R(x) \;-\; C(x)$$

x is the number of items produced and sold.

Profit   Revenue   Cost
function   function   function

The profit function is found by *subtracting* the cost function from the revenue function.

We define the following **operations on functions.**

Adding and Subtracting Functions

If $f(x)$ and $g(x)$ define functions, then

$$(f + g)(x) = f(x) + g(x) \qquad \text{Sum function}$$

and $\qquad\qquad (f - g)(x) = f(x) - g(x). \qquad \text{Difference function}$

In each case, the domain of the new function is the intersection of the domains of $f(x)$ and $g(x)$.

EXAMPLE 3 Adding and Subtracting Functions

Find each of the following for the polynomial functions f and g as defined.

$$f(x) = x^2 - 3x + 7 \quad \text{and} \quad g(x) = -3x^2 - 7x + 7$$

(a) $(f + g)(x)$ This notation does *not* indicate the distributive property.

$= f(x) + g(x)$ Use the definition.

$= (x^2 - 3x + 7) + (-3x^2 - 7x + 7)$ Substitute.

$= -2x^2 - 10x + 14$ Add the polynomials.

**NOW TRY
EXERCISE 3**

For $f(x) = x^3 - 3x^2 + 4$
and $g(x) = -2x^3 + x^2 - 12$,
find each of the following.

(a) $(f + g)(x)$

(b) $(f - g)(x)$

(b) $(f - g)(x)$

$$= f(x) - g(x) \qquad \text{Use the definition.}$$

$$= (x^2 - 3x + 7) - (-3x^2 - 7x + 7) \qquad \text{Substitute.}$$

$$= (x^2 - 3x + 7) + (3x^2 + 7x - 7) \qquad \text{Change subtraction to addition.}$$

$$= 4x^2 + 4x \qquad \text{Add.} \qquad \text{NOW TRY} \quad$$

EXAMPLE 4 Adding and Subtracting Functions

Find each of the following for the polynomial functions f and g as defined.

$$f(x) = 10x^2 - 2x \quad \text{and} \quad g(x) = 2x$$

**NOW TRY
EXERCISE 4**

For $f(x) = x^2 - 4$
and $g(x) = -6x^2$,
find each of the following.

(a) $(f + g)(x)$

(b) $(f - g)(-4)$

(a) $(f + g)(2)$

$$= f(2) + g(2) \qquad \text{Use the definition.}$$

$$\overbrace{f(x) = 10x^2 - 2x}^{} \quad \overbrace{g(x) = 2x}^{}$$

$$\boxed{\text{This is a key step.}} = [10(2)^2 - 2(2)] + 2(2) \qquad \text{Substitute.}$$

$$= [40 - 4] + 4 \qquad \text{Order of operations}$$

$$= 40 \qquad \text{Subtract, and then add.}$$

Alternative method: $(f + g)(x)$ \qquad Find $(f + g)(x)$.

$$= f(x) + g(x) \qquad \text{Use the definition.}$$

$$= (10x^2 - 2x) + 2x \qquad \text{Substitute.}$$

$$= 10x^2 \qquad \text{Combine like terms.}$$

$$(f + g)(2) \qquad \text{Now find } (f + g)(2).$$

$$= 10(2)^2 \qquad (f + g)(x) = 10x^2; \text{ Substitute.}$$

$$= 40 \qquad \text{The result is the same.}$$

(b) $(f - g)(x)$ and $(f - g)(1)$

$$(f - g)(x)$$

$$= f(x) - g(x) \qquad \text{Use the definition.}$$

$$= (10x^2 - 2x) - 2x \qquad \text{Substitute.}$$

$$= 10x^2 - 4x \qquad \text{Combine like terms.}$$

$$(f - g)(1) \qquad \text{Now find } (f - g)(1).$$

$$\boxed{\text{Confirm that } f(1) - g(1) \text{ gives the same result.}} = 10(1)^2 - 4(1) \qquad (f - g)(x) = 10x^2 - 4x; \text{ Substitute.}$$

$$= 6 \qquad \text{Perform the operations.} \quad \text{NOW TRY}$$

OBJECTIVE 4 Find the composition of functions.

The diagram in **FIGURE 2** on the next page shows a function g that assigns, to each element x of set X, some element y of set Y. Suppose that a function f takes each element of set Y and assigns a value z of set Z. Then f and g together assign an element x in X to an element z in Z.

The result of this process is a new function h that takes an element x in X and assigns it an element z in Z.

NOW TRY ANSWERS

3. (a) $-x^3 - 2x^2 - 8$
   (b) $3x^3 - 4x^2 + 16$

4. (a) $-5x^2 - 4$
   (b) 108

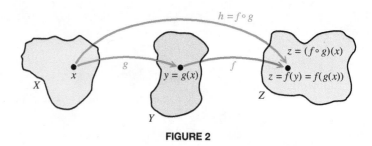

FIGURE 2

Function h is the *composition* of functions f and g, written $\boldsymbol{f \circ g}$.

Composition of Functions

The **composite function,** or **composition,** of functions f and g is defined by

$$(f \circ g)(x) = f(g(x)),$$

for all x in the domain of g such that $g(x)$ is in the domain of f.

Read $f \circ g$ as "f of g" (or "f compose g").

As a real-life example of how composite functions occur, consider the following.

A $40 pair of blue jeans is on sale for 25% off. If we purchase the jeans before noon, the retailer offers an additional 10% off. What is the final sale price of the blue jeans?

We might be tempted to say that the blue jeans are $25\% + 10\% = 35\%$ off and calculate $\$40(0.35) = \$14$, giving a final sale price of

$$\$40 - \$14 = \$26. \quad \text{This is not correct.}$$

To find the correct final sale price, we must first find the price after taking 25% off, and then take an additional 10% off *that* price.

$\$40(0.25) = \$10$, giving a sale price of $\$40 - \$10 = \$30$.   Take 25% off original price.

$\$30(0.10) = \$3$, giving a ***final sale price*** of $\$30 - \$3 = \$27$.   Take additional 10% off.

This is the idea behind composition of functions.

NOW TRY EXERCISE 5

Let $f(x) = 3x + 7$ and $g(x) = x - 2$. Find $(f \circ g)(7)$.

EXAMPLE 5 **Finding a Composite Function**

Let $f(x) = x^2$ and $g(x) = x + 3$. Find $(f \circ g)(4)$.

$(f \circ g)(4)$ Evaluate the "inside" function value first.

$= f(g(4))$ Definition of composition

$= f(4 + 3)$ Use the rule for $g(x)$; $g(4) = 4 + 3$.

$= f(7)$ Add.

Now evaluate the "outside" function. $= 7^2$ Use the rule for $f(x)$; $f(7) = 7^2$.

$= 49$ Square 7.

NOW TRY ANSWER
5. 22

In this composition, g is the innermost "operation" and acts on x (here 4) first. Then the output value of g (here 7) becomes the input (domain) value of f.   NOW TRY

If we interchange the order of functions f and g, the composition $g \circ f$, read "g of f" (or "g compose f"), is defined by

$$(g \circ f)(x) = g(f(x)), \quad \text{for all } x \text{ in the domain of } f \text{ such that } f(x) \text{ is in the domain of } g.$$

NOW TRY EXERCISE 6

As in **Now Try Exercise 5,** let $f(x) = 3x + 7$ and $g(x) = x - 2$. Find $(g \circ f)(7)$.

EXAMPLE 6 Finding a Composite Function

Find $(g \circ f)(4)$ for the functions $f(x) = x^2$ and $g(x) = x + 3$ from **Example 5.**

$$(g \circ f)(4) \quad \text{Evaluate the "inside" function value first.}$$

$$= g(f(4)) \quad \text{Definition of composition}$$

$$= g(4^2) \quad \text{Use the rule for } f(x); f(4) = 4^2.$$

$$= g(16) \quad \text{Square 4.}$$

Now evaluate the "outside" function.

$$= 16 + 3 \quad \text{Use the rule for } g(x); g(16) = 16 + 3.$$

$$= 19 \quad \text{Add.}$$

In this composition, f is the innermost "operation" and acts on x (again 4) first. Then the output value of f (here 16) becomes the input (domain) value of g.   **NOW TRY**

We see in **Examples 5 and 6** that

$$(f \circ g)(4) \neq (g \circ f)(4) \quad \text{because} \quad 49 \neq 19.$$

In general,

$$(f \circ g)(x) \neq (g \circ f)(x).$$

EXAMPLE 7 Finding Composite Functions

Let $f(x) = 4x - 1$ and $g(x) = x^2 + 5$. Find each of the following.

(a) $(f \circ g)(2)$

$$= f(g(2)) \quad \text{Definition of composition}$$

$$= f(2^2 + 5) \quad g(x) = x^2 + 5$$

$$= f(9) \quad \text{Work inside the parentheses.}$$

$$= 4(9) - 1 \quad f(x) = 4x - 1$$

$$= 35 \quad \text{Multiply, and then subtract.}$$

(b) $(f \circ g)(x)$

$$= f(g(x)) \quad \text{Use } g(x) \text{ as the input for function } f.$$

$$= 4(g(x)) - 1 \quad \text{Use the rule for } f(x); f(x) = 4x - 1.$$

$$= 4(x^2 + 5) - 1 \quad g(x) = x^2 + 5$$

$$= 4x^2 + 20 - 1 \quad \text{Distributive property}$$

$$= 4x^2 + 19 \quad \text{Combine like terms.}$$

NOW TRY ANSWER
6. 26

NOW TRY
EXERCISE 7

Let $f(x) = x - 5$
and $g(x) = -x^2 + 2$.
Find each of the following.

(a) $(g \circ f)(-1)$

(b) $(f \circ g)(x)$

(c) Find $(f \circ g)(2)$ again, this time using the rule obtained in part (b).

$$(f \circ g)(x) = 4x^2 + 19 \qquad \text{From part (b)}$$

$$(f \circ g)(2) = 4(2)^2 + 19 \qquad \text{Let } x = 2.$$

$$= 4(4) + 19 \qquad \text{Square 2.}$$

$$= 16 + 19 \qquad \text{Multiply.}$$

Same result as in part (a) → $= 35$ Add.   **NOW TRY**

OBJECTIVE 5 Graph basic polynomial functions.

Recall from **Section 2.5** that each input (or x-value) of a function results in one output (or y-value). The set of input values (for x) defines the domain of the function, and the set of output values (for y) defines the range.

The simplest polynomial function is the **identity function** $f(x) = x$, graphed in **FIGURE 3**. This function pairs each real number with itself.

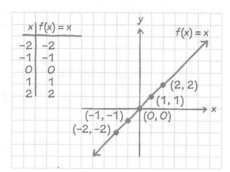

Identity function

$$f(x) = x$$

Domain: $(-\infty, \infty)$

Range: $(-\infty, \infty)$

FIGURE 3

NOTE   A *linear function* **(Section 2.6)** is a specific kind of polynomial function.

Another polynomial function, the **squaring function** $f(x) = x^2$, is graphed in **FIGURE 4**. For this function, every real number is paired with its square. The graph of the squaring function is a *parabola*.

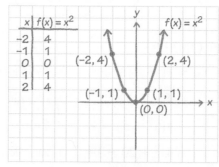

Squaring function

$$f(x) = x^2$$

Domain: $(-\infty, \infty)$

Range: $[0, \infty)$

FIGURE 4

The **cubing function** $f(x) = x^3$ is graphed in **FIGURE 5**. This function pairs every real number with its cube.

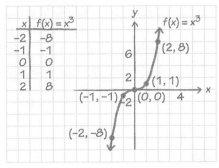

Cubing function

$$f(x) = x^3$$

Domain: $(-\infty, \infty)$
Range: $(-\infty, \infty)$

FIGURE 5

NOW TRY EXERCISE 8
Graph $f(x) = x^2 - 4$. Give the domain and range.

EXAMPLE 8 Graphing Variations of Polynomial Functions

Graph each function by creating a table of ordered pairs. Give the domain and range of each function by observing its graph.

(a) $f(x) = 2x$

To find each range value, multiply the domain value by 2. Plot the points and join them with a straight line. See **FIGURE 6**. Both the domain and the range are $(-\infty, \infty)$.

FIGURE 6

FIGURE 7

(b) $f(x) = -x^2$

For each input x, square it and then take its opposite. Plotting and joining the points gives a parabola that opens down. It is a *reflection* of the graph of the squaring function across the x-axis. See the table and **FIGURE 7**. The domain is $(-\infty, \infty)$ and the range is $(-\infty, 0]$.

(c) $f(x) = x^3 - 2$

For this function, cube the input and then subtract 2 from the result. The graph is that of the cubing function *shifted* 2 units down. See the table and **FIGURE 8**. The domain and range are both $(-\infty, \infty)$.

NOW TRY ANSWER
8.

domain: $(-\infty, \infty)$;
range: $[-4, \infty)$

x	$f(x) = x^3 - 2$
-2	-10
-1	-3
0	-2
1	-1
2	6

FIGURE 8

NOW TRY

4.3 Exercises

▶ FOR EXTRA HELP　　▶ MyMathLab°

▶ *Complete solution available in MyMathLab*

1. *Concept Check*　A polynomial function is a function defined by a _____ in (*one / two / three*) variable(s), consisting of one or more (*factors / terms*) and usually written in descending _____ of the variable.

2. *Concept Check*　Which of the following are *not* polynomial functions?

　A. $P(x) = x^{-2} - 2x$　　**B.** $f(x) = \dfrac{1}{2}x^2 + x - 1$

　C. $g(x) = -4x + 1.5$　　**D.** $p(x) = x^3 - x^2 - \dfrac{5}{x}$

For each polynomial function, find (a) $f(-1)$, (b) $f(2)$, and (c) $f(0)$. See Example 1.

3. $f(x) = 6x - 4$　　　**4.** $f(x) = -2x + 5$　　　**5.** $f(x) = x^2 - 7x$

6. $f(x) = x^2 + 5x$　　　**7.** $f(x) = x^2 - 3x + 4$　　　**8.** $f(x) = x^2 - 5x - 4$

9. $f(x) = 2x^2 - 4x + 1$　　**10.** $f(x) = 3x^2 + x - 5$　　**11.** $f(x) = 5x^4 - 3x^2 + 6$

12. $f(x) = 4x^4 + 2x^2 - 1$　▶ **13.** $f(x) = -x^2 + 2x^3 - 8$　　**14.** $f(x) = -x^2 - x^3 + 11$

Solve each problem. See Example 2.

15. Imports of Fair Trade Certified™ coffee into the United States during the years 2000 through 2012 can be modeled by the polynomial function

$$P(x) = 0.6558x^2 + 5.278x + 1.048,$$

where $x = 0$ represents 2000, $x = 1$ represents 2001, and so on, and $P(x)$ is in millions of pounds. Use this function to approximate the amount of Fair Trade coffee imported into the United States (to the nearest tenth) in each given year. (*Source:* Fair Trade USA.)

(a) 2000　　**(b)** 2006　　**(c)** 2012

FAIR TRADE CERTIFIED™

16. The U.S. population that was foreign-born during the years 1930 through 2011 can be modeled by the polynomial function

$$P(x) = 0.0042x^2 - 0.3187x + 11.49,$$

where $x = 0$ represents 1930, $x = 10$ represents 1940, and so on, and $P(x)$ is percent. Use this function to approximate the percent of the U.S. population that was foreign-born (to the nearest tenth) in each given year. (*Source:* U.S. Census Bureau.)

(a) 1930　　**(b)** 1970　　**(c)** 2011

17. The amount spent by Americans on domestic travel during the years 1990 through 2012 can be modeled by the polynomial function

$$P(x) = -0.00942x^3 + 0.4041x^2 + 15.25x + 280.6,$$

where $x = 0$ represents 1990, $x = 1$ represents 1991, and so on, and $P(x)$ is in billions of dollars. Use this function to approximate the amount spent by Americans on domestic travel (to the nearest tenth) in each given year. (*Source:* U.S. Travel Association.)

(a) 1990   **(b)** 2005   **(c)** 2012

18. World tourism receipts during the years 2000 through 2012 can be modeled by the polynomial function

$$P(x) = -0.4499x^3 + 8.274x^2 + 15.65x + 450.9,$$

where $x = 0$ represents 2000, $x = 1$ represents 2001, and so on, and $P(x)$ is in billions of dollars. Use this function to approximate world tourism receipts (to the nearest tenth) in each given year. (*Source:* World Tourism Association.)

(a) 2000   **(b)** 2006   **(c)** 2012

For each pair of functions, find **(a)** $(f + g)(x)$ *and* **(b)** $(f - g)(x)$. ***See Example 3.***

19. $f(x) = 5x - 10, \quad g(x) = 3x + 7$

20. $f(x) = -4x + 1, \quad g(x) = 6x + 2$

▶ **21.** $f(x) = 4x^2 + 8x - 3, \quad g(x) = -5x^2 + 4x - 9$

22. $f(x) = 3x^2 - 9x + 10, \quad g(x) = -4x^2 + 2x + 12$

Concept Check   *Find two polynomial functions defined by $f(x)$ and $g(x)$ such that each statement is true.*

23. $(f + g)(x) = 3x^3 - x + 3$ **24.** $(f - g)(x) = -x^2 + x - 5$

Let $f(x) = x^2 - 9, g(x) = 2x,$ and $h(x) = x - 3$. Find each of the following. ***See Example 4.***

▶ **25.** $(f + g)(x)$ **26.** $(f - g)(x)$ **27.** $(f + g)(3)$ **28.** $(f - g)(-3)$

29. $(f - h)(x)$ **30.** $(f + h)(x)$ **31.** $(f - h)(-3)$ **32.** $(f + h)(-2)$

33. $(g + h)(-10)$ **34.** $(g - h)(10)$ **35.** $(g - h)(-3)$ **36.** $(g + h)(1)$

37. $(g + h)\left(\dfrac{1}{4}\right)$ **38.** $(g + h)\left(\dfrac{1}{3}\right)$ **39.** $(g + h)\left(-\dfrac{1}{2}\right)$ **40.** $(g + h)\left(-\dfrac{1}{4}\right)$

Solve each problem. ***See Objective 3.***

41. The cost in dollars to produce x t-shirts is $C(x) = 2.5x + 50$. The revenue in dollars from sales of x t-shirts is $R(x) = 10.99x$.

(a) Write and simplify a function P that gives profit in terms of x.

(b) Find the profit if 100 t-shirts are produced and sold.

42. The cost in dollars to produce x baseball caps is $C(x) = 4.3x + 75$. The revenue in dollars from sales of x caps is $R(x) = 25x$.

(a) Write and simplify a function P that gives profit in terms of x.

(b) Find the profit if 50 caps are produced and sold.

Concept Check   Let $f(x) = x^2$ and $g(x) = 2x - 1$. Match each expression in Column I with the description of how to evaluate it in Column II.

I	**II**
43. $(f \circ g)(5)$	**A.** Square 5. Take the result and square it.
44. $(g \circ f)(5)$	**B.** Double 5 and subtract 1. Take the result and square it.
45. $(f \circ f)(5)$	**C.** Double 5 and subtract 1. Take the result, double it, and subtract 1.
46. $(g \circ g)(5)$	**D.** Square 5. Take the result, double it, and subtract 1.

Let $f(x) = x^2 + 4$, $g(x) = 2x + 3$, and $h(x) = x - 5$. Find each value or expression. **See Examples 5–7.**

47. $(h \circ g)(4)$ **48.** $(f \circ g)(4)$ **49.** $(g \circ f)(6)$ **50.** $(h \circ f)(6)$

51. $(f \circ h)(-2)$ **52.** $(h \circ g)(-2)$ **53.** $(f \circ g)(0)$ **54.** $(f \circ h)(0)$

55. $(g \circ f)(x)$ **56.** $(g \circ h)(x)$ **57.** $(h \circ g)(x)$ **58.** $(h \circ f)(x)$

59. $(f \circ h)\left(\dfrac{1}{2}\right)$ **60.** $(h \circ f)\left(\dfrac{1}{2}\right)$ **61.** $(f \circ g)\left(-\dfrac{1}{2}\right)$ **62.** $(g \circ f)\left(-\dfrac{1}{2}\right)$

Extending Skills   The tables give some selected ordered pairs for functions f and g.

x	3	4	6	8
$f(x)$	1	3	9	2

x	2	7	1	9
$g(x)$	3	6	9	12

Tables like these can be used to evaluate composite functions. For example, to evaluate $(g \circ f)(6)$, use the first table to find $f(6) = 9$. Then use the second table to find

$$(g \circ f)(6) = g(f(6)) = g(9) = 12.$$

Find each of the following.

63. $(f \circ g)(2)$ **64.** $(f \circ g)(7)$ **65.** $(g \circ f)(3)$

66. $(g \circ f)(8)$ **67.** $(f \circ f)(4)$ **68.** $(g \circ g)(1)$

Solve each problem. **See Objective 4.**

69. The function $f(x) = 12x$ computes the number of inches in x feet, and the function $g(x) = 5280x$ computes the number of feet in x miles. Find and simplify $(f \circ g)(x)$. What does it compute?

70. The function $f(x) = 60x$ computes the number of minutes in x hours, and the function $g(x) = 24x$ computes the number of hours in x days. Find and simplify $(f \circ g)(x)$. What does it compute?

71. The perimeter x of a square with sides of length s is given by the formula $x = 4s$.

(a) Solve for s in terms of x.

(b) If y represents the area of this square, write y as a function of the perimeter x.

(c) Use the composite function of part (b) to find the area of a square with perimeter 6.

72. The perimeter x of an equilateral triangle with sides of length s is given by the formula $x = 3s$.

(a) Solve for s in terms of x.

(b) The area y of an equilateral triangle with sides of length s is given by the formula $y = \dfrac{s^2\sqrt{3}}{4}$. Write y as a function of the perimeter x.

(c) Use the composite function of part (b) to find the area of an equilateral triangle with perimeter 12.

73. When a thermal inversion layer is over a city (as happens often in Los Angeles), pollutants cannot rise vertically, but are trapped below the layer and must disperse horizontally.

Assume that a factory smokestack begins emitting a pollutant at 8 A.M and that the pollutant disperses horizontally over a circular area. Suppose that t represents the time, in hours, since the factory began emitting pollutants ($t = 0$ represents 8 A.M.), and assume that the radius of the circle of pollution is $r(t) = 2t$ miles. Let $\mathscr{A}(r) = \pi r^2$ represent the area of a circle of radius r. Find and interpret $(\mathscr{A} \circ r)(t)$.

74. An oil well is leaking, with the leak spreading oil over the surface as a circle. At any time t, in minutes, after the beginning of the leak, the radius of the circular oil slick on the surface is $r(t) = 4t$ feet. Let $\mathscr{A}(r) = \pi r^2$ represent the area of a circle of radius r. Find and interpret $(\mathscr{A} \circ r)(t)$.

Graph each polynomial function. Give the domain and range. ***See Example 8.***

75. $f(x) = -2x + 1$

76. $f(x) = 3x + 2$

77. $f(x) = -3x^2$

78. $f(x) = \dfrac{1}{2}x^2$

79. $f(x) = x^3 + 1$

80. $f(x) = -x^3 + 2$

4.4 Multiplying Polynomials

NOW TRY
EXERCISE 1
Find the product.

$$-3s^2t(15s^3t^4)$$

NOW TRY
EXERCISE 2
Find each product.
(a) $3k^3(-2k^5 + 3k^2 - 4)$
(b) $5x(2x - 1)(x + 4)$

OBJECTIVE 1 Multiply terms.

EXAMPLE 1   Multiplying Monomials

Find each product.

(a) $3x^4(5x^3)$

$$= 3 \cdot 5 \cdot x^4 \cdot x^3 \qquad \text{Commutative and associative properties}$$

$$= 15x^{4+3} \qquad \text{Multiply; product rule for exponents}$$

$$= 15x^7 \qquad \text{Add the exponents.}$$

(b) $-4a^3(3a^5)$ **(c)** $2m^2z^4(8m^3z^2)$

$$= -4(3)a^3 \cdot a^5 \qquad\qquad\qquad = 2(8)m^2 \cdot m^3 \cdot z^4 \cdot z^2$$

$$= -12a^8 \qquad\qquad\qquad\qquad = 16m^5z^6 \qquad \text{NOW TRY}$$

OBJECTIVE 2 Multiply any two polynomials.

EXAMPLE 2   Multiplying Polynomials

Find each product.

(a) $-2(8x^3 - 9x^2)$ Be careful with signs.

$$= -2(8x^3) - 2(-9x^2) \qquad \text{Distributive property}$$

$$= -16x^3 + 18x^2 \qquad \text{Multiply.}$$

(b) $5x^2(-4x^2 + 3x - 2)$

$$= 5x^2(-4x^2) + 5x^2(3x) + 5x^2(-2) \qquad \text{Distributive property}$$

$$= -20x^4 + 15x^3 - 10x^2 \qquad \text{Multiply.}$$

(c) $(3x - 4)(2x^2 + x)$ Distributive property; Multiply each term of $2x^2 + x$ by $3x - 4$.

Treat $3x - 4$ as a single expression.

$$= (3x - 4)(2x^2) + (3x - 4)(x)$$

$$= 3x(2x^2) + (-4)(2x^2) + (3x)(x) + (-4)(x)$$
$$\text{Distributive property}$$

$$= 6x^3 - 8x^2 + 3x^2 - 4x \qquad \text{Multiply.}$$

$$= 6x^3 - 5x^2 - 4x \qquad \text{Combine like terms.}$$

(d) $2x^2(x + 1)(x - 3)$

$$= 2x^2[(x + 1)(x) + (x + 1)(-3)] \qquad \text{Distributive property}$$

$$= 2x^2[x^2 + x - 3x - 3] \qquad \text{Distributive property}$$

$$= 2x^2(x^2 - 2x - 3) \qquad \text{Combine like terms.}$$

$$= 2x^4 - 4x^3 - 6x^2 \qquad \text{Distributive property} \qquad \text{NOW TRY}$$

NOW TRY ANSWERS
1. $-45s^5t^5$
2. (a) $-6k^8 + 9k^5 - 12k^3$
    (b) $10x^3 + 35x^2 - 20x$

NOW TRY
EXERCISE 3
Find the product.

$$3t^2 - 5t + 4$$
$$\underline{\qquad t - 3}$$

EXAMPLE 3 Multiplying Polynomials Vertically

Find each product.

(a) $(5a - 2b)(3a + b)$

$$5a \quad - 2b$$
$$\underline{3a \quad + \; b} \qquad \text{Write the factors vertically.}$$
$$5ab - 2b^2 \; \leftarrow \text{Multiply } b(5a - 2b).$$
$$\underline{15a^2 - 6ab} \qquad \leftarrow \text{Multiply } 3a(5a - 2b).$$
$$15a^2 - \; ab - 2b^2 \qquad \text{Combine like terms.}$$

(b) $(3m^3 - 2m^2 + 4)(3m - 5)$

$$3m^3 - 2m^2 + \; 4$$

> Be sure to write like terms in columns.

$$\underline{\qquad\qquad\qquad 3m \; - \; 5}$$
$$-15m^3 + 10m^2 \qquad\quad - 20 \; \leftarrow \text{Multiply } -5(3m^3 - 2m^2 + 4).$$
$$\underline{9m^4 - \; 6m^3 \qquad\qquad + 12m} \qquad \leftarrow \text{Multiply } 3m(3m^3 - 2m^2 + 4).$$
$$9m^4 - 21m^3 + 10m^2 + 12m \; - 20 \qquad \text{Combine like terms.} \quad \textbf{NOW TRY} \; \circlearrowleft$$

NOTE   We can use a rectangle to model polynomial multiplication.

$$(5a - 2b)(3a + b) \qquad \text{See \textbf{Example 3(a)}.}$$

Label a rectangle with each term, as shown below on the left. Then put the product of each pair of monomials in the appropriate box, as shown on the right.

	$3a$	b
$5a$		
$-2b$		

	$3a$	b
$5a$	$15a^2$	$5ab$
$-2b$	$-6ab$	$-2b^2$

$$(5a - 2b)(3a + b)$$
$$= 15a^2 + 5ab - 6ab - 2b^2 \qquad \text{Add the four monomial products.}$$
$$= 15a^2 - ab - 2b^2 \qquad \text{The result is the same as in \textbf{Example 3(a)}.}$$

OBJECTIVE 3 Multiply binomials.

There is a shortcut method for finding the product of two binomials.

$$(3x - 4)(2x + 3)$$
$$= 3x(2x + 3) - 4(2x + 3) \qquad \text{Distributive property}$$
$$= 3x(2x) + 3x(3) - 4(2x) - 4(3) \qquad \text{Distributive property again}$$
$$= 6x^2 + 9x - 8x - 12 \qquad \text{Multiply.}$$

Before combining like terms to find the simplest form of the answer, we check the origin of each of the four terms in the sum

$$6x^2 + 9x - 8x - 12.$$

From the discussion on the preceding page, multiplying

$$(3x - 4)(2x + 3)$$

using the distributive property gave

$$6x^2 + 9x - 8x - 12.$$

The term $6x^2$ is the product of the two *first* terms of the binomials.

$$(3x - 4)(2x + 3) \qquad 3x(2x) = 6x^2 \qquad \text{First terms}$$

To obtain $9x$, the *outer* terms are multiplied.

$$(3x - 4)(2x + 3) \qquad 3x(3) = 9x \qquad \text{Outer terms}$$

The term $-8x$ comes from the *inner* terms.

$$(3x - 4)(2x + 3) \qquad -4(2x) = -8x \qquad \text{Inner terms}$$

Finally, -12 comes from the *last* terms.

$$(3x - 4)(2x + 3) \qquad -4(3) = -12 \qquad \text{Last terms}$$

The product is found by adding these four results.

$$(3x - 4)(2x + 3)$$
$$= 6x^2 + 9x + (-8x) + (-12) \qquad \text{FOIL method}$$
$$= 6x^2 + x - 12 \qquad \text{Combine like terms.}$$

To keep track of the order of multiplying terms, we use the initials FOIL, where the letters refer to the positions of the terms (First, Outer, Inner, Last). The above steps can be done as follows.

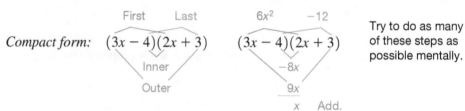

Compact form: First — Last: $(3x - 4)(2x + 3)$ Inner, Outer

$6x^2$ — -12: $(3x - 4)(2x + 3)$ $-8x$, $9x$, x Add.

Try to do as many of these steps as possible mentally.

⚠ **CAUTION**   *The FOIL method applies only to multiplying two binomials.*

EXAMPLE 4 **Using the FOIL Method**

Use the FOIL method to find each product.

(a) $(4m - 5)(3m + 1)$

First terms	$(4m - 5)(3m + 1)$	$4m(3m) = 12m^2$
Outer terms	$(4m - 5)(3m + 1)$	$4m(1) = 4m$
Inner terms	$(4m - 5)(3m + 1)$	$-5(3m) = -15m$
Last terms	$(4m - 5)(3m + 1)$	$-5(1) = -5$

$$(4m - 5)(3m + 1)$$
$$ \quad \text{F} \qquad \text{O} \quad \text{I} \quad \text{L}$$
$$= 12m^2 + 4m - 15m - 5$$
$$= 12m^2 - 11m - 5 \qquad \text{Combine like terms.}$$

NOW TRY EXERCISE 4

Use the FOIL method to find each product.

(a) $(2x + 1)(7x + 2)$

(b) $(3p - k)(5p + 4k)$

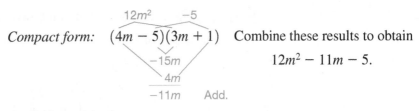

Compact form: $(4m - 5)(3m + 1)$ Combine these results to obtain $12m^2 - 11m - 5$.

$-11m$ Add.

(b) $(5x - 4)(2x - 5)$

    First   Outer   Inner   Last

$= 5x(2x) + 5x(-5) - 4(2x) - 4(-5)$ FOIL method

$= 10x^2 - 25x - 8x + 20$ Multiply.

$= 10x^2 - 33x + 20$ Combine like terms.

(c) $(6a + 5b)(3a - 4b)$

    First   Outer   Inner   Last

$= 18a^2 - 24ab + 15ab - 20b^2$ FOIL method

$= 18a^2 - 9ab - 20b^2$ Combine like terms.

(d) $(2k + 3z)(5k + 3z)$

$= 10k^2 + 6kz + 15kz + 9z^2$ FOIL method

$= 10k^2 + 21kz + 9z^2$ Combine like terms.   NOW TRY

OBJECTIVE 4 Find the product of a sum and difference of two terms.

The product of a sum and difference of the same two terms occurs frequently.

$$(x + y)(x - y)$$
$$= x^2 - xy + xy - y^2 \quad \text{FOIL method}$$
$$= x^2 - y^2 \quad \text{Combine like terms.}$$

> **Product of a Sum and Difference of Two Terms**
>
> The **product of the sum and difference of the two terms** x and y is the difference of the squares of the terms.
> $$(x + y)(x - y) = x^2 - y^2$$

 NOW TRY EXERCISE 5

Find each product.

(a) $(x + 8)(x - 8)$

(b) $(3x - 7y)(3x + 7y)$

(c) $5k(2k - 3)(2k + 3)$

NOW TRY ANSWERS

4. (a) $14x^2 + 11x + 2$
    (b) $15p^2 + 7kp - 4k^2$
5. (a) $x^2 - 64$
    (b) $9x^2 - 49y^2$
    (c) $20k^3 - 45k$

EXAMPLE 5 Multiplying a Sum and Difference of Two Terms

Find each product.

(a) $(p + 7)(p - 7)$

$= p^2 - 7^2$

$= p^2 - 49$

(b) $(2r + 5)(2r - 5)$

$= (2r)^2 - 5^2$

$\boxed{\text{Be careful squaring } 2r.}$ $= 2^2 r^2 - 25$ $(ab)^2 = a^2 b^2$

$= 4r^2 - 25$

(c) $(6m + 5n)(6m - 5n)$

$= (6m)^2 - (5n)^2$

$= 36m^2 - 25n^2$

(d) $2x^3(x + 3)(x - 3)$

$= 2x^3(x^2 - 9)$

$= 2x^5 - 18x^3$ NOW TRY

OBJECTIVE 5 Find the square of a binomial.

To find the square of a binomial sum $x + y$—that is, $(x + y)^2$—multiply $x + y$ by itself.

$$(x + y)^2$$
$$= (x + y)(x + y) \qquad a^2 = a \cdot a$$
$$= x^2 + xy + xy + y^2 \qquad \text{FOIL method}$$
$$= x^2 + 2xy + y^2 \qquad \text{Combine like terms.}$$

A similar result is true for the square of a binomial difference.

Square of a Binomial

The **square of a binomial** is the sum of the square of the first term, twice the product of the two terms, and the square of the last term.

$$(x + y)^2 = x^2 + 2xy + y^2$$
$$(x - y)^2 = x^2 - 2xy + y^2$$

NOW TRY
EXERCISE 6

Find each product.

(a) $(y - 10)^2$

(b) $(4x + 5y)^2$

EXAMPLE 6 Squaring Binomials

Find each product.

(a) $(m + 7)^2$

$$= m^2 + 2 \cdot m \cdot 7 + 7^2 \qquad (x + y)^2 = x^2 + 2xy + y^2$$
$$= m^2 + 14m + 49 \qquad \text{Multiply. Apply the exponent.}$$

(b) $(p - 4)^2$

$$= p^2 - 2 \cdot p \cdot 4 + 4^2 \qquad (x - y)^2 = x^2 - 2xy + y^2$$
$$= p^2 - 8p + 16 \qquad \text{Multiply. Apply the exponent.}$$

(c) $(2p + 3v)^2$

$$= (2p)^2 + 2(2p)(3v) + (3v)^2$$
$$= 4p^2 + 12pv + 9v^2$$

(d) $(3r - 5s)^2$

$$= (3r)^2 - 2(3r)(5s) + (5s)^2$$
$$= 9r^2 - 30rs + 25s^2$$

NOW TRY

> ! **CAUTION** As the products in the formula for the square of a binomial show,
> $$(x + y)^2 \neq x^2 + y^2.$$
> More generally, $\qquad (x + y)^n \neq x^n + y^n \quad$ (where $n \neq 1$).

EXAMPLE 7 Multiplying More Complicated Binomials

Find each product.

(a) $[(3p - 2) + 5q][(3p - 2) - 5q]$

$$= (3p - 2)^2 - (5q)^2 \qquad \text{Product of a sum and difference of terms}$$
$$= 9p^2 - 12p + 4 - 25q^2 \qquad \text{Square both quantities.}$$

(b) $[(2z + r) + 1]^2$

$$= (2z + r)^2 + 2(2z + r)(1) + 1^2 \qquad \text{Square of a binomial}$$
$$= 4z^2 + 4zr + r^2 + 4z + 2r + 1 \qquad \text{Square again; distributive property}$$

NOW TRY ANSWERS

6. (a) $y^2 - 20y + 100$

(b) $16x^2 + 40xy + 25y^2$

**NOW TRY
EXERCISE 7**

Find each product.

(a) $[(4x - y) + 2][(4x - y) - 2]$

(b) $(y - 3)^4$

(c) $(x + y)^3$

This does **not** equal $x^3 + y^3$.

$= (x + y)^2(x + y)$ $a^3 = a^2 \cdot a$

$= (x^2 + 2xy + y^2)(x + y)$ Square $x + y$.

$= x^2(x + y) + 2xy(x + y) + y^2(x + y)$ Distributive property

$= x^3 + x^2y + 2x^2y + 2xy^2 + xy^2 + y^3$ Distributive property

$= x^3 + 3x^2y + 3xy^2 + y^3$ Combine like terms.

(d) $(2a + b)^4$

$= (2a + b)^2(2a + b)^2$ $a^4 = a^2 \cdot a^2$

$= (4a^2 + 4ab + b^2)(4a^2 + 4ab + b^2)$ Square $2a + b$ twice.

$= 4a^2(4a^2 + 4ab + b^2) + 4ab(4a^2 + 4ab + b^2)$ Distributive property

$\quad + b^2(4a^2 + 4ab + b^2)$

$= 16a^4 + 16a^3b + 4a^2b^2 + 16a^3b + 16a^2b^2 + 4ab^3$ Distributive property again

$\quad + 4a^2b^2 + 4ab^3 + b^4$

$= 16a^4 + 32a^3b + 24a^2b^2 + 8ab^3 + b^4$ Combine like terms.

NOW TRY

OBJECTIVE 6 Multiply polynomial functions.

In **Section 4.3,** we added and subtracted functions. Functions can be multiplied.

Multiplying Functions

If $f(x)$ and $g(x)$ define functions, then

$$(fg)(x) = f(x) \cdot g(x).   \text{Product function}$$

The domain of the product function is the intersection of the domains of $f(x)$ and $g(x)$.

! CAUTION Write the product $f(x) \cdot g(x)$ as $(fg)(x)$, **not** $f(g(x))$, which indicates the composition of functions f and g. (See **Section 4.3.**)

EXAMPLE 8 Multiplying Polynomial Functions

For $f(x) = 3x + 4$ and $g(x) = 2x^2 + x$, find $(fg)(x)$ and $(fg)(-1)$.

$(fg)(x)$

This notation indicates function multiplication.

$= f(x) \cdot g(x)$ Use the definition.

$= (3x + 4)(2x^2 + x)$ Substitute.

$= 6x^3 + 3x^2 + 8x^2 + 4x$ FOIL method

$= 6x^3 + 11x^2 + 4x$ Combine like terms.

NOW TRY ANSWERS

7. (a) $16x^2 - 8xy + y^2 - 4$

(b) $y^4 - 12y^3 + 54y^2 - 108y + 81$

NOW TRY
EXERCISE 8
For $f(x) = 3x^2 - 1$
and $g(x) = 8x + 7$,
find $(fg)(x)$ and $(fg)(-2)$.

$(fg)(-1)$

$= 6(-1)^3 + 11(-1)^2 + 4(-1)$

Be careful
with signs. $\quad = -6 + 11 - 4$

$= 1$

$(fg)(x) = 6x^3 + 11x^2 + 4x$

Let $x = -1$ in $(fg)(x)$.

Apply the exponents. Multiply.

Add and subtract.

NOW TRY ANSWER
8. $24x^3 + 21x^2 - 8x - 7; -99$

Another way to find $(fg)(-1)$ is to find $f(-1)$ and $g(-1)$ and multiply the results. Verify that $f(-1) \cdot g(-1) = 1$. This follows from the definition. **NOW TRY**

4.4 Exercises

FOR
EXTRA
HELP

▶ MyMathLab®

▶ Complete solution available
in MyMathLab

Concept Check Match each product in Column I with the correct polynomial in Column II.

I
1. $(2x - 5)(3x + 4)$
2. $(2x + 5)(3x + 4)$
3. $(2x - 5)(3x - 4)$
4. $(2x + 5)(3x - 4)$

II
A. $6x^2 + 23x + 20$
B. $6x^2 + 7x - 20$
C. $6x^2 - 7x - 20$
D. $6x^2 - 23x + 20$

Find each product. **See Examples 1–3.**

 5. $-8m^3(3m^2)$ 6. $-4p^2(5p^4)$ 7. $14x^2y^3(-2x^5y)$ 8. $5m^3n^4(-4m^2n^5)$

9. $3x(-2x + 5)$ 10. $5y(-6y + 1)$ 11. $-q^3(2 + 3q)$ 12. $-3a^4(4 + a)$

13. $6k^2(3k^2 + 2k + 1)$ 14. $5r^3(2r^2 + 3r + 4)$ 15. $(2t + 3)(3t^2 - 4t - 1)$

16. $(4z + 2)(z^2 - 3z - 5)$ 17. $m(m + 5)(m - 8)$ 18. $p(p + 4)(p - 6)$

19. $4z(2z + 1)(3z - 4)$ 20. $2y(2y + 1)(8y - 3)$ 21. $4x^3(x - 3)(x + 2)$

22. $2y^5(y - 8)(y + 2)$ ▶ 23. $(2y + 3)(3y - 4)$ 24. $(2m + 6)(5m - 3)$

25. $\begin{array}{r} 5m - 3n \\ \underline{5m + 3n} \end{array}$ 26. $\begin{array}{r} 2k + 6q \\ \underline{2k - 6q} \end{array}$ 27. $\begin{array}{r} -b^2 + 3b + 3 \\ \underline{2b + 4} \end{array}$

28. $\begin{array}{r} -r^2 - 4r + 8 \\ \underline{3r - 2} \end{array}$ 29. $\begin{array}{r} 2z^3 - 5z^2 + 8z - 1 \\ \underline{4z + 3} \end{array}$ 30. $\begin{array}{r} 3z^4 - 2z^3 + \ z - 5 \\ \underline{2z - 5} \end{array}$

31. $\begin{array}{r} 2p^2 + 3p + 6 \\ \underline{3p^2 - 4p - 1} \end{array}$ 32. $\begin{array}{r} 5y^2 - 2y + 4 \\ \underline{2y^2 + \ y + 3} \end{array}$

Use the FOIL method to find each product. **See Example 4.**

33. $(m + 5)(m - 8)$ 34. $(p + 4)(p - 6)$ ▶ 35. $(4k + 3)(3k - 2)$

36. $(5w + 2)(2w - 5)$ 37. $(3x - 2)(5x - 1)$ 38. $(4x - 1)(6x - 7)$

39. $(5x + 2y)(4x + 3y)$ 40. $(3x + 4y)(2x + 3y)$ 41. $(z - w)(3z + 4w)$

42. $(s - t)(2s + 5t)$ 43. $(6c - d)(2c + 3d)$ 44. $(2m - n)(3m + 5n)$

Find each product. **See Example 5.**

45. $(x + 9)(x - 9)$ 46. $(z + 6)(z - 6)$ ▶ 47. $(2p - 3)(2p + 3)$

48. $(3x - 8)(3x + 8)$ 49. $(5m - 1)(5m + 1)$ 50. $(6y - 3)(6y + 3)$

51. $(3a + 2c)(3a - 2c)$ **52.** $(5r + 4s)(5r - 4s)$ **53.** $(4m + 7n^2)(4m - 7n^2)$

54. $(2k^2 + 6h)(2k^2 - 6h)$ **55.** $3y(5y^3 + 2)(5y^3 - 2)$ **56.** $4x(3x^3 + 4)(3x^3 - 4)$

Find each product. ***See Example 6.***

▶ **57.** $(y - 5)^2$ **58.** $(a - 3)^2$ **59.** $(x + 1)^2$ **60.** $(t + 2)^2$

61. $(2p + 7)^2$ **62.** $(3z + 8)^2$ **63.** $(4n - 3m)^2$ **64.** $(5r - 7s)^2$

Extending Skills   *The factors in the following exercises involve fractions or decimals. Apply the methods of this section, and find each product.*

65. $\left(k - \dfrac{5}{7}p\right)^2$ **66.** $\left(q - \dfrac{3}{4}r\right)^2$ **67.** $(0.2x - 1.4y)^2$

68. $(0.3x - 1.6y)^2$ **69.** $\left(4x - \dfrac{2}{3}\right)\left(4x + \dfrac{2}{3}\right)$ **70.** $\left(3t - \dfrac{5}{4}\right)\left(3t + \dfrac{5}{4}\right)$

71. $(0.2x + 1.3)(0.5x - 0.1)$ **72.** $(0.1y + 2.1)(0.5y - 0.4)$

73. $\left(3w + \dfrac{1}{4}z\right)(w - 2z)$ **74.** $\left(5r + \dfrac{2}{3}y\right)(r - 5y)$

Find each product. ***See Example 7.***

▶ **75.** $[(5x + 1) + 6y]^2$ **76.** $[(3m - 2) + p]^2$

77. $[(2a + b) - 3]^2$ **78.** $[(4k + h) - 4]^2$

79. $[(2a + b) - 3][(2a + b) + 3]$ **80.** $[(m + p) - 5][(m + p) + 5]$

81. $[(2h - k) + j][(2h - k) - j]$ **82.** $[(3m - y) + z][(3m - y) - z]$

83. $(y + 2)^3$ **84.** $(z - 3)^3$ **85.** $(5r - s)^3$

86. $(x + 3y)^3$ **87.** $(q - 2)^4$ **88.** $(r + 3)^4$

Extending Skills   *Find each product.*

89. $(2a + b)(3a^2 + 2ab + b^2)$ **90.** $(m - 5p)(m^2 - 2mp + 3p^2)$

91. $(4z - x)(z^3 - 4z^2x + 2zx^2 - x^3)$ **92.** $(3r + 2s)(r^3 + 2r^2s - rs^2 + 2s^3)$

93. $(m^2 - 2mp + p^2)(m^2 + 2mp - p^2)$ **94.** $(3 + x + y)(-3 + x - y)$

95. $ab(a + b)(a + 2b)(a - 3b)$ **96.** $mp(m - p)(m - 2p)(2m + p)$

In Exercises 97–100, two expressions are given. Replace x with 3 and y with 4 to show that, in general, the two expressions are not equivalent.

97. $(x + y)^2$; $x^2 + y^2$ **98.** $(x + y)^3$; $x^3 + y^3$

99. $(x + y)^4$; $x^4 + y^4$ **100.** $(x + y)^5$; $x^5 + y^5$

Find the area of each figure. Express it as a polynomial in descending powers of the variable x. Refer to the formulas given inside the back cover of this book if necessary.

101.

102.

103.

104.

For each pair of functions, find $(fg)(x)$. **See Example 8.**

105. $f(x) = 2x$, $g(x) = 5x - 1$ **106.** $f(x) = 3x$, $g(x) = 6x - 8$

107. $f(x) = x + 1$, $g(x) = 2x - 3$ **108.** $f(x) = x - 7$, $g(x) = 4x + 5$

109. $f(x) = 2x - 3$, $g(x) = 4x^2 + 6x + 9$

110. $f(x) = 3x + 4$, $g(x) = 9x^2 - 12x + 16$

Let $f(x) = x^2 - 9$, $g(x) = 2x$, and $h(x) = x - 3$. Find each of the following. **See Example 8.**

▶ **111.** $(fg)(x)$ **112.** $(fh)(x)$ **113.** $(fg)(2)$

114. $(fh)(1)$ **115.** $(gh)(x)$ **116.** $(fh)(-1)$

117. $(gh)(-3)$ **118.** $(fg)(-2)$ **119.** $(fg)\left(-\dfrac{1}{2}\right)$

120. $(fg)\left(-\dfrac{1}{3}\right)$ **121.** $(fh)\left(-\dfrac{1}{4}\right)$ **122.** $(fh)\left(-\dfrac{1}{5}\right)$

RELATING CONCEPTS   For Individual or Group Work (Exercises 123–130)

Consider the figure. **Work Exercises 123–130 in order.**

123. What is the length of each side of the blue square in terms of a and b?

124. What is the formula for the area of a square? Use the formula to write an expression, in the form of a product, for the area of the blue square.

125. Each green rectangle has an area of _____. Therefore, the total area in green is represented by the polynomial _____.

126. The yellow square has an area of _____.

127. The area of the entire colored region is represented by _____, because each side of the entire colored region has length _____.

128. The area of the blue square is equal to the area of the entire colored region, minus the total area of the green squares, minus the area of the yellow square. Write this as a simplified polynomial in a and b.

129. (a) What must be true about the expressions for the area of the blue square found in **Exercises 124 and 128?**

(b) Write an equation based on the answer in part (a).

130. Draw a figure and give a similar proof for $(a + b)^2 = a^2 + 2ab + b^2$.

4.5 Dividing Polynomials

OBJECTIVES

1. Divide a polynomial by a monomial.
2. Divide a polynomial by a polynomial of two or more terms.
3. Divide polynomial functions.

OBJECTIVE 1 Divide a polynomial by a monomial.

Recall that a monomial is a single term, such as 3, $5m^2$, or x^2y^2.

> **Dividing a Polynomial by a Monomial**
>
> To divide a polynomial by a monomial, divide each term of the polynomial by the monomial.
>
> $$\frac{a+b}{c} = \frac{a}{c} + \frac{b}{c} \quad (\text{where } c \neq 0)$$
>
> Then write each quotient in lowest terms.

NOW TRY EXERCISE 1

Divide.

(a) $\dfrac{16x^3 - 8x^2 - 4}{4}$

(b) $\dfrac{81y^4 - 54y^3 + 18y}{9y^3}$

EXAMPLE 1 Dividing Polynomials by Monomials

Divide.

(a) $\dfrac{15x^2 - 12x + 3}{3}$ ⟵ Do **not** divide out the 3's.

$= \dfrac{15x^2}{3} - \dfrac{12x}{3} + \dfrac{3}{3}$ Divide *each* term by 3.

$= 5x^2 - 4x + 1$ Write in lowest terms.

CHECK $3\underbrace{(5x^2 - 4x + 1)}_{\text{Quotient}} = \underbrace{15x^2 - 12x + 3}_{\text{Original polynomial (Dividend)}}$ ✓

Divisor   Quotient   Original polynomial (Dividend)

(b) $\dfrac{5m^3 - 9m^2 + 10m}{5m^2}$ Think: $\frac{10m}{5m^2} = \frac{10}{5}m^{1-2} = 2m^{-1} = \frac{2}{m}$

$= \dfrac{5m^3}{5m^2} - \dfrac{9m^2}{5m^2} + \dfrac{10m}{5m^2}$ Divide each term by $5m^2$.

$= m - \dfrac{9}{5} + \dfrac{2}{m}$ Simplify each term. Use the quotient rule for exponents.

CHECK $5m^2\left(m - \dfrac{9}{5} + \dfrac{2}{m}\right) = 5m^3 - 9m^2 + 10m$ ✓   Divisor × Quotient = Original polynomial

The result $m - \dfrac{9}{5} + \dfrac{2}{m}$ is not a polynomial because the last term has a variable in its denominator. The quotient of two polynomials need not be a polynomial.

(c) $\dfrac{8xy^2 - 9x^2y + 6x^2y^2}{x^2y^2}$

$= \dfrac{8xy^2}{x^2y^2} - \dfrac{9x^2y}{x^2y^2} + \dfrac{6x^2y^2}{x^2y^2}$ Divide each term by x^2y^2.

$= \dfrac{8}{x} - \dfrac{9}{y} + 6$ $\dfrac{a^m}{a^n} = a^{m-n}$ **NOW TRY**

NOW TRY ANSWERS

1. (a) $4x^3 - 2x^2 - 1$

(b) $9y - 6 + \dfrac{2}{y^2}$

NOW TRY
EXERCISE 2

Divide.

$$\frac{3x^2 - 4x - 15}{x - 3}$$

OBJECTIVE 2 Divide a polynomial by a polynomial of two or more terms.

This process is similar to that for dividing whole numbers.

EXAMPLE 2   Dividing a Polynomial by a Polynomial

Divide $\dfrac{2x^2 + x - 10}{x - 2}$.

Make sure each polynomial is written in descending powers of the variables.

$$x - 2 \overline{)2x^2 + x - 10} \quad \text{← Write as if dividing whole numbers.}$$

Divide the first term of the dividend $2x^2 + x - 10$ by the first term of the divisor $x - 2$. Here $\dfrac{2x^2}{x} = 2x$.

$$
\begin{array}{r}
2x \quad \text{← Result of } \frac{2x^2}{x} \\
x - 2 \overline{)2x^2 + x - 10}
\end{array}
$$

Multiply $x - 2$ and $2x$, and write the result below $2x^2 + x - 10$.

$$
\begin{array}{r}
2x \\
x - 2 \overline{)2x^2 + \;\; x - 10} \\
\underline{2x^2 - 4x} \quad \text{← } 2x(x - 2) = 2x^2 - 4x
\end{array}
$$

Now subtract by mentally changing the signs on $2x^2 - 4x$ and *adding*.

To subtract, add
the opposite.
$$2x^2 + x$$
$$\oplus \ominus 2x^2 \oplus 4x$$

$$
\begin{array}{r}
2x \\
x - 2 \overline{)2x^2 + \;\; x - 10} \\
\underline{2x^2 - 4x} \\
5x \quad \text{← Subtract. The difference is } 5x.
\end{array}
$$

Bring down -10 and continue by dividing $5x$ by x.

$$
\begin{array}{r}
2x + \;\; 5 \quad \text{← } \frac{5x}{x} = 5 \\
x - 2 \overline{)2x^2 + \;\; x - 10} \\
\underline{2x^2 - 4x} \\
5x - 10 \quad \text{← Bring down } -10. \\
\underline{5x - 10} \quad \text{← } 5(x - 2) = 5x - 10 \\
0 \quad \text{← Subtract. The difference is 0.}
\end{array}
$$

Think:
$$5x - 10$$
$$\oplus \ominus 5x \oplus 10$$

CHECK   Multiply $x - 2$ (the divisor) and $2x + 5$ (the quotient).

$$(x - 2)(2x + 5)$$

$$= 2x^2 + 5x - 4x - 10 \qquad \text{FOIL method}$$

$$= 2x^2 + x - 10 \qquad \text{Combine like terms.}$$

The result is $2x^2 + x - 10$ (the dividend). ✓

NOW TRY

⊘ CAUTION   Remember to do the following when dividing a polynomial by a polynomial of two or more terms.

1. Be sure the terms in both polynomials are written in descending powers.

2. Write any missing terms with 0 placeholders.

NOW TRY ANSWER
2. $3x + 5$

NOW TRY
EXERCISE 3

Divide

$2x^3 - 12x - 10$ by $x - 4$.

EXAMPLE 3   Dividing a Polynomial with a Missing Term

Divide $3x^3 - 2x + 5$ by $x - 3$.

Add a term with 0 coefficient as a placeholder for the missing x^2-term.

$$x - 3 \overline{)3x^3 + 0x^2 - 2x + 5}$$

← Missing term

← Descending powers of the variable

Start with $\dfrac{3x^3}{x} = 3x^2$.

$$
\begin{array}{r}
3x^2 \\
x - 3 \overline{)3x^3 + 0x^2 - 2x + 5} \\
\underline{3x^3 - 9x^2}
\end{array}
$$

← $\dfrac{3x^3}{x} = 3x^2$

← $3x^2(x - 3)$

Subtract by mentally changing the signs on $3x^3 - 9x^2$ and adding.

$$
\begin{array}{r}
3x^2 \\
x - 3 \overline{)3x^3 + 0x^2 - 2x + 5} \\
\underline{3x^3 - 9x^2} \\
9x^2
\end{array}
$$

Add the opposite.

← Subtract.

Bring down the next term.

$$
\begin{array}{r}
3x^2 \\
x - 3 \overline{)3x^3 + 0x^2 - 2x + 5} \\
\underline{3x^3 - 9x^2} \\
9x^2 - 2x
\end{array}
$$

← Bring down $-2x$.

In the next step, $\dfrac{9x^2}{x} = 9x$.

$$
\begin{array}{r}
3x^2 + 9x \\
x - 3 \overline{)3x^3 + 0x^2 - 2x + 5} \\
\underline{3x^3 - 9x^2} \\
9x^2 - 2x \\
\underline{9x^2 - 27x} \\
25x + 5
\end{array}
$$

← $\dfrac{9x^2}{x} = 9x$

Add the opposite.

← $9x(x - 3)$

← Subtract. Bring down 5.

Finally, $\dfrac{25x}{x} = 25$.

$$
\begin{array}{r}
3x^2 + 9x + 25 \\
x - 3 \overline{)3x^3 + 0x^2 - 2x + 5} \\
\underline{3x^3 - 9x^2} \\
9x^2 - 2x \\
\underline{9x^2 - 27x} \\
25x + 5 \\
\underline{25x - 75} \\
80
\end{array}
$$

← $\dfrac{25x}{x} = 25$

Add the opposite.

← $25(x - 3)$

← Remainder

Write the remainder, 80, as the numerator of a fraction, $\dfrac{80}{x - 3}$.

$$3x^2 + 9x + 25 + \dfrac{80}{x - 3}$$

Be sure to add $\dfrac{\text{remainder}}{\text{divisor}}$.
Don't forget the + sign.

NOW TRY ANSWER
3. $2x^2 + 8x + 20 + \dfrac{70}{x - 4}$

CHECK   Multiply $x - 3$ (the divisor) and $3x^2 + 9x + 25$ (the quotient), and then add 80 (the remainder). The result is $3x^3 - 2x + 5$ (the dividend). ✓   NOW TRY

**NOW TRY
EXERCISE 4**
Divide
$$2x^4 + 8x^3 + 2x^2 - 5x - 3$$
by $2x^2 - 2$.

EXAMPLE 4   **Dividing by a Polynomial with a Missing Term**

Divide $6r^4 + 9r^3 + 2r^2 - 8r + 7$ by $3r^2 - 2$.

$$
\begin{array}{r}
2r^2 + 3r + \;\;2 \\
3r^2 + 0r - 2\overline{)\,6r^4 + 9r^3 + 2r^2 - 8r + \;\;7} \\
\underline{6r^4 + 0r^3 - 4r^2} \\
9r^3 + 6r^2 - 8r \\
\underline{9r^3 + 0r^2 - 6r} \\
6r^2 - 2r + \;\;7 \\
\underline{6r^2 + 0r - \;\;4} \\
-2r + 11
\end{array}
$$

Missing term ↑

Stop when the degree of the remainder is less than the degree of the divisor.

$-2r + 11$ ← Remainder

The degree of the remainder, $-2r + 11$, is less than the degree of the divisor, $3r^2 - 2$, so the division process is finished. The result is written as follows.

$$2r^2 + 3r + 2 + \frac{-2r + 11}{3r^2 - 2}$$

Quotient + $\dfrac{\text{remainder}}{\text{divisor}}$ **NOW TRY**

**NOW TRY
EXERCISE 5**
Divide
$$6m^3 - 8m^2 - 5m - 6$$
by $3m - 6$.

EXAMPLE 5   **Finding a Quotient with a Fractional Coefficient**

Divide $2p^3 + 5p^2 + p - 2$ by $2p + 2$.

$$\frac{3p^2}{2p} = \frac{3}{2}p$$

$$
\begin{array}{r}
p^2 + \frac{3}{2}p - 1 \\
2p + 2\overline{)\,2p^3 + 5p^2 + \;\;p - 2} \\
\underline{2p^3 + 2p^2} \\
3p^2 + \;\;p \\
\underline{3p^2 + 3p} \\
-2p - 2 \\
\underline{-2p - 2} \\
0
\end{array}
$$

The remainder is 0, so the quotient is $p^2 + \frac{3}{2}p - 1$.   **NOW TRY**

OBJECTIVE 3   Divide polynomial functions.

Dividing Functions

If $f(x)$ and $g(x)$ define functions, then

$$\left(\frac{f}{g}\right)(x) = \frac{f(x)}{g(x)}.$$ Quotient function

The domain of the quotient function is the intersection of the domains of $f(x)$ and $g(x)$, excluding any values of x for which $g(x) = 0$.

NOW TRY ANSWERS
4. $x^2 + 4x + 2 + \dfrac{3x + 1}{2x^2 - 2}$

5. $2m^2 + \dfrac{4}{3}m + 1$

EXAMPLE 6   **Dividing Polynomial Functions**

For $f(x) = 2x^2 + x - 10$ and $g(x) = x - 2$, find $\left(\frac{f}{g}\right)(x)$ and $\left(\frac{f}{g}\right)(-3)$.

$$\left(\frac{f}{g}\right)(x) = \frac{f(x)}{g(x)} = \frac{2x^2 + x - 10}{x - 2}$$

NOW TRY
EXERCISE 6

For $f(x) = 8x^2 + 2x - 3$
and $g(x) = 2x - 1$,

find $\left(\frac{f}{g}\right)(x)$ and $\left(\frac{f}{g}\right)(8)$.

NOW TRY ANSWER

6. $4x + 3$, $x \neq \frac{1}{2}$; 35

This quotient, found in **Example 2**, is $2x + 5$. Thus,

$$\left(\frac{f}{g}\right)(x) = 2x + 5, \quad x \neq 2. \leftarrow \begin{array}{l} \text{2 is not in the domain.} \\ \text{It causes denominator} \\ g(x) = x - 2 \text{ to equal 0.} \end{array}$$

$$\left(\frac{f}{g}\right)(-3) = 2(-3) + 5 = -1 \quad \text{Let } x = -3 \text{ in } \left(\frac{f}{g}\right)(x) = 2x + 5.$$

Verify that the same value is found by evaluating $\frac{f(-3)}{g(-3)}$.

NOW TRY

4.5 Exercises

FOR
EXTRA
HELP

▶ MyMathLab®

● *Complete solution available
in MyMathLab*

Concept Check   *Complete each statement.*

1. We find the quotient of two monomials using the _____ rule for _____.

2. When dividing polynomials that are not monomials, first write them in _____ powers.

3. If a polynomial in a division problem has a missing term, insert a term with coefficient equal to _____ as a placeholder.

4. To check a division problem, multiply the _____ by the quotient. Then add the _____.

Divide. See Example 1.

5. $\dfrac{15x^3 - 10x^2 + 5}{5}$

6. $\dfrac{27m^4 - 18m^3 - 9}{9}$

7. $\dfrac{9y^2 + 12y - 15}{3y}$

8. $\dfrac{80r^2 - 40r + 10}{10r}$

9. $\dfrac{15m^3 + 25m^2 + 30m}{5m^3}$

10. $\dfrac{64x^3 - 72x^2 + 12x}{8x^3}$

11. $\dfrac{4m^2n^2 - 21mn^3 + 18mn^2}{14m^2n^3}$

12. $\dfrac{24h^2k + 56hk^2 - 28hk}{16h^2k^2}$

13. $\dfrac{8wxy^2 + 3wx^2y + 12w^2xy}{4wx^2y}$

14. $\dfrac{12ab^2c + 10a^2bc + 18abc^2}{6a^2bc}$

Complete the division. See Example 2.

15.
$$\begin{array}{r} r^2 \\ 3r - 1\overline{)3r^3 - 22r^2 + 25r - 6} \\ \underline{3r^3 - r^2} \\ -21r^2 \end{array}$$

16.
$$\begin{array}{r} 3b^2 \\ 2b - 5\overline{)6b^3 - 7b^2 - 4b - 40} \\ \underline{6b^3 - 15b^2} \\ 8b^2 \end{array}$$

Divide. See Examples 2–5.

17. $\dfrac{y^2 + y - 20}{y + 5}$

18. $\dfrac{y^2 + 3y - 18}{y + 6}$

19. $\dfrac{q^2 + 4q - 32}{q - 4}$

20. $\dfrac{q^2 + 2q - 35}{q - 5}$

21. $\dfrac{3t^2 + 17t + 10}{3t + 2}$

22. $\dfrac{2k^2 - 3k - 20}{2k + 5}$

23. $\dfrac{p^2 + 2p + 20}{p + 6}$

24. $\dfrac{x^2 + 11x + 16}{x + 8}$

25. $\dfrac{3m^3 + 5m^2 - 5m + 1}{3m - 1}$

26. $\dfrac{8z^3 - 6z^2 - 5z + 3}{4z + 3}$

27. $\dfrac{m^3 - 2m^2 - 9}{m - 3}$

28. $\dfrac{p^3 + 3p^2 - 4}{p + 2}$

29. $(4x^3 + 9x^2 - 10x + 3) \div (4x + 1)$

30. $(10z^3 - 26z^2 + 17z - 13) \div (5z - 3)$

31. $\dfrac{6x^3 - 19x^2 + 14x - 15}{3x^2 - 2x + 4}$

32. $\dfrac{8m^3 - 18m^2 + 37m - 13}{2m^2 - 3m + 6}$

33. $(x^3 + 2x - 3) \div (x - 1)$

34. $(x^3 + 5x^2 - 18) \div (x + 3)$

35. $(2x^3 - 11x^2 + 25) \div (x - 5)$

36. $(2x^3 + 3x^2 - 5) \div (x - 1)$

⊙ **37.** $(3x^3 - x + 4) \div (x - 2)$

38. $(3k^3 + 9k - 14) \div (k - 2)$

39. $\dfrac{4k^4 + 6k^3 + 3k - 1}{2k^2 + 1}$

40. $\dfrac{9k^4 + 12k^3 - 4k - 1}{3k^2 - 1}$

41. $(2z^3 - 5z^2 + 6z - 15) \div (2z - 5)$

42. $(3p^3 + p^2 + 18p + 6) \div (3p + 1)$

43. $\dfrac{6y^4 + 4y^3 + 4y - 6}{3y^2 + 2y - 3}$

44. $\dfrac{8t^4 + 6t^3 + 12t - 32}{4t^2 + 3t - 8}$

45. $\dfrac{p^3 - 1}{p - 1}$

46. $\dfrac{8a^3 + 1}{2a + 1}$

⊙ **47.** $(x^4 - 4x^3 + 5x^2 - 3x + 2) \div (x^2 + 3)$

48. $(3t^4 + 5t^3 - 8t^2 - 13t + 2) \div (t^2 - 5)$

⊙ **49.** $(2p^3 + 7p^2 + 9p + 3) \div (2p + 2)$

50. $(3x^3 + 4x^2 + 7x + 4) \div (3x + 3)$

51. $(3a^2 - 11a + 17) \div (2a + 6)$

52. $(5t^2 + 19t + 7) \div (4t + 12)$

Extending Skills   *Divide.*

53. $\left(2x^2 - \dfrac{7}{3}x - 1\right) \div (3x + 1)$

54. $\left(m^2 + \dfrac{7}{2}m + 3\right) \div (2m + 3)$

55. $\left(3a^2 - \dfrac{23}{4}a - 5\right) \div (4a + 3)$

56. $\left(3q^2 + \dfrac{19}{5}q - 3\right) \div (5q - 2)$

Solve each problem.

57. Suppose that the volume of a box is

$$(2p^3 + 15p^2 + 28p) \text{ cubic feet.}$$

The height is p feet and the length is $(p + 4)$ feet. Find an expression in p that represents the width.

58. Suppose that a minivan travels

$$(2m^3 + 15m^2 + 35m + 36) \text{ miles}$$

in $(2m + 9)$ hours. Find an expression in m that represents the rate of the van in mph.

59. For $P(x) = x^3 - 4x^2 + 3x - 5$, find $P(-1)$. Then divide $P(x)$ by $D(x) = x + 1$. Compare the remainder with $P(-1)$. What do these results suggest?

60. *Concept Check*   Let $P(x) = 4x^3 - 8x^2 + 13x - 2$ and $D(x) = 2x - 1$. Use division to find polynomials $Q(x)$ and $R(x)$ such that

$$P(x) = Q(x) \cdot D(x) + R(x).$$

*For each pair of functions, find $\left(\dfrac{f}{g}\right)(x)$ and give any x-values that are not in the domain of the quotient function. **See Example 6.***

61. $f(x) = 10x^2 - 2x$, $g(x) = 2x$

62. $f(x) = 18x^2 - 24x$, $g(x) = 3x$

63. $f(x) = 2x^2 - x - 3$, $g(x) = x + 1$

64. $f(x) = 4x^2 - 23x - 35$, $g(x) = x - 7$

65. $f(x) = 8x^3 - 27$, $g(x) = 2x - 3$

66. $f(x) = 27x^3 + 64$, $g(x) = 3x + 4$

*Let $f(x) = x^2 - 9$, $g(x) = 2x$, and $h(x) = x - 3$. Find each of the following. **See Example 6.***

▶ **67.** $\left(\dfrac{f}{g}\right)(x)$ **68.** $\left(\dfrac{f}{h}\right)(x)$ **69.** $\left(\dfrac{f}{g}\right)(2)$ **70.** $\left(\dfrac{f}{h}\right)(1)$

71. $\left(\dfrac{h}{g}\right)(x)$ **72.** $\left(\dfrac{g}{h}\right)(x)$ **73.** $\left(\dfrac{h}{g}\right)(3)$ **74.** $\left(\dfrac{g}{h}\right)(-1)$

75. $\left(\dfrac{f}{g}\right)\left(\dfrac{1}{2}\right)$ **76.** $\left(\dfrac{f}{g}\right)\left(\dfrac{3}{2}\right)$ **77.** $\left(\dfrac{h}{g}\right)\left(-\dfrac{1}{2}\right)$ **78.** $\left(\dfrac{h}{g}\right)\left(-\dfrac{3}{2}\right)$

Chapter 4   Summary

Key Terms

4.1
exponent (power)
base
exponential expression

4.2
term
algebraic expression

polynomial
numerical coefficient
  (coefficient)
degree of a term
polynomial in x
descending powers
leading term
leading coefficient

trinomial
binomial
monomial
degree of a polynomial
like terms
negative of a polynomial

4.3
polynomial function
composite function
  (composition of functions)
identity function
squaring function
cubing function

New Symbols

$(f \circ g)(x) = f(g(x))$ composite function

Test Your Word Power

See how well you have learned the vocabulary in this chapter.

1. A **polynomial** is an algebraic expression made up of
  A. a term or a finite product of terms with positive coefficients and exponents
  B. the sum of two or more terms with whole number coefficients and exponents
  C. the product of two or more terms
  D. a term or a finite sum of terms with real number coefficients and whole number exponents.

2. A **monomial** is a polynomial with
  A. only one term
  B. exactly two terms
  C. exactly three terms
  D. more than three terms.

3. A **binomial** is a polynomial with
  A. only one term
  B. exactly two terms
  C. exactly three terms
  D. more than three terms.

4. A **trinomial** is a polynomial with
  A. only one term
  B. exactly two terms
  C. exactly three terms
  D. more than three terms.

5. The **FOIL** method is used to
  A. add two binomials
  B. add two trinomials
  C. multiply two binomials
  D. multiply two trinomials.

ANSWERS

1. D; *Example:* $5x^3 + 2x^2 - 7$ **2.** A; *Examples:* $-4, 2x^3, 15a^2b$ **3.** B; *Example:* $3t^3 + 5t$ **4.** C; *Example:* $2a^2 - 3ab + b^2$

5. C; *Example:* $(m + 4)(m - 3) = m(m) - 3m + 4m + 4(-3) = m^2 + m - 12$

     F   O   I   L

Quick Review

CONCEPTS   **EXAMPLES**

4.1 Integer Exponents and Scientific Notation

Definitions and Rules for Exponents

For all integers m and n and all real numbers a and b, the following hold.

Apply the rules for exponents.

Product Rule $a^m \cdot a^n = a^{m+n}$

$$3^4 \cdot 3^2 = 3^6$$

Quotient Rule $\dfrac{a^m}{a^n} = a^{m-n}$ $(a \neq 0)$

$$\frac{2^5}{2^3} = 2^2$$

Zero Exponent $a^0 = 1$ $(a \neq 0)$

$$27^0 = 1, \quad (-5)^0 = 1$$

Negative Exponent $a^{-n} = \dfrac{1}{a^n}$ $(a \neq 0)$

$$5^{-2} = \frac{1}{5^2}$$

Power Rules   (a) $(a^m)^n = a^{mn}$ (b) $(ab)^m = a^m b^m$

$$(6^3)^4 = 6^{12}, \quad (5p)^4 = 5^4 p^4$$

(c) $\left(\dfrac{a}{b}\right)^n = \dfrac{a^n}{b^n}$ $(b \neq 0)$

$$\left(\frac{2}{3}\right)^5 = \frac{2^5}{3^5}$$

Special Rules for Negative Exponents

$\dfrac{1}{a^{-n}} = a^n$ $(a \neq 0)$ $\dfrac{a^{-n}}{b^{-m}} = \dfrac{b^m}{a^n}$ $(a, b \neq 0)$

$a^{-n} = \left(\dfrac{1}{a}\right)^n$ $(a \neq 0)$ $\left(\dfrac{a}{b}\right)^{-n} = \left(\dfrac{b}{a}\right)^n$ $(a, b \neq 0)$

$$\frac{1}{3^{-2}} = 3^2, \qquad \frac{5^{-3}}{4^{-6}} = \frac{4^6}{5^3}$$

$$4^{-3} = \left(\frac{1}{4}\right)^3, \quad \left(\frac{4}{7}\right)^{-2} = \left(\frac{7}{4}\right)^2$$

Scientific Notation

A number is written in scientific notation when it is expressed in the form

$$a \times 10^n,$$

where $1 \leq |a| < 10$ and n is an integer.

Write 23,500,000,000 in scientific notation.

$$23{,}500{,}000{,}000 = 2.35 \times 10^{10}$$

Write 4.3×10^{-6} in standard notation.

$$4.3 \times 10^{-6} = 0.0000043$$

4.2 Adding and Subtracting Polynomials

Add or subtract polynomials by combining like terms.

Subtract. $(5x^4 + 3x^2) - (7x^4 + x^2 - x)$

$$= 5x^4 + 3x^2 - 7x^4 - x^2 + x$$

$$= -2x^4 + 2x^2 + x$$

4.3 Polynomial Functions, Graphs, and Composition

Adding and Subtracting Functions

If $f(x)$ and $g(x)$ define functions, then

$$(f + g)(x) = f(x) + g(x)$$

and $(f - g)(x) = f(x) - g(x).$

Let $f(x) = x^2$ and $g(x) = 2x + 1$. Find $(f + g)(x)$ and $(f - g)(x)$.

$(f + g)(x)$ $\qquad\qquad$ $(f - g)(x)$

$= f(x) + g(x)$ $\qquad$ $= f(x) - g(x)$

$= x^2 + 2x + 1$ $\qquad$ $= x^2 - (2x + 1)$

$\qquad\qquad\qquad\qquad = x^2 - 2x - 1$

Composition of f and g

$$(f \circ g)(x) = f(g(x))$$

$$(g \circ f)(x) = g(f(x))$$

Let $f(x) = x^2$ and $g(x) = 2x + 1$. Find $(f \circ g)(x)$ and $(g \circ f)(x)$.

$(f \circ g)(x) = f(g(x))$ $\qquad$ $(g \circ f)(x) = g(f(x))$

$= f(2x + 1)$ $\qquad\qquad$ $= g(x^2)$

$= (2x + 1)^2$ $\qquad\qquad$ $= 2x^2 + 1$

CONCEPTS | **EXAMPLES**

Graphs of Basic Polynomial Functions

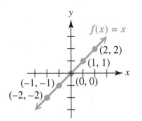

Identity function
$f(x) = x$
Domain: $(-\infty, \infty)$
Range: $(-\infty, \infty)$

Squaring function
$f(x) = x^2$
Domain: $(-\infty, \infty)$
Range: $[0, \infty)$

Cubing function
$f(x) = x^3$
Domain: $(-\infty, \infty)$
Range: $(-\infty, \infty)$

4.4 Multiplying Polynomials

To multiply two polynomials, multiply each term of one by each term of the other.

Multiply.

$$(x^3 + 3x)(4x^2 - 5x + 2)$$
$$= x^3(4x^2 - 5x + 2) + 3x(4x^2 - 5x - 2)$$
$$= 4x^5 - 5x^4 + 2x^3 + 12x^3 - 15x^2 - 6x$$
$$= 4x^5 - 5x^4 + 14x^3 - 15x^2 + 6x$$

To multiply two binomials, use the **FOIL method.** Multiply the **First** terms, the **Outer** terms, the **Inner** terms, and the **Last** terms. Then add these products.

$(2x + 3)(x - 7)$

$= 2x(x) + 2x(-7) + 3x + 3(-7)$ FOIL method

$= 2x^2 - 14x + 3x - 21$ Multiply.

$= 2x^2 - 11x - 21$ Combine like terms.

Special Products

$$(x + y)(x - y) = x^2 - y^2$$
$$(x + y)^2 = x^2 + 2xy + y^2$$
$$(x - y)^2 = x^2 - 2xy + y^2$$

$(3m + 8)(3m - 8)$

$= 9m^2 - 64$

$(5a + 3b)^2$ $\bigg|$ $(2k - 1)^2$

$= 25a^2 + 30ab + 9b^2$ $\bigg|$ $= 4k^2 - 4k + 1$

Multiplying Functions

If $f(x)$ and $g(x)$ define functions, then

$$(fg)(x) = f(x) \cdot g(x).$$

Let $f(x) = x^2$ and $g(x) = 2x + 1$. Find $(fg)(x)$.

$$(fg)(x)$$
$$= f(x) \cdot g(x)$$
$$= x^2(2x + 1)$$
$$= 2x^3 + x^2$$

4.5 Dividing Polynomials

Dividing by a Monomial

To divide a polynomial by a monomial, divide each term in the polynomial by the monomial, and then write each fraction in lowest terms.

Divide.

$$\frac{2x^3 - 4x^2 + 6x - 8}{2x}$$

$$= \frac{2x^3}{2x} - \frac{4x^2}{2x} + \frac{6x}{2x} - \frac{8}{2x}$$

$$= x^2 - 2x + 3 - \frac{4}{x}$$

CONCEPTS	EXAMPLES

Dividing by a Polynomial
Use the "long division" process. The process ends when the remainder is 0 or when the degree of the remainder is less than the degree of the divisor.

Find $(m^3 - m^2 + 2m + 5) \div (m + 1)$.

$$\begin{array}{r} m^2 - 2m + 4 \\ m+1{\overline{\smash{\big)}\,m^3 - m^2 + 2m + 5}} \\ \underline{m^3 + m^2} \\ -2m^2 + 2m \\ \underline{-2m^2 - 2m} \\ 4m + 5 \\ \underline{4m + 4} \\ 1 \leftarrow \text{Remainder} \end{array}$$

The answer is

$$m^2 - 2m + 4 + \frac{1}{m + 1}.$$

Dividing Functions
If $f(x)$ and $g(x)$ define functions, then

$$\left(\frac{f}{g}\right)(x) = \frac{f(x)}{g(x)}, \quad (\text{where } g(x) \neq 0).$$

Let $f(x) = x^2$ and $g(x) = 2x + 1$. Find $\left(\frac{f}{g}\right)(x)$.

$$\left(\frac{f}{g}\right)(x) = \frac{f(x)}{g(x)} = \frac{x^2}{2x + 1}, \quad x \neq -\frac{1}{2}$$

Chapter 4   Review Exercises

4.1 *Simplify. Write answers with only positive exponents. Assume that all variables represent nonzero real numbers.*

1. 4^3

2. $\left(\frac{1}{3}\right)^4$

3. $(-5)^3$

4. $\dfrac{2}{(-3)^{-2}}$

5. $\left(\frac{2}{3}\right)^{-4}$

6. $\left(\frac{5}{4}\right)^{-2}$

7. $5^{-1} - 6^{-1}$

8. $2^{-1} + 4^{-1}$

9. $-3^0 + 3^0$

10. $(3^{-4})^2$

11. $(x^{-4})^{-2}$

12. $(xy^{-3})^{-2}$

13. $(z^{-3})^3 z^{-6}$

14. $(5m^{-3})^2 (m^4)^{-3}$

15. $\dfrac{(3r)^2 r^4}{r^{-2} r^{-3}} (9r^{-3})^{-2}$

16. $\left(\dfrac{5z^{-3}}{z^{-1}}\right) \dfrac{5}{z^2}$

17. $\left(\dfrac{6m^{-4}}{m^{-9}}\right)^{-1} \left(\dfrac{m^{-2}}{16}\right)$

18. $\left(\dfrac{3r^5}{5r^{-3}}\right)^{-2} \left(\dfrac{9r^{-1}}{2r^{-5}}\right)^3$

19. $(-3x^4 y^3)(4x^{-2} y^5)$

20. $\dfrac{6m^{-4} n^3}{-3mn^2}$

21. $\dfrac{(5p^{-2}q)(4p^5 q^{-3})}{2p^{-5} q^5}$

22. Explain the difference between the expressions $(-6)^0$ and -6^0.

Write each number in scientific notation.

23. 13,450

24. 0.0000000765

25. 0.138

26. The total population of the United States was recently estimated at **308,700,000**. Of this amount, about **53,000** Americans were centenarians, that is, age **100** or older. Write the three bold-faced numbers using scientific notation. (*Source:* U.S. Census Bureau.)

1. 64

2. $\dfrac{1}{81}$

3. -125

4. 18

5. $\dfrac{81}{16}$

6. $\dfrac{16}{25}$

7. $\dfrac{1}{30}$

8. $\dfrac{3}{4}$

9. 0

10. $\dfrac{1}{3^8}$

11. x^8

12. $\dfrac{y^6}{x^2}$

13. $\dfrac{1}{z^{15}}$

14. $\dfrac{25}{m^{18}}$

15. $\dfrac{r^{17}}{9}$

16. $\dfrac{25}{z^4}$

17. $\dfrac{1}{96m^7}$

18. $\dfrac{2025}{8r^4}$

19. $-12x^2 y^8$

20. $-\dfrac{2n}{m^5}$

21. $\dfrac{10p^8}{q^7}$

22. In $(-6)^0$, the base is -6 and the expression simplifies to 1. In -6^0, the base is 6 and the expression simplifies to -1.

23. 1.345×10^4

24. 7.65×10^{-8}

25. 1.38×10^{-1}

26. 3.087×10^8; 5.3×10^4; 1×10^2 (or 10^2)

27. 1,210,000

28. 0.0058

29. 2×10^{-4}; 0.0002

30. 1.5×10^3; 1500

31. 4.1×10^{-5}; 0.000041

32. 2.7×10^{-2}; 0.027

33. (a) 20,000 hr
  (b) 833 days

34. 14; 5   **35.** $-1; 2$

36. $\dfrac{1}{10}; 1$ **37.** 504; 8

38. (a) $11k^3 - 3k^2 + 9k$
  (b) trinomial   (c) 3

39. (a) $9m^7 + 14m^6$
  (b) binomial   (c) 7

40. (a) $-5y^4 + 3y^3 + 7y^2 - 2y$
  (b) none of these   (c) 4

41. (a) $-7q^5r^3$ (b) monomial
  (c) 8

42. One example is
  $x^5 + 2x^4 - x^2 + x + 2$.

43. $-x^2 - 3x + 1$

44. $-5y^3 - 4y^2 + 6y - 12$

45. $6a^3 - 4a^2 - 16a + 15$

46. $8y^2 - 9y + 5$

47. (a) -11 (b) 4   (c) 7

48. (a) $5x^2 - x + 5$
  (b) $-5x^2 + 5x + 1$
  (c) 11   (d) -9

49. (a) 167   (b) 1495
  (c) 20   (d) 42
  (e) $75x^2 + 220x + 160$
  (f) $15x^2 + 10x + 2$

Write each number in standard notation.

27. 1.21×10^6

28. 5.8×10^{-3}

Evaluate. Give answers in both scientific notation and standard notation.

29. $\dfrac{16 \times 10^4}{8 \times 10^8}$

30. $\dfrac{6 \times 10^{-2}}{4 \times 10^{-5}}$

31. $\dfrac{0.0000000164}{0.0004}$

32. $\dfrac{0.0009 \times 12{,}000{,}000}{400{,}000}$

33. The planet Mercury has an average distance from the sun of 3.6×10^7 mi, while the average distance from Venus to the sun is 6.7×10^7 mi.

  (a) How long would it take a spacecraft traveling at 1.55×10^3 mph to travel from Venus to Mercury? Give the answer in hours, in standard notation.

  (b) Use the answer from part (a) to find the number of days it would take the spacecraft to travel from Venus to Mercury, to the nearest whole number.

4.2 *Give the numerical coefficient and the degree of each term.*

34. $14p^5$ **35.** $-z^2$ **36.** $\dfrac{x}{10}$ **37.** $504p^3r^5$

For each polynomial, (a) write it in descending powers, (b) identify it as a monomial, binomial, trinomial, or none of these, and (c) give its degree.

38. $9k + 11k^3 - 3k^2$

39. $14m^6 + 9m^7$

40. $-5y^4 + 3y^3 + 7y^2 - 2y$

41. $-7q^5r^3$

42. Give an example of a polynomial in the variable x such that the polynomial has degree 5, is lacking a third-degree term, and is in descending powers of the variable.

Add or subtract as indicated.

43. Add.
$$3x^2 - 5x + 6$$
$$-4x^2 + 2x - 5$$

44. Subtract.
$$-5y^3 \quad\quad + 8y - 3$$
$$\quad\quad 4y^2 + 2y + 9$$

45. $(4a^3 - 9a + 15) - (-2a^3 + 4a^2 + 7a)$ **46.** $(3y^2 + 2y - 1) + (5y^2 - 11y + 6)$

4.3 *Work each problem.*

47. For the polynomial function $f(x) = -2x^2 + 5x + 7$, find each value.
  (a) $f(-2)$ (b) $f(3)$ (c) $f(0)$

48. Find each of the following for the polynomial functions
$$f(x) = 2x + 3 \quad \text{and} \quad g(x) = 5x^2 - 3x + 2.$$
  (a) $(f + g)(x)$ (b) $(f - g)(x)$ (c) $(f + g)(-1)$ (d) $(f - g)(-1)$

49. Find each of the following for the polynomial functions
$$f(x) = 3x^2 + 2x - 1 \quad \text{and} \quad g(x) = 5x + 7.$$
  (a) $(g \circ f)(3)$ (b) $(f \circ g)(3)$ (c) $(f \circ g)(-2)$
  (d) $(g \circ f)(-2)$ (e) $(f \circ g)(x)$ (f) $(g \circ f)(x)$

50. (a) 95,408
 (b) 117,556
 (c) 130,792

51.

$f(x) = -2x + 5$
domain: $(-\infty, \infty)$;
range: $(-\infty, \infty)$

52.

$f(x) = x^2 - 6$
domain: $(-\infty, \infty)$;
range: $[-6, \infty)$

53.

$f(x) = -x^3 + 1$
domain: $(-\infty, \infty)$;
range: $(-\infty, \infty)$

54. $-12k^3 - 42k$
55. $2x^3 + 22x^2 + 56x$
56. $15m^2 - 7m - 2$
57. $6w^2 - 13wt + 6t^2$
58. $10p^4 + 30p^3 - 8p^2 - 24p$
59. $3q^3 - 13q^2 - 14q + 20$
60. $36r^4 - 1$
61. $16m^2 + 24m + 9$
62. $9t^2 - 12ts + 4s^2$

63. $y^2 - 3y + \dfrac{5}{4}$

64. $x^2 - 4x + 6$

65. $p^2 + 6p + 9 + \dfrac{54}{2p - 3}$

66. $p^2 + 3p - 6$
67. (a) $36x^3 - 9x^2$ (b) -45
68. (a) $4x - 1, \ x \neq 0$ (b) 7

50. The number of twin births in the United States during the years 1990 through 2011 can be modeled by the polynomial function

$$P(x) = -21.769x^3 + 626.67x^2$$
$$- 1875.0x + 95,408,$$

where $x = 0$ represents 1990, $x = 1$ represents 1991, and so on. Use this function to approximate number of twin births (to the nearest whole number) in each given year. (*Source:* National Center for Health Statistics.)

 (a) 1990 (b) 2000 (c) 2011

Graph each polynomial function. Give the domain and range.

51. $f(x) = -2x + 5$ **52.** $f(x) = x^2 - 6$ **53.** $f(x) = -x^3 + 1$

4.4 *Find each product.*

54. $-6k(2k^2 + 7)$ **55.** $2x(x + 4)(x + 7)$ **56.** $(3m - 2)(5m + 1)$

57. $(3w - 2t)(2w - 3t)$ **58.** $(2p^2 + 6p)(5p^2 - 4)$ **59.** $(3q^2 + 2q - 4)(q - 5)$

60. $(6r^2 - 1)(6r^2 + 1)$ **61.** $(4m + 3)^2$ **62.** $(3t - 2s)^2$

4.5 *Divide.*

63. $\dfrac{4y^3 - 12y^2 + 5y}{4y}$

64. $\dfrac{x^3 - 9x^2 + 26x - 30}{x - 5}$

65. $\dfrac{2p^3 + 9p^2 + 27}{2p - 3}$

66. $\dfrac{5p^4 + 15p^3 - 33p^2 - 9p + 18}{5p^2 - 3}$

4.4, 4.5 *Find each of the following for the polynomial functions*
$$f(x) = 12x^2 - 3x \quad and \quad g(x) = 3x.$$

67. (a) $(fg)(x)$ (b) $(fg)(-1)$ **68.** (a) $\left(\dfrac{f}{g}\right)(x)$ (b) $\left(\dfrac{f}{g}\right)(2)$

Chapter 4 Mixed Review Exercises

Solve each problem.

1. (a) A (b) G (c) C
 (d) C (e) A (f) E
 (g) B (h) H (i) F
 (j) I

1. Match each expression (a)–(j) in Column I with its equivalent expression A – J in Column II. Choices may be used once, more than once, or not at all.

I		II	
(a) 4^{-2}	(b) -4^2	A. $\dfrac{1}{16}$	B. 0
(c) 4^0	(d) $(-4)^0$	C. 1	D. $-\dfrac{1}{16}$
(e) $(-4)^{-2}$	(f) -4^0	E. -1	F. $\dfrac{5}{16}$
(g) $-4^0 + 4^0$	(h) $-4^0 - 4^0$	G. -16	H. -2
(i) $4^{-2} + 4^{-1}$	(j) 4^2	I. 16	J. none of these

2. 103,363 mi²

3. $\dfrac{y^4}{36}$ **4.** $\dfrac{1}{125}$

5. -9 **6.** $-\dfrac{1}{5z^9}$

7. $21p^9 + 7p^8 + 14p^7$

8. $4x^2 - 36x + 81$

9. $\dfrac{1}{16y^{18}}$

10. $8x + 1 + \dfrac{5}{x-3}$

11. $8x^2 - 10x - 3$

12. $\dfrac{1250z^7x^6}{9}$

13. $9m^2 - 30mn + 25n^2 - p^2$

14. $2y^2x + \dfrac{3y^3}{2x} + \dfrac{5x^2}{2}$

15. $-3k^2 + 4k - 7$

2. In 2013, the estimated population of New Zealand was 4.365×10^6. The population density was 42.23 people per square mile. What is the area of New Zealand to the nearest square mile? (*Source: The World Factbook.*)

Perform the indicated operations and then simplify. Write answers with only positive exponents. Assume that all variables represent nonzero real numbers.

3. $\dfrac{6^{-1}y^3(y^2)^{-2}}{6y^{-4}(y^{-1})}$ **4.** 5^{-3} **5.** $-(-3)^2$

6. $\dfrac{(-z^{-2})^3}{5(z^{-3})^{-1}}$ **7.** $7p^5(3p^4 + p^3 + 2p^2)$ **8.** $(2x - 9)^2$

9. $(y^6)^{-5}(2y^{-3})^{-4}$ **10.** $\dfrac{8x^2 - 23x + 2}{x - 3}$ **11.** $(4x + 1)(2x - 3)$

12. $\dfrac{(5z^2x^3)^2(2zx^2)^{-1}}{(-10zx^{-3})^{-2}(3z^{-1}x^{-4})^2}$ **13.** $[(3m - 5n) + p][(3m - 5n) - p]$

14. $\dfrac{20y^3x^3 + 15y^4x + 25yx^4}{10yx^2}$ **15.** $(2k - 1) - (3k^2 - 2k + 6)$

| Chapter 4 | Test | FOR EXTRA HELP | *Step-by-step test solutions are found on the Chapter Test Prep Videos available in* MyMathLab® *or on* You Tube™. |

▶ *View the complete solutions to all Chapter Test exercises in MyMathLab.*

[4.1]
1. (a) C   (b) A   (c) D
    (d) A   (e) E   (f) F
    (g) B   (h) G   (i) I
    (j) C

2. $\dfrac{4x^7}{9y^{10}}$

3. $\dfrac{6}{r^{14}}$ **4.** $\dfrac{16}{9p^{10}q^{28}}$

5. $\dfrac{16}{x^6y^{16}}$

6. 0.00000091

7. 3×10^{-4}; 0.0003

[4.3]
8. (a) -18
    (b) $-2x^2 + 12x - 9$
    (c) $-2x^2 - 2x - 3$
    (d) -7

1. Match each expression (a)–(j) in Column I with its equivalent expression A–J in Column II. Choices may be used once, more than once, or not at all.

I

(a) 7^{-2} (b) 7^0

(c) -7^0 (d) $(-7)^0$

(e) -7^2 (f) $7^{-1} + 2^{-1}$

(g) $(7 + 2)^{-1}$ (h) $\dfrac{7^{-1}}{2^{-1}}$

(i) 7^2 (j) $(-7)^{-2}$

II

A. 1   B. $\dfrac{1}{9}$

C. $\dfrac{1}{49}$ D. -1

E. -49 F. $\dfrac{9}{14}$

G. $\dfrac{2}{7}$ H. 0

I. 49   J. none of these

Simplify. Write answers with only positive exponents. Assume that all variables represent nonzero real numbers.

2. $(3x^{-2}y^3)^{-2}(4x^3y^{-4})$ **3.** $\dfrac{36r^{-4}(r^2)^{-3}}{6r^4}$

4. $\left(\dfrac{4p^2}{q^4}\right)^3\left(\dfrac{6p^8}{q^{-8}}\right)^{-2}$ **5.** $(-2x^4y^{-3})^0(-4x^{-3}y^{-8})^2$

6. Write 9.1×10^{-7} in standard notation.

7. Evaluate. Give the answer in both scientific notation and standard notation.

$$\dfrac{2,500,000 \times 0.00003}{0.05 \times 5,000,000}$$

9. (a) 23   (b) $3x^2 + 11$
   (c) $9x^2 + 30x + 27$

10.   11.

domain: $(-\infty, \infty)$;   domain: $(-\infty, \infty)$;
range: $(-\infty, 3]$ range: $(-\infty, \infty)$

[4.4]

12. $10x^2 - x - 3$
13. $6m^3 - 7m^2 - 30m + 25$
14. $36x^2 - y^2$
15. $9k^2 + 6kq + q^2$
16. $4y^2 - 9z^2 + 6zx - x^2$

[4.5]

17. $4p - 8 + \dfrac{6}{p}$

18. $x^2 + 4x + 4$

[4.2]

19. $x^3 - 2x^2 - 10x - 13$

[4.4, 4.5]

20. (a) $x^3 + 4x^2 + 5x + 2$
    (b) 0
    (c) $x + 2$, $x \neq -1$
    (d) 0

8. Find each of the following for the polynomial functions

$$f(x) = -2x^2 + 5x - 6 \quad \text{and} \quad g(x) = 7x - 3.$$

(a) $f(4)$ (b) $(f + g)(x)$ (c) $(f - g)(x)$ (d) $(f - g)(-2)$

9. Find each of the following for the polynomial functions

$$f(x) = 3x + 5 \quad \text{and} \quad g(x) = x^2 + 2.$$

(a) $(f \circ g)(-2)$ (b) $(f \circ g)(x)$ (c) $(g \circ f)(x)$

Graph each polynomial function. Give the domain and range.

10. $f(x) = -2x^2 + 3$ **11.** $f(x) = -x^3 + 3$

Perform the indicated operations.

12. $(5x - 3)(2x + 1)$ **13.** $(2m - 5)(3m^2 + 4m - 5)$

14. $(6x + y)(6x - y)$ **15.** $(3k + q)^2$

16. $[2y + (3z - x)][2y - (3z - x)]$ **17.** $\dfrac{16p^3 - 32p^2 + 24p}{4p^2}$

18. $(x^3 + 3x^2 - 4) \div (x - 1)$

19. $(4x^3 - 3x^2 + 2x - 5) - (3x^3 + 11x + 8) + (x^2 - x)$

20. Find each of the following for the polynomial functions

$$f(x) = x^2 + 3x + 2 \quad \text{and} \quad g(x) = x + 1.$$

(a) $(fg)(x)$ (b) $(fg)(-2)$ (c) $\left(\dfrac{f}{g}\right)(x)$ (d) $\left(\dfrac{f}{g}\right)(-2)$

Chapters R–4   Cumulative Review Exercises

[R.1]
1. (a) A, B, C, D, F
   (b) B, C, D, F
   (c) D, F   (d) C, D, F
   (e) E, F   (f) D, F

[R.3]
2. 32

3. $-\dfrac{1}{72}$ 4. 0

[1.1]
5. $\{-65\}$
6. {all real numbers}

[1.2]   **[1.5]**

7. $t = \dfrac{A - p}{pr}$ 8. $(-\infty, 6)$

[1.7]

9. $\left\{-\dfrac{1}{3}, 1\right\}$

10. $\left(-\infty, -\dfrac{8}{3}\right] \cup [2, \infty)$

1. Match each number in Column I with the choice or choices of sets of numbers in Column II to which the number belongs.

I		II	
(a) 34	(b) 0	**A.** Natural numbers	**B.** Whole numbers
(c) 2.16	(d) $-\sqrt{36}$	**C.** Integers	**D.** Rational numbers
(e) $\sqrt{13}$	(f) $-\dfrac{4}{5}$	**E.** Irrational numbers	**F.** Real numbers

Evaluate.

2. $9 \cdot 4 - 16 \div 4$ **3.** $\left(\dfrac{1}{3}\right)^2 - \left(\dfrac{1}{2}\right)^3$ **4.** $-|8 - 13| - |-4| + |-9|$

Solve.

5. $-5(8 - 2z) + 4(7 - z) = 7(8 + z) - 3$ **6.** $3(x + 2) - 5(x + 2) = -2x - 4$

7. $A = p + prt$ for t **8.** $2(m + 5) - 3m + 1 > 5$

9. $|3x - 1| = 2$ **10.** $|3z + 1| \geq 7$

11. A survey polled Internet users age 12 and older about their most frequent daily Internet activities. Complete the results shown in the table if 5000 such users were surveyed.

Internet Activity	Percent	Number
Look for news	33%	
Check email		1600
Find or check a fact		1050
Play games	14%	

Source: The 2013 Digital Future Report.

12. Find the measure of each angle of the triangle.

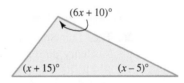

Find the slope of each line described.

13. Through $(-4, 5)$ and $(2, -3)$ **14.** Through $(4, 5)$; horizontal

Write an equation of each line that satisfies the given conditions. Give the equation (a) in slope-intercept form and (b) in standard form.

15. Through $(4, -1)$; $m = -4$ **16.** Through $(0, 0)$ and $(1, 4)$

Graph each equation or inequality.

17. $-3x + 4y = 12$ **18.** $y \le 2x - 6$ **19.** $3x + 2y < 0$

20. Per capita consumption of whole milk in the United States (in gallons) is shown in the graph, where $x = 0$ represents 1970.

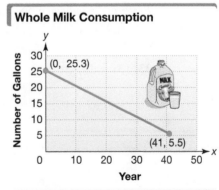

Source: U.S. Department of Agriculture.

(a) Use the given ordered pairs to find the average rate of change in per capita consumption of whole milk (in gallons, to the nearest hundredth) per year during this period. Interpret the answer.

(b) Use the answer from part (a) to write an equation of the line in slope-intercept form that models per capita consumption of whole milk y (in gallons).

(c) Use the equation from part (b) to approximate per capita consumption of whole milk in 2000.

21. Give the domain and range of the relation

$$\{(-4, -2), (-1, 0), (2, 0), (5, 2)\}.$$

Does this relation define a function?

22. If $g(x) = -x^2 - 2x + 6$, find $g(3)$.

Solve each system.

23. $3x - 4y = 1$
$2x + 3y = 12$

24. $3x - 2y = 4$
$-6x + 4y = 7$

25. $x + 3y - 6z = 7$
$2x - y + z = 1$
$x + 2y + 2z = -1$

Solve each problem.

26. The Star-Spangled Banner that flew over Fort McHenry during the War of 1812 had a perimeter of 144 ft. Its length measured 12 ft more than its width. Find the dimensions of this flag, which is displayed in the Smithsonian Institution's Museum of American History in Washington, DC. (*Source:* National Park Service brochure.)

27. Agbe needs 9 L of a 20% solution of alcohol. Agbe has a 15% solution on hand, as well as a 30% solution. How many liters of the 15% solution and the 30% solution should Agbe mix to obtain the 20% solution needed?

Simplify. Write answers with only positive exponents. Assume that all variables represent positive real numbers.

28. $\left(\dfrac{2m^3n}{p^2}\right)^3$

29. $\dfrac{x^{-6}y^3z^{-1}}{x^7y^{-4}z}$

30. $(2m^{-2}n^3)^{-3}$

Perform the indicated operations.

31. $(3x^2 - 8x + 1) - (x^2 - 3x - 9)$

32. $(x + 2y)(x^2 - 2xy + 4y^2)$

33. $(3x + 2y)(5x - y)$

34. $\dfrac{16x^3y^5 - 8x^2y^2 + 4}{4x^2y}$

35. $\dfrac{m^3 - 3m^2 + 5m - 3}{m - 1}$

5

Factoring

Determining the maximum area that can be enclosed by a fence of fixed perimeter is accomplished by solving a *quadratic equation,* one of the topics covered in this chapter on *factoring*.

5.1 Greatest Common Factors and Factoring by Grouping

OBJECTIVES

1   Factor out the greatest common factor.
2   Factor by grouping.

VOCABULARY

☐ factoring
☐ greatest common factor (GCF)

Writing a polynomial as the product of two or more simpler polynomials is called **factoring** the polynomial. For example, consider the following.

$$3x(5x - 2) = 15x^2 - 6x \qquad \text{Multiplying}$$

$$15x^2 - 6x = 3x(5x - 2) \qquad \text{Factoring}$$

Notice that both multiplying and factoring use the distributive property, but in opposite directions. *Factoring "undoes," or reverses, multiplying.*

OBJECTIVE 1 Factor out the greatest common factor.

The first step in factoring a polynomial is to find the *greatest common factor* for the terms of the polynomial. The product of the greatest common numerical factor and each variable factor of least degree common to every term in a polynomial is the **greatest common factor (GCF)** of the terms of the polynomial.

For example, the greatest common factor for $8x + 12$ is 4, because 4 is the greatest factor that *divides into* both $8x$ and 12.

$$8x + 12$$

$$= 4(2x) + 4(3) \qquad \text{Factor 4 from each term.}$$

$$= 4(2x + 3) \qquad \text{Distributive property, } ab + ac = a(b + c)$$

CHECK   Multiply $4(2x + 3)$ to obtain $8x + 12.$ ✓ Original polynomial

Using the distributive property in this way is called **factoring out the greatest common factor.**

NOW TRY
EXERCISE 1

Factor out the greatest common factor.

(a) $54m - 45$

(b) $2k - 7$

EXAMPLE 1   Factoring Out the Greatest Common Factor

Factor out the greatest common factor.

(a) $9z - 18$

$$= 9 \cdot z - 9 \cdot 2 \qquad \text{GCF = 9; Factor 9 from each term.}$$

$$= 9(z - 2) \qquad \text{Distributive property}$$

CHECK   Multiply $9(z - 2)$ to obtain $9z - 18.$ ✓ Original polynomial

(b) $56m + 35p$

$$= 7(8m + 5p)$$

(c) $2y + 5$

There is no common factor other than 1.

(d) $12 + 24z$

Remember to write the 1.

$$= 12 \cdot 1 + 12 \cdot 2z \qquad \text{Identity property}$$

$$= 12(1 + 2z) \qquad \text{12 is the GCF.}$$

CHECK $12(1 + 2z)$

$$= 12(1) + 12(2z) \qquad \text{Distributive property}$$

$$= 12 + 24z \text{ ✓} \qquad \text{Original polynomial}$$

NOW TRY ANSWERS
1. (a) $9(6m - 5)$
(b) There is no common factor other than 1.

NOW TRY

NOW TRY EXERCISE 2

Factor out the greatest common factor.

(a) $16y^4 + 8y^3$

(b) $14p^2 - 9p^3 + 6p^4$

(c) $9x^3y^2 - 3x^2y^2 + 6x^2y^3$

EXAMPLE 2 Factoring Out the Greatest Common Factor

Factor out the greatest common factor.

(a) $9x^2 + 12x^3$

The numerical part of the GCF is 3, the greatest integer that divides into both 9 and 12. The least exponent that appears on x is 2. The GCF is $3x^2$.

$$9x^2 + 12x^3$$
$$= 3x^2(3) + 3x^2(4x) \qquad \text{GCF} = 3x^2$$
$$= 3x^2(3 + 4x) \qquad \text{Distributive property}$$

(b) $32p^4 - 24p^3 + 40p^5$
$$= 8p^3(4p) + 8p^3(-3) + 8p^3(5p^2) \qquad \text{GCF} = 8p^3$$
$$= 8p^3(4p - 3 + 5p^2) \qquad \text{Distributive property}$$

(c) $\quad 3k^4 - 15k^7 + 24k^9$

Remember the 1.
$$= 3k^4(1 - 5k^3 + 8k^5) \qquad \text{GCF} = 3k^4$$

(d) $24m^3n^2 - 18m^2n + 6m^4n^3$
$$= 6m^2n(4mn) + 6m^2n(-3) + 6m^2n(m^2n^2) \qquad \text{GCF} = 6m^2n$$
$$= 6m^2n(4mn - 3 + m^2n^2) \qquad \text{Distributive property}$$

(e) $25x^2y^3 + 30y^5 - 15x^4y^7$
$$= 5y^3(5x^2 + 6y^2 - 3x^4y^4)$$

In each case, check the factored form by multiplying. NOW TRY

 NOW TRY EXERCISE 3

Factor out the greatest common factor.

(a) $(3x - 2)(x + 1) +$
$\quad (3x - 2)(2x - 5)$

(b) $z(a - b)^3 - 2w(a - b)^2$

EXAMPLE 3 Factoring Out a Binomial Factor

Factor out the greatest common factor.

(a) $(x - 5)(x + 6) + (x - 5)(2x + 5) \qquad$ The greatest common factor is $x - 5$.
$$= (x - 5)[(x + 6) + (2x + 5)] \qquad \text{Factor out } x - 5.$$
$$= (x - 5)(3x + 11) \qquad \text{Combine like terms inside the brackets.}$$

(b) $z^2(m + n) + x^2(m + n)$
$$= (m + n)(z^2 + x^2) \qquad \text{Factor out the common factor } (m + n).$$

(c) $p(r + 2s)^2 - q(r + 2s)^3$
$$= (r + 2s)^2[p - q(r + 2s)] \qquad \text{Factor out the common factor } (r + 2s)^2.$$
$$= (r + 2s)^2(p - qr - 2qs) \qquad \text{Be careful with signs.}$$

(d) $(p - 5)(p + 2) - (p - 5)(3p + 4)$
$$= (p - 5)[(p + 2) - (3p + 4)] \qquad \text{Factor out the common factor } p - 5.$$
$$= (p - 5)[p + 2 - 3p - 4] \qquad \text{Distributive property}$$
$$= (p - 5)[-2p - 2] \qquad \text{Combine like terms.}$$
$$= (p - 5)[-2(p + 1)] \qquad \text{Look for a common factor.}$$
$$= -2(p - 5)(p + 1) \qquad \text{Commutative property}$$ NOW TRY

NOW TRY ANSWERS

2. (a) $8y^3(2y + 1)$
  (b) $p^2(14 - 9p + 6p^2)$
  (c) $3x^2y^2(3x - 1 + 2y)$
3. (a) $(3x - 2)(3x - 4)$
  (b) $(a - b)^2(za - zb - 2w)$

NOW TRY
EXERCISE 4
Factor $-4y^5 - 3y^3 + 8y$ in two ways.

EXAMPLE 4 Factoring Out a Negative Common Factor

Factor $-a^3 + 3a^2 - 5a$ in two ways.

First, a could be used as the common factor.

$$-a^3 + 3a^2 - 5a$$

$$= a(-a^2) + a(3a) + a(-5) \qquad \text{Factor out } a.$$

$$= a(-a^2 + 3a - 5) \qquad \text{Distributive property}$$

CHECK Multiply $a(-a^2 + 3a - 5)$ to obtain $-a^3 + 3a^2 - 5a$. ✓

Because of the leading negative sign, $-a$ could also be used as the common factor.

$$-a^3 + 3a^2 - 5a$$

$$= -a(a^2) + (-a)(-3a) + (-a)(5) \qquad \text{Factor out } -a.$$

$$= -a(a^2 - 3a + 5) \qquad \text{Distributive property}$$

CHECK Multiply $-a(a^2 - 3a + 5)$ to obtain $-a^3 + 3a^2 - 5a$. ✓

Sometimes there may be a reason to prefer one of these forms, but either is correct.

NOW TRY

NOTE The answer section in this book will usually give the factored form where the common factor has a positive coefficient.

OBJECTIVE 2 Factor by grouping.

Sometimes the *individual terms* of a polynomial have a greatest common factor of 1, but it still may be possible to factor the polynomial by using a process called **factoring by grouping**. *We usually factor by grouping when a polynomial has more than three terms.*

NOW TRY
EXERCISE 5
Factor.

$$3m - 3n + xm - xn$$

EXAMPLE 5 Factoring by Grouping

Factor $ax - ay + bx - by$.

Group the terms in pairs so that each pair has a common factor.

$$ax - ay + bx - by$$

Terms with common factor a ↓ ↓   Terms with common factor b ↓ ↓

$$= (ax - ay) + (bx - by)$$

$$= a(x - y) + b(x - y) \qquad \text{Factor each group.}$$

By the commutative property, $(a + b)(x - y)$ is also correct.

$$= (x - y)(a + b) \qquad \text{The common factor is } x - y.$$

CHECK $(x - y)(a + b)$

$$= xa + xb - ya - yb \qquad \text{Multiply using the FOIL method.}$$

$$= ax + bx - ay - by \qquad \text{Commutative property}$$

$$= ax - ay + bx - by \quad ✓ \qquad \text{Original polynomial}$$

NOW TRY

NOW TRY ANSWERS
4. $y(-4y^4 - 3y^2 + 8)$;
$-y(4y^4 + 3y^2 - 8)$
5. $(m - n)(3 + x)$

**NOW TRY
EXERCISE 6**

Factor.

$ab - 7a - 5b + 35$

EXAMPLE 6 Factoring by Grouping

Factor $3x - 3y - ax + ay$.

$$3x - 3y - ax + ay \quad \text{Pay close attention here.}$$

$$= (3x - 3y) + (-ax + ay) \qquad \text{Group the terms.}$$

$$= 3(x - y) + a(-x + y) \qquad \text{Factor out 3, and factor out } a.$$

The factors $(x - y)$ and $(-x + y)$ are opposites. If we factor out $-a$ instead of a in the second group, we obtain the common binomial factor $(x - y)$. So we start over.

$$(3x - 3y) + (-ax + ay)$$

$$= 3(x - y) - a(x - y) \qquad \text{Be careful with signs.}$$

$$= (x - y)(3 - a) \qquad \text{Factor out } x - y.$$

CHECK $(x - y)(3 - a)$

$$= 3x - ax - 3y + ay \qquad \text{Multiply using the FOIL method.}$$

$$= 3x - 3y - ax + ay \checkmark \quad \text{Original polynomial} \qquad \text{NOW TRY} \ \text{}$$

NOTE   In **Example 6,** a different grouping would lead to the factored form $(a - 3)(y - x)$. Verify by multiplying that this is also correct.

Factoring by Grouping

Step 1   **Group terms.** Collect the terms into groups so that each group has a common factor.

Step 2   **Factor within the groups.** Factor out the common factor in each group.

Step 3   **Factor the entire polynomial.** If each group now has a common factor, factor it out. If not, try a different grouping.

Always check the factored form by multiplying.

**NOW TRY
EXERCISE 7**

Factor.

$3ax - 6xy - a + 2y$

EXAMPLE 7 Factoring by Grouping

Factor $6ax + 12bx + a + 2b$.

$$6ax + 12bx + a + 2b$$

$$= (6ax + 12bx) + (a + 2b) \qquad \text{Group the terms.}$$

Now factor $6x$ from the first group, and use the identity property of multiplication to introduce the factor 1 in the second group.   Remember to write the 1.

$$= 6x(a + 2b) + 1(a + 2b) \qquad \text{Factor each group.}$$

$$= (a + 2b)(6x + 1) \qquad \text{Factor out } a + 2b.$$

CHECK $(a + 2b)(6x + 1)$

$$= 6ax + a + 12bx + 2b \qquad \text{Use the FOIL method.}$$

$$= 6ax + 12bx + a + 2b \checkmark \quad \text{Original polynomial} \qquad \text{NOW TRY} \ \text{}$$

NOW TRY ANSWERS
6. $(b - 7)(a - 5)$
7. $(a - 2y)(3x - 1)$

**NOW TRY
EXERCISE 8**

Factor.

$2kp^2 + 6 - 3p^2 - 4k$

EXAMPLE 8 **Rearranging Terms before Factoring by Grouping**

Factor $p^2q^2 - 10 - 2q^2 + 5p^2$.

Neither the first two terms nor the last two terms have a common factor except 1. We can rearrange and group the terms as follows.

$$p^2q^2 - 10 - 2q^2 + 5p^2$$

$$= (p^2q^2 - 2q^2) + (5p^2 - 10) \qquad \text{Rearrange and group the terms.}$$

$$= q^2(p^2 - 2) + 5(p^2 - 2) \qquad \text{Factor out the common factors.}$$

Don't stop here.

$$= (p^2 - 2)(q^2 + 5) \qquad \text{Factor out } p^2 - 2. \text{ Use parentheses.}$$

CHECK $(p^2 - 2)(q^2 + 5)$

$$= p^2q^2 + 5p^2 - 2q^2 - 10 \qquad \text{Use the FOIL method.}$$

$$= p^2q^2 - 10 - 2q^2 + 5p^2 \checkmark \qquad \text{Original polynomial} \qquad \text{NOW TRY}$$

⚠ **CAUTION** In **Example 8,** do not stop at the step

$$q^2(p^2 - 2) + 5(p^2 - 2).$$

This expression is *not in factored form* because it is a *sum* of two terms, $q^2(p^2 - 2)$ and $5(p^2 - 2)$, not a *product*.

 **NOW TRY
EXERCISE 9**

Factor.

$12wy - 24xy + 4wz - 8xz$

EXAMPLE 9 **Factoring Out a GCF before Factoring by Grouping**

Factor $10ax - 5ay + 10bx - 5by$.

Always start by factoring out any greatest common factor from the terms.

$$10ax - 5ay + 10bx - 5by$$

$$= 5(2ax - ay + 2bx - by) \qquad \text{Factor out the GCF, 5.}$$

$$= 5[(2ax - ay) + (2bx - by)] \qquad \text{Group the terms inside the brackets.}$$

$$= 5[a(2x - y) + b(2x - y)] \qquad \text{Factor out the common factors.}$$

$$= 5[(2x - y)(a + b)] \qquad \text{Factor out } 2x - y.$$

$$= 5(2x - y)(a + b) \qquad \text{Write without the brackets.}$$

CHECK $5(2x - y)(a + b)$

$$= 5(2ax + 2bx - ay - by) \qquad \text{Use the FOIL method.}$$

$$= 10ax + 10bx - 5ay - 5by \qquad \text{Distributive property}$$

$$= 10ax - 5ay + 10bx - 5by \checkmark \qquad \text{Original polynomial} \qquad \text{NOW TRY}$$

NOTE Verify that the result in **Example 9** can also be obtained by grouping the terms of the polynomial

$$2ax - ay + 2bx - by \quad \text{as} \quad (2ax + 2bx) + (-ay - by).$$

5.1 Exercises

FOR EXTRA HELP

 MyMathLab®

● *Complete solution available in MyMathLab*

1. *Concept Check* Which choice is an example of a polynomial in factored form?

A. $3x^2y^3 + 6x^2(2x + y)$

B. $5(x + y)^2 - 10(x + y)^3$

C. $(-2 + 3x)(5y^2 + 4y + 3)$

D. $(3x + 4)(5x - y) - (3x + 4)(2x - 1)$

2. *Concept Check* When directed to factor the polynomial $4x^2y^5 - 8xy^3$ completely, a student wrote

$$2xy^3(2xy^2 - 4).$$

The teacher did not give the student full credit. *WHAT WENT WRONG?* Give the correct answer.

Concept Check To prepare for the exercises that follow, find the greatest common factor for each list of terms.

3. $9m^3,\ 3m^2,\ 15m$

4. $4a^2,\ 6a,\ 2a^3$

5. $16xy^3,\ 24x^2y^2,\ 8x^2y$

6. $10m^2n^2,\ 25mn^3,\ 50m^2n$

7. $6m(r + t)^2,\ 3p(r + t)^4$

8. $7z^2(m + n)^4,\ 9z^3(m + n)^5$

Factor out the greatest common factor. See Examples 1–4.

● 9. $12m - 60$

10. $15r - 45$

11. $4 + 20z$

12. $9 + 27x$

13. $8y - 15$

14. $7x - 40$

● 15. $8k^3 + 24k$

16. $9z^4 + 81z$

17. $-4p^3q^4 - 2p^2q^5$

18. $-3z^5w^2 - 18z^3w^4$

19. $7x^3 + 35x^4 - 14x^5$

20. $6k^3 - 36k^4 - 48k^5$

21. $10t^5 - 2t^3 - 4t^4$

22. $6p^3 - 3p^2 - 9p^4$

23. $15a^2c^3 - 25ac^2 + 5ac$

24. $15y^3z^3 - 27y^2z^4 + 3yz^3$

25. $16z^2n^6 + 64zn^7 - 32z^3n^3$

26. $5r^3s^5 + 10r^2s^2 - 15r^4s^2$

27. $14a^3b^2 + 7a^2b - 21a^5b^3 + 42ab^4$

28. $12km^3 - 24k^3m^2 + 36k^2m^4 - 60k^4m^3$

● 29. $(m - 4)(m + 2) + (m - 4)(m + 3)$

30. $(z - 5)(z + 7) + (z - 5)(z + 10)$

31. $(2z - 1)(z + 6) - (2z - 1)(z - 5)$

32. $(3x + 2)(x - 4) - (3x + 2)(x + 8)$

● 33. $5(2 - x)^2 - 2(2 - x)^3$

34. $2(5 - x)^3 - 3(5 - x)^2$

35. $4(3 - x)^2 - (3 - x)^3 + 3(3 - x)$

36. $2(t - s) + 4(t - s)^2 - (t - s)^3$

37. $15(2z + 1)^3 + 10(2z + 1)^2 - 25(2z + 1)$

38. $6(a + 2b)^2 - 4(a + 2b)^3 + 12(a + 2b)^4$

39. $5(m + p)^3 - 10(m + p)^2 - 15(m + p)^4$

40. $-9a^2(p + q) - 3a^3(p + q)^2 + 6a(p + q)^3$

Factor each polynomial twice. First use a common factor with a positive coefficient, and then use a common factor with a negative coefficient. See Example 4.

41. $-r^3 + 3r^2 + 5r$

42. $-t^4 + 8t^3 - 12t$

43. $-12s^5 + 48s^4$

44. $-16y^4 + 64y^3$

45. $-2x^5 + 6x^3 + 4x^2$

46. $-5a^3 + 10a^4 - 15a^5$

Factor by grouping. See Examples 5–9.

● 47. $mx + qx + my + qy$

48. $2k + 2h + jk + jh$

49. $10m + 2n + 5mk + nk$

50. $3ma + 3mb + 2ab + 2b^2$

▶ **51.** $4 - 2q - 6p + 3pq$

52. $20 + 5m + 12n + 3mn$

53. $p^2 - 4zq + pq - 4pz$

54. $r^2 - 9tw + 3rw - 3rt$

▶ **55.** $2xy + 3y + 2x + 3$

56. $7ab + 35bc + a + 5c$

57. $m^3 + 4m^2 - 6m - 24$

58. $2a^3 + a^2 - 14a - 7$

59. $-3a^3 - 3ab^2 + 2a^2b + 2b^3$

60. $-16m^3 + 4m^2p^2 - 4mp + p^3$

▶ **61.** $4 + xy - 2y - 2x$

62. $10ab - 21 - 6b + 35a$

63. $8 + 9y^4 - 6y^3 - 12y$

64. $x^3y^2 - 3 - 3y^2 + x^3$

65. $1 - a + ab - b$

66. $2ab^2 - 8b^2 + a - 4$

67. $2mx - 6qx + 2my - 6qy$

68. $12 - 6q - 18p + 9pq$

69. $4a^3 - 4a^2b^2 + 8ab - 8b^3$

70. $5x^3 + 15x^2y^2 - 5xy - 15y^3$

71. $2x^3y^2 + x^2y^2 - 14xy^2 - 7y^2$

72. $3m^2n^3 + 15m^2n - 2m^2n^2 - 10m^2$

Extending Skills   *Factor out the variable that is raised to the lesser exponent. (For example, in* **Exercise 73,** *factor out* m^{-5}.*)*

73. $3m^{-5} + m^{-3}$ **74.** $k^{-2} + 2k^{-4}$ **75.** $3p^{-3} + 2p^{-2}$ **76.** $-5q^{-3} + 8q^{-2}$

5.2 Factoring Trinomials

OBJECTIVES

1. Factor trinomials when the coefficient of the second-degree term is 1.
2. Factor trinomials when the coefficient of the second-degree term is not 1.
3. Use an alternative method for factoring trinomials.
4. Factor by substitution.

VOCABULARY

☐ prime polynomial

OBJECTIVE 1   Factor trinomials when the coefficient of the second-degree term is 1.

We begin by finding the product of $x + 3$ and $x - 5$.

$$(x + 3)(x - 5)$$
$$= x^2 - 5x + 3x - 15 \qquad \text{FOIL method}$$
$$= x^2 - 2x - 15 \qquad \text{Combine like terms.}$$

By this result, the factored form of $x^2 - 2x - 15$ is $(x + 3)(x - 5)$.

$$\text{Factored form} \longrightarrow (x + 3)(x - 5) = x^2 - 2x - 15 \longleftarrow \text{Product}$$

Multiplication →

← Factoring

Because multiplying and factoring are operations that "undo" each other, factoring trinomials involves using the FOIL method in reverse. As shown here, the x^2-term comes from multiplying x and x, and -15 comes from multiplying 3 and -5.

Product of x and x is x^2.

$$(x + 3)(x - 5) = x^2 - 2x - 15$$

Product of 3   and -5 is -15.

We find the $-2x$ in $x^2 - 2x - 15$ by multiplying the outer terms, multiplying the inner terms, and adding the results.

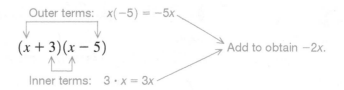

Outer terms: $x(-5) = -5x$

$(x + 3)(x - 5)$ ⟶ Add to obtain $-2x$.

Inner terms: $3 \cdot x = 3x$

Factoring $x^2 + bx + c$

Step 1 **Find pairs whose product is c.** Find all pairs of integers whose product is c, the third term of the trinomial.

Step 2 **Find pairs whose sum is b.** Choose the pair whose sum is b, the coefficient of the middle term.

If there are no such integers, the polynomial cannot be factored. A polynomial that cannot be factored with integer coefficients is a **prime polynomial.**

Examples: $x^2 + x + 2, \quad x^2 - x - 1, \quad 2x^2 + x + 7$ Prime polynomials

---

NOW TRY
EXERCISE 1

Factor each trinomial.

(a) $t^2 - t - 30$

(b) $w^2 + 12w + 32$

EXAMPLE 1 Factoring Trinomials in $x^2 + bx + c$ Form

Factor each trinomial.

(a) $x^2 + 2x - 35$

Step 1 Find pairs of integers whose product is -35.

$$35(-1)$$
$$-35(1)$$
$$7(-5)$$
$$-7(5)$$

Step 2 Write sums of those pairs of integers.

$$35 + (-1) = 34$$
$$-35 + 1 = -34$$
$$7 + (-5) = 2 \leftarrow \text{Coefficient of the middle term}$$
$$-7 + 5 = -2$$

The integers 7 and -5 have the necessary product and sum.

$$x^2 + 2x - 35 \quad \text{factors as} \quad (x + 7)(x - 5). \quad \boxed{\text{Multiply to check.}}$$

(b) $r^2 + 8r + 12$

Look for two integers with a product of 12 and a sum of 8. Of all pairs having a product of 12, only the pair 6 and 2 has a sum of 8.

$$r^2 + 8r + 12 \quad \text{factors as} \quad (r + 6)(r + 2).$$

By the commutative property, it is equally correct to write $(r + 2)(r + 6)$. ***Check by using the FOIL method to multiply the factored form.***   **NOW TRY** ↻

NOW TRY
EXERCISE 2

Factor $m^2 + 12m - 11$.

EXAMPLE 2 Recognizing a Prime Polynomial

Factor $m^2 + 6m + 7$.

Look for two integers whose product is 7 and whose sum is 6. Only two pairs of integers, 7 and 1 and -7 and -1, give a product of 7. Neither of these pairs has a sum of 6, so $m^2 + 6m + 7$ cannot be factored with integer coefficients and is prime.   **NOW TRY** ↻

NOW TRY ANSWERS

1. (a) $(t - 6)(t + 5)$
   (b) $(w + 4)(w + 8)$
2. prime

**NOW TRY
EXERCISE 3**

Factor $a^2 + ab - 20b^2$.

EXAMPLE 3   Factoring a Multivariable Trinomial

Factor $x^2 + 6ax - 16a^2$.

This trinomial is in the form $x^2 + bx + c$, where $b = 6a$ and $c = -16a^2$.

Step 1   Find pairs of expressions whose product is $-16a^2$.

| **Step 2** | Write sums of those pairs of expressions. |

$$16a(-a)$$ $16a + (-a) = 15a$

$$-16a(a)$$ $-16a + a = -15a$

$$8a(-2a)$$ $8a + (-2a) = 6a$ ← Coefficient of the middle term

$$-8a(2a)$$ $-8a + 2a = -6a$

$$-4a(4a)$$ $-4a + 4a = 0$

The expressions $8a$ and $-2a$ have the necessary product and sum.

$$x^2 + 6ax - 16a^2 \quad \text{factors as} \quad (x + 8a)(x - 2a).$$

CHECK $(x + 8a)(x - 2a)$

$$= x^2 - 2ax + 8ax - 16a^2 \qquad \text{FOIL method}$$

$$= x^2 + 6ax - 16a^2 \checkmark \qquad \text{Original polynomial}$$ NOW TRY

**NOW TRY
EXERCISE 4**

Factor $5w^3 - 40w^2 + 60w$.

EXAMPLE 4   Factoring a Trinomial with a Common Factor

Factor $16y^3 - 32y^2 - 48y$.

$$16y^3 - 32y^2 - 48y$$

$$= 16y(y^2 - 2y - 3) \qquad \text{Factor out the GCF, } 16y.$$

To factor $y^2 - 2y - 3$, look for two integers whose product is -3 and whose sum is -2. The necessary integers are -3 and 1.

$$= 16y(y - 3)(y + 1) \qquad \text{Factor the trinomial.}$$

Remember to include the GCF, $16y$.   NOW TRY

> ⚠ **CAUTION**   *When factoring, always look for a common factor first. Remember to write the common factor as part of the answer.*

OBJECTIVE 2   Factor trinomials when the coefficient of the second-degree term is not 1.

We can use a generalization of the method shown in **Objective 1** to factor a trinomial of the form $ax^2 + bx + c$, where $a \neq 1$.

To factor $3x^2 + 7x + 2$, for example, we first identify the values a, b, and c.

$$ax^2 + bx + c$$
$$3x^2 + 7x + 2, \quad \text{so} \quad a = 3, \quad b = 7, \quad c = 2$$

The product ac is $3 \cdot 2 = 6$, so we must find integers having a product of 6 and a sum of 7 (because the middle term has coefficient 7). The necessary integers are 1 and 6, so we write $7x$ as $1x + 6x$, or $x + 6x$.

NOW TRY ANSWERS

3. $(a + 5b)(a - 4b)$

4. $5w(w - 6)(w - 2)$

$$3x^2 + 7x + 2$$

$$= 3x^2 + \underbrace{x + 6x}_{} + 2$$

$$x + 6x = 7x$$

$$= (3x^2 + x) + (6x + 2) \qquad \text{Group the terms.}$$

$$= x(3x + 1) + 2(3x + 1) \qquad \text{Factor by grouping.}$$

Check by multiplying. $\quad = (3x + 1)(x + 2) \qquad \text{Factor out the common factor.}$

NOW TRY EXERCISE 5

Factor $8y^2 - 10y - 3$.

EXAMPLE 5   Factoring a Trinomial in $ax^2 + bx + c$ Form

Factor $12r^2 - 5r - 2$.

Here $a = 12$, $b = -5$, and $c = -2$, so the product ac is -24. The two integers whose product is -24 and whose sum b is -5, are 3 and -8.

$$12r^2 - 5r - 2$$

$$= 12r^2 + 3r - 8r - 2 \qquad \text{Write } -5r \text{ as } 3r - 8r.$$

$$= 3r(4r + 1) - 2(4r + 1) \qquad \text{Factor by grouping.}$$

Check by multiplying. $\quad = (4r + 1)(3r - 2) \qquad \text{Factor out the common factor.}$

NOW TRY

OBJECTIVE 3   Use an alternative method for factoring trinomials.

This method involves trying repeated combinations and using the FOIL method.

EXAMPLE 6   Factoring Trinomials in $ax^2 + bx + c$ Form

Factor each trinomial.

(a) $3x^2 + 7x + 2$

The goal is to find the correct numbers to put in the blanks.

$$(\underline{\quad\quad} x + \underline{\quad\quad})(\underline{\quad\quad} x + \underline{\quad\quad})$$

Addition signs are used because all the signs in the polynomial indicate addition. The first two expressions have a product of $3x^2$, so they must be $3x$ and x.

$$(3x + \underline{\quad\quad})(x + \underline{\quad\quad})$$

The product of the two last terms must be 2, so the numbers must be 2 and 1. There is a choice. The 2 could be placed with the $3x$ or with the x. Only one of these choices will give the correct middle term, $7x$.

	$3x$			$6x$	

$$(3x + 2)(x + 1) \qquad \qquad (3x + 1)(x + 2)$$

$$2x \qquad \qquad \qquad \qquad x$$

$$3x + 2x = 5x \qquad \qquad 6x + x = 7x$$

Wrong middle term $\qquad$ Correct middle term

Therefore, $3x^2 + 7x + 2$ factors as $(3x + 1)(x + 2)$. (Compare to the solution obtained by factoring by grouping at the top of this page.)

NOW TRY
EXERCISE 6
Factor $10r^2 + 19r + 6$.

(b) $12r^2 - 5r - 2$

To reduce the number of trials, we note that the terms of the trinomial have greatest common factor 1. This means that neither of its factors can have a common factor except 1. We should keep this in mind as we choose factors. We try 4 and 3 for the two first terms.

$$(4r \underline{\qquad})(3r \underline{\qquad})$$

The factors of -2 are -2 and 1 or -1 and 2. We try both possibilities.

$(4r - 2)(3r + 1)$

Wrong: $4r - 2$ has a
factor of 2, which
cannot be correct,
because 2 is not a factor
of $12r^2 - 5r - 2$.

$(4r - 1)(3r + 2)$

$8r$
$-3r$
$8r - 3r = 5r$
Wrong middle term

The middle term on the right is $5r$, instead of the $-5r$ that is needed. We obtain $-5r$ by interchanging the signs of the second terms in the factors.

$-8r$
$(4r + 1)(3r - 2)$
$3r$

$-8r + 3r = -5r$
Correct middle term

Thus, $12r^2 - 5r - 2$ factors as $(4r + 1)(3r - 2)$. (Compare to **Example 5.**)

CHECK $\quad (4r + 1)(3r - 2)$

$$= 12r^2 - 8r + 3r - 2 \qquad \text{FOIL method}$$

$$= 12r^2 - 5r - 2 \checkmark \qquad \text{Original polynomial}$$

NOW TRY

NOTE As shown in **Example 6(b),** if the terms of a polynomial have greatest common factor 1, then none of the terms of its factors can have a common factor (except 1). Remembering this will eliminate some potential factors.

Factoring $ax^2 + bx + c$ (GCF of a, b, c is 1)

Step 1 **Find pairs whose product is a.** Write all pairs of integer factors of a, the coefficient of the second-degree term.

Step 2 **Find pairs whose product is c.** Write all pairs of integer factors of c, the last term.

Step 3 **Choose inner and outer terms.** Use the FOIL method and various combinations of the factors from Steps 1 and 2 until the necessary middle term is obtained.

If no such combinations exist, the trinomial is prime.

NOW TRY ANSWER
6. $(2r + 3)(5r + 2)$

NOW TRY
EXERCISE 7
Factor $12a^2 - 19ab - 21b^2$.

EXAMPLE 7 Factoring a Multivariable Trinomial

Factor $18m^2 - 19mx - 12x^2$.

The terms of the polynomial have greatest common factor 1. Follow the steps in the preceding box to factor the trinomial. There are many possible factors of both 18 and -12. Try 6 and 3 for 18 and -3 and 4 for -12.

$$(6m - 3x)(3m + 4x) \qquad (6m + 4x)(3m - 3x)$$

Wrong: common factor   Wrong: common factors

Because 6 and 3 do not work as factors of 18, try 9 and 2 instead, with 3 and -4 as factors of -12.

$$(9m + 3x)(2m - 4x) \qquad \overbrace{(9m - 4x)(2m + 3x)}^{27mx}$$

Wrong: common factors $\underbrace{}_{-8mx}$

$27mx + (-8mx) = 19mx$
Wrong middle term

The result on the right differs from the correct middle term only in sign, so interchange the signs of the second terms in the factors.

$$18m^2 - 19mx - 12x^2 \quad \text{factors as} \quad (9m + 4x)(2m - 3x)$$

Check by multiplying.

NOW TRY

NOW TRY
EXERCISE 8
Factor $-8x^2 + 22x - 15$.

EXAMPLE 8 Factoring a Trinomial in $ax^2 + bx + c$ Form ($a < 0$)

Factor $-3x^2 + 16x + 12$.

While we could factor directly, it is helpful to first factor out -1 so that the coefficient of the x^2-term is positive.

$$-3x^2 + 16x + 12$$

$$= -1(3x^2 - 16x - 12) \qquad \text{Factor out } -1.$$

$$= -1(3x + 2)(x - 6) \qquad \text{Factor the trinomial.}$$

$$= -(3x + 2)(x - 6) \qquad -1a = -a \qquad \text{NOW TRY}$$

NOTE The factored form in **Example 8** can be written in other ways, such as

$$(-3x - 2)(x - 6) \quad \text{and} \quad (3x + 2)(-x + 6).$$

Verify that these both give the original trinomial when multiplied.

NOW TRY
EXERCISE 9
Factor $12y^3 + 33y^2 - 9y$.

EXAMPLE 9 Factoring a Trinomial with a Common Factor

Factor $16y^3 + 24y^2 - 16y$.

$$16y^3 + 24y^2 - 16y$$

$$= 8y(2y^2 + 3y - 2) \qquad \text{GCF} = 8y$$

Remember the common factor.

$$= 8y(2y - 1)(y + 2) \qquad \text{Factor the trinomial.} \qquad \text{NOW TRY}$$

NOW TRY ANSWERS
7. $(4a + 3b)(3a - 7b)$
8. $-(4x - 5)(2x - 3)$
9. $3y(4y - 1)(y + 3)$

OBJECTIVE 4 Factor by substitution.

NOW TRY
EXERCISE 10

Factor.

$3(a+2)^2 - 11(a+2) - 4$

EXAMPLE 10 Factoring a Polynomial by Substitution

Factor $2(x+3)^2 + 5(x+3) - 12$.

The binomial $x + 3$ appears to powers 2 and 1, so we let a substitution variable represent $x + 3$. We may choose any letter we wish except x. We choose t.

$$2(x+3)^2 + 5(x+3) - 12$$

$$= 2t^2 + 5t - 12 \qquad\qquad \text{Let } t = x + 3.$$

> Don't stop here.

$$= (2t - 3)(t + 4) \qquad\qquad \text{Factor.}$$

> Be sure to make the final substitution.

$$= [2(x+3) - 3][(x+3) + 4] \qquad \text{Replace } t \text{ with } x + 3.$$

$$= (2x + 6 - 3)(x + 7) \qquad\qquad \text{Simplify.}$$

$$= (2x + 3)(x + 7) \qquad\qquad\qquad\qquad \text{NOW TRY}$$

NOW TRY
EXERCISE 11

Factor $6x^4 + 11x^2 + 3$.

EXAMPLE 11 Factoring a Trinomial in $ax^4 + bx^2 + c$ Form

Factor $6y^4 + 7y^2 - 20$.

The variable y appears to powers in which the greater exponent is twice the lesser exponent. We can let a substitution variable represent the variable to the lesser power.

$$6y^4 + 7y^2 - 20$$

$$= 6(y^2)^2 + 7y^2 - 20 \qquad y^4 = (y^2)^2$$

$$= 6t^2 + 7t - 20 \qquad\qquad \text{Let } t = y^2.$$

> Don't stop here.
> Replace t with y^2.

$$= (3t - 4)(2t + 5) \qquad\qquad \text{Factor.}$$

$$= (3y^2 - 4)(2y^2 + 5) \qquad \text{Replace } t \text{ with } y^2. \qquad \text{NOW TRY}$$

NOTE Some students feel comfortable factoring polynomials like the one in **Example 11** directly, without using the substitution method. We try 3 and 2 as factors of 6 and -4 and 5 as factors of -20.

$$6y^4 + 7y^2 - 20$$

$$
\overset{\displaystyle 15y^2}{= (3y^2 - 4)(2y^2 + 5)}
$$
$$\underset{\displaystyle -8y^2}{} \qquad \begin{array}{l} 3y^2 \cdot 2y^2 = 6y^4 \\ -4(5) = 20 \end{array}$$

$$15y^2 - 8y^2 = 7y^2$$

Correct middle term

NOW TRY ANSWERS
10. $(3a + 7)(a - 2)$
11. $(3x^2 + 1)(2x^2 + 3)$

5.2 Exercises

FOR EXTRA HELP

MyMathLab®

● *Complete solution available in MyMathLab*

Concept Check   *Choose the correct response.*

1. Which is *not* a valid way of starting the process of factoring the trinomial $12x^2 + 29x + 10$?

   A. $(12x \quad)(x \quad)$

   B. $(4x \quad)(3x \quad)$

   C. $(6x \quad)(2x \quad)$

   D. $(8x \quad)(4x \quad)$

2. Which is the completely factored form of the trinomial $2x^6 - 5x^5 - 3x^4$?

    A. $x^4(2x + 1)(x - 3)$ **B.** $x^4(2x - 1)(x + 3)$

    C. $(2x^5 + x^4)(x - 3)$ **D.** $x^3(2x^2 + x)(x - 3)$

3. Which is the completely factored form of the trinomial $4x^2 - 4x - 24$?

    A. $4(x - 2)(x + 3)$ **B.** $4(x + 2)(x + 3)$

    C. $4(x + 2)(x - 3)$ **D.** $4(x - 2)(x - 3)$

4. Which is *not* a factored form of the trinomial $-x^2 + 16x - 60$?

    A. $(x - 10)(-x + 6)$ **B.** $(-x - 10)(x + 6)$

    C. $(-x + 10)(x - 6)$ **D.** $-1(x - 10)(x - 6)$

5. *Concept Check* When a student was given the polynomial $4x^2 + 2x - 20$ to factor completely on a test, the student lost some credit when her answer was

$$(4x + 10)(x - 2).$$

WHAT WENT WRONG? Give the correct answer.

6. *Concept Check* When factoring the polynomial

$$-4x^2 - 29x + 24,$$

Terry obtained $(-4x + 3)(x + 8)$. Johnny wrote $(4x - 3)(-x - 8)$. Who is correct?

Complete each factoring. **See Examples 1 and 3–8.**

7. $x^2 + 8x + 15$ **8.** $y^2 + 11y + 18$ **9.** $m^2 - 10m + 21$

   $= (x + 5)(\underline{\quad})$ $= (y + 2)(\underline{\quad})$ $= (m - 3)(\underline{\quad})$

10. $n^2 - 14n + 48$ **11.** $r^2 - r - 20$ **12.** $x^2 + 4x - 32$

   $= (n - 6)(\underline{\quad})$ $= (r + 4)(\underline{\quad})$ $= (x - 4)(\underline{\quad})$

13. $x^2 + ax - 6a^2$ **14.** $m^2 - 3mn - 10n^2$ **15.** $4x^2 - 4x - 3$

   $= (x + 3a)(\underline{\quad})$ $= (m + 2n)(\underline{\quad})$ $= (2x + 1)(\underline{\quad})$

16. $6z^2 - 11z + 4$ **17.** $12u^2 + 10uv + 2v^2$ **18.** $16p^2 - 4pq - 2q^2$

   $= (3z - 4)(\underline{\quad})$ $= 2(3u + v)(\underline{\quad})$ $= 2(2p - q)(\underline{\quad})$

Factor each trinomial. **See Examples 1–9.**

▶ **19.** $y^2 + 7y - 30$ **20.** $z^2 + 2z - 24$ **21.** $p^2 + 15p + 56$

22. $k^2 - 11k + 30$ ▶ **23.** $m^2 - 11m + 60$ **24.** $p^2 - 12p - 27$

▶ **25.** $a^2 - 2ab - 35b^2$ **26.** $z^2 + 8zw + 15w^2$ **27.** $a^2 - 9ab + 18b^2$

28. $k^2 - 11hk + 28h^2$ **29.** $x^2y^2 + 12xy + 18$ **30.** $p^2q^2 - 5pq - 18$

31. $-6m^2 - 13m + 15$ **32.** $-15y^2 + 17y + 18$ ▶ **33.** $10x^2 + 3x - 18$

34. $8k^2 + 34k + 35$ ▶ **35.** $20k^2 + 47k + 24$ **36.** $27z^2 + 42z - 5$

▶ **37.** $15a^2 - 22ab + 8b^2$ **38.** $14c^2 - 17cd - 6d^2$ **39.** $36m^2 - 60m + 25$

40. $25r^2 - 90r + 81$ **41.** $40x^2 + xy + 6y^2$ **42.** $15p^2 + 24pq + 8q^2$

43. $6x^2z^2 + 5xz - 4$ **44.** $8m^2n^2 - 10mn + 3$ ▶ **45.** $24x^2 + 42x + 15$

46. $36x^2 + 18x - 4$ ▶ **47.** $-15a^2 - 70a + 120$ **48.** $-12a^2 - 10a + 42$

49. $-11x^3 + 110x^2 - 264x$ **50.** $-9k^3 - 36k^2 + 189k$

51. $2x^3y^3 - 48x^2y^4 + 288xy^5$ **52.** $6m^3n^2 - 60m^2n^3 + 150mn^4$

▶ **53.** $6a^3 + 12a^2 - 90a$ **54.** $3m^4 + 6m^3 - 72m^2$

55. $13y^3 + 39y^2 - 52y$ **56.** $4p^3 + 24p^2 - 64p$

57. $12p^3 - 12p^2 + 3p$ **58.** $45t^3 + 60t^2 + 20t$

Factor each trinomial. See Example 10.

59. $12p^6 - 32p^3r + 5r^2$ **60.** $2y^6 + 7xy^3 + 6x^2$

▶ **61.** $10(k + 1)^2 - 7(k + 1) + 1$ **62.** $4(m - 5)^2 - 4(m - 5) - 15$

63. $3(m + p)^2 - 7(m + p) - 20$ **64.** $4(x - y)^2 - 23(x - y) - 6$

Extending Skills   *Factor each trinomial. (Hint: Factor out the GCF first.)*

65. $a^2(a + b)^2 - ab(a + b)^2 - 6b^2(a + b)^2$

66. $m^2(m - p)^2 - mp(m - p)^2 - 12p^2(m - p)^2$

67. $p^2(p + q) + 4pq(p + q) + 3q^2(p + q)$

68. $2k^2(5 - y) - 7k(5 - y) + 5(5 - y)$

69. $z^2(z - x) - zx(x - z) - 2x^2(z - x)$

70. $r^2(r - s) - 5rs(s - r) - 6s^2(r - s)$

Factor each trinomial. See Example 11.

▶ **71.** $p^4 - 10p^2 + 16$ **72.** $k^4 + 10k^2 + 9$ **73.** $2x^4 - 9x^2 - 18$

74. $6z^4 + z^2 - 1$ **75.** $16x^4 + 16x^2 + 3$ **76.** $9r^4 + 9r^2 + 2$

5.3   Special Factoring

OBJECTIVES

1. Factor a difference of squares.
2. Factor a perfect square trinomial.
3. Factor a difference of cubes.
4. Factor a sum of cubes.

VOCABULARY

☐ difference of squares
☐ perfect square trinomial
☐ difference of cubes
☐ sum of cubes

OBJECTIVE 1   Factor a difference of squares.

The special products introduced in **Section 4.4** are used in reverse when factoring. Recall that the product of the sum and difference of two terms leads to a **difference of squares.**

> **Factoring a Difference of Squares**
> $$x^2 - y^2 = (x + y)(x - y)$$

EXAMPLE 1   Factoring Differences of Squares

Factor each polynomial.

(a) $t^2 - 36$

$= t^2 - 6^2$ $36 = 6^2$

$= (t + 6)(t - 6)$ Factor the difference of squares.

(b) $4a^2 - 64$ *Always check for a common factor first.*

$= 4(a^2 - 16)$ Factor out the common factor, 4.

$= 4(a + 4)(a - 4)$ Factor the difference of squares.

$$x^2 \;-\; y^2 \;=\; (x \;+\; y)\;(x \;-\; y)$$

(c) $16m^2 - 49p^2 = (4m)^2 - (7p)^2 = (4m + 7p)(4m - 7p)$

NOW TRY
EXERCISE 1

Factor each polynomial.

(a) $4m^2 - 25n^2$

(b) $9x^2 - 729$

(c) $(a + b)^2 - 25$

(d) $v^4 - 1$

$$x^2 \quad - \quad y^2 \quad = \quad (x \ + \ y) \quad (x \ - \ y)$$

(d) $81k^2 - (a + 2)^2 = (9k)^2 - (a + 2)^2 = (9k + a + 2)(9k - (a + 2))$

$$= (9k + a + 2)(9k - a - 2)$$

We could have used the method of substitution here.

(e) $x^4 - 81$

$$= (x^2 + 9)(x^2 - 9) \qquad \text{Factor the difference of squares.}$$

$$= (x^2 + 9)(x + 3)(x - 3) \qquad \text{Factor the difference of squares again.}$$

NOW TRY

❗ **CAUTION** *Assuming that the greatest common factor is 1, it is not possible to factor (with real numbers) a sum of squares* such as $x^2 + 9$ in **Example 1(e)**. In particular, $x^2 + y^2 \neq (x + y)^2$, as shown next.

OBJECTIVE 2 Factor a perfect square trinomial.

Two other special products from **Section 4.4** lead to the following rules for factoring.

> **Factoring a Perfect Square Trinomial**
>
> $$x^2 + 2xy + y^2 = (x + y)^2$$
> $$x^2 - 2xy + y^2 = (x - y)^2$$

Because the trinomial $x^2 + 2xy + y^2$ is the square of $x + y$, it is called a **perfect square trinomial.** In this pattern, both the first and the last terms of the trinomial must be perfect squares. In the factored form $(x + y)^2$, twice the product of the first and the last terms must give the middle term of the trinomial.

$$4m^2 + 20m + 25 \qquad\qquad\qquad p^2 - 8p + 64$$

Perfect square trinomial;
$4m^2 = (2m)^2$, $25 = 5^2$,
and $2(2m)(5) = 20m$.

Not a perfect square trinomial;
middle term would have to be
$16p$ or $-16p$.

EXAMPLE 2 Factoring Perfect Square Trinomials

Factor each polynomial.

(a) $144p^2 - 120p + 25$

Here, $144p^2 = (12p)^2$ and $25 = 5^2$. The sign on the middle term is $-$, so if $144p^2 - 120p + 25$ is a perfect square trinomial, the factored form will have to be

$$(12p - 5)^2.$$

Determine twice the product of the two terms to see if this is correct.

$$2(12p)(-5) = -120p \longleftarrow \text{Desired middle term}$$

This is the middle term of the given trinomial.

$$144p^2 - 120p + 25 \quad \text{factors as} \quad (12p - 5)^2.$$

NOW TRY ANSWERS

1. (a) $(2m + 5n)(2m - 5n)$

(b) $9(x + 9)(x - 9)$

(c) $(a + b + 5)(a + b - 5)$

(d) $(v^2 + 1)(v + 1)(v - 1)$

Factor each polynomial.

(a) $a^2 + 12a + 36$

(b) $16x^2 - 56xy + 49y^2$

(c) $y^2 - 16y + 64 - z^2$

(b) $4m^2 + 20mn + 49n^2$

If this is a perfect square trinomial, it will equal $(2m + 7n)^2$. By the pattern in the box, if multiplied out, this squared binomial has a middle term of

$$2(2m)(7n) = 28mn, \quad \textit{which does not equal} \quad 20mn.$$

Verify that this trinomial cannot be factored by the methods of the previous section either. It is prime.

(c) $(r + 5)^2 + 6(r + 5) + 9$

$$= [(r + 5) + 3]^2 \qquad 2(r + 5)(3) = 6(r + 5) \text{ is the middle term.}$$

$$= (r + 8)^2 \qquad \text{Add.}$$

(d) $m^2 - 8m + 16 - p^2$

There are four terms, so we will use factoring by grouping. The first three terms here form a perfect square trinomial.

$$m^2 - 8m + 16 - p^2$$

$$= (m^2 - 8m + 16) - p^2 \qquad \text{Group the terms of the perfect square trinomial.}$$

$$= (m - 4)^2 - p^2 \qquad \text{Factor the perfect square trinomial.}$$

$$= (m - 4 + p)(m - 4 - p) \qquad \text{Factor the difference of squares.} \qquad \textbf{NOW TRY} \; \circlearrowleft$$

> **NOTE**   Perfect square trinomials can be factored by the general methods shown earlier for other trinomials. The patterns given here provide "shortcuts."

OBJECTIVE 3   Factor a difference of cubes.

A **difference of cubes,** $x^3 - y^3$, can be factored as follows.

Factoring a Difference of Cubes

$$x^3 - y^3 = (x - y)(x^2 + xy + y^2)$$

Check by showing that the product of $x - y$ and $x^2 + xy + y^2$ is $x^3 - y^3$.

EXAMPLE 3   **Factoring Differences of Cubes**

Factor each polynomial.

$$x^3 - y^3 = (x - y)(x^2 + x \cdot y + y^2)$$
$$\downarrow \quad \downarrow \quad \downarrow \quad \downarrow \; \downarrow \quad \downarrow \; \downarrow \quad \downarrow$$

(a) $m^3 - 8 = m^3 - 2^3 = (m - 2)(m^2 + m \cdot 2 + 2^2)$

$$= (m - 2)(m^2 + 2m + 4)$$

CHECK $(m - 2)(m^2 + 2m + 4)$

$$= m^3 + 2m^2 + 4m - 2m^2 - 4m - 8 \qquad \text{Distributive property}$$

$$= m^3 - 8 \; \checkmark \qquad \text{Combine like terms.}$$

NOW TRY
EXERCISE 3
Factor each polynomial.

(a) $t^3 - 1$

(b) $125a^3 - 8b^3$

(b) $27x^3 - 8y^3$

$= (3x)^3 - (2y)^3$ Difference of cubes

$= (3x - 2y)[(3x)^2 + (3x)(2y) + (2y)^2]$ Factor.

$= (3x - 2y)(9x^2 + 6xy + 4y^2)$

> $(3x)^2 = 3^2 x^2$, not $3x^2$.
> $(2y)^2 = 2^2 y^2$, not $2y^2$.

(c) $1000k^3 - 27n^3$

$= (10k)^3 - (3n)^3$ Difference of cubes

$= (10k - 3n)[(10k)^2 + (10k)(3n) + (3n)^2]$ Factor.

$= (10k - 3n)(100k^2 + 30kn + 9n^2)$ Multiply.   NOW TRY

OBJECTIVE 4 Factor a sum of cubes.

While the binomial $x^2 + y^2$ cannot be factored with real numbers, a **sum of cubes,** such as $x^3 + y^3$, is factored as follows.

> **Factoring a Sum of Cubes**
>
> $$x^3 + y^3 = (x + y)(x^2 - xy + y^2)$$

To verify this result, find the product of $x + y$ and $x^2 - xy + y^2$.

NOTE In a sum or difference of cubes, the following are true.

- In the binomial factor, the sign of the second term is *always the same* as the sign of the second term in the original polynomial.

- In the trinomial factor, the first and last terms are *always positive.*

- In the trinomial factor, the sign of the middle term is *the opposite of* the sign of the second term in the binomial factor.

EXAMPLE 4 Factoring Sums of Cubes

Factor each polynomial.

(a) $r^3 + 27$

$= r^3 + 3^3$ Sum of cubes

$= (r + 3)(r^2 - 3r + 3^2)$ Factor.

$= (r + 3)(r^2 - 3r + 9)$
> This trinomial cannot be factored further.

(b) $27z^3 + 125$

$= (3z)^3 + 5^3$ Sum of cubes

$= (3z + 5)[(3z)^2 - (3z)(5) + 5^2]$ Factor.

$= (3z + 5)(9z^2 - 15z + 25)$ Multiply.

(c) $125t^3 + 216s^6$

$= (5t)^3 + (6s^2)^3$ Sum of cubes

$= (5t + 6s^2)[(5t)^2 - (5t)(6s^2) + (6s^2)^2]$ Factor.

$= (5t + 6s^2)(25t^2 - 30ts^2 + 36s^4)$ Multiply.

NOW TRY ANSWERS

3. (a) $(t - 1)(t^2 + t + 1)$

   (b) $(5a - 2b)(25a^2 + 10ab + 4b^2)$

NOW TRY
EXERCISE 4
Factor each polynomial.
(a) $1000 + z^3$
(b) $81a^6 + 3b^3$
(c) $(x-3)^3 + y^3$

(d) $3x^2 + 192$

$= 3(x^3 + 64)$ Factor out the common factor.

$= 3(x^3 + 4^3)$ Write as a sum of cubes.

Remember the common factor. $= 3(x+4)(x^2 - 4x + 16)$ Factor.

(e) $(x+2)^3 + t^3$

$= [(x+2) + t][(x+2)^2 - (x+2)t + t^2]$ Sum of cubes

$= (x+2+t)(x^2 + 4x + 4 - xt - 2t + t^2)$ Multiply.   **NOW TRY**

> ⚠ **CAUTION** A common error when factoring $x^3 + y^3$ or $x^3 - y^3$ is to think that the *xy*-term has a coefficient of 2. Because there is no coefficient of 2, expressions of the form $x^2 + xy + y^2$ and $x^2 - xy + y^2$ usually cannot be factored further.

NOW TRY ANSWERS
4. (a) $(10+z) \cdot$
    $(100 - 10z + z^2)$
(b) $3(3a^2 + b) \cdot$
    $(9a^4 - 3a^2b + b^2)$
(c) $(x-3+y) \cdot$
    $(x^2 - 6x + 9 - xy + 3y + y^2)$

Summary of Special Types of Factoring

Difference of Squares	$x^2 - y^2 = (x+y)(x-y)$
Perfect Square Trinomial	$x^2 + 2xy + y^2 = (x+y)^2$
	$x^2 - 2xy + y^2 = (x-y)^2$
Difference of Cubes	$x^3 - y^3 = (x-y)(x^2 + xy + y^2)$
Sum of Cubes	$x^3 + y^3 = (x+y)(x^2 - xy + y^2)$

5.3 Exercises

FOR EXTRA HELP   ▶ MyMathLab®

▶ *Complete solution available in MyMathLab*

Concept Check *Work each problem.*

1. Which of the following binomials are differences of squares?
    A. $64 - k^2$ **B.** $2x^2 - 25$ **C.** $k^2 + 9$ **D.** $4z^4 - 49$

2. Which of the following binomials are sums or differences of cubes?
    A. $64 + r^3$ **B.** $125 - p^6$ **C.** $9x^3 + 125$ **D.** $(x+y)^3 - 1$

3. Which of the following trinomials are perfect squares?
    A. $x^2 - 8x - 16$ **B.** $4m^2 + 20m + 25$
    C. $9z^4 + 30z^2 + 25$ **D.** $25p^2 - 45p + 81$

4. Of the twelve polynomials listed in **Exercises 1–3,** which ones can be factored by the methods of this section?

5. The binomial $4x^2 + 64$ is an example of a sum of two squares that can be factored. Under what conditions can a sum of two squares be factored?

6. Insert the correct signs in the blanks.
    (a) $8 + m^3$ **(b)** $n^3 - 1$
    $= (2 \underline{\quad} m)(4 \underline{\quad} 2m \underline{\quad} m^2)$ $= (n \underline{\quad} 1)(n^2 \underline{\quad} n \underline{\quad} 1)$

Factor each polynomial. ***See Examples 1–4.***

▶ **7.** $p^2 - 16$

8. $k^2 - 9$

9. $25x^2 - 4$

10. $36m^2 - 25$

11. $18a^2 - 98b^2$

12. $32c^2 - 98d^2$

13. $64m^4 - 4y^4$

14. $243x^4 - 3t^4$

15. $(y + z)^2 - 81$

16. $(h + k)^2 - 9$

17. $16 - (x + 3y)^2$

18. $64 - (r + 2t)^2$

19. $p^4 - 256$

20. $a^4 - 625$

21. $k^2 - 6k + 9$

22. $x^2 + 10x + 25$

▶ **23.** $4z^2 + 4zw + w^2$

24. $9y^2 + 6yz + z^2$

25. $16m^2 - 8m + 1 - n^2$

26. $25c^2 - 20c + 4 - d^2$

27. $4r^2 - 12r + 9 - s^2$

28. $9a^2 - 24a + 16 - b^2$

29. $x^2 - y^2 + 2y - 1$

30. $-k^2 - h^2 + 2kh + 4$

31. $98m^2 + 84mn + 18n^2$

32. $80z^2 - 40zw + 5w^2$

33. $(p + q)^2 + 2(p + q) + 1$

34. $(x + y)^2 + 6(x + y) + 9$

35. $(a - b)^2 + 8(a - b) + 16$

36. $(m - n)^2 + 4(m - n) + 4$

▶ **37.** $x^3 - 27$

38. $y^3 - 64$

39. $216 - t^3$

40. $512 - m^3$

▶ **41.** $x^3 + 64$

42. $r^3 + 343$

43. $1000 + y^3$

44. $729 + x^3$

45. $8x^3 + 1$

46. $27y^3 + 1$

47. $125x^3 - 216$

48. $8w^3 - 125$

49. $x^3 - 8y^3$

50. $z^3 - 125p^3$

51. $64g^3 - 27h^3$

52. $27a^3 - 8b^3$

53. $343p^3 + 125q^3$

54. $512t^3 + 27s^3$

55. $24n^3 + 81p^3$

56. $250x^3 + 16y^3$

57. $(y + z)^3 + 64$

58. $(p - q)^3 + 125$

59. $m^6 - 125$

60. $27r^6 + 1$

61. $27 - 1000x^9$

62. $64 - 729p^9$

63. $125y^6 + z^3$

64. *Concept Check*   Consider $(x - y)^2 - 25$. To factor this polynomial, is the first step $x^2 - 2xy + y^2 - 25$ correct?

Extending Skills   *In some cases, the method of factoring by grouping can be combined with the methods of special factoring discussed in this section. Consider this example.*

$$8x^3 + 4x^2 + 27y^3 - 9y^2$$

$$= (8x^3 + 27y^3) + (4x^2 - 9y^2) \qquad \text{Associative and commutative properties}$$

$$= (2x + 3y)(4x^2 - 6xy + 9y^2) + (2x + 3y)(2x - 3y) \qquad \text{Factor within groups.}$$

$$= (2x + 3y)\left[(4x^2 - 6xy + 9y^2) + (2x - 3y)\right] \qquad \text{Factor out the greatest common factor, } 2x + 3y.$$

$$= (2x + 3y)(4x^2 - 6xy + 9y^2 + 2x - 3y) \qquad \text{Combine like terms.}$$

In problems such as this, how we choose to group in the first step is essential to factoring correctly. If we reach a "dead end," then we should group differently and try again.

Use the method just described to factor each polynomial.

65. $125p^3 + 25p^2 + 8q^3 - 4q^2$

66. $27x^3 + 9x^2 + y^3 - y^2$

67. $27a^3 + 15a - 64b^3 - 20b$

68. $1000k^3 + 20k - m^3 - 2m$

69. $8t^4 - 24t^3 + t - 3$

70. $y^4 + y^3 + y + 1$

71. $64m^2 - 512m^3 - 81n^2 + 729n^3$

72. $10x^2 + 5x^3 - 10y^2 + 5y^3$

RELATING CONCEPTS   For Individual or Group Work   **(Exercises 73–78)**

The binomial $x^6 - y^6$ may be considered either as a difference of squares or a difference of cubes. **Work Exercises 73–78 in order.**

73. Factor $x^6 - y^6$ by first factoring as a difference of squares. Then factor further by considering one of the factors as a sum of cubes and the other factor as a difference of cubes.

74. Based on the answer in **Exercise 73,** fill in the blank with the correct factors so that $x^6 - y^6$ is factored completely.

$$x^6 - y^6 = (x - y)(x + y) \underline{\hspace{4cm}}$$

75. Factor $x^6 - y^6$ by first factoring as a difference of cubes. Then factor further by considering one of the factors as a difference of squares.

76. Based on the answer in **Exercise 75,** fill in the blank with the correct factor so that $x^6 - y^6$ is factored.

$$x^6 - y^6 = (x - y)(x + y) \underline{\hspace{4cm}}$$

77. Notice that the factor written in the blank in **Exercise 76** is a fourth-degree polynomial, while the two factors written in the blank in **Exercise 74** are both second-degree polynomials. What must be true about the product of the two factors written in the blank in **Exercise 74?** Verify this.

78. If we have a choice of factoring as a difference of squares or a difference of cubes, how should we start to more easily obtain the completely factored form of the polynomial? Base the answer on the results in **Exercises 73–77.**

5.4 A General Approach to Factoring

OBJECTIVE

1 Factor any polynomial.

A polynomial is *completely factored* when it is written as a product of prime polynomials with integer coefficients.

Factoring a Polynomial

Step 1 **Factor out any common factor.**

Step 2 **If the polynomial is a binomial,** check to see if it is a difference of squares, a difference of cubes, or a sum of cubes.

If the polynomial is a trinomial, check to see if it is a perfect square trinomial. If it is not, factor as in **Section 5.2.**

If the polynomial has more than three terms, try to factor by grouping.

Step 3 **If any of the factors can be factored further, do so.**

Step 4 **Check the factored form by multiplying.**

OBJECTIVE 1 Factor any polynomial.

We use the various methods of factoring introduced in **Sections 5.1–5.3.**

**NOW TRY
EXERCISE 1**

Factor each polynomial.
(a) $13x + 39$
(b) $21x^3y^2 - 27x^2y^4$
(c) $8y(m - n) - 5(m - n)$

EXAMPLE 1 Factoring Out a Common Factor

Factor each polynomial.

(a) $9p + 45$

$= 9(p + 5)$ GCF $= 9$

(b) $8m^2p^2 + 4mp$

$= 4mp(2mp + 1)$

(c) $5x(a + b) - y(a + b)$

$= (a + b)(5x - y)$ Factor out $(a + b)$.   NOW TRY

Factoring a Binomial

For a **binomial** (two terms), check for the following patterns.

Difference of squares	$x^2 - y^2 = (x + y)(x - y)$
Difference of cubes	$x^3 - y^3 = (x - y)(x^2 + xy + y^2)$
Sum of cubes	$x^3 + y^3 = (x + y)(x^2 - xy + y^2)$

**NOW TRY
EXERCISE 2**

Factor each binomial if possible.
(a) $4a^2 - 49b^2$
(b) $9x^2 + 100$
(c) $27v^3 - 1000$

EXAMPLE 2 Factoring Binomials

Factor each binomial if possible.

(a) $64m^2 - 9n^2$

$= (8m)^2 - (3n)^2$ Difference of squares

$= (8m + 3n)(8m - 3n)$ $x^2 - y^2 = (x + y)(x - y)$

(b) $8p^3 - 27$

$= (2p)^3 - 3^3$ Difference of cubes

$= (2p - 3)[(2p)^2 + (2p)(3) + 3^2]$ $x^3 - y^3 = (x - y)(x^2 + xy + y^2)$

$= (2p - 3)(4p^2 + 6p + 9)$ $(2p)^2 = 2^2p^2 = 4p^2$

(c) $1000m^3 + 1$

$= (10m)^3 + 1^3$ Sum of cubes

$= (10m + 1)[(10m)^2 - (10m)(1) + 1^2]$ $x^3 + y^3 = (x + y)(x^2 - xy + y^2)$

$= (10m + 1)(100m^2 - 10m + 1)$ $(10m)^2 = 10^2m^2 = 100m^2$

(d) $25m^2 + 121$ is prime. It is a *sum* of squares, with no common factor (except 1).

NOW TRY

NOW TRY ANSWERS
1. (a) $13(x + 3)$
    (b) $3x^2y^2(7x - 9y^2)$
    (c) $(m - n)(8y - 5)$
2. (a) $(2a + 7b)(2a - 7b)$
    (b) prime
    (c) $(3v - 10)(9v^2 + 30v + 100)$

NOTE   Although the binomial $25m^2 + 625$ is a sum of squares, it can be factored because the greatest common factor of the terms is *not* 1.

$$25m^2 + 625 = 25\underbrace{(m^2 + 25)}$$ Factor out the common factor 25.

This sum of squares cannot
be factored further.

Factoring a Trinomial

For a **trinomial** (three terms), decide whether it is a perfect square trinomial of either of these forms.

$$x^2 + 2xy + y^2 = (x + y)^2 \quad \text{or} \quad x^2 - 2xy + y^2 = (x - y)^2$$

If not, use the methods of **Section 5.2.**

NOW TRY
EXERCISE 3

Factor each trinomial.

(a) $25x^2 - 90x + 81$

(b) $7x^2 - 7xy - 84y^2$

(c) $12m^2 + 5m - 28$

EXAMPLE 3   Factoring Trinomials

Factor each trinomial.

(a) $p^2 + 10p + 25$

$= (p + 5)^2$ Perfect square trinomial

(b) $49z^2 - 42z + 9$

$= (7z - 3)^2$ Perfect square trinomial

(c) $y^2 - 5y - 6$

$= (y - 6)(y + 1)$ The numbers -6 and 1 have a product of -6 and a sum of -5.

(d) $2k^2 - k - 6$

$= (2k + 3)(k - 2)$ Use either method from **Section 5.2.**

(e) $28z^2 + 6z - 10$

> Remember the common factor.

$= 2(14z^2 + 3z - 5)$ Factor out the common factor.

$= 2(7z + 5)(2z - 1)$ Factor the trinomial.   **NOW TRY**

If a polynomial has more than three terms, consider factoring by grouping.

EXAMPLE 4   Factoring Polynomials with More Than Three Terms

Factor each polynomial.

(a) $xy^2 - y^3 + x^3 - x^2y$

$= (xy^2 - y^3) + (x^3 - x^2y)$ Group the terms.

$= y^2(x - y) + x^2(x - y)$ Factor each group.

$= (x - y)(y^2 + x^2)$ $x - y$ is a common factor.

(b) $20k^3 + 4k^2 - 45k - 9$ > Be careful with signs.

$= (20k^3 + 4k^2) - (45k + 9)$

$= 4k^2(5k + 1) - 9(5k + 1)$ Factor each group.

$= (5k + 1)(4k^2 - 9)$ $5k + 1$ is a common factor.

$= (5k + 1)(2k + 3)(2k - 3)$ Difference of squares

(c) $4a^2 + 4a + 1 - b^2$

$= (4a^2 + 4a + 1) - b^2$ Associative property

$= (2a + 1)^2 - b^2$ Perfect square trinomial

$= (2a + 1 + b)(2a + 1 - b)$ Difference of squares

NOW TRY ANSWERS

3. (a) $(5x - 9)^2$
   (b) $7(x + 3y)(x - 4y)$
   (c) $(4m + 7)(3m - 4)$

NOW TRY EXERCISE 4

Factor each polynomial.
(a) $5a^3 + 5a^2b - ab^2 - b^3$
(b) $9u^2 - 48u + 64 - v^2$
(c) $x^3 - 9y^2 - 27y^3 + x^2$

(d) $8m^3 + 4m^2 - n^3 - n^2$

$= \underbrace{(8m^3 - n^3)}_{\text{Difference of cubes}} + \underbrace{(4m^2 - n^2)}_{\text{Difference of squares}}$ Rearrange and group the terms.

$= (2m - n)(4m^2 + 2mn + n^2) + (2m - n)(2m + n)$ Factor each group.

$= (2m - n)(4m^2 + 2mn + n^2 + 2m + n)$ Factor out the common factor $2m - n$.   **NOW TRY**

NOW TRY ANSWERS
4. **(a)** $(a + b)(5a^2 - b^2)$
 (b) $(3u - 8 + v)(3u - 8 - v)$
 (c) $(x - 3y)(x^2 + 3xy + 9y^2 + x + 3y)$

NOTE Observe the final two lines in **Example 4(d).** Students often ask, *"What happened to the other $(2m - n)$?"* Think of the variable a in the expression $ax + ay$, which is factored as $a(x + y)$. The binomial $(2m - n)$ is handled just like a in this simpler example.

5.4 Exercises

FOR EXTRA HELP   MyMathLab®

 Complete solution available in MyMathLab

Concept Check In Exercises 1 and 2, match each polynomial in Column I with the method or methods for factoring it in Column II. The choices in Column II may be used once, more than once, or not at all.

I	II
1. (a) $49x^2 - 81y^2$	**A.** Factor out the GCF.
(b) $125z^6 + 1$	**B.** Factor a difference of squares.
(c) $88r^2 - 55s^2$	**C.** Factor a difference of cubes.
(d) $64a^3 - 8b^9$	**D.** Factor a sum of cubes.
(e) $50x^2 - 128y^4$	**E.** The polynomial is prime.

I	II
2. (a) $ab - 5a + 3b - 15$	**A.** Factor out the GCF.
(b) $z^2 - 3z + 6$	**B.** Factor a perfect square trinomial.
(c) $x^2 - 12x + 36 - 4p^2$	**C.** Factor by grouping.
(d) $r^2 - 24r + 144$	**D.** Factor into two distinct binomials.
(e) $2y^2 + 36y + 162$	**E.** The polynomial is prime.

*The following exercises are of mixed variety. Factor each polynomial. **See Examples 1–4.***

3. $3p^4 - 3p^3 - 90p^2$

4. $k^4 - 16$

5. $3a^2pq + 3abpq - 90b^2pq$

6. $49z^2 - 16$

 7. $225p^2 + 256$

8. $18m^3n + 3m^2n^2 - 6mn^3$

 9. $6b^2 - 17b - 3$

10. $k^2 - 6k - 16$

11. $x^3 - 1000$

12. $6t^2 + 19tu - 77u^2$

 13. $4(p + 2) + m(p + 2)$

14. $40p - 32r$

15. $9m^2 - 45m + 18m^3$

16. $4k^2 + 28kr + 49r^2$

17. $54m^3 - 2000$

18. $mn - 2n + 5m - 10$

19. $9m^2 - 30mn + 25n^2$

20. $2a^2 - 7a - 4$

▶ **21.** $kq - 9q + kr - 9r$

22. $56k^3 - 875$

23. $16z^3x^2 - 32z^2x$

24. $9r^2 + 100$

25. $x^2 + 2x - 35$

26. $9 - a^2 + 2ab - b^2$

27. $625 - x^4$

28. $2m^2 - mn - 15n^2$

29. $p^3 + 1$

30. $48y^2z^3 - 28y^3z^4$

31. $64m^2 - 625$

32. $14z^2 - 3zk - 2k^2$

33. $12z^3 - 6z^2 + 18z$

34. $225k^2 - 36r^2$

35. $256b^2 - 400c^2$

36. $z^2 - zp - 20p^2$

37. $512 + 1000z^3$

38. $64m^2 - 25n^2$

39. $10r^2 + 23rs - 5s^2$

40. $12k^2 - 17kq - 5q^2$

41. $24p^3q + 52p^2q^2 + 20pq^3$

42. $32x^2 + 16x^3 - 24x^5$

43. $48k^4 - 243$

44. $14x^2 - 25xq - 25q^2$

45. $m^3 + m^2 - n^3 - n^2$

46. $64x^3 + y^3 - 16x^2 + y^2$

47. $x^2 - 4m^2 - 4mn - n^2$

48. $4r^2 - s^2 - 2st - t^2$

49. $18p^5 - 24p^3 + 12p^6$

50. $k^2 - 6k + 16$

51. $2x^2 - 2x - 40$

52. $27x^3 - 3y^3$

53. $(2m + n)^2 - (2m - n)^2$

54. $(3k + 5)^2 - 4(3k + 5) + 4$

55. $50p^2 - 162$

56. $y^2 + 3y - 10$

57. $12m^2rx + 4mnrx + 40n^2rx$

58. $18p^2 + 53pr - 35r^2$

59. $21a^2 - 5ab - 4b^2$

60. $x^2 - 2xy + y^2 - 4$

61. $x^2 - y^2 - 4$

62. $(5r + 2s)^2 - 6(5r + 2s) + 9$

63. $(p + 8q)^2 - 10(p + 8q) + 25$

64. $z^4 - 9z^2 + 20$

65. $21m^4 - 32m^2 - 5$

66. $(x - y)^3 - (27 - y)^3$

67. $(r + 2t)^3 + (r - 3t)^3$

68. $16x^3 + 32x^2 - 9x - 18$

69. $x^5 + 3x^4 - x - 3$

70. $1 - x^{16}$

71. $m^2 - 4m + 4 - n^2 + 6n - 9$

72. $x^2 + 4 + x^2y + 4y$

(5.5) Solving Equations by the Zero-Factor Property

OBJECTIVES

1 Learn and use the zero-factor property.

2 Solve applied problems that require the zero-factor property.

3 Solve a formula for a specified variable, where factoring is necessary.

VOCABULARY

☐ quadratic equation
☐ double solution

In **Chapter 1,** we developed methods for solving linear, or first-degree, equations. Solving higher degree polynomial equations requires other methods, one of which involves factoring.

OBJECTIVE 1 Learn and use the zero-factor property.

The **zero-factor property** is a special property of the number 0.

Zero-Factor Property

If two numbers have a product of 0, then at least one of the numbers must be 0.

If $ab = 0,$ then either $a = 0$ or $b = 0.$

To prove the zero-factor property, we first assume that $a \neq 0$. (If a does equal 0, then the property is proved already.) If $a \neq 0$, then $\frac{1}{a}$ exists, and both sides of $ab = 0$ can be multiplied by $\frac{1}{a}$.

$$\frac{1}{a} \cdot ab = \frac{1}{a} \cdot 0 \qquad \text{Multiply each side of } ab = 0 \text{ by } \tfrac{1}{a}.$$

$$b = 0 \qquad \text{Multiply.}$$

Thus, if $a \neq 0$, then $b = 0$, and the property is proved.

⚠ CAUTION If $ab = 0$, then $a = 0$ or $b = 0$. However, if $ab = 6$, for example, it is not necessarily true that $a = 6$ or $b = 6$. In fact, it is very likely that *neither a = 6 nor b = 6*. **The zero-factor property works only for a product equal to 0.**

NOW TRY EXERCISE 1
Solve.

$$(x + 5)(4x - 7) = 0$$

EXAMPLE 1 Using the Zero-Factor Property to Solve an Equation

Solve $(x + 6)(2x - 3) = 0$.

Here, the product of $x + 6$ and $2x - 3$ is 0. By the zero-factor property, the following must hold true.

$$x + 6 = 0 \quad \text{or} \quad 2x - 3 = 0 \qquad \text{Zero-factor property}$$

$$x = -6 \quad \text{or} \qquad 2x = 3 \qquad \text{Solve each of these equations.}$$

$$x = \frac{3}{2}$$

CHECK $(x + 6)(2x - 3) = 0$ $(x + 6)(2x - 3) = 0$

$$(-6 + 6)[2(-6) - 3] \overset{?}{=} 0 \qquad \left(\frac{3}{2} + 6\right)\left(2 \cdot \frac{3}{2} - 3\right) \overset{?}{=} 0 \quad \text{Let } x = \tfrac{3}{2}.$$
$$\text{Let } x = -6.$$

$$0(-15) \overset{?}{=} 0 \qquad\qquad\qquad \frac{15}{2}(0) \overset{?}{=} 0$$

$$0 = 0 \; \checkmark \; \text{True} \qquad\qquad\qquad 0 = 0 \; \checkmark \; \text{True}$$

NOW TRY ANSWER

1. $\left\{-5, \frac{7}{4}\right\}$

Both values check, so the solution set is $\left\{-6, \frac{3}{2}\right\}$.   **NOW TRY** ↻

Because the product $(x + 6)(2x - 3)$ equals $2x^2 + 9x - 18$, the equation of **Example 1** has a term with a squared variable and is an example of a *quadratic equation*. *A quadratic equation has degree 2.*

Quadratic Equation

A **quadratic equation** (in x here) can be written in the form

$$ax^2 + bx + c = 0,$$

where a, b, and c are real numbers, and $a \neq 0$. The given form is called **standard form.**

Solving a Quadratic Equation Using the Zero-Factor Property

Step 1 **Write the equation in standard form**—that is, with all terms on one side of the equality symbol in descending powers of the variable and 0 on the other side.

Step 2 **Factor** completely.

Step 3 **Apply the zero-factor property.** Set each factor with a variable equal to 0.

Step 4 **Solve** the resulting equations.

Step 5 **Check** each value in the *original* equation. Write the solution set.

EXAMPLE 2 Solving Quadratic Equations

Solve each equation.

(a) $\qquad\qquad\qquad 2x^2 + 3x = 2$

Step 1	$2x^2 + 3x - 2 = 0$	Standard form
Step 2	$(2x - 1)(x + 2) = 0$	Factor.
Step 3	$2x - 1 = 0 \quad$ or $\quad x + 2 = 0$	Zero-factor property
Step 4	$2x = 1 \quad$ or $\qquad x = -2$	Solve each equation.
	$x = \dfrac{1}{2}$	

Step 5 *Check* each value in the original equation.

CHECK $\qquad 2x^2 + 3x = 2$ $\qquad\qquad\qquad\qquad\qquad 2x^2 + 3x = 2$

$2\left(\dfrac{1}{2}\right)^2 + 3\left(\dfrac{1}{2}\right) \overset{?}{=} 2 \qquad$ Let $x = \frac{1}{2}$. $\qquad 2(-2)^2 + 3(-2) \overset{?}{=} 2 \qquad$ Let $x = -2$.

$2\left(\dfrac{1}{4}\right) + \dfrac{3}{2} \overset{?}{=} 2 \qquad\qquad\qquad\qquad\qquad\qquad 2(4) - 6 \overset{?}{=} 2$

$\dfrac{1}{2} + \dfrac{3}{2} \overset{?}{=} 2 \qquad\qquad\qquad\qquad\qquad\qquad\qquad 8 - 6 \overset{?}{=} 2$

$2 = 2 \ \checkmark \ $ True $\qquad\qquad\qquad\qquad\qquad\qquad\qquad\qquad 2 = 2 \ \checkmark \ $ True

Because both values check, the solution set is $\left\{-2, \dfrac{1}{2}\right\}$. ⟵ We give solutions from least to greatest.

**NOW TRY
EXERCISE 2**
Solve each equation.
(a) $7x = 3 - 6x^2$
(b) $16x^2 + 40x + 25 = 0$

(b)

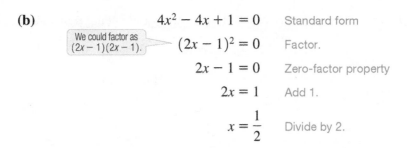

$$4x^2 - 4x + 1 = 0 \qquad \text{Standard form}$$

We could factor as
$(2x - 1)(2x - 1)$.

$$(2x - 1)^2 = 0 \qquad \text{Factor.}$$

$$2x - 1 = 0 \qquad \text{Zero-factor property}$$

$$2x = 1 \qquad \text{Add 1.}$$

$$x = \frac{1}{2} \qquad \text{Divide by 2.}$$

There is only one *distinct* solution, called a **double solution,** because the trinomial is a perfect square. The solution set is $\left\{\frac{1}{2}\right\}$. **NOW TRY**

**NOW TRY
EXERCISE 3**
Solve $3x^2 + 12x = 0$.

EXAMPLE 3 Solving a Quadratic Equation (Missing Constant Term)

Solve $4x^2 - 20x = 0$.

This quadratic equation has a missing constant term. Comparing it with the standard form $ax^2 + bx + c = 0$ shows that $c = 0$. The zero-factor property can still be used.

$$4x^2 - 20x = 0$$

$$4x(x - 5) = 0 \qquad \text{Factor.}$$

Set each *variable* factor equal to 0.

$$4x = 0 \quad \text{or} \quad x - 5 = 0 \qquad \text{Zero-factor property}$$

$$x = 0 \quad \text{or} \qquad x = 5 \qquad \text{Solve each equation.}$$

CHECK

$$4x^2 - 20x = 0 \qquad\qquad\qquad 4x^2 - 20x = 0$$

$$4(0)^2 - 20(0) \overset{?}{=} 0 \quad \text{Let } x = 0. \qquad 4(5)^2 - 20(5) \overset{?}{=} 0 \quad \text{Let } x = 5.$$

$$0 - 0 = 0 \ \checkmark \ \text{True} \qquad\qquad 100 - 100 = 0 \ \checkmark \ \text{True}$$

The solution set is $\{0, 5\}$. **NOW TRY**

⊘ **CAUTION** Remember to include 0 as a solution in **Example 3.**

**NOW TRY
EXERCISE 4**
Solve $4x^2 - 100 = 0$.

EXAMPLE 4 Solving a Quadratic Equation (Missing Linear Term)

Solve $3x^2 - 108 = 0$.

$$3x^2 - 108 = 0$$

$$3(x^2 - 36) = 0 \qquad \text{Factor out 3.}$$

The factor 3
does *not* lead to
a solution.

$$3(x + 6)(x - 6) = 0 \qquad \text{Factor } x^2 - 36.$$

$$x + 6 = 0 \quad \text{or} \quad x - 6 = 0 \qquad \text{Zero-factor property}$$

$$x = -6 \quad \text{or} \qquad x = 6 \qquad \text{Solve each equation.}$$

Check that the solution set is $\{-6, 6\}$. **NOW TRY**

NOW TRY ANSWERS
2. (a) $\left\{-\frac{3}{2}, \frac{1}{3}\right\}$ (b) $\left\{-\frac{5}{4}\right\}$
3. $\{0, -4\}$ 4. $\{-5, 5\}$

⊘ **CAUTION** The factor 3 in **Example 4** is not a ***variable*** factor, so it does *not* lead to a solution of the equation. However, the factor x in **Example 3** is a variable factor and leads to the solution 0.

NOW TRY
EXERCISE 5

Solve.

$$(x + 3)(2x - 1)$$
$$= 4(x + 4) - 4$$

EXAMPLE 5   **Solving an Equation That Requires Rewriting**

Solve $(2x + 1)(x + 1) = 2(1 - x) + 6$.

$$(2x + 1)(x + 1) = 2(1 - x) + 6$$

$$2x^2 + 3x + 1 = 2 - 2x + 6 \qquad \text{Multiply on each side.}$$

$$2x^2 + 3x + 1 = 8 - 2x \qquad \text{Add on the right.}$$

$$\boxed{\text{Write in standard form.}} \quad 2x^2 + 5x - 7 = 0 \qquad \text{Add } 2x. \text{ Subtract 8.}$$

$$(2x + 7)(x - 1) = 0 \qquad \text{Factor.}$$

$$2x + 7 = 0 \quad \text{or} \quad x - 1 = 0 \qquad \text{Zero-factor property}$$

$$x = -\frac{7}{2} \quad \text{or} \qquad x = 1 \qquad \text{Solve each equation.}$$

CHECK
$$(2x + 1)(x + 1) = 2(1 - x) + 6$$

$$\left[2\left(-\frac{7}{2}\right) + 1\right]\left(-\frac{7}{2} + 1\right) \overset{?}{=} 2\left[1 - \left(-\frac{7}{2}\right)\right] + 6 \qquad \text{Let } x = -\frac{7}{2}.$$

$$(-7 + 1)\left(-\frac{5}{2}\right) \overset{?}{=} 2\left(\frac{9}{2}\right) + 6 \qquad \text{Simplify; } 1 = \frac{2}{2}.$$

$$(-6)\left(-\frac{5}{2}\right) \overset{?}{=} 9 + 6$$

$$15 = 15 \checkmark \qquad \text{True}$$

Check that 1 is also a solution. The solution set is $\left\{-\frac{7}{2}, 1\right\}$.   NOW TRY

The zero-factor property can be extended to solve certain polynomial equations of degree 3 or greater, as shown in the next example.

NOW TRY
EXERCISE 6

Solve $12x = 2x^3 + 5x^2$.

EXAMPLE 6   **Solving an Equation of Degree 3**

Solve $-x^3 + x^2 = -6x$.

$$-x^3 + x^2 = -6x$$

$$-x^3 + x^2 + 6x = 0 \qquad \text{Add } 6x \text{ to each side.}$$

$$x^3 - x^2 - 6x = 0 \qquad \text{Multiply each side by } -1.$$

$$x(x^2 - x - 6) = 0 \qquad \text{Factor out } x.$$

$$\boxed{\text{Remember to set } x \text{ equal to 0.}} \quad x(x - 3)(x + 2) = 0 \qquad \text{Factor the trinomial.}$$

$$x = 0 \quad \text{or} \quad x - 3 = 0 \quad \text{or} \quad x + 2 = 0 \qquad \begin{array}{l}\text{Extend the zero-factor property}\\\text{to the three } \textit{variable} \text{ factors.}\end{array}$$

$$x = 3 \quad \text{or} \qquad x = -2$$

NOW TRY ANSWERS
5. $\left\{-3, \frac{5}{2}\right\}$ 6. $\left\{-4, 0, \frac{3}{2}\right\}$

Check that the solution set is $\{-2, 0, 3\}$.   NOW TRY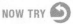

OBJECTIVE 2 Solve applied problems that require the zero-factor property.

An application may lead to a quadratic equation.

**NOW TRY
EXERCISE 7**

The height of a triangle is 1 ft less than twice the length of the base. The area is 14 ft². What are the measures of the base and the height?

EXAMPLE 7 Using a Quadratic Equation in an Application

A piece of sheet metal is in the shape of a parallelogram. The longer sides of the parallelogram are each 8 m longer than the distance between them. The area of the piece is 48 m². Find the length of the longer sides and the distance between them.

Step 1 **Read** the problem again. There will be two answers.

Step 2 **Assign a variable.**

Let x = the distance between the longer sides

and $x + 8$ = the length of each longer side. (See **FIGURE 1**.)

FIGURE 1

Step 3 **Write an equation.** The area of a parallelogram is given by $\mathcal{A} = bh$, where b is the length of the longer side and h is the distance between the longer sides. Here, $b = x + 8$ and $h = x$.

$$\mathcal{A} = bh \qquad \text{Formula for area of a parallelogram}$$
$$48 = (x + 8)x \qquad \text{Let } \mathcal{A} = 48, b = x + 8, h = x.$$

Step 4 **Solve.**
$$48 = x^2 + 8x \qquad \text{Distributive property}$$
$$x^2 + 8x - 48 = 0 \qquad \text{Standard form}$$
$$(x + 12)(x - 4) = 0 \qquad \text{Factor.}$$
$$x + 12 = 0 \quad \text{or} \quad x - 4 = 0 \qquad \text{Zero-factor property}$$
$$x = -12 \quad \text{or} \qquad x = 4 \qquad \text{Solve each equation.}$$

Step 5 **State the answer.** *The distance between the longer sides cannot be negative, so reject* -12 *as an answer.* The only possible answer is 4, so the required distance is 4 m. The length of the longer sides is $4 + 8 = 12$ m.

Step 6 **Check.** The length of the longer sides is 8 m more than the distance between them, and the area is

$$4 \cdot 12 = 48 \text{ m}^2, \quad \text{as required.}$$

The answer checks.

NOW TRY

⚠ CAUTION When an application leads to a quadratic equation, a solution of the equation may not satisfy the physical requirements of the problem, as in **Example 7**. Reject such solutions as answers.

NOW TRY ANSWER
7. base: 4 ft; height: 7 ft

A function defined by a quadratic polynomial is a *quadratic function.* Quadratic functions are used to describe the height a falling object or a projected object reaches in a specific time. The next example uses such a function.

NOW TRY
EXERCISE 8

Refer to **Example 8.** After how many seconds will the rocket be 192 ft above the ground?

EXAMPLE 8   Using a Quadratic Function in an Application

If a small rocket is launched vertically upward from ground level with an initial velocity of 128 ft per sec, then its height in feet after t seconds (if air resistance is neglected) can be modeled by the function

$$h(t) = -16t^2 + 128t.$$

After how many seconds will the rocket be 220 ft above the ground?

    We let $h(t) = 220$ and solve for t.

$$220 = -16t^2 + 128t \qquad \text{Let } h(t) = 220.$$
$$16t^2 - 128t + 220 = 0 \qquad \text{Standard form}$$
$$4t^2 - 32t + 55 = 0 \qquad \text{Divide by 4.}$$
$$(2t - 5)(2t - 11) = 0 \qquad \text{Factor.}$$
$$2t - 5 = 0 \quad \text{or} \quad 2t - 11 = 0 \qquad \text{Zero-factor property}$$
$$t = 2.5 \quad \text{or} \qquad t = 5.5 \qquad \text{Solve each equation.}$$

The rocket will reach a height of 220 ft twice: on its way up at 2.5 sec and again on its way down at 5.5 sec.   NOW TRY

OBJECTIVE 3 Solve a formula for a specified variable, where factoring is necessary.

A rectangular solid has the shape of a box, but is solid. See **FIGURE 2**. The surface area of any solid three-dimensional figure is the total area of its surface. For a rectangular solid, the surface area S is

$$S = 2HW + 2LW + 2LH. \qquad \substack{H,\ W,\text{ and } L \text{ represent height,} \\ \text{width, and length.}}$$

Rectangular solid
$S = 2HW + 2LW + 2LH$

FIGURE 2

NOW TRY
EXERCISE 9

Solve the formula for H.

$$S = 2HW + 2LW + 2LH$$

EXAMPLE 9   Using Factoring to Solve for a Specified Variable

Solve the formula $S = 2HW + 2LW + 2LH$ for L.

    To solve for the length L, treat L as the only variable and treat all other variables as constants.

$$S = 2HW + 2LW + 2LH \quad \substack{\text{We must isolate} \\ \text{the } L\text{-terms.}}$$
$$S - 2HW = 2LW + 2LH \qquad \text{Subtract } 2HW.$$
$$\boxed{\substack{\text{This is a} \\ \text{key step.}}} \ S - 2HW = L(2W + 2H) \qquad \text{Factor out } L.$$
$$\frac{S - 2HW}{2W + 2H} = L, \quad \text{or} \quad L = \frac{S - 2HW}{2W + 2H} \qquad \text{Divide by } 2W + 2H.$$

NOW TRY

NOW TRY ANSWERS
8. 2 sec and 6 sec
9. $H = \frac{S - 2LW}{2W + 2L}$

❗ **CAUTION** *In Example 9, we must write the expression so that the specified variable is a factor. Then we can divide by its coefficient in the final step.*

NOTE In **Section 4.3,** we saw that the graph of $f(x) = x^2$ is a parabola. In general, the graph of

$$f(x) = ax^2 + bx + c \quad \text{(where } a \neq 0\text{)}$$

is a parabola, and the x-intercepts of its graph give the real number solutions of the equation $ax^2 + bx + c = 0$.

A graphing calculator can locate these x-intercepts (called **zeros** of the function) for $f(x) = 2x^2 + 3x - 2$. Notice that this quadratic expression was found on the left side of the equation in **Example 2(a)** earlier in this section, where the equation was written in standard form. The x-intercepts (zeros) given with the graphs in **FIGURE 3** are the same as the solutions found in **Example 2(a).**

FIGURE 3

5.5 Exercises

FOR EXTRA HELP

▶ MyMathLab®

▶ *Complete solution available in MyMathLab*

Concept Check *Choose the correct response.*

1. Which equation is *not* in proper form for using the zero-factor property? Tell why it is not in proper form.

   A. $(x + 2)(x - 6) = 0$ **B.** $x(3x - 7) = 0$

   C. $3t(t + 8)(t - 9) = 0$ **D.** $y(y - 3) + 6(y - 3) = 0$

2. Without actually solving, determine which equation has 0 in its solution set.

   A. $4x^2 - 25 = 0$ **B.** $x^2 + 2x - 3 = 0$

   C. $6x^2 + 9x + 1 = 0$ **D.** $x^3 + 4x^2 = 3x$

Solve each equation. **See Examples 1–5.**

3. $(x + 10)(x - 5) = 0$ **4.** $(x + 7)(x + 3) = 0$ ▶ **5.** $(2k - 5)(3k + 8) = 0$

6. $(3q - 4)(2q + 5) = 0$ **7.** $x^2 - 3x - 10 = 0$ **8.** $x^2 + x - 12 = 0$

9. $x^2 + 9x + 18 = 0$ **10.** $x^2 - 18x + 80 = 0$ ▶ **11.** $2x^2 = 7x + 4$

12. $2x^2 = 3 - x$ **13.** $15x^2 - 7x = 4$ **14.** $3x^2 + 3 = -10x$

▶ **15.** $4p^2 + 16p = 0$ **16.** $2t^2 - 8t = 0$ **17.** $6x^2 - 36x = 0$

18. $3x^2 - 27x = 0$ ▶ **19.** $4p^2 - 16 = 0$ **20.** $9z^2 - 81 = 0$

21. $-3x^2 + 27 = 0$ **22.** $-2x^2 + 8 = 0$ **23.** $-x^2 = 9 - 6x$

24. $-x^2 - 8x = 16$ **25.** $9x^2 + 24x + 16 = 0$ **26.** $4x^2 - 20x + 25 = 0$

27. $(x - 3)(x + 5) = -7$ **28.** $(x + 8)(x - 2) = -21$

29. $(2x + 1)(x - 3) = 6x + 3$

30. $(3x + 2)(x - 3) = 7x - 1$

31. $2x^2 - 12 - 4x = x^2 - 3x$

32. $3x^2 + 9x + 30 = 2x^2 - 2x$

33. $(5x + 1)(x + 3) = -2(5x + 1)$

34. $(3x + 1)(x - 3) = 2 + 3(x + 5)$

▶ **35.** $(x + 3)(x - 6) = (2x + 2)(x - 6)$

36. $(2x + 1)(x + 5) = (x + 11)(x + 3)$

*Solve each equation. **See Example 6.***

37. $2x^3 - 9x^2 - 5x = 0$

38. $6x^3 - 13x^2 - 5x = 0$

▶ **39.** $x^3 - 2x^2 = 3x$

40. $x^3 - 6x^2 = -8x$

41. $9x^3 = 16x$

42. $25x^3 = 64x$

43. $2x^3 + 5x^2 - 2x - 5 = 0$

44. $2x^3 + x^2 - 98x - 49 = 0$

45. $x^3 - 6x^2 - 9x + 54 = 0$

46. $x^3 - 3x^2 - 4x + 12 = 0$

47. *Concept Check*   A student tried to solve the equation in **Exercise 41** by first dividing each side by x, obtaining

$$9x^2 = 16.$$

She then solved the resulting equation by the zero-factor property to obtain the solution set $\left\{-\frac{4}{3}, \frac{4}{3}\right\}$. ***WHAT WENT WRONG?*** Give the correct solution set.

48. *Concept Check*   A student tried to solve the equation in **Exercise 45** by first writing it as

$$x^3 - 6x^2 = 9x - 54$$

$$x^2(x - 6) = 9(x - 6)$$

and then dividing both sides by $x - 6$, to obtain $x^2 = 9$. He then gave the solution set as $\{-3, 3\}$. ***WHAT WENT WRONG?*** Give the correct solution set.

Extending Skills   Solve each equation. (*Hint: In Exercises 49–52, use the substitution of variable method.*)

49. $2(x - 1)^2 - 7(x - 1) - 15 = 0$

50. $4(2x + 3)^2 - (2x + 3) - 3 = 0$

51. $5(3x - 1)^2 + 3 = -16(3x - 1)$

52. $2(x + 3)^2 = 5(x + 3) - 2$

53. $(2x - 3)^2 = 16x^2$

54. $9x^2 = (5x + 2)^2$

*Solve each problem. **See Examples 7 and 8.***

55. A garden has an area of 320 ft². Its length is 4 ft more than its width. What are the dimensions of the garden?

56. A square mirror has sides measuring 2 ft less than the sides of a square painting. If the difference between their areas is 32 ft², find the lengths of the sides of the mirror and the painting.

$x + 4$

x

x

$x - 2$

$x - 2$

57. The base of a parallelogram is 7 ft more than the height. If the area of the parallelogram is 60 ft², what are the measures of the base and the height?

58. A sign has the shape of a triangle. The length of the base is 3 m less than the height. What are the measures of the base and the height if the area is 44 m²?

59. A farmer has 300 ft of fencing and wants to enclose a rectangular area of 5000 ft². What dimensions should she use?

60. A rectangular landfill has an area of 30,000 ft². Its length is 200 ft more than its width. What are the dimensions of the landfill?

61. Find two consecutive integers such that the sum of their squares is 61.

62. Find two consecutive integers such that their product is 72.

63. A box with no top is to be constructed from a piece of cardboard whose length measures 6 in. more than its width. The box is to be formed by cutting squares that measure 2 in. on each side from the four corners and then folding up the sides. If the volume of the box will be 110 in.³, what are the dimensions of the piece of cardboard?

64. The surface area of the box with open top shown in the figure is 161 in.². Find the dimensions of the base. (*Hint:* The surface area of the box is modeled by the function $S(x) = x^2 + 16x$.)

65. If an object is projected upward with an initial velocity of 64 ft per sec from a height of 80 ft, then its height in feet t seconds after it is projected is modeled by the function

$$f(t) = -16t^2 + 64t + 80.$$

How long after it is projected will it hit the ground? (*Hint:* When it hits the ground, its height is 0 ft.)

66. Refer to **Example 8.** After how many seconds will the rocket be

(a) 240 ft above the ground?   (b) 112 ft above the ground?

67. If a baseball is dropped from a helicopter 625 ft above the ground, then its distance in feet from the ground t seconds later is modeled by the function

$$f(t) = -16t^2 + 625.$$

How long after it is dropped will it hit the ground?

68. If a rock is dropped from a building 576 ft high, then its distance in feet from the ground t seconds later is modeled by the function

$$f(t) = -16t^2 + 576.$$

How long after it is dropped will it hit the ground?

69. *Concept Check*   A student solved the formula $S = 2HW + 2LW + 2LH$ for L as follows. **WHAT WENT WRONG?**

$$S = 2HW + 2LW + 2LH$$

$$S - 2LW - 2HW = 2LH$$

$$\frac{S - 2LW - 2HW}{2H} = L$$

70. *Concept Check*   Which is the correct result when solving the following equation for t?

$$2t + c = kt$$

A. $t = \dfrac{-c}{2 - k}$ **B.** $t = \dfrac{c - kt}{-2}$

C. $t = \dfrac{2t + c}{k}$ **D.** $t = \dfrac{kt - c}{2}$

Solve each equation for the specified variable. **See Example 9.**

71. $k = dF - DF$ for F

72. $Mv = mv - Vm$ for m

▶ **73.** $2k + ar = r - 3y$ for r

74. $4s + 7p = tp - 7$ for p

75. $w = \dfrac{3y - x}{y}$ for y

76. $c = \dfrac{-2t + 4}{t}$ for t

Chapter 5   Summary

Key Terms

5.1
factoring
greatest common factor
   (GCF)

5.2
prime polynomial

5.3
difference of squares
perfect square trinomial
difference of cubes
sum of cubes

5.5
quadratic equation
double solution

Test Your Word Power

See how well you have learned the vocabulary in this chapter.

1. Factoring is
   A. a method of multiplying polynomials
   B. the process of writing a polynomial as a product of prime factors
   C. the answer in a multiplication problem
   D. a way to add the terms of a polynomial.

2. The **greatest common factor** of a polynomial is
   A. the least integer that divides evenly into all its terms

   B. the least expression that is a factor of all its terms
   C. the greatest expression that is a factor of all its terms
   D. the variable that is common to all its terms.

3. A **difference of squares** is a binomial
   A. that can be factored as the difference of two cubes
   B. that cannot be factored
   C. that is squared
   D. that can be factored as the product of the sum and difference of two terms.

4. A **perfect square trinomial** is a trinomial
   A. that can be factored as the square of a binomial
   B. that cannot be factored
   C. that is multiplied by a binomial
   D. where all terms are perfect squares.

5. A **quadratic equation** is a polynomial equation of
   A. degree one
   B. degree two
   C. degree three
   D. degree four.

ANSWERS

1. B; *Example:* $x^2 - 5x - 14$ factors as $(x - 7)(x + 2)$.   **2.** C; *Example:* The greatest common factor of $8x^2$, $22xy$, and $16x^3y^2$ is $2x$.
3. D; *Example:* $b^2 - 49$ is the difference of the squares b^2 and 7^2. It can be factored as $(b + 7)(b - 7)$.   **4.** A; *Example:* $a^2 + 2a + 1$ is a perfect square trinomial. Its factored form is $(a + 1)^2$.   **5.** B; *Examples:* $x^2 - 3x + 2 = 0$, $x^2 - 9 = 0$, and $2x^2 = 6x + 8$

Quick Review

CONCEPTS

EXAMPLES

5.1 Greatest Common Factors and Factoring by Grouping

Factoring Out the Greatest Common Factor

Use the distributive property to write the given polynomial as a product of two factors, one of which is the greatest common factor of the terms of the polynomial.

Factor $4x^2y - 50xy^2$.

$$4x^2y - 50xy^2$$
$$= 2xy(2x - 25y) \quad \text{The greatest common factor is } 2xy.$$

Factoring by Grouping

Step 1 Group the terms so that each group has a common factor.

Step 2 Factor out the common factor in each group.

Step 3 If the groups now have a common factor, factor it out. If not, try a different grouping.

Always check the factored form by multiplying.

Factor by grouping.

$$5a - 5b - ax + bx$$
$$= (5a - 5b) + (-ax + bx) \quad \text{Group the terms.}$$
$$= 5(a - b) - x(a - b) \quad \text{Factor out 5 and } -x.$$
$$= (a - b)(5 - x) \quad \text{Factor out } a - b.$$

5.2 Factoring Trinomials

To factor a trinomial, choose factors of the first term and factors of the last term. Then place them within a pair of parentheses of this form.

$$(\qquad)(\qquad)$$

Try various combinations of the factors until the correct middle term of the trinomial is found.

Factor $15x^2 + 14x - 8$.
The factors of 15 are 5 and 3, and 15 and 1.

The factors of -8 are

$$-4 \text{ and } 2, \quad 4 \text{ and } -2, \quad -1 \text{ and } 8, \quad \text{and} \quad 1 \text{ and } -8.$$

Various combinations lead to the correct factorization.

$$15x^2 + 14x - 8$$
$$= (5x - 2)(3x + 4) \quad \text{Check by multiplying.}$$

5.3 Special Factoring

Difference of Squares

$$x^2 - y^2 = (x + y)(x - y)$$

Factor. $\qquad 4m^2 - 25n^2$

$$= (2m)^2 - (5n)^2$$
$$= (2m + 5n)(2m - 5n)$$

Perfect Square Trinomials

$$x^2 + 2xy + y^2 = (x + y)^2$$
$$x^2 - 2xy + y^2 = (x - y)^2$$

$9y^2 + 6y + 1$ $\qquad$ $16p^2 - 56p + 49$

$= (3y + 1)^2$ $\qquad$ $= (4p - 7)^2$

Difference of Cubes

$$x^3 - y^3 = (x - y)(x^2 + xy + y^2)$$

Factor. $\qquad 8 - 27a^3$

$$= (2 - 3a)(4 + 6a + 9a^2)$$

Sum of Cubes

$$x^3 + y^3 = (x + y)(x^2 - xy + y^2)$$

$64z^3 + 1$

$$= (4z + 1)(16z^2 - 4z + 1)$$

CONCEPTS	**EXAMPLES**

5.5 **Solving Equations by the Zero-Factor Property**

Zero-Factor Property

If two numbers have a product of 0, then at least one of the numbers must be 0.

If $ab = 0$, then either $a = 0$ or $b = 0$.

If $(2x - 1)(x + 4) = 0$, then by the zero-factor property

$$2x - 1 = 0 \quad \text{or} \quad x + 4 = 0.$$

Solving a Quadratic Equation Using the Zero-Factor Property.

Step 1   Rewrite the equation if necessary so that one side is 0.

Step 2   Factor the polynomial.

Step 3   Set each factor equal to 0.

Step 4   Solve each equation from Step 3.

Step 5   Check each value, and write the solution set.

Solve.
$$2x^2 + 5x = 3$$
$$2x^2 + 5x - 3 = 0 \qquad \text{Standard form}$$
$$(2x - 1)(x + 3) = 0 \qquad \text{Factor.}$$
$$2x - 1 = 0 \quad \text{or} \quad x + 3 = 0 \qquad \text{Zero-factor property}$$
$$x = \frac{1}{2} \quad \text{or} \qquad x = -3 \qquad \text{Solve each equation.}$$

A check verifies that the solution set is $\left\{-3, \frac{1}{2}\right\}$.

Chapter 5 Review Exercises

1. $6p(2p - 1)$

2. $7x(3x + 5)$

3. $4qb(3q + 2b - 5q^2b)$

4. $6rt(r^2 - 5rt + 3t^2)$

5. $(x + 3)(x - 3)$

6. $(z + 1)(3z - 1)$

7. $(m + q)(4 + n)$

8. $(x + y)(x + 5)$

9. $(m + 3)(2 - a)$

10. $(x + 3)(x - y)$

11. $(3p - 4)(p + 1)$

12. $(3k - 2)(2k + 5)$

13. $(3r + 1)(4r - 3)$

14. $(2m + 5)(5m + 6)$

15. $(2k - h)(5k - 3h)$

16. prime

17. $2x(4 + x)(3 - x)$

18. $3b(2b - 5)(b + 1)$

19. $(y^2 + 4)(y^2 - 2)$

20. $(2k^2 + 1)(k^2 - 3)$

21. $(p + 2)^2(p + 3)(p - 2)$

22. $(3r + 16)(r + 1)$

5.1   *Factor out the greatest common factor.*

1. $12p^2 - 6p$

2. $21x^2 + 35x$

3. $12q^2b + 8qb^2 - 20q^3b^2$

4. $6r^3t - 30r^2t^2 + 18rt^3$

5. $(x + 3)(4x - 1) - (x + 3)(3x + 2)$

6. $(z + 1)(z - 4) + (z + 1)(2z + 3)$

Factor by grouping.

7. $4m + nq + mn + 4q$

8. $x^2 + 5y + 5x + xy$

9. $2m + 6 - am - 3a$

10. $x^2 + 3x - 3y - xy$

5.2   *Factor completely.*

11. $3p^2 - p - 4$

12. $6k^2 + 11k - 10$

13. $12r^2 - 5r - 3$

14. $10m^2 + 37m + 30$

15. $10k^2 - 11kh + 3h^2$

16. $9x^2 + 4xy - 2y^2$

17. $24x - 2x^2 - 2x^3$

18. $6b^3 - 9b^2 - 15b$

19. $y^4 + 2y^2 - 8$

20. $2k^4 - 5k^2 - 3$

21. $p^2(p + 2)^2 + p(p + 2)^2 - 6(p + 2)^2$

22. $3(r + 5)^2 - 11(r + 5) - 4$

23. When asked to factor $x^2y^2 - 6x^2 + 5y^2 - 30$, a student gave the following incorrect answer.

$$x^2(y^2 - 6) + 5(y^2 - 6)$$

WHAT WENT WRONG? What is the correct answer?

23. It is not factored because there are two terms: $x^2(y^2 - 6)$ and $5(y^2 - 6)$. The correct answer is $(y^2 - 6)(x^2 + 5)$.

24. $p + 1$

25. $(4x + 5)(4x - 5)$

26. $(3t + 7)(3t - 7)$

27. $(6m - 5n)(6m + 5n)$

28. $(x + 7)^2$

29. $(3k - 2)^2$

30. $(r + 3)(r^2 - 3r + 9)$

31. $(5x - 1)(25x^2 + 5x + 1)$

32. $(m + 1)(m^2 - m + 1) \cdot$ $(m - 1)(m^2 + m + 1)$

33. $(x^4 + 1)(x^2 + 1)(x + 1) \cdot$ $(x - 1)$

34. $(x + 3 + 5y)(x + 3 - 5y)$

35. $2b(3a^2 + b^2)$

36. $(x + 1)(x - 1)(x - 2) \cdot$ $(x^2 + 2x + 4)$

37. $\{4\}$

38. $\left\{-1, -\dfrac{2}{5}\right\}$

39. $\{2, 3\}$

40. $\{-4, 2\}$

41. $\left\{-\dfrac{5}{2}, \dfrac{10}{3}\right\}$

42. $\left\{-\dfrac{3}{2}, \dfrac{1}{3}\right\}$

43. $\left\{-\dfrac{3}{2}, -\dfrac{1}{4}\right\}$

44. $\{-3, 3\}$

45. $\left\{-\dfrac{3}{2}, 0\right\}$

46. $\left\{\dfrac{1}{2}, 1\right\}$

47. $\{1, 4\}$

48. $\left\{-\dfrac{7}{2}, 0, 4\right\}$

49. $\{-3, -2, 2\}$

50. $\left\{-2, -\dfrac{6}{5}, 3\right\}$

51. 3 ft

52. length: 60 ft; width: 40 ft

53. 16 sec

54. 1 sec and 15 sec

55. 8 sec

56. The rock reaches a height of 240 ft once on its way up and once on its way down.

57. $k = \dfrac{-3s - 2t}{b - 1}$, or $k = \dfrac{3s + 2t}{1 - b}$

58. $w = \dfrac{7}{z - 3}$, or $w = \dfrac{-7}{3 - z}$

---

24. If the area of this rectangle is represented by
$$4p^2 + 3p - 1,$$
what is the width in terms of p?

5.3 *Factor completely.*

25. $16x^2 - 25$

26. $9t^2 - 49$

27. $36m^2 - 25n^2$

28. $x^2 + 14x + 49$

29. $9k^2 - 12k + 4$

30. $r^3 + 27$

31. $125x^3 - 1$

32. $m^6 - 1$

33. $x^8 - 1$

34. $x^2 + 6x + 9 - 25y^2$

35. $(a + b)^3 - (a - b)^3$

36. $x^5 - x^3 - 8x^2 + 8$

5.5 *Solve each equation.*

37. $x^2 - 8x + 16 = 0$

38. $(5x + 2)(x + 1) = 0$

39. $x^2 - 5x + 6 = 0$

40. $x^2 + 2x = 8$

41. $6x^2 = 5x + 50$

42. $6x^2 + 7x = 3$

43. $8x^2 + 14x + 3 = 0$

44. $-4x^2 + 36 = 0$

45. $6x^2 + 9x = 0$

46. $(2x + 1)(x - 2) = -3$

47. $(x - 1)(x + 3) = (2x - 1)(x - 1)$

48. $2x^3 - x^2 - 28x = 0$

49. $-x^3 - 3x^2 + 4x + 12 = 0$

50. $(x + 2)(5x^2 - 9x - 18) = 0$

Solve each problem.

51. A triangular wall brace has the shape of a right triangle. One of the perpendicular sides is 1 ft longer than twice the other. The area enclosed by the triangle is 10.5 ft². Find the shorter of the perpendicular sides.

52. A rectangular parking lot has a length 20 ft more than its width. Its area is 2400 ft². What are the dimensions of the lot?

The area is 10.5 ft².

The area is 2400 ft².

A rock is projected directly upward from ground level. After t seconds, its height (if air resistance is neglected) is modeled by the function
$$f(t) = -16t^2 + 256t.$$

53. After how many seconds will the rock return to the ground?

54. After how many seconds will it be 240 ft above the ground?

55. After how many seconds does the rock reach its maximum height, 1024 ft?

56. Why does the question in **Exercise 54** have two answers?

Solve each equation for the specified variable.

57. $3s + bk = k - 2t$ for k

58. $z = \dfrac{3w + 7}{w}$ for w

Chapter 5	Mixed Review Exercises

Factor completely.

1. $(4 + 9k)(4 - 9k)$

2. $a(6 - m)(5 + m)$

3. prime

4. $(2 - a)(4 + 2a + a^2)$

5. $(5z - 3m)^2$

6. $5y^2(3y + 4)$

7. $\left\{ -\dfrac{3}{5}, 4 \right\}$

8. $\{-1, 0, 1\}$

9. 6 in.

10. width: 25 ft; length: 110 ft

Factor completely.

1. $16 - 81k^2$

2. $30a + am - am^2$

3. $9x^2 + 13xy - 3y^2$

4. $8 - a^3$

5. $25z^2 - 30zm + 9m^2$

6. $15y^3 + 20y^2$

Solve.

7. $5x^2 - 17x = 12$

8. $x^3 - x = 0$

9. The length of a rectangular picture frame is 2 in. longer than its width. The area enclosed by the frame is 48 in.^{2}. What is the width?

10. When Europeans arrived in America, many Native Americans of the Northeast lived in *longhouses* that sheltered several related families. The rectangular floor area of a typical Huron longhouse was about 2750 ft^2. The length was 85 ft greater than the width. What were the dimensions of the floor?

Chapter 5	Test	FOR EXTRA HELP	*Step-by-step test solutions are found on the Chapter Test Prep Videos available in* MyMathLab® *or on* You Tube".

▶ *View the complete solutions to all Chapter Test exercises in MyMathLab.*

[5.1–5.4]

1. $11z(z - 4)$

2. $5x^2y^3(2y^2 - 1 - 5x^3)$

3. $(x + y)(3 + b)$

4. $-(2x + 9)(x - 4)$

5. $(3x - 5)(2x + 7)$

6. $(4p - q)(p + q)$

7. $(4a + 5b)^2$

8. $(x + 1 + 2z)(x + 1 - 2z)$

9. $(a + b)(a - b)(a + 2)$

10. $(3k + 11j)(3k - 11j)$

11. $(y - 6)(y^2 + 6y + 36)$

12. $(2k^2 - 5)(3k^2 + 7)$

13. $(3x^2 + 1)(9x^4 - 3x^2 + 1)$

[5.2]

14. D

[5.5]

15. $\left\{ -2, -\dfrac{2}{3} \right\}$ **16.** $\left\{ 0, \dfrac{5}{3} \right\}$

17. $\left\{ -\dfrac{2}{5}, 1 \right\}$

18. $r = \dfrac{-2 - 6t}{a - 3}$, or $r = \dfrac{2 + 6t}{3 - a}$

19. length: 8 in.; width: 5 in.

20. 2 sec and 4 sec

Factor.

1. $11z^2 - 44z$

2. $10x^2y^5 - 5x^2y^3 - 25x^5y^3$

3. $3x + by + bx + 3y$

4. $-2x^2 - x + 36$

5. $6x^2 + 11x - 35$

6. $4p^2 + 3pq - q^2$

7. $16a^2 + 40ab + 25b^2$

8. $x^2 + 2x + 1 - 4z^2$

9. $a^3 + 2a^2 - ab^2 - 2b^2$

10. $9k^2 - 121j^2$

11. $y^3 - 216$

12. $6k^4 - k^2 - 35$

13. $27x^6 + 1$

14. Which one of the following is *not* a factored form of $-x^2 - x + 12$?

   A. $(3 - x)(x + 4)$ **B.** $-(x - 3)(x + 4)$

   C. $(-x + 3)(x + 4)$ **D.** $(x - 3)(-x + 4)$

Solve each equation.

15. $3x^2 + 8x = -4$

16. $3x^2 - 5x = 0$

17. $5m(m - 1) = 2(1 - m)$

18. $ar + 2 = 3r - 6t$ for r

Solve each problem.

19. The area of the rectangle shown is 40 in.^{2}. Find the length and the width of the rectangle.

$x + 7$

$2x + 3$

The area is 40 in.^{2}.

20. A ball is projected upward from ground level. After t seconds, its height in feet is modeled by the function

$$f(t) = -16t^2 + 96t.$$

After how many seconds will it reach a height of 128 ft?

Chapters R–5 Cumulative Review Exercises

[R.4]
1. $-2m + 6$
2. $2x^2 + 5x + 4$

[R.3]
3. 10   4. undefined

[1.1]
5. $\left\{\dfrac{7}{6}\right\}$ 6. $\{-1\}$

[1.5]
7. $\left(-\dfrac{1}{2}, \infty\right)$

[1.6]
8. $(2, 3)$
9. $(-\infty, 2) \cup (3, \infty)$

[1.7]
10. $\left\{-\dfrac{16}{5}, 2\right\}$ 11. $(-11, 7)$
12. $(-\infty, -2] \cup [7, \infty)$

[1.4]
13. 2 hr

[2.2]
14. 0   15. -1

[2.1]
16.

[2.6]
17. -1 18. $\left(-\dfrac{7}{2}, 0\right)$

19. $(0, 7)$

[3.1]
20. $\{(1, 5)\}$ 21. $\varnothing$

[3.2]
22. $\{(1, 1, 0)\}$

Simplify.

1. $-2(m - 3)$

2. $3x^2 - 4x + 4 + 9x - x^2$

Evaluate for $p = -4$, $q = -2$, and $r = 5$.

3. $\dfrac{5p + 6r^2}{p^2 + q - 1}$

4. $\dfrac{\sqrt{r}}{-p + 2q}$

Solve.

5. $2x - 5 + 3x = 4 - (x + 2)$

6. $\dfrac{3x - 1}{5} + \dfrac{x + 2}{2} = -\dfrac{3}{10}$

7. $3 - 2(x + 3) < 4x$

8. $2x + 4 < 10$ and $3x - 1 > 5$

9. $2x + 4 > 10$ or $3x - 1 < 5$

10. $|5x + 3| - 10 = 3$

11. $|x + 2| < 9$

12. $|2x - 5| \geq 9$

13. Two planes leave the Dallas–Fort Worth airport at the same time. One travels east at 550 mph, and the other travels west at 500 mph. Assuming no wind, how long will it take for the planes to be 2100 mi apart?

Plane	r	t	d
Eastbound	550	x	
Westbound	500	x	

← Total

14. What is the slope of the line shown here?

15. Find the slope of the line passing through the points $(-4, 8)$ and $(-2, 6)$.

16. Graph $4x + 2y = -8$.

Use the function $f(x) = 2x + 7$ to find each of the following.

17. $f(-4)$

18. The x-intercept of its graph

19. The y-intercept of its graph

Solve each system.

20. $3x - 2y = -7$
       $2x + 3y = 17$

21. $y = 5x + 6$
       $-10x = -2y - 12$

22. $2x + 3y - 6z = 5$
       $8x - y + 3z = 7$
       $3x + 4y - 3z = 7$

Perform the indicated operations. In Exercises 23 and 26, assume that variables represent nonzero real numbers.

23. $(3x^2y^{-1})^{-2}(2x^{-3}y)^{-1}$

24. $(7x + 3y)^2$

25. $(3x^3 + 4x^2 - 7) - (2x^3 - 8x^2 + 3x)$

26. $\dfrac{2x^4 + x^3 + 7x^2 + 2x + 6}{x^2 + 2}$

Factor.

27. $16w^2 + 50wz - 21z^2$

28. $4x^2 - 4x + 1 - y^2$

29. $100x^4 - 81$

30. $8p^3 + 27$

Solve.

31. $(x - 1)(2x + 3)(x + 4) = 0$

32. $9x^2 = 6x - 1$

33. A sign is to have the shape of a triangle with a height 3 ft greater than the length of the base. How long should the base be if the area is to be 14 ft^2?

34. A game board has the shape of a rectangle. The longer sides are each 2 in. longer than the distance between them. The area of the board is 288 in.^{2}. Find the length of the longer sides and the distance between them.

ANSWERS TO SELECTED EXERCISES

In this section, we provide the answers that we think most students will obtain when they work the exercises using the methods explained in the text. If your answer does not look exactly like the one given here, it is not necessarily wrong. In many cases, there are equivalent forms of the answer that are correct. For example, if the answer section shows $\frac{3}{4}$ and your answer is 0.75, you have obtained the right answer, but written it in a different (yet equivalent) form. Unless the directions specify otherwise, 0.75 is just as valid an answer as $\frac{3}{4}$.

In general, if your answer does not agree with the one given in the text, see whether it can be transformed into the other form. If it can, then it is the correct answer. If you still have doubts, consult your instructor.

R REVIEW OF THE REAL NUMBER SYSTEM

Section R.1 (pages 9–12)

1. yes **3.** $\{1, 2, 3, 4, 5\}$ **5.** $\{5, 6, 7, 8, \ldots\}$

7. $\{\ldots, -1, 0, 1, 2, 3, 4\}$ **9.** $\{10, 12, 14, 16, \ldots\}$

11. $\{-4, 4\}$ **13.** $\varnothing$

In Exercises 15 and 17, we give one possible answer.

15. $\{x \mid x$ is an even natural number less than or equal to 8$\}$

17. $\{x \mid x$ is a positive multiple of 4$\}$

19.

21.

23. (a) $8, 13, \frac{75}{5}$ (or 15) (b) $0, 8, 13, \frac{75}{5}$ (c) $-9, 0, 8, 13, \frac{75}{5}$
(d) $-9, -0.7, 0, \frac{6}{7}, 4.\overline{6}, 8, \frac{21}{2}, 13, \frac{75}{5}$ (e) $-\sqrt{6}, \sqrt{7}$ (f) All are real numbers. **25.** false; Some are whole numbers, but negative integers are not.
27. false; No irrational number is an integer. **29.** true **31.** true
33. true **35.** (a) A (b) A (c) B (d) B **37.** (a) -6 (b) 6
39. (a) 12 (b) 12 **41.** (a) $-\frac{6}{5}$ (b) $\frac{6}{5}$ **43.** 8 **45.** $\frac{3}{2}$ **47.** -5
49. -2 **51.** -4.5 **53.** 5 **55.** 6 **57.** 0 **59.** (a) Las Vegas; The population increased by 45.4%. (b) Detroit; The population decreased by 3.6%. **61.** Pacific Ocean, Indian Ocean, Caribbean Sea, South China Sea, Gulf of California **63.** true **65.** true **67.** false
69. true **71.** true **73.** $2 < 6$ **75.** $4 > -9$ **77.** $-10 < -5$
79. $x > 0$ **81.** $7 > y$ **83.** $5 \geq 5$ **85.** $3t - 4 \leq 10$ **87.** $5x + 3 \neq 0$
89. $t \leq -3$ **91.** $3x < 4$ **93.** $-6 < 10$; true **95.** $10 \geq 10$; true
97. $-3 \geq -3$; true **99.** $-8 > -6$; false **101.** $5 \geq -5$; true
103. Iowa (IA), Ohio (OH), Pennsylvania (PA) **105.** $x < y$

Section R.2 (pages 19–23)

1. positive; $18 + 6 = 24$ **3.** greater; $-14 + 9 = -5$ **5.** the number with greater absolute value is subtracted from the one with lesser absolute value; $5 - 12 = -7$ **7.** additive inverses; $4 + (-4) = 0$
9. negative; $-5(15) = -75$ **11.** -19 **13.** 9 **15.** $-\frac{19}{12}$ **17.** -1.85
19. -11 **21.** 21 **23.** -13 **25.** -10.18 **27.** $\frac{67}{30}$ **29.** 14 **31.** -5

33. -6 **35.** -11 **37.** 16 **39.** -4 **41.** 8 **43.** 3.018 **45.** $-\frac{7}{4}$
47. $-\frac{7}{8}$ **49.** 1 **51.** 6 **53.** $\frac{13}{2}$, or $6\frac{1}{2}$ **55.** It is true for multiplication (and division). It is false for addition and false for subtraction when the number to be subtracted has the lesser absolute value. A more precise statement is, "The product or quotient of two negative numbers is positive."
57. -35 **59.** 40 **61.** 2 **63.** -12 **65.** $\frac{6}{5}$ **67.** 1 **69.** 0 **71.** 0
73. -7 **75.** 6 **77.** -4 **79.** 0 **81.** undefined **83.** $\frac{25}{102}$ **85.** $-\frac{9}{13}$
87. -2.1 **89.** 10,000 **91.** $\frac{17}{18}$ **93.** $\frac{17}{36}$ **95.** $-\frac{19}{24}$ **97.** $-\frac{22}{45}$
99. $-\frac{2}{15}$ **101.** $\frac{3}{5}$ **103.** $-\frac{35}{27}$ **105.** $-\frac{1}{3}$ **107.** $-\frac{4}{3}$ **109.** -12.351
111. -15.876 **113.** -4.14 **115.** 4800 **117.** $\frac{1}{3}$ **119.** 70.21
121. The two quotients are reciprocals by inspection. So once the correct answer to Exercise 117 is known $\left(\frac{1}{3}\right)$, the answer to Exercise 118 is simply its reciprocal (3). **123.** 112°F **125.** $30.13
127. (a) $466.02 (b) $190.68 **129.** (a) 59.53% (b) -36.87%
(c) 58.64% **131.** 1995: $-$164 billion; 2000: $236 billion;
2005: $-$318 billion; 2012: $-$1087 billion

Section R.3 (pages 28–31)

1. false; $-7^6 = -(7^6)$ **3.** true **5.** true **7.** true **9.** false; The base is 8. **11.** (a) 64 (b) -64 (c) 64 (d) -64 **13.** 10^4 **15.** $\left(\frac{3}{4}\right)^5$
17. $(-9)^3$ **19.** z^7 **21.** 0^6 **23.** 16 **25.** 0.021952 **27.** $\frac{1}{125}$ **29.** $\frac{256}{625}$
31. -125 **33.** 256 **35.** -729 **37.** -4096 **39.** 9 **41.** 13
43. -20 **45.** $\frac{10}{11}$ **47.** -0.7 **49.** not a real number **51.** (a) not a real number (b) negative **53.** 24 **55.** 15 **57.** 55 **59.** -91
61. -8 **63.** -48 **65.** -2 **67.** -79 **69.** -10 **71.** 2 **73.** -2
75. undefined **77.** -7 **79.** -1 **81.** 17 **83.** -96 **85.** $-\frac{15}{238}$
87. 8 **89.** $-\frac{5}{16}$ **91.** $-\frac{11}{4}$, or -2.75 **93.** $-\frac{3}{16}$ **95.** $1572 **97.** $3296
99. 0.035 **101.** (a) $28.3 billion (b) $42.2 billion (c) $56.0 billion
(d) The amount spent on pets almost exactly doubled from 2001 to 2013.

Section R.4 (pages 37–39)

1. B **3.** A **5.** order **7.** same; same **9.** -7 **11.** $2m + 2p$
13. $-12x + 12y$ **15.** $8k$ **17.** $-2r$ **19.** cannot be simplified
21. $8a$ **23.** $-2d + f$ **25.** $x + y$ **27.** $-6y + 3$ **29.** $p + 11$
31. $-2k + 15$ **33.** $-3m + 2$ **35.** -1 **37.** $2p + 7$ **39.** $-6z - 39$
41. $(5 + 8)x = 13x$ **43.** $(5 \cdot 9)r = 45r$ **45.** $9y + 5x$ **47.** 7
49. 0 **51.** $8(-4) + 8x = -32 + 8x$ **53.** 0 **55.** Answers will vary. One example of commutativity is washing your face and brushing your teeth. An example of non-commutativity is putting on your socks and putting on your shoes. **57.** 1900 **59.** 75 **61.** 431 **63.** No. One example is $7 + (5 \cdot 3) = (7 + 5)(7 + 3)$, which is false.
65. associative property **66.** associative property **67.** commutative property **68.** associative property **69.** distributive property
70. arithmetic facts

1 LINEAR EQUATIONS, INEQUALITIES, AND APPLICATIONS

Section 1.1 (pages 50–53)

1. algebraic expression; does; is not   **3.** true; solution; solution set
5. identity; all real numbers   **7.** A, C   **9.** Both sides are evaluated as
30, so 6 is a solution.   **11.** equation   **13.** expression   **15.** equation
17. A sign error was made when the distributive property was applied.
The left side of the second line should be $8x - 4x + 6$. The correct
solution is 1.   **19.** $\{-1\}$ **21.** $\{-4\}$ **23.** $\{-7\}$ **25.** $\{0\}$ **27.** $\{4\}$
29. $\left\{-\frac{7}{8}\right\}$ **31.** $\varnothing$; contradiction   **33.** $\left\{-\frac{5}{3}\right\}$ **35.** $\left\{-\frac{1}{2}\right\}$ **37.** $\{2\}$
39. $\{-2\}$ **41.** $\{$ all real numbers $\}$; identity   **43.** $\{-1\}$ **45.** $\{7\}$
47. $\{2\}$ **49.** $\{$ all real numbers $\}$; identity   **51.** $\left\{\frac{3}{2}\right\}$ **53.** 12
55. (a) 10^2, or 100   (b) 10^3, or 1000   **57.** $\left\{-\frac{18}{5}\right\}$ **59.** $\left\{-\frac{5}{6}\right\}$
61. $\{6\}$ **63.** $\{4\}$ **65.** $\{3\}$ **67.** $\{3\}$ **69.** $\{0\}$ **71.** $\{35\}$
73. $\{-10\}$ **75.** $\{2000\}$ **77.** $\{25\}$ **79.** $\{40\}$ **81.** $\{3\}$

Section 1.2 (pages 60–65)

1. formula   **3.** (a) 35% (b) 18% (c) 2% (d) 7.5% (e) 150%
There may be other acceptable forms of the answers in Exercises 5–35.
5. $r = \dfrac{I}{pt}$ **7.** (a) $b = \dfrac{\mathcal{A}}{h}$ (b) $h = \dfrac{\mathcal{A}}{b}$ **9.** $L = \dfrac{P - 2W}{2}$, or $L = \dfrac{P}{2} - W$
11. (a) $W = \dfrac{V}{LH}$ (b) $H = \dfrac{V}{LW}$ **13.** $r = \dfrac{C}{2\pi}$
15. (a) $b = \dfrac{2\mathcal{A} - hB}{h}$, or $b = \dfrac{2\mathcal{A}}{h} - B$ (b) $B = \dfrac{2\mathcal{A} - hb}{h}$, or
$B = \dfrac{2\mathcal{A}}{h} - b$ **17.** $C = \frac{5}{9}(F - 32)$ **19.** (a) $x = \dfrac{C - B}{A}$
(b) $A = \dfrac{C - B}{x}$ **21.** $t = \dfrac{A - P}{Pr}$ **23.** D   **25.** $y = -4x + 1$
27. $y = \frac{1}{2}x + 3$ **29.** $y = -\frac{4}{9}x + \frac{11}{9}$ **31.** $y = \frac{3}{2}x + \frac{5}{2}$ **33.** $y = \frac{6}{5}x - \frac{7}{5}$
35. $y = \frac{3}{2}x - 3$ **37.** 3.140 hr   **39.** 52 mph   **41.** 113°F   **43.** 230 m
45. (a) 240 in.   (b) 480 in.   **47.** 2 in.   **49.** 75% water; 25% alcohol
51. 3%   **53.** (a) .558 (b) .481 (c) .438 (d) .315
55. 34%   **57.** 103.4 million   **59.** $72,324   **61.** $14,465
63. 12%   **65.** 23.8%   **67.** 49.9%   **69.** (a) 0.79 m² (b) 0.96 m²
71. (a) 116 mg   (b) 141 mg

Section 1.3 (pages 73–78)

1. (a) $x + 15$ (b) $15 > x$ **3.** (a) $x - 8$ (b) $8 < x$ **5.** D
7. $2x - 13$ **9.** $12 + 4x$ **11.** $8(x - 16)$ **13.** $\dfrac{3x}{10}$ **15.** $x + 6 = -31; -37$
17. $x - (-4x) = x + 9; \frac{9}{4}$ **19.** $14 - \frac{2}{3}x = 10; 6$
21. expression; $-11x + 63$ **23.** equation; $\left\{\frac{51}{11}\right\}$ **25.** expression; $\frac{1}{3}x - \frac{13}{2}$
27. *Step 1:* the number of patents each corporation secured;
Step 2: patents that Samsung secured; *Step 3:* x; $x - 1414$;
Step 4: 6457; *Step 5:* 6457; 5043; *Step 6:* 1414; IBM patents; 5043; 11,500
29. width: 165 ft; length: 265 ft   **31.** 24.34 in. by 29.88 in.
33. 850 mi; 925 mi; 1300 mi   **35.** Exxon Mobil: $449.9 billion;
Wal-Mart: $469.2 billion   **37.** Eiffel Tower: 984 ft; Leaning Tower: 180 ft

39. Obama: 332 votes; Romney: 206 votes   **41.** 49.3%
43. $8265   **45.** $49.48   **47.** $225   **49.** $4000 at 3%; $8000 at 4%
51. $10,000 at 4.5%; $19,000 at 3%   **53.** $24,000   **55.** 5 L   **57.** 4 L
59. 1 gal   **61.** 150 lb   **63.** We cannot expect the final mixture to be worth
more than the more expensive of the two ingredients.   **65.** (a) $800 - x$
(b) $800 - y$ **66.** (a) $0.05x; 0.10(800 - x)$ (b) $0.05y; 0.10(800 - y)$
67. (a) $0.05x + 0.10(800 - x) = 800(0.0875)$
(b) $0.05y + 0.10(800 - y) = 800(0.0875)$
68. (a) $200 at 5%; $600 at 10%   (b) 200 L of 5% acid; 600 L of
10% acid   (c) The processes are the same. The amounts of money in
Problem A correspond to the amounts of solution in Problem B.

Section 1.4 (pages 83–87)

1. $5.70   **3.** 30 mph   **5.** The problem asks for the *distance* to the
workplace. To find this distance, we must multiply the rate, 10 mph, by
the time, $\frac{3}{4}$ hr.   **7.** No, the answers must be whole numbers because they
represent the numbers of coins.   **9.** 17 pennies; 17 dimes; 10 quarters
11. 23 loonies; 14 toonies   **13.** 28 $10 coins; 13 $20 coins
15. 872 adult tickets   **17.** 8.10 m per sec   **19.** 10.35 m per sec
21. $2\frac{1}{2}$ hr   **23.** 7:50 P.M.   **25.** 45 mph   **27.** $\frac{1}{2}$ hr   **29.** 60°, 60°, 60°
31. 40°, 45°, 95°   **33.** Both measure 122°.   **35.** 64°, 26°
37. 65°, 115°   **39.** 19, 20, 21   **41.** 27, 28, 29, 30   **43.** 61 yr old
45. 28, 30, 32   **47.** 21, 23, 25   **49.** 40°, 80°   **50.** 120°
51. The sum is equal to the measure of the angle found in **Exercise 50.**
52. The sum of the measures of angles ① and ② is equal to the measure
of angle ③.

Section 1.5 (pages 99–102)

1. D   **3.** B   **5.** F   **7.** (a) $x < 100$ (b) $100 \le x \le 129$
(c) $130 \le x \le 159$ (d) $160 \le x \le 189$ (e) $x \ge 190$
9. $[16, \infty)$

11. $(7, \infty)$

13. $(-\infty, -4)$

15. $(-\infty, -40]$

17. $(-\infty, 4]$

19. $(-\infty, -10]$

21. $(-\infty, 14)$

23. $\left(-\infty, -\frac{15}{2}\right)$

25. $\left[\frac{1}{2}, \infty\right)$

27. $[2, \infty)$

29. $(3, \infty)$

31. $(-\infty, 4)$

33. $\left(-\infty, \frac{23}{6}\right]$

35. $\left(-\infty, \frac{76}{11}\right)$

37. $(-\infty, \infty)$

39. $\varnothing$

41. A; B

43. $(1, 11)$

45. $[-14, 10]$

47. $[-5, 6]$

49. $\left[-\frac{14}{3}, 2\right]$

51. $\left(-\frac{1}{3}, \frac{1}{9}\right]$

53. $\left[-1, \frac{5}{2}\right]$

55. $\left[-\frac{1}{2}, \frac{35}{2}\right]$

57. $(0, 1)$ **59.** $(-2, 2)$ **61.** $[3, \infty)$
63. $[-9, \infty)$ **65.** at least 80
67. 26 months   **69.** more than 4.4 in.
71. **(a)** 140 to 184 lb   **(b)** 107 to 141 lb
(c) Answers will vary.   **73.** 26 DVDs

Section 1.6 (pages 108–110)

1. true   **3.** false; The union is $(-\infty, 7) \cup (7, \infty)$.   **5.** false; The intersection is $\varnothing$.   **7.** $\{1, 3, 5\}$, or B **9.** $\{4\}$, or D **11.** $\varnothing$
13. $\{1, 2, 3, 4, 5, 6\}$, or A
15.

17.

19. $(-3, 2)$

21. $(-\infty, 2]$

23. $\varnothing$

25. $[5, 9]$

27. $(-3, -1)$

29. $(-\infty, 4]$

31.

33.

35. $(-\infty, 8]$

37. $[-2, \infty)$

39. $(-\infty, \infty)$

41. $(-\infty, -5) \cup (5, \infty)$

43. $(-\infty, -1) \cup (2, \infty)$

45. $(-\infty, \infty)$

47. $[-4, -1]$ **49.** $[-9, -6]$
51. $(-\infty, 3)$ **53.** $[3, 9)$

55. intersection; $(-5, -1)$ **57.** union; $(-\infty, 4)$

59. union; $(-\infty, 0] \cup [2, \infty)$ **61.** intersection; $[4, 12]$

63. $\{$Tuition and fees$\}$ **65.** $\{$Tuition and fees, Board rates, Dormitory charges$\}$ **67.** Maria, Joe   **68.** none of them   **69.** none of them
70. Luigi, Than   **71.** Maria, Joe   **72.** all of them

Section 1.7 (pages 118–121)

1. E; C; D; B; A   **3.** **(a)** one   **(b)** two   **(c)** none   **5.** $\{-12, 12\}$
7. $\{-5, 5\}$ **9.** $\{-6, 12\}$ **11.** $\{-5, 6\}$ **13.** $\left\{-3, \frac{11}{2}\right\}$
15. $\left\{-\frac{19}{2}, \frac{9}{2}\right\}$ **17.** $\left\{\frac{7}{3}, 3\right\}$ **19.** $\{12, 36\}$ **21.** $\{-12, 12\}$
23. $\{-10, -2\}$ **25.** $\left\{-\frac{32}{3}, 8\right\}$ **27.** $\{-75, 175\}$
29. $(-\infty, -3) \cup (3, \infty)$ **31.** $(-\infty, -4] \cup [4, \infty)$

33. $(-\infty, -25] \cup [15, \infty)$ **35.** $\left(-\infty, -\frac{12}{5}\right) \cup \left(\frac{8}{5}, \infty\right)$

37. $(-\infty, -2) \cup (8, \infty)$ **39.** $\left(-\infty, -\frac{9}{5}\right] \cup [3, \infty)$

41. **(a)**   **(b)**

43. $[-3, 3]$ **45.** $(-4, 4)$

47. $(-25, 15)$ **49.** $\left[-\frac{12}{5}, \frac{8}{5}\right]$

51. $[-2, 8]$ **53.** $\left(-\frac{9}{5}, 3\right)$

55. $(-\infty, -5) \cup (13, \infty)$ **57.** $\left(-\frac{13}{3}, 3\right)$

59. $\{-6, -1\}$ **61.** $\left[-\frac{10}{3}, 4\right]$

63. $\left[-\frac{7}{6}, -\frac{5}{6}\right]$ **65.** $[3, 13]$

67. $\left(-\infty, \frac{1}{2}\right] \cup \left[\frac{7}{6}, \infty\right)$ **69.** $\left\{-\frac{5}{3}, \frac{11}{3}\right\}$ **71.** $(-\infty, -20) \cup (40, \infty)$

73. $\{-5, 1\}$ **75.** $\{3, 9\}$ **77.** $\{0, 20\}$ **79.** $\{-5, 5\}$

81. $\{-5, -3\}$ **83.** $(-\infty, -3) \cup (2, \infty)$ **85.** $[-10, 0]$

87. $(-\infty, 20] \cup [30, \infty)$ **89.** $\left\{-\frac{5}{3}, \frac{1}{3}\right\}$ **91.** $\{-1, 3\}$ **93.** $\left\{-3, \frac{5}{3}\right\}$

95. $\left\{-\frac{1}{3}, -\frac{1}{15}\right\}$ **97.** $\left\{-\frac{5}{4}\right\}$ **99.** $(-\infty, \infty)$ **101.** $\varnothing$ **103.** $\left\{-\frac{1}{4}\right\}$

105. $\varnothing$ **107.** $(-\infty, \infty)$ **109.** $\left\{-\frac{3}{7}\right\}$ **111.** $\left\{\frac{2}{5}\right\}$ **113.** $(-\infty, \infty)$

115. $\varnothing$ **117.** between 30.72 and 33.28 oz, inclusive   **119.** between 31.2 and 32.8 oz, inclusive   **121.** $(-0.05, 0.05)$

123. $(2.74975, 2.75025)$ **125.** between 6.8 and 9.8 lb

127. $|x - 1000| \le 100;\ 900 \le x \le 1100$ **129.** 810.5 ft

130. Bank of America Center, Texaco Heritage Plaza   **131.** Williams Tower, Bank of America Center, Texaco Heritage Plaza, Enterprise Plaza, Centerpoint Energy Plaza, Continental Center I, Fulbright Tower

132. (a) $|x - 810.5| \ge 95$ **(b)** $x \ge 905.5$ or $x \le 715.5$

(c) JPMorgan Chase Tower, Wells Fargo Plaza, One Shell Plaza

(d) It makes sense because it includes all buildings *not* listed in the answer to **Exercise 131.**

---

2   LINEAR EQUATIONS, GRAPHS, AND FUNCTIONS

Section 2.1 (pages 143–146)

1. origin   **3.** $y; x; x; y$ **5.** two; 2; 6   **7. (a)** x represents the year; y represents personal spending on medical care in billions of dollars.
(b) about $2360 billion   **(c)** $(2012, 2360)$ **(d)** 2008   **9. (a)** I
(b) III   **(c)** II   **(d)** IV   **(e)** none   **(f)** none   **11. (a)** I or III
(b) II or IV   **(c)** II or IV   **(d)** I or III

13.–21.

23. (a) $-4; -3; -2; -1; 0$
(b)

25. (a) $-3; 3; 2; -1$
(b)

27. (a) $\frac{5}{2}; 5; \frac{3}{2}; 1$
(b)

29. (a) $-4; 5; -\frac{12}{5}; \frac{5}{4}$
(b)

31. (a) $3; 1; -1; -3$
(b)

33. (a) 1   **(b)** 2   **(c)** For every increase in x by 1 unit, y increases by 2 units.

35. $(6, 0); (0, 4)$

37. $(6, 0); (0, -2)$

39. $(-2, 0); \left(0, -\frac{5}{3}\right)$

41. $\left(\frac{21}{2}, 0\right); \left(0, -\frac{7}{3}\right)$

43. none; $(0, 5)$

45. $(2, 0)$; none

47. $(-4, 0)$; none

49. none; $(0, -2)$

51. $(0, 0); (0, 0)$

53. $(0, 0); (0, 0)$

55. $(0, 0); (0, 0)$

57. (a) $(-2, 0); (0, 3)$
(b) B
(c)

59. (a) none; $(0, -1)$
(b) A
(c)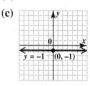

61. C   **63.** B   **65.** $(-5, -1)$ **67.** $\left(\frac{9}{2}, -\frac{3}{2}\right)$ **69.** $\left(0, \frac{11}{2}\right)$

71. $(2.1, 0.9)$ **73.** $(1, 1)$ **75.** $\left(-\frac{5}{12}, \frac{5}{28}\right)$ **77.** $Q(11, -4)$

79. $Q(4.5, 0.75)$

Section 2.2 (pages 156–162)

1. A, B, D, F   **3.** 5 ft   **5. (a)** C   **(b)** A   **(c)** D   **(d)** B   **7.** 2
9. undefined   **11.** 1   **13.** -1 **15. (a)** B **(b)** C **(c)** A **(d)** D
17. 2   **19.** $\frac{5}{2}$ **21.** 0   **23.** undefined   **25. (a)** 8   **(b)** rises
27. (a) $\frac{5}{6}$ **(b)** rises   **29. (a)** 0   **(b)** horizontal   **31. (a)** $-\frac{1}{2}$
(b) falls   **33. (a)** undefined   **(b)** vertical   **35. (a)** -1 **(b)** falls
37. 6   **39.** -3 **41.** -2 **43.** $\frac{4}{3}$ **45.** $-\frac{5}{2}$ **47.** undefined

In part (a) of Exercises 49–53, we used the intercepts. Other points can be used.

49. (a) $(4, 0)$ and $(0, -8)$; 2   **(b)** $y = 2x - 8$; 2   **(c)** $A = 2, B = -1$; 2
51. (a) $(4, 0)$ and $(0, -3)$; $-\frac{3}{4}$ **(b)** $y = -\frac{3}{4}x + 3$; $-\frac{3}{4}$
(c) $A = 3, B = 4$; $-\frac{3}{4}$ **53. (a)** $(-3, 0)$ and $(0, -3)$; -1
(b) $y = -x - 3$; -1 **(c)** $A = 1, B = 1$; -1

55. $-\frac{1}{2}$

57. $\frac{5}{2}$

59. 4

61. undefined   **63.** 0   **65.** 0

67.   **69.**   **71.**

73.   **75.**   **77.** $-\frac{4}{9}; \frac{9}{4}$ **79.** parallel
81. perpendicular
83. neither   **85.** parallel
87. neither

89. perpendicular   **91.** 19.5 ft   **93.** −$4000 per year; The value of the machine is decreasing $4000 per year during these years.   **95.** 0% per year (or no change); The percent of pay raise is not changing—it is 3% per year during these years.   **97.** **(a)** In 2012, there were 326 million wireless subscriber connections in the U.S.   **(b)** 14.2   **(c)** The number of subscribers increased by an average of 14.2 million per year from 2007 to 2012.   **99.** **(a)** −7 theaters per yr   **(b)** The negative slope means that the number of drive-in theaters decreased by an average of 7 per year from 2005 to 2012.   **101.** $0.08 per year; The price of a gallon of gasoline increased by an average of $0.08 per year from 1980 to 2012.   **103.** −1859 thousand cameras per year; The number of digital cameras sold decreased by an average of 1859 thousand per year from 2010 to 2013.   **105.** Because the slopes of both pairs of opposite sides are equal, the figure is a parallelogram.   **107.** $\frac{1}{3}$ **108.** $\frac{1}{3}$ **109.** $\frac{1}{3}$ **110.** $\frac{1}{3} = \frac{1}{3} = \frac{1}{3}$ is true.   **111.** collinear   **112.** not collinear

Section 2.3 (pages 172–176)

1. A   **3.** A   **5.** $3x + y = 10$ **7.** A   **9.** C   **11.** H   **13.** B
15. $y = 5x + 15$ **17.** $y = -\frac{2}{3}x + \frac{4}{5}$ **19.** $y = x - 1$ **21.** $y = \frac{2}{5}x + 5$
23. $y = \frac{2}{3}x + 1$ **25.** $y = -x - 2$ **27.** $y = 2x - 4$ **29.** $y = -\frac{3}{5}x + 3$
31. **(a)** $y = x + 4$ **(b)** 1   **33.** **(a)** $y = -\frac{6}{5}x + 6$ **(b)** $-\frac{6}{5}$
(c) $(0, 4)$ **(c)** $(0, 6)$
(d)   **(d)**

35. **(a)** $y = \frac{4}{5}x - 4$ **(b)** $\frac{4}{5}$ **37.** **(a)** $y = -\frac{1}{2}x - 2$ **(b)** $-\frac{1}{2}$
(c) $(0, -4)$ **(c)** $(0, -2)$
(d)   **(d)**

39. **(a)** $y = -2x + 18$ **(b)** $2x + y = 18$ **41.** **(a)** $y = -\frac{3}{4}x + \frac{5}{2}$
(b) $3x + 4y = 10$ **43.** **(a)** $y = \frac{1}{2}x + \frac{13}{2}$ **(b)** $x - 2y = -13$

45. **(a)** $y = 4x - 12$ **(b)** $4x - y = 12$ **47.** **(a)** $y = 1.4x + 4$
(b) $7x - 5y = -20$ **49.** $2x - y = 2$ **51.** $x + 2y = 8$
53. $y = 5$ **55.** $x = 7$ **57.** $y = -3$ **59.** $2x - 13y = -6$
61. $y = 5$ **63.** $x = 9$ **65.** $y = -\frac{3}{2}$ **67.** $y = 8$ **69.** $x = 0.5$
71. **(a)** $y = 3x - 19$ **(b)** $3x - y = 19$ **73.** **(a)** $y = \frac{1}{2}x - 1$
(b) $x - 2y = 2$ **75.** **(a)** $y = -\frac{1}{2}x + 9$ **(b)** $x + 2y = 18$
77. **(a)** $y = 7$ **(b)** $y = 7$ **79.** $y = 45x$; $(0, 0)$, $(5, 225)$, $(10, 450)$
81. $y = 3.75x$; $(0, 0)$, $(5, 18.75)$, $(10, 37.50)$
83. $y = 140x$; $(0, 0)$, $(5, 700)$, $(10, 1400)$
85. **(a)** $y = 149x + 15$ **(b)** $(5, 760)$; The cost for 5 tickets and a parking pass is $760.   **(c)** $313   **87.** **(a)** $y = 41x + 99$ **(b)** $(5, 304)$; The cost for a 5-month membership is $304.   **(c)** $591
89. **(a)** $y = 95x + 36$ **(b)** $(5, 511)$; The cost of the plan for 5 months is $511.   **(c)** $2316   **91.** **(a)** $y = 6x + 30$ **(b)** $(5, 60)$; It costs $60 to rent the saw for 5 days.   **(c)** 18 days   **93.** **(a)** $y = -1357x + 7030$; Sales of portable media/MP3 players in the United States decreased by $1357 million per year from 2010 to 2013.   **(b)** $5673 million
95. **(a)** $y = 3.875x + 31.3$ **(b)** $73.9 billion; It is very close to the actual value.   **97.** 32; 212   **98.** $(0, 32)$ and $(100, 212)$
99. $\frac{9}{5}$ **100.** $F = \frac{9}{5}C + 32$ **101.** $C = \frac{5}{9}(F - 32)$ **102.** 86°
103. 10°   **104.** −40°

Section 2.4 (pages 183–185)

1. **(a)** yes   **(b)** yes   **(c)** no   **(d)** yes   **3.** **(a)** no   **(b)** no   **(c)** no
(d) yes   **5.** solid; below   **7.** dashed; above   **9.** $\le$ **11.** $>$
13.   **15.**   **17.**
19.   **21.**   **23.**
25.   **27.**   **29.**
31.   **33.**   **35.**
37. 2; $(0, -4)$; $2x - 4$; solid; above; $\ge$; $\ge 2x - 4$
39.   **41.**   **43.**

45. $-3 < x < 3$ **47.** $-2 < x + 1 < 2$ **49.**
$-3 < \quad x \quad < 1$

51.   **53.**   **55.** $x \le 200$,
$x \ge 100$,
$y \ge 3000$

56.   **57.** $C = 50x + 100y$ **58.** Some examples are $(100, 5000)$, $(150, 3000)$, and $(150, 5000)$. The corner points are $(100, 3000)$ and $(200, 3000)$.

59. The least value occurs when $x = 100$ and $y = 3000$.   **60.** The company should use 100 workers and manufacture 3000 units to achieve the least possible cost.

Section 2.5 (pages 193–195)

1. relation; ordered pairs   **3.** domain; range
5. independent variable; dependent variable   **7.** $\{(2, -2), (2, 0), (2, 1)\}$
9. $\{(1960, 0.76), (1980, 2.69), (2000, 5.39), (2013, 8.38)\}$
11. $\{(A, 4), (B, 3), (C, 2), (D, 1), (F, 0)\}$

In Exercises 13 and 15, answers will vary.

13.   **15.**

x	y
-3	-4
-3	1
2	0

17. function; domain: $\{5, 3, 4, 7\}$; range: $\{1, 2, 9, 6\}$ **19.** not a function; domain: $\{2, 0\}$; range: $\{4, 2, 5\}$ **21.** function; domain: $\{-3, 4, -2\}$; range: $\{1, 7\}$ **23.** not a function; domain: $\{1, 0, 2\}$; range: $\{1, -1, 0, 4, -4\}$ **25.** function; domain: $\{2, 5, 11, 17, 3\}$; range: $\{1, 7, 20\}$ **27.** not a function; domain: $\{1\}$; range: $\{5, 2, -1, -4\}$ **29.** function; domain: $\{4, 2, 0, -2\}$; range: $\{-3\}$ **31.** function; domain: $\{-2, 0, 3\}$; range: $\{2, 3\}$ **33.** function; domain: $(-\infty, \infty)$; range: $(-\infty, \infty)$ **35.** not a function; domain: $\{-2\}$; range: $(-\infty, \infty)$
37. not a function; domain: $(-\infty, 0]$; range: $(-\infty, \infty)$ **39.** function; domain: $(-\infty, \infty)$; range: $(-\infty, 4]$ **41.** not a function; domain: $[-4, 4]$; range: $[-3, 3]$ **43.** not a function; domain: $(-\infty, \infty)$; range: $[2, \infty)$ **45.** function; $(-\infty, \infty)$ **47.** function; $(-\infty, \infty)$
49. function; $(-\infty, \infty)$ **51.** not a function; $[0, \infty)$ **53.** not a function; $(-\infty, \infty)$ **55.** function; $[0, \infty)$ **57.** function; $[3, \infty)$
59. function; $\left[-\frac{1}{2}, \infty\right)$ **61.** function; $(-\infty, \infty)$
63. function; $(-\infty, 0) \cup (0, \infty)$ **65.** function; $(-\infty, 4) \cup (4, \infty)$
67. function; $(-\infty, 0) \cup (0, \infty)$ **69. (a)** yes   **(b)** domain: $\{2009, 2010, 2011, 2012, 2013\}$; range: $\{44.0, 43.4, 43.1, 42.9\}$
(c) 42.9; 2010   **(d)** Answers will vary. Two possible answers are $(2010, 43.4)$ and $(2013, 43.1)$.

Section 2.6 (pages 201–205)

1. $f(x)$; function; domain: x; f of x (or "f at x")   **3.** line; -2; linear; $-2x + 4$; -2; 3; -2 **5.** 4   **7.** 13   **9.** -11 **11.** 4   **13.** -296 **15.** 3
17. 2.75   **19.** $-3p + 4$ **21.** $3x + 4$ **23.** $-3x - 2$ **25.** $-6t + 1$
27. $-\pi^2 + 4\pi + 1$ **29.** $-3x - 3h + 4$ **31.** $-\frac{p^2}{9} + \frac{4p}{3} + 1$
33. (a) -1 **(b)** -1 **35. (a)** 2   **(b)** 3   **37. (a)** 15   **(b)** 10
39. (a) 4   **(b)** 1   **41. (a)** 3   **(b)** -3 **43. (a)** -3 **(b)** 2
45. (a) 2   **(b)** 0   **(c)** -1 **47. (a)** $f(x) = -\frac{1}{3}x + 4$ **(b)** 3
49. (a) $f(x) = 3 - 2x^2$ **(b)** -15 **51. (a)** $f(x) = \frac{4}{3}x - \frac{8}{3}$ **(b)** $\frac{4}{3}$
53. domain: $(-\infty, \infty)$;   **55.** domain: $(-\infty, \infty)$;   **57.** domain: $(-\infty, \infty)$;
range: $(-\infty, \infty)$ range: $(-\infty, \infty)$ range: $(-\infty, \infty)$

59. domain: $(-\infty, \infty)$;   **61.** domain: $(-\infty, \infty)$;
range: $\{-4\}$ range: $\{0\}$

63. x-axis   **65. (a)** 11.25 (dollars)   **(b)** 3 is the value of the independent variable, which represents a package weight of 3 lb. $f(3)$ is the value of the dependent variable, which represents the cost to mail a 3-lb package.
(c) $18.75; $f(5) = 18.75$ **67. (a)** $f(x) = 12x + 100$
(b) 1600; The cost to print 125 t-shirts is $1600.   **(c)** 75; $f(75) = 1000$; The cost to print 75 t-shirts is $1000.   **69. (a)** 1.1   **(b)** 5   **(c)** -1.2
(d) $(0, 3.5)$ **(e)** $f(x) = -1.2x + 3.5$ **71. (a)** $[0, 100]$; $[0, 3000]$
(b) 25 hr; 25 hr   **(c)** 2000 gal   **(d)** $f(0) = 0$; The pool is empty at time 0.   **(e)** $f(25) = 3000$; After 25 hr, there are 3000 gal of water in the pool.   **73. (a)** 194.53 cm   **(b)** 177.29 cm   **(c)** 177.41 cm
(d) 163.65 cm   **75.** Because it falls from left to right, the slope is negative.
76. $-\frac{3}{2}$ **77.** $-\frac{3}{2}, \frac{2}{3}$ **78.** $\left(\frac{7}{3}, 0\right)$ **79.** $\left(0, \frac{7}{2}\right)$ **80.** $f(x) = -\frac{3}{2}x + \frac{7}{2}$
81. $-\frac{17}{2}$ **82.** $\frac{23}{3}$

3   SYSTEMS OF LINEAR EQUATIONS

Section 3.1 (pages 225–230)

1. 4; -3 **3.** $\varnothing$ **5.** no   **7.** D; The ordered-pair solution must be in quadrant IV because that is where the graphs of the equations intersect.
9. (a) B   **(b)** C   **(c)** A   **(d)** D   **11.** solution   **13.** not a solution
15. $\{(-2, -3)\}$ **17.** $\{(0, 1)\}$ **19.** $\{(2, 0)\}$

21. $\{(1, 2)\}$ **23.** $\{(2, 3)\}$ **25.** $\left\{\left(\frac{22}{9}, \frac{22}{3}\right)\right\}$ **27.** $\{(5, 4)\}$

29. $\{(1, 3)\}$ **31.** $\left\{\left(-5, -\frac{10}{3}\right)\right\}$ **33.** $\{(2, 6)\}$

35. $\{(x, y) \mid 2x - y = 0\}$; dependent equations   **37.** $\varnothing$; inconsistent system

39. $\{(4, 2)\}$ **41.** $\{(-8, 4)\}$ **43.** $\{(0, 0)\}$ **45.** $\{(2, -4)\}$

47. $\{(3, -1)\}$ **49.** $\{(2, -3)\}$ **51.** $\{(x, y) \mid 7x + 2y = 6\}$; dependent equations   **53.** $\left\{\left(\frac{3}{2}, -\frac{3}{2}\right)\right\}$ **55.** $\varnothing$; inconsistent system   **57.** $\{(0, 0)\}$

59. $\{(0, -4)\}$ **61.** $\left\{\left(6, -\frac{5}{6}\right)\right\}$ **63.** $y = -\frac{3}{7}x + \frac{4}{7}$; $y = -\frac{3}{7}x + \frac{3}{14}$;

no solution   **65.** Both are $y = -\frac{2}{3}x + \frac{1}{3}$; infinitely many solutions

67. $\{(-3, 2)\}$ **69.** $\left\{\left(\frac{1}{3}, \frac{1}{2}\right)\right\}$ **71.** $\{(-4, 6)\}$

73. $\{(x, y) \mid 4x - y = -2\}$ **75.** $\left\{\left(1, \frac{1}{2}\right)\right\}$ **77.** None of the coefficients in the first system are -1 or 1, and solving by substitution would involve fractions. In the second system, we can solve for x in the first equation to avoid using fractions as coefficients.

79. (a) \$4   (b) 300 half-gallons   (c) supply: 200 half-gallons; demand: 400 half-gallons   **81.** (a) 2009–2011   (b) 2011 and 2012   (c) 2010; 13,000   (d) (2010, 13,000)   (e) *The Big Bang Theory* viewership was increasing, *Dancing with the Stars* viewership was decreasing, and *60 Minutes* viewership remained fairly constant.

83. hiking   **85.** (8.7, 35.9)   **87.** $\{(2, 4)\}$ **89.** $\left\{\left(\frac{1}{2}, 2\right)\right\}$

91. $\left\{\left(\frac{c}{a}, 0\right)\right\}$ **93.** $\left\{\left(-\frac{1}{a}, -5\right)\right\}$

Section 3.2 (pages 237–239)

1. Answers will vary. Some possible answers are (a) two perpendicular walls and the ceiling in a normal room, (b) the floors of three different levels of an office building, and (c) three pages of a book (because they intersect in the spine).   **3.** The statement means that when -1 is substituted for x, 2 is substituted for y, and 3 is substituted for z in the three equations, the resulting three statements are true.   **5.** 4   **7.** $\{(3, 2, 1)\}$

9. $\{(1, 4, -3)\}$ **11.** $\{(0, 2, -5)\}$ **13.** $\{(1, 0, 3)\}$ **15.** $\left\{\left(1, \frac{3}{10}, \frac{2}{5}\right)\right\}$

17. $\left\{\left(-\frac{7}{3}, \frac{22}{3}, 7\right)\right\}$ **19.** $\{(-12, 18, 0)\}$ **21.** $\{(0.8, -1.5, 2.3)\}$

23. $\{(4, 5, 3)\}$ **25.** $\{(2, 2, 2)\}$ **27.** $\left\{\left(\frac{8}{3}, \frac{2}{3}, 3\right)\right\}$ **29.** $\{(-1, 0, 0)\}$

31. $\{(-4, 6, 2)\}$ **33.** $\{(-3, 5, -6)\}$ **35.** $\varnothing$; inconsistent system

37. $\{(x, y, z) \mid x - y + 4z = 8\}$; dependent equations   **39.** $\{(3, 0, 2)\}$

41. $\{(x, y, z) \mid 2x + y - z = 6\}$; dependent equations   **43.** $\{(0, 0, 0)\}$

45. $\varnothing$; inconsistent system   **47.** $\{(2, 1, 5, 3)\}$ **49.** $\{(-2, 0, 1, 4)\}$

Section 3.3 (pages 250–256)

1. (a) 6 oz   (b) 15 oz   (c) 24 oz   (d) 30 oz   **3.** $\$1.89x$

5. (a) $(10 - x)$ mph   (b) $(10 + x)$ mph   **7.** wins: 92; losses: 70

9. length: 78 ft; width: 36 ft   **11.** AT&T: \$126.4 billion; Verizon: \$115.8 billion   **13.** $x = 40$ and $y = 50$, so the angles measure 40° and 50°.

15. hockey: \$354.84; basketball: \$315.66   **17.** ribeye: \$17.29; salmon: \$14.99   **19.** DVD: \$12.96; Blu-ray: \$19.49   **21.** 6 gal of 25%; 14 gal of 35%   **23.** pure acid: 6 L; 10% acid: 48 L   **25.** nuts: 14 kg; cereal: 16 kg   **27.** \$1000 at 2%; \$2000 at 4%   **29.** train: 60 km per hr; plane: 160 km per hr   **31.** scooter: 25 mph; bicycle: 10 mph

33. boat: 21 mph; current: 3 mph   **35.** \$0.75-per-lb candy: 5.22 lb; \$1.25-per-lb candy: 3.78 lb   **37.** general admission: 76; with student ID: 108

39. 8 for a citron; 5 for a wood apple   **41.** $x + y + z = 180$; angle measures: 70°, 30°, 80°   **43.** first: 20°; second: 70°; third: 90°

45. shortest: 12 cm; middle: 25 cm; longest: 33 cm   **47.** gold: 13; silver: 11; bronze: 9   **49.** general admission: 1170; courtside: 985; bench: 130   **51.** bookstore A: 140; bookstore B: 280; bookstore C: 380

53. first chemical: 50 kg; second chemical: 400 kg; third chemical: 300 kg

55. wins: 30; losses: 12; overtime losses: 6   **57.** box of fish: 8 oz; box of bugs: 2 oz; box of worms: 5 oz

4 EXPONENTS, POLYNOMIALS, AND POLYNOMIAL FUNCTIONS

Section 4.1 (pages 276–280)

1. incorrect; $(ab)^2 = a^2 b^2$ **3.** incorrect; $\left(\frac{4}{a}\right)^3 = \frac{4^3}{a^3}$ **5.** correct

7. Do not multiply the bases. $4^5 \cdot 4^2 = 4^7$ **9.** 13^{12} **11.** 8^{10} **13.** x^{17}

15. $-27w^8$ **17.** $18x^3 y^8$ **19.** The product rule does not apply.

21. (a) B   (b) C   (c) B   (d) C   **23.** 1   **25.** -1 **27.** 1   **29.** 2

31. 0   **33.** -2 **35.** (a) B   (b) D   (c) B   (d) D   **37.** $\frac{1}{5^4}$, or $\frac{1}{625}$

39. $\frac{1}{3^5}$, or $\frac{1}{243}$ **41.** $\frac{1}{9}$ **43.** $\frac{1}{(4x)^2}$, or $\frac{1}{16x^2}$ **45.** $\frac{4}{x^2}$ **47.** $-\frac{1}{a^3}$

49. $\frac{1}{(-a)^4}$, or $\frac{1}{a^4}$ **51.** $\frac{1}{(-3x)^3}$, or $-\frac{1}{27x^3}$ **53.** $\frac{11}{30}$ **55.** $-\frac{5}{24}$

57. $-\frac{3}{4}$ **59.** 16   **61.** $\frac{27}{4}$ **63.** 4^2, or 16   **65.** x^4 **67.** $\frac{1}{r^3}$ **69.** 6^6

71. $\frac{1}{6^{10}}$ **73.** 7^2, or 49   **75.** r^3 **77.** The quotient rule does not apply.

79. x^{18} **81.** $\frac{27}{125}$ **83.** $64t^3$ **85.** $-216x^6$ **87.** $-\frac{64m^6}{t^3}$ **89.** $\frac{s^{12}}{t^{20}}$

91. (a) B   (b) D   (c) D   (d) B   **93.** 64   **95.** $\frac{27}{8}$ **97.** $\frac{25}{16}$

99. $\frac{81}{16t^4}$ **101.** $16x^2$ **103.** $\frac{32}{x^5}$ **105.** $\frac{1}{3}$ **107.** $\frac{1}{a^5}$ **109.** 5^6 **111.** $\frac{1}{x^{12}}$

113. $\frac{1}{k^2}$ **115.** $-4r^6$ **117.** $\frac{625}{a^{10}}$ **119.** $\frac{z^4}{x^3}$ **121.** $-14k^3$ **123.** $\frac{p^4}{5}$

125. $\frac{m^8}{n^{11}}$ **127.** $\frac{1}{2pq}$ **129.** $\frac{4}{a^2}$ **131.** $\frac{1}{6y^{13}}$ **133.** $\frac{4k^5}{m^2}$ **135.** $\frac{2k^5}{3}$

137. $\frac{8}{3pq^{10}}$ **139.** $\frac{y^9}{8}$ **141.** $\frac{n^{10}}{25m^{18}}$ **143.** $-\frac{125y^3}{x^{30}}$ **145.** $\frac{4k^{17}}{125}$

147. $-\frac{3}{32m^8 p^4}$ **149.** $\frac{2}{3y^4}$ **151.** $\frac{3p^8}{16q^{14}}$ **153.** after; power; a; 10^n

155. 5.3×10^2 **157.** 8.3×10^{-1} **159.** 6.92×10^{-6} **161.** -3.85×10^4

163. $\$1 \times 10^9$ (or \$10⁹); $\$1 \times 10^{12}$ (or \$10¹²); $\$3.8 \times 10^{12}$; 2.57891×10^5 **165.** 72,000   **167.** 0.00254   **169.** $-60,000$

171. 0.000012   **173.** 0.06   **175.** 0.0000025   **177.** 200,000   **179.** 3000

181. 7.5×10^9 **183.** 4×10^{17} **185.** (a) 3.174×10^8 (b) $\$1 \times 10^{12}$ (or \$10¹²)   (c) \$3151   **187.** 30,500, or 3.05×10^4 **189.** 300 sec

191. approximately 5.87×10^{12} mi   **193.** (a) 5.16×10^2 (b) 998 mi²

Section 4.2 (pages 284–286)

1. A   **3.** 7; 1   **5.** -15; 2   **7.** 1; 4   **9.** $\frac{1}{6}$; 1   **11.** 8; 0   **13.** -1; 3

15. $2x^3 - 3x^2 + x + 4$; $2x^3$; 2   **17.** $p^7 - 8p^5 + 4p^3$; p^7; 1

19. $-3m^4 - m^3 + 10$; $-3m^4$; -3 **21.** monomial; 0 **23.** binomial; 1

25. binomial; 8 **27.** monomial; 6 **29.** trinomial; 3 **31.** none of these; 5

33. $8z^4$ **35.** $7m^3$ **37.** $5x$ **39.** already simplified **41.** $-t + 13s$

43. $8k^2 + 2k - 7$ **45.** $-2n^4 - n^3 + n^2$ **47.** $-2ab^2 + 20a^2b$

49. $3m + 11$ **51.** $-p - 4$ **53.** $8x^2 + x - 2$ **55.** $-t^4 + 2t^2 - t + 5$

57. $5y^3 - 3y^2 + 5y + 1$ **59.** $r + 13$ **61.** $-2a^2 - 2a - 7$

63. $-3z^5 + z^2 + 7z$ **65.** $12p - 4$ **67.** $-9p^2 + 11p - 9$ **69.** $5a + 18$

71. $14m^2 - 13m + 6$ **73.** $13z^2 + 10z - 3$ **75.** $10y^3 - 7y^2 + 5y + 8$

77. $-5a^4 - 6a^3 + 9a^2 - 11$ **79.** $3y^2 - 4y + 2$ **81.** $-4m^2 + 4n^2 - 7n$

83. $y^4 - 4y^2 - 4$ **85.** $10z^2 - 16z$ **87.** $12x^2 + 8x + 5$

Section 4.3 (pages 294–297)

1. polynomial; one; terms; powers **3.** (a) -10 (b) 8 (c) -4

5. (a) 8 (b) -10 (c) 0 **7.** (a) 8 (b) 2 (c) 4

9. (a) 7 (b) 1 (c) 1 **11.** (a) 8 (b) 74 (c) 6

13. (a) -11 (b) 4 (c) -8 **15.** (a) 1.0 million lb

(b) 56.3 million lb (c) 158.8 million lb **17.** (a) $280.6 billion

(b) $568.5 billion (c) $711.4 billion **19.** (a) $8x - 3$ (b) $2x - 17$

21. (a) $-x^2 + 12x - 12$ (b) $9x^2 + 4x + 6$ **23.** $f(x)$ and $g(x)$

can be any two polynomials that have a sum of $3x^3 - x + 3$, such as

$f(x) = 3x^3 + 1$ and $g(x) = -x + 2$. **25.** $x^2 + 2x - 9$ **27.** 6

29. $x^2 - x - 6$ **31.** 6 **33.** -33 **35.** 0 **37.** $-\frac{9}{4}$ **39.** $-\frac{9}{2}$

41. (a) $P(x) = 8.49x - 50$ (b) $799 **43.** B **45.** A **47.** 6

49. 83 **51.** 53 **53.** 13 **55.** $2x^2 + 11$ **57.** $2x - 2$ **59.** $\frac{97}{4}$ **61.** 8

63. 1 **65.** 9 **67.** 1 **69.** $(f \circ g)(x) = 63{,}360x$; It computes the

number of inches in x miles. **71.** (a) $s = \dfrac{x}{4}$ (b) $y = \dfrac{x^2}{16}$ (c) 2.25

73. $(\mathcal{A} \circ r)(t) = 4\pi t^2$; This is the area of the circular layer as a function

of time.

75.

domain: $(-\infty, \infty)$;

range: $(-\infty, \infty)$

77.

domain: $(-\infty, \infty)$;

range: $(-\infty, 0]$

79.

domain: $(-\infty, \infty)$;

range: $(-\infty, \infty)$

Section 4.4 (pages 304–306)

1. C **3.** D **5.** $-24m^5$ **7.** $-28x^7y^4$ **9.** $-6x^2 + 15x$

11. $-2q^3 - 3q^4$ **13.** $18k^4 + 12k^3 + 6k^2$ **15.** $6t^3 + t^2 - 14t - 3$

17. $m^3 - 3m^2 - 40m$ **19.** $24z^3 - 20z^2 - 16z$ **21.** $4x^5 - 4x^4 - 24x^3$

23. $6y^2 + y - 12$ **25.** $25m^2 - 9n^2$ **27.** $-2b^3 + 2b^2 + 18b + 12$

29. $8z^4 - 14z^3 + 17z^2 + 20z - 3$ **31.** $6p^4 + p^3 + 4p^2 - 27p - 6$

33. $m^2 - 3m - 40$ **35.** $12k^2 + k - 6$ **37.** $15x^2 - 13x + 2$

39. $20x^2 + 23xy + 6y^2$ **41.** $3z^2 + zw - 4w^2$ **43.** $12c^2 + 16cd - 3d^2$

45. $x^2 - 81$ **47.** $4p^2 - 9$ **49.** $25m^2 - 1$ **51.** $9a^2 - 4c^2$

53. $16m^2 - 49n^4$ **55.** $75y^7 - 12y$ **57.** $y^2 - 10y + 25$ **59.** $x^2 + 2x + 1$

61. $4p^2 + 28p + 49$ **63.** $16n^2 - 24nm + 9m^2$ **65.** $k^2 - \frac{10}{7}kp + \frac{25}{49}p^2$

67. $0.04x^2 - 0.56xy + 1.96y^2$ **69.** $16x^2 - \frac{4}{9}$ **71.** $0.1x^2 + 0.63x - 0.13$

73. $3w^2 - \frac{23}{4}wz - \frac{1}{2}z^2$ **75.** $25x^2 + 10x + 1 + 60xy + 12y + 36y^2$

77. $4a^2 + 4ab + b^2 - 12a - 6b + 9$ **79.** $4a^2 + 4ab + b^2 - 9$

81. $4h^2 - 4hk + k^2 - j^2$ **83.** $y^3 + 6y^2 + 12y + 8$

85. $125r^3 - 75r^2s + 15rs^2 - s^3$ **87.** $q^4 - 8q^3 + 24q^2 - 32q + 16$

89. $6a^3 + 7a^2b + 4ab^2 + b^3$ **91.** $4z^4 - 17z^3x + 12z^2x^2 - 6zx^3 + x^4$

93. $m^4 - 4m^2p^2 + 4mp^3 - p^4$ **95.** $a^4b - 7a^2b^3 - 6ab^4$

97. $49; 25; 49 \neq 25$ **99.** $2401; 337; 2401 \neq 337$ **101.** $\frac{9}{2}x^2 - 2y^2$

103. $15x^2 - 2x - 24$ **105.** $10x^2 - 2x$ **107.** $2x^2 - x - 3$

109. $8x^3 - 27$ **111.** $2x^3 - 18x$ **113.** -20 **115.** $2x^2 - 6x$ **117.** 36

119. $\frac{35}{4}$ **121.** $\frac{1859}{64}$ **123.** $a - b$ **124.** $\mathcal{A} = s^2$; $(a - b)^2$

125. $(a - b)b$, or $ab - b^2$; $2ab - 2b^2$ **126.** b^2 **127.** a^2; a

128. $a^2 - (2ab - 2b^2) - b^2 = a^2 - 2ab + b^2$ **129.** (a) They must be

equal. (b) $(a - b)^2 = a^2 - 2ab + b^2$

130.

Area: a^2	Area: ab
Area: ab	Area: b^2

The large square is made up of two smaller squares
and two congruent rectangles. The sum of the areas
is $a^2 + 2ab + b^2$. Because $(a + b)^2$ must represent the same quantity, they must be equal. Thus,
$(a + b)^2 = a^2 + 2ab + b^2$.

Section 4.5 (pages 311–313)

1. quotient; exponents **3.** 0 **5.** $3x^3 - 2x^2 + 1$ **7.** $3y + 4 - \dfrac{5}{y}$

9. $3 + \dfrac{5}{m} + \dfrac{6}{m^2}$ **11.** $\dfrac{2}{7n} - \dfrac{3}{2m} + \dfrac{9}{7mn}$ **13.** $\dfrac{2y}{x} + \dfrac{3}{4} + \dfrac{3w}{x}$

15. $r^2 - 7r + 6$ **17.** $y - 4$ **19.** $q + 8$ **21.** $t + 5$

23. $p - 4 + \dfrac{44}{p + 6}$ **25.** $m^2 + 2m - 1$ **27.** $m^2 + m + 3$

29. $x^2 + 2x - 3 + \dfrac{6}{4x + 1}$ **31.** $2x - 5 + \dfrac{-4x + 5}{3x^2 - 2x + 4}$

33. $x^2 + x + 3$ **35.** $2x^2 - x - 5$ **37.** $3x^2 + 6x + 11 + \dfrac{26}{x - 2}$

39. $2k^2 + 3k - 1$ **41.** $z^2 + 3$ **43.** $2y^2 + 2$ **45.** $p^2 + p + 1$

47. $x^2 - 4x + 2 + \dfrac{9x - 4}{x^2 + 3}$ **49.** $p^2 + \dfrac{5}{2}p + 2 + \dfrac{-1}{2p + 2}$

51. $\dfrac{3}{2}a - 10 + \dfrac{77}{2a + 6}$ **53.** $\dfrac{2}{3}x - 1$ **55.** $\dfrac{3}{4}a - 2 + \dfrac{1}{4a + 3}$

57. $(2p + 7)$ feet **59.** -13; -13; They are the same, which suggests

that when $P(x)$ is divided by $x - r$, the result is $P(r)$. Here, $r = -1$.

61. $5x - 1$; 0 **63.** $2x - 3$; -1 **65.** $4x^2 + 6x + 9$; $\frac{3}{2}$

67. $\dfrac{x^2 - 9}{2x}$, $x \neq 0$ **69.** $-\frac{5}{4}$ **71.** $\dfrac{x - 3}{2x}$, $x \neq 0$ **73.** 0

75. $-\frac{35}{4}$ **77.** $\frac{7}{2}$

---

5 **FACTORING**

Section 5.1 (pages 329–330)

1. C **3.** $3m$ **5.** $8xy$ **7.** $3(r + t)^2$ **9.** $12(m - 5)$ **11.** $4(1 + 5z)$

13. cannot be factored **15.** $8k(k^2 + 3)$ **17.** $-2p^2q^4(2p + q)$

19. $7x^3(1 + 5x - 2x^2)$ **21.** $2t^3(5t^2 - 1 - 2t)$ **23.** $5ac(3ac^2 - 5c + 1)$

25. $16zn^3(zn^3 + 4n^4 - 2z^2)$ **27.** $7ab(2a^2b + a - 3a^4b^2 + 6b^3)$

29. $(m - 4)(2m + 5)$ **31.** $11(2z - 1)$ **33.** $(2 - x)^2(1 + 2x)$
35. $(3 - x)(6 + 2x - x^2)$ **37.** $20z(2z + 1)(3z + 4)$
39. $5(m + p)^2(m + p - 2 - 3m^2 - 6mp - 3p^2)$ **41.** $r(-r^2 + 3r + 5)$;
$-r(r^2 - 3r - 5)$ **43.** $12s^4(-s + 4)$; $-12s^4(s - 4)$
45. $2x^2(-x^3 + 3x + 2)$; $-2x^2(x^3 - 3x - 2)$ **47.** $(m + q)(x + y)$
49. $(5m + n)(2 + k)$ **51.** $(2 - q)(2 - 3p)$ **53.** $(p + q)(p - 4z)$
55. $(2x + 3)(y + 1)$ **57.** $(m + 4)(m^2 - 6)$ **59.** $(a^2 + b^2)(-3a + 2b)$
61. $(y - 2)(x - 2)$ **63.** $(3y - 2)(3y^3 - 4)$ **65.** $(1 - a)(1 - b)$
67. $2(m - 3q)(x + y)$ **69.** $4(a^2 + 2b)(a - b^2)$
71. $y^2(2x + 1)(x^2 - 7)$ **73.** $m^{-5}(3 + m^2)$ **75.** $p^{-3}(3 + 2p)$

Section 5.2 (pages 336–338)

1. D   **3.** C   **5.** The factor $(4x + 10)$ can be factored further into
$2(2x + 5)$, giving the *completely* factored form as $2(2x + 5)(x - 2)$.
7. $x + 3$ **9.** $m - 7$ **11.** $r - 5$ **13.** $x - 2a$ **15.** $2x - 3$
17. $2u + v$ **19.** $(y - 3)(y + 10)$ **21.** $(p + 8)(p + 7)$ **23.** prime
25. $(a + 5b)(a - 7b)$ **27.** $(a - 6b)(a - 3b)$ **29.** prime
31. $-(6m - 5)(m + 3)$ **33.** $(5x - 6)(2x + 3)$ **35.** $(4k + 3)(5k + 8)$
37. $(3a - 2b)(5a - 4b)$ **39.** $(6m - 5)^2$ **41.** prime
43. $(2xz - 1)(3xz + 4)$ **45.** $3(4x + 5)(2x + 1)$
47. $-5(a + 6)(3a - 4)$ **49.** $-11x(x - 6)(x - 4)$
51. $2xy^3(x - 12y)^2$ **53.** $6a(a - 3)(a + 5)$ **55.** $13y(y + 4)(y - 1)$
57. $3p(2p - 1)^2$ **59.** $(6p^3 - r)(2p^3 - 5r)$ **61.** $(5k + 4)(2k + 1)$
63. $(3m + 3p + 5)(m + p - 4)$ **65.** $(a + b)^2(a - 3b)(a + 2b)$
67. $(p + q)^2(p + 3q)$ **69.** $(z - x)^2(z + 2x)$ **71.** $(p^2 - 8)(p^2 - 2)$
73. $(2x^2 + 3)(x^2 - 6)$ **75.** $(4x^2 + 3)(4x^2 + 1)$

Section 5.3 (pages 342–344)

1. A, D   **3.** B, C   **5.** A sum of two squares can be factored
if the binomial terms have a common factor greater than 1.
7. $(p + 4)(p - 4)$ **9.** $(5x + 2)(5x - 2)$ **11.** $2(3a + 7b)(3a - 7b)$
13. $4(4m^2 + y^2)(2m + y)(2m - y)$ **15.** $(y + z + 9)(y + z - 9)$
17. $(4 + x + 3y)(4 - x - 3y)$ **19.** $(p^2 + 16)(p + 4)(p - 4)$
21. $(k - 3)^2$ **23.** $(2z + w)^2$ **25.** $(4m - 1 + n)(4m - 1 - n)$
27. $(2r - 3 + s)(2r - 3 - s)$ **29.** $(x + y - 1)(x - y + 1)$
31. $2(7m + 3n)^2$ **33.** $(p + q + 1)^2$ **35.** $(a - b + 4)^2$
37. $(x - 3)(x^2 + 3x + 9)$ **39.** $(6 - t)(36 + 6t + t^2)$
41. $(x + 4)(x^2 - 4x + 16)$ **43.** $(10 + y)(100 - 10y + y^2)$
45. $(2x + 1)(4x^2 - 2x + 1)$ **47.** $(5x - 6)(25x^2 + 30x + 36)$
49. $(x - 2y)(x^2 + 2xy + 4y^2)$ **51.** $(4g - 3h)(16g^2 + 12gh + 9h^2)$
53. $(7p + 5q)(49p^2 - 35pq + 25q^2)$
55. $3(2n + 3p)(4n^2 - 6np + 9p^2)$
57. $(y + z + 4)(y^2 + 2yz + z^2 - 4y - 4z + 16)$
59. $(m^2 - 5)(m^4 + 5m^2 + 25)$ **61.** $(3 - 10x^3)(9 + 30x^3 + 100x^6)$
63. $(5y^2 + z)(25y^4 - 5y^2z + z^2)$
65. $(5p + 2q)(25p^2 - 10pq + 4q^2 + 5p - 2q)$
67. $(3a - 4b)(9a^2 + 12ab + 16b^2 + 5)$
69. $(t - 3)(2t + 1)(4t^2 - 2t + 1)$
71. $(8m - 9n)(8m + 9n - 64m^2 - 72mn - 81n^2)$
73. $(x^3 - y^3)(x^3 + y^3)$; $(x - y)(x^2 + xy + y^2)(x + y)(x^2 - xy + y^2)$

74. $(x^2 + xy + y^2)(x^2 - xy + y^2)$ **75.** $(x^2 - y^2)(x^4 + x^2y^2 + y^4)$;
$(x - y)(x + y)(x^4 + x^2y^2 + y^4)$ **76.** $x^4 + x^2y^2 + y^4$
77. The product must equal $x^4 + x^2y^2 + y^4$.
Multiply $(x^2 + xy + y^2)(x^2 - xy + y^2)$ to verify this.
78. Start by factoring as a difference of squares.

Section 5.4 (pages 347–348)

1. (a) B   **(b)** D   **(c)** A   **(d)** A, C   **(e)** A, B   **3.** $3p^2(p - 6)(p + 5)$
5. $3pq(a + 6b)(a - 5b)$ **7.** prime   **9.** $(6b + 1)(b - 3)$
11. $(x - 10)(x^2 + 10x + 100)$ **13.** $(p + 2)(4 + m)$
15. $9m(m - 5 + 2m^2)$ **17.** $2(3m - 10)(9m^2 + 30m + 100)$
19. $(3m - 5n)^2$ **21.** $(k - 9)(q + r)$ **23.** $16z^2x(zx - 2)$
25. $(x + 7)(x - 5)$ **27.** $(25 + x^2)(5 - x)(5 + x)$
29. $(p + 1)(p^2 - p + 1)$ **31.** $(8m + 25)(8m - 25)$
33. $6z(2z^2 - z + 3)$ **35.** $16(4b + 5c)(4b - 5c)$
37. $8(4 + 5z)(16 - 20z + 25z^2)$ **39.** $(5r - s)(2r + 5s)$
41. $4pq(2p + q)(3p + 5q)$ **43.** $3(4k^2 + 9)(2k + 3)(2k - 3)$
45. $(m - n)(m^2 + mn + n^2 + m + n)$ **47.** $(x - 2m - n)(x + 2m + n)$
49. $6p^3(3p^2 - 4 + 2p^3)$ **51.** $2(x + 4)(x - 5)$ **53.** $8mn$
55. $2(5p + 9)(5p - 9)$ **57.** $4rx(3m^2 + mn + 10n^2)$
59. $(7a - 4b)(3a + b)$ **61.** prime   **63.** $(p + 8q - 5)^2$
65. $(7m^2 + 1)(3m^2 - 5)$ **67.** $(2r - t)(r^2 - rt + 19t^2)$
69. $(x + 3)(x^2 + 1)(x + 1)(x - 1)$ **71.** $(m + n - 5)(m - n + 1)$

Section 5.5 (pages 355–358)

1. D; The polynomial is not factored.   **3.** $\{-10, 5\}$ **5.** $\left\{-\frac{8}{3}, \frac{5}{2}\right\}$
7. $\{-2, 5\}$ **9.** $\{-6, -3\}$ **11.** $\left\{-\frac{1}{2}, 4\right\}$ **13.** $\left\{-\frac{1}{3}, \frac{4}{5}\right\}$ **15.** $\{-4, 0\}$
17. $\{0, 6\}$ **19.** $\{-2, 2\}$ **21.** $\{-3, 3\}$ **23.** $\{3\}$ **25.** $\left\{-\frac{4}{3}\right\}$
27. $\{-4, 2\}$ **29.** $\left\{-\frac{1}{2}, 6\right\}$ **31.** $\{-3, 4\}$ **33.** $\left\{-5, -\frac{1}{5}\right\}$ **35.** $\{1, 6\}$
37. $\left\{-\frac{1}{2}, 0, 5\right\}$ **39.** $\{-1, 0, 3\}$ **41.** $\left\{-\frac{4}{3}, 0, \frac{4}{3}\right\}$ **43.** $\left\{-\frac{5}{2}, -1, 1\right\}$
45. $\{-3, 3, 6\}$ **47.** By dividing each side by a variable expression, she
lost the solution 0. The solution set is $\left\{-\frac{4}{3}, 0, \frac{4}{3}\right\}$.
49. $\left\{-\frac{1}{2}, 6\right\}$ **51.** $\left\{-\frac{2}{3}, \frac{4}{15}\right\}$ **53.** $\left\{-\frac{3}{2}, \frac{1}{2}\right\}$
55. width: 16 ft; length: 20 ft   **57.** base: 12 ft; height: 5 ft
59. 50 ft by 100 ft   **61.** -6 and -5 or 5 and 6
63. length: 15 in.; width: 9 in.   **65.** 5 sec   **67.** $6\frac{1}{4}$ sec
69. L appears on both sides of the equation.
71. $F = \dfrac{k}{d - D}$ **73.** $r = \dfrac{-2k - 3y}{a - 1}$, or $r = \dfrac{2k + 3y}{1 - a}$
75. $y = \dfrac{-x}{w - 3}$, or $y = \dfrac{x}{3 - w}$

GLOSSARY

For a more complete discussion, see the section(s) in parentheses.

A

absolute value The absolute value of a number is the undirected distance between 0 and the number on a number line. (Section R.1)

absolute value equation An absolute value equation is an equation that involves the absolute value of a variable expression. (Section 1.7)

absolute value inequality An absolute value inequality is an inequality that involves the absolute value of a variable expression. (Section 1.7)

additive inverse (opposite, negative) The additive inverse of a number x, symbolized $-x$, is the number that is the same distance from 0 on the number line as x, but on the opposite side of 0. The number 0 is its own additive inverse. For all real numbers x, $x + (-x) = (-x) + x = 0$. (Section R.1)

algebraic expression An algebraic expression is a collection of constants, variables, operation symbols, and/or grouping symbols. (Sections R.3, 4.2)

asymptote A line that a graph more and more closely approaches as the graph gets farther away from the origin is an asymptote of the graph. (Sections 6.4, 9.2)

axis of symmetry (axis) The axis of symmetry of a parabola is the vertical or horizontal line (depending on the orientation of the graph) through the vertex of the parabola. (Section 8.5)

B

base The base in an exponential expression is the expression that is the repeated factor. In b^x, b is the base. (Sections R.3, 4.1)

binomial A binomial is a polynomial consisting of exactly two terms. (Section 4.2)

boundary line In the graph of an inequality, the boundary line separates the region that satisfies the inequality from the region that does not satisfy the inequality. (Section 2.4)

C

center The fixed point that is a fixed distance from all the points that form a circle is the center of the circle. (Section 7.3)

circle A circle is the set of all points in a plane that lie a fixed distance from a fixed point. (Section 7.3)

coefficient (See **numerical coefficient**.)

combined variation A relationship among variables that involves both direct and inverse variation is combined variation. (Section 6.6)

common logarithm A common logarithm is a logarithm having base 10. (Section 9.5)

complex conjugates The complex numbers $a + bi$ and $a - bi$ are complex conjugates. (Section 7.7)

complex fraction A complex fraction is a quotient with one or more fractions in the numerator, denominator, or both. (Section 6.3)

complex number A complex number is any number that can be written in the form $a + bi$, where a and b are real numbers and i is the imaginary unit. (Section 7.7)

components In an ordered pair (x, y), x and y are the components of the ordered pair. (Section 2.1)

composite function If g is a function of x, and f is a function of $g(x)$, then $f(g(x))$ defines the composite function of f and g. It is symbolized $(f \circ g)(x)$. (Section 4.3)

composition of functions The process of finding a composite function is called composition of functions. (Section 4.3)

compound inequality A compound inequality consists of two inequalities linked by a connective word such as *and* or *or*. (Section 1.6)

compound interest Compound interest is paid or charged on both principal and previous interest. (Section 9.6)

conditional equation A conditional equation is true for some replacements of the variable and false for others. (Section 1.1)

conjugates The binomials $x + y$ and $x - y$ are conjugates. (Section 7.5)

consecutive even (or odd) integers Two even (or odd) integers that differ by two are consecutive even (or odd) integers. (Section 1.4)

consecutive integers Two integers that differ by one are consecutive integers. (Section 1.4)

consistent system A system of equations with a solution is a consistent system. (Section 3.1)

constant A constant is a fixed, unchanging number. (Section R.3)

constant function A constant function is a linear function whose graph is a horizontal line. It has the form $f(x) = b$, where b is a real number. (Section 2.6)

constant of variation In the variation equations $y = kx$, $y = \frac{k}{x}$, and $y = kxz$, the real number k is the constant of variation. (Section 6.6)

continuous compounding Continuous compounding of interest involves compounding where the number of compounding periods is allowed to increase without bound, leading to a formula with the number e. (Section 9.6)

contradiction A contradiction is an equation that is never true. It has no solution. (Section 1.1)

coordinate Every point on a number line is associated with a unique real number, called the coordinate of the point. (Section R.1)

coordinates of a point The numbers in an ordered pair are the coordinates of the corresponding point in the plane. (Section 2.1)

cube root function The function $f(x) = \sqrt[3]{x}$ is the cube root function. (Section 7.1)

cubing function The polynomial function $f(x) = x^3$ is the cubing function. (Section 4.3)

D

degree of a polynomial The degree of a polynomial is the greatest degree of any of the terms in the polynomial. (Section 4.2)

degree of a term The degree of a term is the sum of the exponents on the variables in the term. (Section 4.2)

dependent equations Equations of a system that have the same graph (because they are different forms of the same equation) are dependent equations. (Section 3.1)

dependent variable In an equation relating x and y, if the value of the variable y depends on the value of the variable x, then y is the dependent variable. (Section 2.5)

descending powers   A polynomial in one variable is written in descending powers of the variable if the exponents on the variables of the terms of the polynomial decrease from left to right. (Section 4.2)

difference   The answer to a subtraction problem is the difference. (Section R.2)

difference of cubes   The difference of cubes, $x^3 - y^3$, can be factored as $x^3 - y^3 = (x - y)(x^2 + xy + y^2)$. (Section 5.3)

difference of squares   The difference of squares, $x^2 - y^2$, can be factored as the product of the sum and difference of two terms, or $x^2 - y^2 = (x + y)(x - y)$. (Section 5.3)

direct variation y varies directly as x if there exists a real number k such that $y = kx$. (Section 6.6)

discontinuous   A graph that has one or more breaks due to excluded values of the domain is discontinuous. (Section 6.4)

discriminant   The discriminant of the equation $ax^2 + bx + c = 0$ is the quantity $b^2 - 4ac$ under the radical symbol in the quadratic formula. (Section 8.2)

domain   The set of all first components (x-values) in the ordered pairs of a relation is the domain. (Section 2.5)

domain of the variable in a rational equation   The domain of the variable in a rational equation is the intersection of the domains of the rational expressions in the equation. (Section 6.4)

double solution   If a quadratic equation has two solutions that are not distinct, that solution is a double solution. (Section 5.5)

E

elements (members)   The elements (members) of a set are the objects that belong to the set. (Section R.1)

empty (null) set   The empty (null) set, denoted by { } or $\varnothing$, is the set containing no elements. (Section R.1)

equation   An equation is a statement that two quantities are equal. (Section R.1)

equivalent equations   Equivalent equations are equations that have the same solution set. (Section 1.1)

equivalent inequalities   Equivalent inequalities are inequalities that have the same solution set. (Section 1.5)

exponent (power)   An exponent, or power, is a number that indicates how many times its base is used as a factor. In b^x, x is the exponent. (Sections R.3, 4.1)

exponential equation   An exponential equation is an equation that has a variable in at least one exponent. (Section 9.2)

exponential expression   A number or letter (variable) written with an exponent is an exponential expression. (Sections R.3, 4.1)

exponential function with base a   An exponential function with base a is a function of the form $f(x) = a^x$, where $a > 0$ and $a \neq 1$ for all real numbers x. (Section 9.2)

extraneous solution   A proposed solution to an equation that does not satisfy the original equation is an extraneous solution. (Sections 6.4 and 7.6)

F

factoring   Factoring is the process of writing a polynomial as the product of two or more simpler polynomials. (Section 5.1)

factors   Two numbers whose product is a third number are factors of that third number. (Section R.3)

finite set   A finite set is a set where the counting of its elements comes to an end. (Section R.1)

first-degree equation   A first-degree (linear) equation has no term with the variable to a power greater than 1. (Section 2.1)

focus variable   In the elimination method for solving a system of equations in three variables, the first variable to be eliminated is the focus variable. (Section 3.2)

formula   A formula is an equation in which variables are used to describe a relationship among several quantities. (Section 1.2)

function   A function is a relation in which, for each distinct value of the first component of the ordered pairs, there is exactly one value of the second component. (Section 2.5)

G

graph of an equation   The graph of an equation in two variables is the set of all points that correspond to all of the ordered pairs that satisfy the equation. (Section 2.1)

graph of a number   The point on a number line that corresponds to a number is its graph. (Section R.1)

greatest common factor (GCF)   The greatest common factor of a list of integers is the largest factor of all those integers. The greatest common factor of the terms of a polynomial is the largest factor of all the terms in the polynomial. (Section 5.1)

H

horizontal asymptote   If the y-values of a rational function approach a real number b as $|x|$ increases without bound, then the horizontal line $y = b$ is a horizontal asymptote of the graph. (Section 6.4)

hypotenuse   The hypotenuse is the longest side in a right triangle. It is the side opposite the right angle. (Section 7.3)

I

identity   An identity is an equation that is true for all valid replacements of the variable. It has an infinite number of solutions. (Section 1.1)

identity element for addition (additive identity)   For all real numbers a, $a + 0 = 0 + a = a$. The number 0 is the identity element for addition. (Section R.4)

identity element for multiplication (multiplicative identity)   For all real numbers a, $a \cdot 1 = 1 \cdot a = a$. The number 1 is the identity element for multiplication. (Section R.4)

identity function   The simplest polynomial function is the identity function, $f(x) = x$. (Section 4.3)

imaginary part   The imaginary part of the complex number $a + bi$ is b. (Section 7.7)

inconsistent system   A system of equations with no solution is an inconsistent system. (Section 3.1)

independent equations   Equations of a system that have different graphs are independent equations. (Section 3.1)

independent variable   In an equation relating x and y, if the value of the variable y depends on the value of the variable x, then x is the independent variable. (Section 2.5)

index (order)   In a radical of the form $\sqrt[n]{a}$, n is the index or order. (Section 7.1)

inequality   An inequality is a statement that two expressions are not equal. (Sections R.1, 1.5)

infinite set   An infinite set is a set where the counting of its elements does not come to an end. (Section R.1)

integers   The set of integers is $\{ \ldots, -3, -2, -1, 0, 1, 2, 3, \ldots \}$. (Section R.1)

intersection   The intersection of two sets A and B, symbolized $A \cap B$, is the set of elements that belong to *both A and B*. (Section 1.6)

interval   An interval is a portion of a number line. (Section 1.5)

inverse of a function f   The inverse of a one-to-one function f, written f^{-1}, is the set of all ordered pairs of the form (y, x) where (x, y) belongs to f. (Section 9.1)

inverse variation y varies inversely as x if there exists a real number k such that $y = \frac{k}{x}$. (Section 6.6)

irrational numbers   An irrational number cannot be written as the quotient of two integers, but can be represented by a point on a number line. (Section R.1)

J

joint variation y varies jointly as x and z if there exists a real number k such that $y = kxz$. (Section 6.6)

L

leading coefficient   The numerical coefficient of the leading term of a polynomial is the leading coefficient. (Section 4.2)

leading term   When a polynomial is written in descending powers of the variable, the greatest-degree term is written first and is the leading term of the polynomial. (Section 4.2)

least common denominator (LCD)   Given several denominators, the least multiple that is divisible by all the denominators is the least common denominator. (Section 6.2)

legs (of a right triangle)   The two shorter perpendicular sides of a right triangle are its legs. (Section 7.3)

like terms   Terms with exactly the same variables raised to exactly the same powers are like terms. (Sections R.4, 4.2)

linear equation in one variable   A linear equation in one variable (here x) can be written in the form $Ax + B = C$, where A, B, and C are real numbers and $A \neq 0$. (Section 1.1)

linear equation in two variables   A linear equation in two variables (here x and y) is an equation that can be written in the form $Ax + By = C$, where A, B, and C are real numbers and A and B are not both 0. (Section 2.1)

linear function   A function f that can be written in the form $f(x) = ax + b$, where a and b are real numbers, is a linear function. The value of a is the slope m of the graph of the function. (Section 2.6)

linear inequality in one variable   A linear inequality in one variable (here x) can be written in the form $Ax + B < C$ or $Ax + B > C$ (or with $\leq$ or $\geq$), where A, B, and C are real numbers and $A \neq 0$. (Section 1.5)

linear inequality in two variables   A linear inequality in two variables (here x and y) can be written in the form $Ax + By < C$ or $Ax + By > C$ (or with $\leq$ or $\geq$), where A, B, and C are real numbers and A and B are not both 0. (Section 2.4)

logarithm   A logarithm is an exponent. The expression $\log_a x$ represents the exponent to which the base a must be raised to obtain x. (Section 9.3)

logarithmic equation   A logarithmic equation is an equation with a logarithm of a variable expression in at least one term. (Section 9.3)

logarithmic function with base a   A logarithmic function with base a is a function of the form $g(x) = \log_a x$, where $a > 0$ and $a \neq 1$ for all positive real numbers x. (Section 9.3)

M

mathematical model   In a real-world problem, a mathematical model is one or more equations (or inequalities) that describe the situation. (Section 1.2)

monomial   A monomial is a polynomial consisting of exactly one term. (Section 4.2)

multiplicative inverse (reciprocal)   The multiplicative inverse (reciprocal) of a nonzero number x, symbolized $\frac{1}{x}$, is the real number which has the property that the product of the two numbers is 1. For all nonzero real numbers x, $\frac{1}{x} \cdot x = x \cdot \frac{1}{x} = 1$. (Sections R.2, 6.1)

N

natural (counting) numbers   The set of natural numbers is the set of numbers used for counting, $\{1, 2, 3, 4, \ldots\}$. (Section R.1)

natural logarithm   A natural logarithm is a logarithm having base e. (Section 9.5)

negative of a polynomial   The negative of a polynomial is that polynomial with the sign of every term changed. (Section 4.2)

negative square root   The negative square root of a positive number x, written with a radical symbol as $-\sqrt{x}$, is the negative number which, when squared, gives x as the result. (Section R.3)

nonreal complex number   If $a + bi$ has $b \neq 0$, then it is a nonreal complex number. (Section 7.7)

number line   A line that has a point designated to correspond to the real number 0, and a standard unit chosen to represent the distance between 0 and 1, is a number line. All real numbers correspond to one and only one number on such a line. (Section R.1)

numerical coefficient   The numerical factor in a term is the numerical coefficient, or simply, the coefficient of the other factors. (Sections R.4, 4.2)

O

one-to-one function   In a one-to-one function each x-value corresponds to only one y-value, and each y-value corresponds to only one x-value. (Section 9.1)

order (See **index.**)

ordered pair   An ordered pair is a pair of numbers (x, y) written within parentheses in which the order of the numbers is important. (Section 2.1)

ordered triple   An ordered triple is a triple of numbers written within parentheses in the form (x, y, z). (Section 3.2)

origin   The point at which the x-axis and y-axis of a rectangular coordinate system intersect is the origin. (Section 2.1)

P

parabola   The graph of a quadratic function is a parabola. (Section 8.5)

percent   Percent, written with the symbol %, means "per one hundred." (Section 1.2)

percent decrease   If a quantity decreases from one measure to another, the amount of decrease compared to the original amount, when expressed as a percent, is the percent decrease. (Section 1.2)

percent increase   If a quantity increases from one measure to another, the amount of increase compared to the original amount, when expressed as a percent, is the percent decrease. (Section 1.2)

perfect square trinomial   A perfect square trinomial is a trinomial that can be factored as the square of a binomial. (Section 5.3)

plot   To plot a point in a rectangular coordinate system is to locate it based on its x- and y-coordinates. (Section 2.1)

polynomial   A polynomial is a term or a finite sum of terms of the form ax^n, where a is a real number, x is a variable, and the exponent n is a whole number. (Section 4.2)

polynomial function   A function defined by a polynomial in one variable, consisting of one or more terms, is a polynomial function. (Section 4.3)

polynomial in x   A polynomial containing only the variable x is a polynomial in x. (Section 4.2)

positive (principal) square root   The positive (principal) square root of a positive number x, written with a radical symbol as $\sqrt{x}$, is the positive number which, when squared, gives x as the result. (Section R.3)

prime polynomial   A prime polynomial is a polynomial that cannot be factored into factors having only integer coefficients. (Section 5.1)

principal root   For even indexes, the symbols $\sqrt{}$, $\sqrt[4]{}$, $\sqrt[6]{}$, $\ldots$, $\sqrt[n]{}$ are used for nonnegative roots, which are principal roots. (Section 7.1)

product   The answer to a multiplication problem is the product. (Section R.2)

proportion   A proportion is a statement that two ratios are equal. (Section 6.5)

proposed solution   A value of the variable that appears to be a solution of an equation before checking is a proposed solution. (Sections 6.4 and 7.6)

pure imaginary number   A complex number $a + bi$ where $a = 0$ and $b \neq 0$ is a pure imaginary number. (Section 7.7)

Q

quadrant   A quadrant is one of the four regions in the plane determined by the axes in a rectangular coordinate system. (Section 2.1)

quadratic equation   A quadratic equation (in x here) can be written in the form $ax^2 + bx + c = 0$, where a, b, and c are real numbers and $a \neq 0$. (Sections 5.5, 8.1)

quadratic formula   The solutions of the equation $ax^2 + bx + c = 0$ (where $a \neq 0$) are given by the quadratic formula,
$$x = \frac{-b \pm \sqrt{b^2 - 4ac}}{2a}.$$
(Section 8.2)

quadratic function   A function that can be written in the form $f(x) = ax^2 + bx + c$, for real numbers a, b, and c, where $a \neq 0$, is a quadratic function. (Section 8.5)

quadratic inequality   A quadratic inequality (in x here) can be written in the form $ax^2 + bx + c < 0$ or $ax^2 + bx + c > 0$ (or with $\leq$ or $\geq$), where a, b, and c are real numbers and $a \neq 0$. (Section 8.7)

quadratic in form   A nonquadratic equation that can be written in the form $au^2 + bu + c = 0$, for $a \neq 0$ and an algebraic expression u, is quadratic in form. (Section 8.3)

quotient   The answer to a division problem is the quotient. (Section R.2)

R

radical   An expression consisting of a radical symbol, root index, and radicand is a radical. (Section 7.1)

radical equation   A radical equation is an equation with a variable in at least one radicand. (Section 7.6)

radical expression   A radical expression is an algebraic expression that contains radicals. (Section 7.1)

radicand   The number or expression under a radical symbol is the radicand. (Section 7.1)

radius   The radius of a circle is the fixed distance between the center and any point on the circle. (Section 7.3)

range   The set of all second components (y-values) in the ordered pairs of a relation is the range. (Section 2.5)

ratio   A ratio is a comparison of two quantities using a quotient. (Section 6.5)

rational equation   An equation that involves rational expressions is a rational equation. (Section 6.4)

rational expression   The quotient of two polynomials with denominator not 0 is a rational expression. (Section 6.1)

rational function   A function that is defined by a quotient of polynomials is a rational function. (Section 6.1)

rational inequality   An inequality that involves rational expressions is a rational inequality. (Section 8.7)

rational numbers   Rational numbers can be written as the quotient of two integers, with denominator not 0. (Section R.1)

real numbers   Real numbers include all numbers that can be represented by points on a number line—that is, all rational and irrational numbers. (Section R.1)

real part   The real part of the complex number $a + bi$ is a. (Section 7.7)

reciprocal   (See **multiplicative inverse.**)

reciprocal function   The rational function $f(x) = \frac{1}{x}$, where $x \neq 0$, is the reciprocal function. (Section 6.4)

rectangular (Cartesian) coordinate system   The x-axis and y-axis placed at a right angle at their zero points form a rectangular coordinate system, also called a Cartesian coordinate system. (Section 2.1)

relation   A relation is any set of ordered pairs. (Section 2.5)

rise   Rise refers to the vertical change between two points on a line—that is, the change in y-values. (Section 2.2)

run   Run refers to the horizontal change between two points on a line—that is, the change in x-values. (Section 2.2)

S

scatter diagram   A scatter diagram is a graph of ordered pairs of data (usually real-world data). (Section 2.3)

second-degree equation   (See **quadratic equation.**)

set   A set is a collection of objects. (Section R.1)

signed numbers   Signed numbers are numbers that can be written with a positive or negative sign. (Section R.1)

slope   The ratio of the change in y to the change in x for any two points on a line is the slope of the line. (Section 2.2)

solution   A solution of an equation is any replacement for the variable that makes the equation true. (Section 1.1)

solution set   The solution set of an equation is the set of all solutions of the equation. (Section 1.1)

solution set of a linear system   The solution set of a linear system of equations consists of all ordered pairs that satisfy all the equations of the system at the same time. (Section 3.1)

square root   The inverse of squaring a number is taking its square root. That is, a number a is a square root of k if $a^2 = k$. (Section R.3)

square root function   The root function $f(x) = \sqrt{x}$, where $x \geq 0$, is the square root function. (Section 7.1)

squaring function   The polynomial function $f(x) = x^2$ is the squaring function. (Section 4.3)

sum   The answer to an addition problem is the sum. (Section R.2)

sum of cubes   The sum of cubes, $x^3 + y^3$, can be factored as $x^3 + y^3 = (x + y) \cdot (x^2 - xy + y^2)$. (Section 5.3)

system of equations   A system of equations consists of two or more equations to be solved at the same time. (Section 3.1)

system of linear equations   A system of linear equations consists of two or more linear equations to be solved at the same time. (Section 3.1)

T

table of ordered pairs (table of values)   A table of ordered pairs (table of values) is a systematic method for listing corresponding x- and y-coordinates when graphing an equation in two variables. (Section 2.1)

term   A term is a number, a variable, or the product or quotient of a number and one or more variables raised to powers. (Sections R.4, 4.2)

three-part inequality   An inequality that says that one number is between two other numbers is a three-part inequality. (Section 1.5)

trinomial   A trinomial is a polynomial consisting of exactly three terms. (Section 4.2)

U

union   The union of two sets A and B, symbolized $A \cup B$, is the set of elements that belong to *either A or B* (or both). (Section 1.6)

unlike terms   Unlike terms are terms that do not satisfy the conditions that define like terms. (Section R.4)

V

variable   A variable is a symbol, usually a letter, used to represent an unknown number. (Section R.1)

vertex   The point on a parabola that has the least y-value (if the parabola opens up) or the greatest y-value (if the parabola opens down) is the vertex of the parabola. (Section 8.5)

vertical asymptote   If the y-values of a rational function approach $-\infty$ or ∞ as the x-values approach a real number a, then the vertical line $x = a$ is a vertical asymptote of the graph. (Section 6.4)

W

whole numbers   The set of whole numbers is $\{0, 1, 2, 3, 4, \ldots\}$. (Section R.1)

working equation   In the elimination method for solving a system of equations in three variables, the working equation is used twice to eliminate the focus variable. (Section 3.2)

X

x-axis   The horizontal number line in a rectangular coordinate system is the x-axis. (Section 2.1)

x-intercept   A point where a graph intersects the x-axis is an x-intercept. (Section 2.1)

Y

y-axis   The vertical number line in a rectangular coordinate system is the y-axis. (Section 2.1)

y-intercept   A point where a graph intersects the y-axis is a y-intercept. (Section 2.1)

PHOTO CREDITS

INDEX